COMPOSITE RELIABILITY

A symposium
presented at
Las Vegas, Nev., 15–16 April 1974
AMERICAN SOCIETY FOR
TESTING AND MATERIALS

ASTM SPECIAL TECHNICAL PUBLICATION 580
E. M. Wu, symposium chairman

List price $49.75
04-580000-33

AMERICAN SOCIETY FOR TESTING AND MATERIALS
1916 Race Street, Philadelphia, Pa. 19103

NOTE

The Society is not responsible, as a body,
for the statements and opinions
advanced in this publication.

Printed in Baltimore, Md.
August 1975

Foreword

The symposium on Composite Reliability was presented in Las Vegas, Nev., 15–16 April 1974. The symposium was sponsored by Committee D-30 on High Modulus Fibers and Their Composites, American Society for Testing and Materials, in cooperation with the American Institute of Aeronautics and Astronautics, American Society of Mechanical Engineers, and the American Institute of Mining, Metallurgical, and Petroleum Engineers. E. M. Wu, Washington University, presided as symposium chairman.

Related
ASTM Publications

Analysis of the Test Methods for High Modulus Fibers and Composites, STP 521 (1973), $30.75, 04-521000-33

Applications of Composite Materials, STP 524 (1973), $16.75, 04-524000-33

Composite Materials: Testing and Design (Third Conference), STP 546 (1974), $39.75, 04-546000-33

A Note of Appreciation
to Reviewers

This publication is made possible by the authors and, also, the unheralded efforts of the reviewers. This body of technical experts whose dedication, sacrifice of time and effort, and collective wisdom in reviewing the papers must be acknowledged. The quality level of ASTM publications is a direct function of their respected opinions. On behalf of ASTM we acknowledge with appreciation their contribution.

ASTM Committee on Publications

Editorial Staff

Jane B. Wheeler, *Managing Editor*
Helen M. Hoersch, *Associate Editor*
Charlotte E. Wilson, *Senior Assistant Editor*
Ellen J. McGlinchey, *Assistant Editor*

Contents

CREEP, FATIGUE, AND IMPACT

Introduction

It is now clearly evident that composites have become viable engineering materials. Prime examples of this are the components now being used in the aerospace, ground transportation, recreational, and appliance industries. In the advanced applications, Northrop's YF-17 contains 900 lb of graphite-epoxy secondary structure, while the Air Force's F-15 has boron-epoxy horizontal stabilizers, vertical stabilizers, and rudders. Two phenomena have recently occurred, however, which could potentially accelerate advanced composite systems toward high-volume structural use in the civilian sphere of technology. The first is a breakthrough in producing high-performance carbon fibers from a low-cost pitch precursor. This will eventually result in a tenfold cost reduction for carbon fibers and thereby contribute to placing carbon-epoxy composites in the economic ball park with metal systems. The second boost toward new high-volume markets arises from a consideration of the total life-cycle cost of an end product. In many cases it can now be demonstrated that it is more efficient on a life-cycle basis to invest a pound of hydrocarbon in an optimized, lightweight composite structure, through advanced materials technology, than to burn that pound of hydrocarbon to transport a heavier structure. Thus, the combined effects of a decreasing initial cost and lower total life-cycle cost are now driving advanced composites, particularly the resin matrix systems, toward successful economic competition with traditional technologies in such high-volume industries as auto and truck transportation and household appliances.

With the advent of structural composite systems in high-performance military and civilian aircraft and particularly in the people-intensive transportation industry, the question of system reliability and durability takes on primary importance. We must know what fraction of the structural items produced will exhibit a specific lifetime under a given-use environment (reliability), as well as how long a given structural item will survive under a specified-use environment (durability). Both factors are indeed indispensable in accurately evaluating the total life-cycle cost of a structural end product. As Colonel Keating pointed out in his opening remarks to the conference, the consumer today obtains a product which is well defined by specifications, codes, and safety factors, but ill defined in terms of reliability and durability, and hence very expensive on a life-cycle cost basis.

With the need to conserve our valuable energy resources becoming

1

more and more evient and with an attendant skyrocketing energy cost, society is now looking to the technical community to use advanced technology to drive reliability and durability up and cost down. This conference attempts to answer that call by bringing together leading scientists and engineers who are attacking the reliability and durability problem from a number of different viewpoints. Roughly half of the conference is devoted to the material performance behavior aspects of reliability, including strength, fracture, creep, impact and fatigue, utilizing both theoretical and experimental approaches. In addition, several papers discuss the very important area of nondestructive testing as a means of assessing damage and incipient failure. Equally important are several papers dealing with the effects on reliability brought about by exposure of the composite material to various extremes of temperature and chemical environment. Taken as a whole, the conference proceedings provide a balanced, state-of-the-art look at composite material reliability and should be a welcome source of information to those in the technical community concerned with optimizing composite structures to reduce total life-cycles costs.

Edward M. Wu

Washington University, St. Louis, Mo.
63130; symposium chairman.

Opening

J. F. McCarthy, Jr.,[1] *and O. Orringer*[1]

Some Approaches to Assessing Failure Probabilities of Redundant Structures

REFERENCE: McCarthy, J. F., Jr., and Orringer, O., **"Some Approaches to Assessing Failure Probabilities of Redundant Structures,"** *Composite Reliability, ASTM STP 580,* American Society for Testing and Materials, 1975, pp. 5-31.

ABSTRACT: The growing acceptance of the concept of variability in the properties of structural materials (fracture toughness of metals, differences in composite fibers, etc.), along with the inherent randomness of loading due to nature, has caused the approach of analyzing structural systems using reliability techniques to become increasingly important. Classical reliability analysis is traced from basic probability theory to the development of fiber bundle theory with its resulting features and limitations. Recent applications of reliability analysis to "weak-link" structural systems are cited. Current research in the probabilistic treatment of physically redundant structures is then discussed with emphasis on the proper definition of convolution integral limits and the problems involved in the statistical modeling of real engineering components. Recent and anticipated trends in the application of reliability techniques to analyzing redundant structures are examined, including risk analyses of current Air Force aircraft and the "wearout" approach to life expectancy. Conclusions are drawn concerning the role that risk analysis could play in modern aerospace design and in establishing structural design criteria.

KEY WORDS: reliability, composite materials, structural analyses, risk assessments, redundancy, design criteria, fiber composites, mechanical properties

Nomenclature

a	Crack length
C	Cost or empirical constant
F, G	Cumulative probability distribution functions
f, g	Probability density functions
l	Length
P, p	Numerical probabilities

[1] Professor and lecturer, respectively, in Aeronautics and Astronautics, Massachusetts Institute of Technology, Cambridge, Mass. 02139.

$Pr \{ \ \}$ Probability that event in braces will occur
r Crack growth rate exponent
s System load or stress range
T, t Time
X, Y, Z Component loads
x Component strength variate
α Weibull distribution shape parameter
β Weibull distribution scale parameter
σ Standard deviation

Subscripts

A Applied load
B Bundle
c, cr Critical
I Initial
F, f Failure
R Redundant
WL   Weak link

Traditional structural analysis and design methods treat physical systems as if they were deterministic. The properties of the structure itself (for example, Young's modulus, tensile strength, design dimensions) are presumed to be known exactly; the service loads which the structure will experience during its life are presumed to be perfectly predictable; and the analysis method used to predict the response of a given design to given loads is assumed to be exact, at least to the accuracy required for engineering purposes. These assumptions are directly reflected in the manner in which structural design codes for many fields are organized. However, the idea of variability has always hovered in the shadows, in terms of the safety factors which are found in every design code. The purpose of a safety factor, based on extensive past experience with specific structures constructed of specific materials and designed to a specific code, is to provide a concise accounting for the combined inaccuracies of current knowledge of properties, loads, and analysis methods. Indeed, tracing of the development of such widely varied fields as bridge construction [1-3][2] and early naval architecture [4-6] shows that the history of safety factors corresponds to the history of state-of-the-art knowledge. The fundamental philosophy which underlies this traditional approach is that only man's imperfect abilities prevent the design of a safe structure with a safety factor of one.

The past generation has witnessed a growing awareness that variability in the behavior of structures arises, not just from imperfect knowledge,

[2] The italic numbers in brackets refer to the list of references appended to this paper.

but also from the random effects inherent in nature. The first motivations for bringing variability from shadow to light were the study of brittle material strength *[7]* and attempts to predict the fatigue life of a structure *[8,9]*. This effort continues today as attempts are made to predict fatigue life in random service-load environments *[10]*, and is of special interest to the aerospace industry. There are also some special applications in modern civil engineering and naval architecture (for example, earthquake response, effects of storms on supertankers), and more recently, natural randomness has become a special concern in numerous aspects of the structural design of nuclear power reactors *[11,12]*.

The past decade has witnessed many attempts to incorporate natural randomness into structural design codes, either based on some combination of the principles of probability and statistics with structural mechanics *[13]*, or on attempts to refine ultimate load estimates with probability theory *[14]*. None of these attempts has received general acceptance, and some have caused bitter controversy *[15]*. However, research on the impact of random effects on design codes still continues, with current emphasis on the micromechanics or single-specimen level *[16]*. For lack of a better term, we lump all of these activities under the general heading of "structural reliability analysis methods," recognizing that this term means different things to different people.

The purpose of this paper is to provide a perspective view of structural reliability analysis by reviewing briefly its three primary antecedents: classical system reliability analysis, fiber bundle theory, and the probabilistic theory of structural dynamics. No attempt at completeness is made; indeed entire areas such as quality control and fleet analysis *[17]* have been virtually ignored. We assume that the reader is familiar with the fundamental concepts of probability theory *[18]*. The latter part of the paper reviews some prior contributions to structural reliability analysis and presents a more detailed discussion of some recent analytical work done at the Massachusetts Institute of Technology.

Classical Reliability Analysis

Classical reliability analysis concerns itself with the derivation of general statistical properties of systems from the corresponding properties of their components. The first important engineering applications were avionics, electronics, and guidance systems during the 1940's and 1950's. Subsequent applications include automobile warranty policies and aircraft maintenance guarantees. Reference *19* contains an excellent distillation of the theory. Figure 1 illustrates some typical examples of "systems" as viewed by the classical reliability analyst. The weak-link system fails when its first component failure occurs, and the failure probability for the system can be calculated from

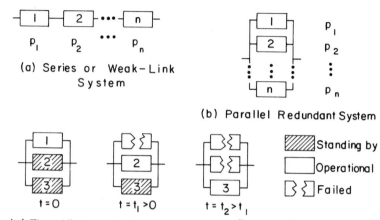

(a) Series or Weak-Link System

(b) Parallel Redundant System

(c) Time History of a Three-Component "Standby" Redundant System

FIG. 1—*Typical systems in classical reliability analysis.*

$$P_{WL} = 1 - \prod_{i=1}^{n} (1 - p_i) = 1 - (1 - p_1)(1 - p_2)\cdots(1 - p_n) \qquad (1)$$

where p_1, p_2, ..., p_n are the failure probabilities of the individual components. In a similar manner, the parallel redundant system, which does not fail until all of its components have failed, has the failure probability

$$P_R = \prod_{i=1}^{n} p_i = p_1 p_2 \cdots p_n \qquad (2)$$

Equations 1 and 2 assume that the component failure probabilities have specific numerical values. However, the main concern of classical reliability analysis is how components and systems behave with time. For example, component failures might be correlated experimentally with an exponential time distribution function

$$F_i(t) = Pr\,\{i^{\text{th}} \text{ component fails at time} \leq t\} = 1 - e^{-t/T_i} \qquad (3)$$

where T_i is a given mean time to failure (MTTF). In terms of the density function $f_i(t) = dF_i/dt$, $\text{MTTF}_i = \int_0^\infty t f_i(t)dt = T_i$. Substitution of Eq 3 into Eqs 1 or 2 produces the derived system distribution function. Continuing with the weak-link system example, we find

$$F_{WL}(t) = 1 - \prod_{i=1}^{n} [1 - F_i(t)] = 1 - \prod^n e^{-t/T_i} \qquad (4)$$

Equation 4 may be differentiated to produce the corresponding system density function, and to permit calculation of the weak-link system MTTF

$$f_{WL}(t) = \sum_{j=1}^{n} \frac{1}{T_j} e^{-t/T_j} \left(\prod_{i(\neq j)}^{n} e^{-t/T_i} \right) = \left(\sum_{i=1}^{n} \frac{1}{T_i} \right) \exp - t \left(\sum_{i=1}^{n} \frac{1}{T_i} \right) \quad (5)$$

$$MTTF_{WL} = \int_0^\infty t f_{WL}(t) dt = 1 \bigg/ \left(\sum_{i=1}^{n} \frac{1}{T_i} \right) \quad (6)$$

Similar although somewhat more complicated calculations may be made for the parallel redundant system. Figure 1c illustrates a more sophisticated type of redundancy known as "standby." A possible time-history of a three-component system is shown. At $t = 0$, only component 1 is operational. The system is assumed to be constructed such that component 2 is turned on when 1 fails, and component 3 is turned on when 2 fails. Again, although the combinatorial algebra is still more complicated, it is possible to produce an analytical expression for the system MTTF. Other generic system types, such as the "k out of n" (system fails when any k of its n components fails), have been subjects of classical reliability analysis. Combinations of these fundamental systems may be analyzed, and there has recently occurred an extension of classical reliability theory to the optimization of such combinations [20].

The numerous practical applications of classical reliability analysis include aircraft autopilots (parallel redundant), "majority decision" missile guidance systems ("k out of n") and mechanical system maintenance analysis (weak-link). Mean time between failures (MTBF) is normally the statistic of interest in the latter case.

System reliability analysis is often applied to the design of space vehicles. In the Apollo Program, for example, the initial criterion for overall mission success was 0.9 and for overall crew safety 0.999. These requirements dictated the necessary parallel redundancy in subsystems and the required reliability of components. The initial requirements were subdivided into values for each major module (command module, service module, second-stage booster, etc.) and subsequently into values for each major subsystem. They literally forced the nature of the design. For the electrical power system, the power sources consisted of 3 fuel cells, 3 batteries, and 3 inverters with redundant d-c and a-c busses. If any one module failed, for example a fuel cell, the mission could still be completed successfully. If any two modules failed, for example two fuel cells, the mission had to be aborted, but crew safety was assured. The initial allocation for the reliability of the fuel cells was 0.9977 for mission success and 0.999 for crew safety. (The requirements of 0.999 for overall crew safety had to be relaxed later in the program to 0.99 because the weight and complexity for adequate parallel redundancy became excessive.) Similar philosophies for mission success and crew safety are currently being exercised on the Space Shuttle Program in an iterative process where requirements are traded off against weight and complexity.

Several prominent features characterize classical reliability analysis, and should be kept in mind when structural applications are considered. First, the environment of each component is described by a single generalized parameter (time in the examples treated in the foregoing, but equally as well voltage supplied or mechanical load); further, component failure distributions F_i are well known, and usually correlated in terms of one of the simpler one- or two-parameter distribution families. Second, there is a one-to-one correspondence between the statistical component and the physical component; that is, distributions $F_i(x_j)$ (x = load in component, $j \neq i$) are not permitted. Third, only the simplest kinds of interconnection (in a probabilistic sense) between components are considered: series or parallel. Finally, classical reliability analysis presumes that the load (voltage, time, etc.) applied to one component is not changed directly by the event of failure of a neighboring component. (However, this presumption is relaxed in a restricted manner in the case of "standby" systems.) The relative simplicity of the foregoing assumptions has made possible the derivation of many analytical expressions for MTTF, MTBF, and other important statistical performance measures for a wide variety of systems of practical interest.

Fiber Bundle Theory

A paper by Daniels [21] is currently recognized as the first contribution to fiber bundle theory; the theory was developed by Daniels to predict the statistical properties of the combined strength of bundles of threads in textile yarns, given the statistics of the individual threads. Figure 2a illustrates a bundle of N fibers, each assumed to have unit cross-sectional area for simplicity. The entire bundle supports a load s, which is borne equally as s/N by each fiber. All fibers are assumed to belong to the same statisti-

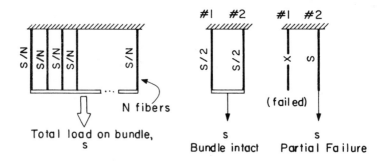

(a) Bundle of N fibers   (b) Possible Sequence of Events in a Bundle of Two Fibers

FIG. 2—*Some examples of fiber bundles.*

cal population, which is characterized by given strength distribution and density functions $F(x) = Pr$ {Strength of a fiber $\leqslant x$} and $f(x) = dF/dx$. Failure of the bundle is characterized by a sequence of events in which fibers 1, 2, ..., N fail successively in some order. It is evident that when (say) j fibers have failed $(0 < j < N)$, each of the $N - j$ surviving fibers bears an increased load $s/(N - j)$. The bundle thus incorporates a component reloading property, in contrast to the classical parallel redundant system of Fig. 1b. (Dynamic overload effects are neglected.)

Derivation of the strength distribution function for the bundle is best understood by taking the case of a two-fiber bundle (Fig. 2b). We may postulate, as a typical sequence, failure of fiber 1 followed by failure of fiber 2. The probability of occurence of this sequence may be calculated from

Pr {1, 2 fail in order at total load $\leqslant s$}

$$= Pr \text{ \{Strength of 1, } x_1 \leqslant s/2\} \cdot Pr \text{ \{} x_1 \leqslant \text{Strength of 2} \leqslant s\} \quad (7)$$

$$= \int_0^{s/2} f(x_1) \int_{x_1}^s f(x_2) \, dx_2 \, dx_1$$

Equation 7 is referred to as a convolution integral; the distribution function for the bundle is now obtained by recognizing that the other possible sequence, 2 followed by 1, is statistically identical to the sequence just discussed. Thus, we find

$$F_B(s) = 2 \int_0^{s/2} f(x_1) \int_{x_1}^s f(x_2) \, dx_2 \, dx_1 \quad (8)$$

Equation 8 may be integrated analytically to the form

$$F_B(s) = 2F(s)F(s/2) - [F(s/2)]^2 \quad (9)$$

a result quite different from the corresponding classical redundant system, for which $F_R(s) = [F(s/2)]^2$. Equation 7 may be readily extended to the general bundle of N fibers by recognizing that there are $N!$ possible failure sequences, each statistically identical to 1, 2, ..., N. Therefore

$$F_B(s) = (N!) \int_0^{s/N} f(x_1) \int_{x_1}^{s/(N-1)} f(x_2) \cdots \int_{x_{N-1}}^s f(x_N) \, dx_N \cdots dx_2 \, dx_1 \quad (10)$$

for a bundle of N fibers. Although a general analytical expression cannot be given for the integrated form of Eq 10, recursion formulas can be developed if one of the common one- or two-parameter distributions is assumed for $f(x)$.

Equation 10 has recently had a direct impact on specifications to material suppliers. Suppose a two-parameter Weibull distribution is assumed for the fibers (Fig. 3)

$$F(x) = 1 - e^{-(x/\beta)^\alpha} \qquad f(x) = \frac{\alpha x^{\alpha-1}}{\beta^\alpha} e^{-(x/\beta)^\alpha}$$

$$0 \leqslant x < \infty; \qquad \alpha, \beta > 0 \tag{11}$$

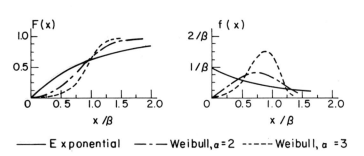

——— Exponential   —·— Weibull, $\alpha = 2$ ----- Weibull, $\alpha = 3$

FIG. 3—*Comparison of exponential and Weibull distributions.*

where α, β are respectively the shape and scale parameters of the distribution; that is, (Coefficient of variation) $\approx 1/\alpha$ and Pr {Strength $\leqslant \beta$} = 0.632. It can be shown that $\beta_B \rightarrow \beta/N^{1/\alpha}$ for large N, and this has led some manufacturers of composite aircraft components to specify narrow distribution of graphite fiber strength in yarns, $(\alpha \gg 1)$, in preference to high mean strength [22].

A more detailed statistical description of the possible outcomes of applying a load s to a fiber bundle may be derived by equating to one the sum of the probabilities of all mutually exclusive events which may occur [23]. A typical term in the sum is given by

Pr {j fibers fail in some order}$\cdot Pr$ {$N - j$ fibers survive system load s}

$$= \left(\int_0^{s/N} f(x_1) \int_{x_1}^{s/(N-1)} f(x_2) \cdots \int_{x_{j-1}}^{s/(N+1-j)} f(x_j) dx_j \cdots dx_2 dx_1 \right)$$

$$\times \left[1 - F\left(\frac{s}{N-j}\right) \right]^{N-j} \tag{12}$$

The complete sample space is thus characterized by

$$\left[1 - F\left(\frac{s}{N}\right)\right]^{N} + \sum_{j=1}^{N-1}\left(\frac{N!}{(N-j)!}\left[1 - F\left(\frac{s}{N-j}\right)\right]^{N-j}\right.$$

$$\left. \times \int_{0}^{s/N} f(x_1) \cdots \int_{x_{j-1}}^{s/(N+1-j)} f(x_j)dx_j \cdots dx_1\right)$$

$$+ (N!) \int_{0}^{s/N} f(x_1) \cdots \int_{x_{N-1}}^{s} f(x_N)dx_N \cdots dx_1 = 1 \qquad (13)$$

The first and last terms on the left side of Eq 13 are the probabilities for the extremes of complete survival and complete failure, respectively, while each term in the summation represents the probability for failure of all $N!/(N - j)!$ possible sequences of j fibers. It is easily shown that Eq 13 contains the complete set of "k out of N" calculations, by shifting some terms to the right side to obtain an expression of the form

Pr {At least k fibers fail}

$= 1 - Pr$ {Less than k fibers fail}

$$= 1 - \left[1 - F\left(\frac{s}{N}\right)\right]^{N} - \sum_{j=1}^{k-1}\left(\frac{N!}{(N-j)!}\left[1 - F\left(\frac{s}{N-j}\right)\right]^{N-j}\right.$$

$$\left. \times \int_{0}^{s/N} f(x_1) \cdots \int_{x_{j-1}}^{s/(N+1-j)} f(x_j)dx_j \cdots dx_1\right) \qquad (14)$$

While Eq 14 is of little interest for the fiber bundle per se, it will prove useful in subsequent developments for redundant structures.

Rosen [24] extended fiber bundle theory ten years ago to a method for predicting the strength statistics of a composite material single-ply tape. Briefly, he treated the tape as a weak-link series of fiber bundles, as shown in Fig. 4. A typical broken fiber is assumed to be ineffective as a load-carrier for a distance l_c to either side of the break. The parameter l_c is determined by a shear-lag calculation to find the distance along which the surrounding matrix material can reintroduce some arbitrary fraction (say, 0.9) of the unbroken fiber stress back into the broken fiber. The quantity $2l_c$ then sizes the typical bundle, and Rosen defines failure of the structure to occur when another arbitrarily chosen fraction of the fibers in any one bundle has broken. An expression for the ply-strength distribution function can be formulated on this basis, and Rosen makes some numerical calculations by restricting attention to the lower tail of a

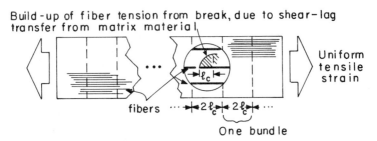

Build-up of fiber tension from break, due to shear-lag transfer from matrix material

Uniform tensile strain

fibers

One bundle

FIG. 4—*Rosen's probability model of a composite tape ply.*

Weibull distribution for the fibers, which permits approximation of $1 - \exp[- (x/\beta)^a]$ by a quadratic polynominal.

We make the following observations in comparing fiber bundle theory with classical reliability analysis of a parallel redundant system. First, the properties of description by one generalized load parameter, the identity of physical and statistical components, and simplicity of interconnection are retained. Second, the fiber bundle possesses a component reloading property absent from the classical system. However, the simplicity of interconnection and the fact that only tension is considered combine to make the reloading property quite simple: the surviving fibers share the current system load equally at any stage, and the effect of a fiber failure will always be to increase the loads on the remaining fibers.

We conclude this section by noting two important weaknesses in Rosen's composite-ply statistical model. First, since the strengths of individual fibers are controlled by the presence of flaws of random severity, it is to be expected that the parameters of a correlated distribution for strength will be quite sensitive to the unsupported fiber length, l, tested experimentally. While $l \approx O$ [1 in.] in many fiber quality-control tests, the critical shear-lag length $l_c \approx O$ [10 fiber diameters] for boron, graphite, or glass fibers in epoxy matrix material, and the largest commercially manufactured fiber (boron) has a 0.0056-in. diameter. Therefore, the size of one of Rosen's bundles is approximately O [0.10 in.] at most, and may be as small as O [0.01 in.] for glass and graphite. Hence, it is doubtful whether the normally available fiber quality statistics can properly be applied to Rosen's model, although some argument in favor may be made on the basis that glass and graphite are supplied as yarns containing roughly 1000 fibers. A second and more serious weakness is that the reloading property in a composite ply does not really correspond to the ideal fiber bundle situation. Rather, it has been demonstrated both analytically [25] and experimentally [26] that the static overload caused by a broken fiber is borne disproportionately by its near neighbors when the bundle is embedded in a shear-transferring medium.

Probabilistic Theory of Structural Dynamics

The analysis methods reviewed in the foregoing approach a physical problem from the viewpoint of a system possessing randomness, which is subjected to a load in the form of a deterministric number (design voltage level, required strength of a bundle, etc.) or a deterministic variable (time, load range for calculation of $F_B(s)$, etc.). In contrast, the probabilistic theory of structural dynamics assumes a deterministic physical system, and seeks to make statistical predictions about the system's response to random loading which can be described only by a probability distribution for load amplitude [27]. The probabilistic theory of structural dynamics has had little direct impact on structural reliability methods, most of the workers in the latter field preferring to ignore dynamic overload effects. The common justification for this quasi-static viewpoint is that the frequencies of the first few natural vibration modes of a structure, in which most of the vibrational energy is concentrated, tend to be very low compared with the frequency content of the random load sources. Notable exceptions to this premise are the analyses required to verify the structural integrity of spacecraft during the launch phase [28], and the ability of nuclear power reactors to survive earthquakes [29].

However, probabilistic structural dynamics does influence structural reliability analysis in that the methods for characterizing random loads developed in the former field have been carried over to the latter. The standard technique in theoretical investigations is to assume that the loading can be modeled as a stationary Gaussian process with zero mean

$$f_A(s) = \frac{1}{\sigma\sqrt{2\pi}}\, e^{-s^2/2\sigma^2}; \qquad -\infty < s < \infty, \qquad \sigma > 0 \qquad (15)$$

where σ is the standard deviation of the distribution. Although Eq 15 cannot be integrated analytically to produce the distribution function $F_A(s)$, tables are available in most texts on probability theory. These can be used to plot an exceedance curve, which gives a summary of the fraction of applied loads that exceed a specified value in a sample comprising a large total number of applied loads. The Gaussian exceedance curve is given by

$$Pr\,\{\text{Load} > +s\} = 1 - F_A(s) \qquad (16)$$

and will be symmetrical for $Pr\,\{\text{Load} < -s\}$. The limitations of the Gaussian distribution for practical analysis are illustrated by Fig. 5, which compares the Gaussian exceedance curve with a typical experimental curve derived from aircraft flight test data. The experiment is generally asymmetric because aircraft usually fly at positive load factors.

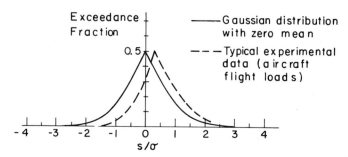

FIG. 5—*Theoretical and experimental exceedance curves.*

One of the most important current applications of random load characterization is the production of program tapes to control the loads applied to components or full-scale structures during design verification tests. The sophistication of these load programs has grown as understanding of the effect of random loading on crack growth has increased [10]. The general procedure for cutting a program tape follows these lines. An experimental exceedance curve is calculated from service load histories similar to that expected for the new design. The parameters of a parametric distribution (for example, mean and standard deviation for a Gaussian distribution) are estimated from the exceedance curve, and an appropriate random number generator subroutine is then used to produce series of load peaks. Also, each test facility adds its own refinement for censoring of large load peaks which exceed test capacity or are not expected within service life, and for elimination of small nondamaging peaks to speed up the test. Vaicaitas and Shinozuka [30] have recently proposed direct use of the statistical theory of structural dynamics to match the random process at critical stress locations within the structure, rather than at the applied load locations. This new approach is advantageous for large structure tests because it accounts rationally for inertial effects which are present in service but absent in tests.

Weak-Link Methods for Structural Reliability Analysis

The past 15 years have witnessed a research boom in structural reliability analysis methods, led primarily by civil engineers, and drawing mainly upon classical reliability theory and the random loading concepts from statistical dynamics. The focus has been on weak-link models, principally because of the difficulty of handling structural redundancy without matrix computer analysis programs, which were only beginning to become available during the early 1960's. Most of these studies deal with pin-jointed, plane truss structures to avoid tedious stress analysis, and they assume various convenient distribution functions for the individual member strengths. The truss structure also possesses the inherent advantage of identity of physical and statistical components, with the mechanical load (or stress) induced in the member by applied loads corresponding to the member's strength measure. Concentration on probability for the first member to fail then removes the requirement to investigate mechanical reloading properties, and a classical reliability analysis can be performed. Shinozuka and his colleagues [31] have justified this approach with a numerical study of a bundle of three fibers with Gaussian distributed strength, subjected to a Gaussian random load. Failure probabilities calculated for the bundle from

$$P_{F\text{WL}} = \int_0^\infty F_{\text{WL}}(s)f_A(s)\,ds \qquad P_{FB} = \int_0^\infty F_B(s)f_A(s)\,ds \qquad (17)$$

were in close agreement, where $F_{wL}(s) = 1 - [1 - F(s/3)]^3$; $F_B(s)$ is obtained from Eq 10 with $N = 3$; $f_A(s)$ is a Gaussian density function for the applied load; and where all of the calculations were adjusted for a one-sided load range.

Similar weak-line calculations for truss structures have been carried out, but are of little interest. Rather, the primary contributions have dealt with situations in which two or more statistically independent sources of random applied loading are considered. Moses and Kinser [32] have shown that the presence of structure interconnections partially correlates the member load, even though the external sources are uncorrelated. They also formulated a scheme for optimizing the design of a truss subjected to several random load sources, by varying the member cross-sectional areas to meet a reliability requirement with minimum weight. Many other authors have played similar optimization games. One notable example is the work of Mau [33], who formulated and carried out extensive numerical studies with a steepest descent procedure on a cost-constraint criterion of the form

$$C_I + P_{F\text{WL}}C_F = C_o \qquad (18)$$

where

C_I = initial cost of the structural system,
$P_{F\text{WL}}$ = weak-link system failure probability,
C_F = cost of failure, and
C_o = cost constraint.

The quantities C_I, $P_{F\text{WL}}$ are functions of the design variables (member cross-sectional areas), while C_F, C_o have arbitrarily assigned values. Mau pointed out that any value assigned to C_F must necessarily be imprecise, since social or strategic, as well as economic costs, must be considered for analysis of a real structure. However, Mau concluded from sensitivity analyses that the optimized design was not changed significantly by variations of C_F over one or two orders of magnitude. Mau's report also contains an excellent bibliography of the extensive literature on weak-link structural reliability analysis.

We conclude this section by observing that the methods for straightforward calculation of the probability for failure of the first component in a structure possessing random component strengths and subjected to multiple sources of random loading are now in an advanced state of development, and can be useful in themselves, but that serious questions remain with regard to the utility of the optimization procedures. The classic example of minimum weight optimization of a simple truss to meet deterministic load conditions [34,35] should serve as a warning to the unwary.

Reliability Analysis of Redundant Structures

Theoretical work started at MIT under Air Force sponsorship in 1971 has taken a different direction, attempting to develop practical methods of accounting for redundancy when assessing the failure probability of a random-strength structure, but restricting consideration to deterministic or single-source random loads. The intuitive rationale for this effort is (to continue with a simple example) that a redundant truss ought to be inherently more reliable than a similar statically determinate truss when the components of both structures are designed to equal individual failure probabilities, yet a weak-link calculation for the redundant truss gives the opposite result.

Orringer [23] and Peterson [36] extended fiber bundle theory to general redundant structures having arbitrary reloading properties. The extension was made by recognizing that sequences of failures of j out of N components are no longer necessarily statistically identical, but that each of the mutually exclusive events which are possible outcomes of loading the structure can still be assigned probabilities of the form given by Eq 12. Accounting formally for a reloading property which may generally be different for every failure path, we may replace Eq 12 with

$$Pr\{n_1 n_2 \cdots n_j\}$$

$$= \left(\int_0^{Z_{n_1}(s)} f_{n_1}(x_1) \int_{\lambda_2 x_1}^{X_{n_2}(s)} f_{n_2}(x_2) \cdots \int_{\lambda_j x_{j-1}}^{X_{n_j}(s)} f_{n_j}(x_j) dx_j \cdots dx_1 \right.$$

$$\times \prod_{\substack{\text{Surviving} \\ \text{Components, } n_i}} [1 - F(Y_{n_i}(s))] \tag{19}$$

where n_1, n_2, ..., n_j are a typical group of j of the components of the structure, and where

$$Pr\{n_1 n_2 \cdots n_j\} = Pr\{\text{Failure of } n_1, n_2, \ldots, n_j \text{ in order and survival of all other components}\},$$

$Z_{n_1}(s)$ = maximum load attainable in n_1 due to applied load s, with the structure intact,

$X_{n_k}(s)$ = maximum load attainable in n_k due to applied load s, with $n_1, n_2, \ldots, n_{k-1}$ failed,

λ_k = ratio of load in n_k to load in n_{k-1} just before n_{k-1} fails, and

$Y_{n_i}(s)$ = maximum load attainable in surviving component n_i due to s, with $n_1, n_2, \ldots, n_j$ failed.

It is evident that all of the load parameters which appear as integration limits, or in the survival product of Eq 19 may be obtained with any modular, user-programmable matrix structural analysis software. Thus, the general reloading property can be derived, as portions of it are required, by standard finite-element analysis techniques.

Orringer [23] also pointed out the one crucial difference between a true fiber bundle and the bundle-like behavior of a redundant structure, namely, that the state reached by the structure just before complete failure will generally consist of many components which form a physically weak-link surviving structure, unlike the bundle which always consists of a single fiber just before failure. Furthermore, the number of components required to fail in a structure in order to cause collapse generally depends upon the specific failure path examined. Figure 6 illustrates a simple example of this property; failure of four diagonals is required to collapse a three-bay truss if the failure sequence is A, B, C, D, but collapse can also occur after the sequence B, D. The net result is that there exists no valid analog to Eq 10 for the complete collapse probability of a structure. Instead, the "k out of N" approach, Eq 14, must be used. With Eq 19, we may replace Eq 14 by the following expression for a general structure

$$Pr\{\text{At least } k \text{ components fail}\} = 1 - \prod_{\substack{\text{All} \\ \text{Components}}} [1 - F(Z_i(s))]$$

$$- \sum_{j=1}^{k-1} \left(\sum_{\substack{\text{All Permutations} \\ \text{of } j \text{ components}}} Pr\{n_1 n_2 \cdots n_j\} \right) \qquad (20)$$

with the understanding that k may be censored by the presence of internal kinematic modes for certain failure sequences. The singularity

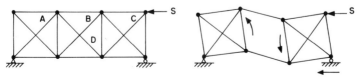

FIG. 6—*Example of an internal kinematic mode.*

test in the matrix analysis software can be used to test for the presence of these modes.

The probability for complete collapse of a structure results if all possible terms in Eq 20 are calculated. However, the number of possible sequences grows rapidly with both the amount of redundancy and the total number of components in a structure, making the cost of a complete calculation for a practical structure prohibitive.

Peterson [36] proposed a "most probable route" (MPR) procedure to reduce the computing burden. Peterson's MPR procedure extends the envelope of failure paths examined by searching for the next most probable sequence after each separate term in Eq 20 is calculated. If a path of $j - 1$ failures has already been calculated, then enough stress analysis information has already been obtained to calculate the convolution integrals for all possible sequences of j which continue from this particular path. The MPR procedure greatly reduces the amount of finite-element analysis required if it is stopped by a constraint; for example, convergence of the approximation to collapse probability, maximum allowable number of failed components per path, etc. Peterson ran some numerical studies of the truss shown in Fig. 6. Figure 7 reproduces his

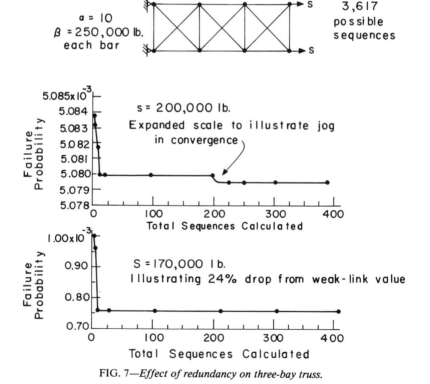

FIG. 7—*Effect of redundancy on three-bay truss.*

results. It is apparent that a weak-link calculation is a poor approximation for collapse failure probability in some cases. Peterson's result also illustrates an inherent weakness in the MPR procedure; convergence occurs with occasional steps, due to the impossibility of calculating the survival product portion of a term (see Eq 19) until the next finite-element analysis with j failures has been completed.

A fundamental inaccuracy in the generalized bundle theory was discovered during the past year. Strictly speaking, Eq 19 is not valid unless the structure reloading property is such that failure of a component always increases the load magnitudes in the surviving components without changing their algebraic signs. Thus, the failure probabilities calculated by Peterson are somewhat high, except for the weak-link value. However, load decreases and sign changes can be properly accounted for by examining the load history of a component, as other components fail, and making adjustments to the integration limits in Eq 19. Seppanen [37] has recently completed the required corrections for failure sequences of three components. Figure 8 illustrates an example of a correction required by a load decrease. The load history for the second component in the sequence is such that it may already have demonstrated a strength greater than the maximum load it can attain after failure of the first component. In that case, the sequence probability must be zero. Similar corrections are required for sign changes. In conclusion, we remark that the computing burden is so severe, with redundancy present, that automated design optimization schemes are out of the question.

Probability Models for Engineering Components

Additional complications arise in both weak-link and redundant structural reliability analysis when attempts are made to model structures of current engineering interest, rather than pin-jointed trusses. For example, consider a composite laminate box beam with bolt holes and cutouts. Continuum finite-element methods are required to produce a reasonable stress analysis, but this complication destroys the simple correspondence between physical and probabilistic components enjoyed by the truss structure. A carefully developed probability model, solidly based on the applicable failure mechanics, will be required for each type of component. Orringer [38] conducted a brief investigation of the problems associated with modeling a tension wing skin consisting of three planks separated by ideally effective crack-stoppers. Formulation of an adequate statistical model for the strength of an individual plank proved to be extremely difficult when logical sources of variability (for example, location, orientation) were added to an assumed flaw size distribution, even under the simplifying restriction that unstable crack propagation is presumed to

Failure events AAA with n_1 in range Oa are possible, but events BBB with n_1 in range ab are impossible for sequence n_1, n_2:

$$\int_0^{Z_{n1}} f_1(t_1) \int_{\lambda_2 t_1}^{X_{n2}} f_2(t_2)\, dt_2 dt_1 \quad \text{is incorrect}$$

$$\int_0^{Z_{n1}^*} f_1(t_1) \int_{\lambda_2 t_1}^{X_{n2}} f_2(t_2)\, dt_2 dt_1 \quad \text{is required}$$

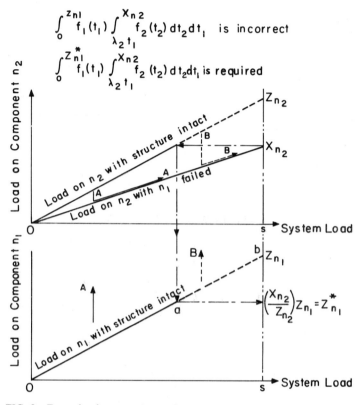

FIG. 8—*Example of a correction to the original generalized bundle theory.*

occur before any crack becomes large enough to change the effective stiffness of a plank.

Another "identity crisis" occurred when attempts were made to create a one-dimensional mechanical/probabilistic model for a line of bolts in a buffer strip of a composite laminate box beam skin [39]. The model is illustrated by Fig. 9. Mechanically, the structure is composed of two types of finite elements: quadratic-assumed-displacement bars representing the skin buffer strip and web flange, which receive running shear loads from the main skin and web, and linear-assumed-displacement shear transfer elements representing the bolts. The figure also shows a much idealized statistical model, which restricts consideration to one possible bolt-bearing and one possible tension failure site each in the buffer strip and flange, at each bolt location. Additional complication is introduced by the fact that

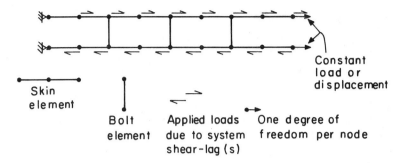

Skin element

Bolt element

Applied loads due to system shear-lag (s)

Constant load or displacement

One degree of freedom per node

(a) Finite Element Model of a Line of Three Bolts

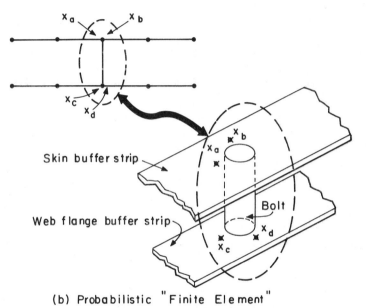

Skin buffer strip

Web flange buffer strip

Bolt

(b) Probabilistic "Finite Element"

FIG. 9—*Mechanical/probability model for bolt-line.*

failure at any site makes the adjacent bolt "disappear" mechanically, while the element in which the failure actually occurred remains in the structure! The symbolic expression for the probability of the disappearance of a typical bolt can be written

$$Pr \{\text{Bolt becomes ineffective}\} = 1 - \prod [1 - F(x_a)] \cdots [1 - F(x_d)] \quad (21)$$

However, there remains the difficult question of how the bookkeeping between applied load and stresses $x_a, \ldots, x_d$ must be done to produce valid convolution integral limits for a redundant reliability analysis. This difficulty is still unresolved.

Current Trends in Reliability Assessment

The topics reviewed in the foregoing have been confined to mathematical techniques for the calculation of the probabilities for various events to occur, without much discussion of what these "failures" might mean in a practical sense. However, no review of structural reliability analysis can achieve adequate perspective without at least a brief focus on the latter subject. Since design criteria are involved, as well as failure definitions currently in vogue or proposed, together with associated physical/probability models for material behavior, we choose to narrow our focus to the field of aerospace vehicles.

Current typical aircraft design criteria have been devised more or less independently of one another, and consider reliability only in general terms. Either the "fail-safe" (FS) or "safe crack growth" (SCG) criteria may be used for the design of military aircraft; each is based in part on statistics characterizing manufacturing flaws which may escape detection in a nondestructive inspection (NDI) program, or which may appear in the airframe during service. Not only do the FS and SCG statistics differ, the two criteria normally result in different design structural weights for the same aircraft mission, and no basis exists for comparison between FS and SCG designs. Hence, there is a strong motivation to employ the mathematical reliability analysis methods to adjust these criteria to provide designs having equal probabilities of "safety." (A large part of the problem is, of course, what is meant by the term "safety" in this context.)

The traditional approach to airframe reliability assessment has been from a fatigue viewpoint, with the Palmgren-Miner rule entering in the design phase, and with a full-scale fatigue test to demonstrate airframe life. Even these assessments were not made until the 1950's. For example, the B-47 (designed in the early 1940's) had no full-scale fatigue test. Also, no full-scale fatigue test was included in the original B-52 program (1955 to 1962 production) until several aircraft were lost during low-level operation, a penetration mode which had not been part of the original operational concept. As a result of problems with the F-111, which was originally designed as a safe-life structure, the SCG concept was applied (by analysis and inspection) to establish proof-test inspection intervals for the F-111 fleet to assure flight safety. By proof-testing each airframe at low temperature, assurance was obtained that no flaw size above a given value existed in the structure at the time of test. (The proof-test inspection intervals were based on the flaw growth calculations discussed in the following.) The C-5A is the first Air Force aircraft to have had a contractual life guarantee, but fracture mechanics analysis had not reached a point where it could influence design and choice of materials during the initial design cycle.

The operational structural failures and fatigue test failures experienced by the F-111 and C-5A have caused intensive program reviews [40,41], which included mathematical reliability analysis for comparative assessment of the risks associated with alternate retrofit programs [42,43]. Mathematical reliability analyses are currently being employed to assess possible courses of action for improving the safety of other fleets already in service, for example, the B-52D, KC-135, and F-4 [44–46]. As existing fleets of aircraft continue to age, and in some cases begin to serve on missions not originally considered as part of the design envelope, there is additional motivation to use the available mathematical techniques to make meaningful assessments of safety.

Two statistical concepts of material behavior occupy prominent positions in the current literature on structural realiability analysis; both attempt to make statements about the life expectancy of structural materials. The first concept models the time history of stable flaw growth in terms of a rate equation, which takes the following form for constant-amplitude fatigue

$$da/dn = Cs^{2r}a^r \qquad (22)$$

where

a = instantaneous crack length,

s = stress range = $S_{max} - S_{min}$ for constant-amplitude fatigue,

r = experimentally determined growth-rate exponent,

C = an experimentally determined constant, and

n = number of fatigue cycles experienced by the material.

The parameters r, C must be determined for each material; generally, $r > 1$, with many materials having $r \approx 2$. Extensive da/dn data are now available for most aircraft metal alloys [47]. Integration of Eq 22 to produce an expression for crack length after n fatigue cycles is straightforward

$$a_0^{1-r} - a_n^{1-r} = (r - 1)Cns^{2r} \qquad (23)$$

where a_o, a_n, represent the initial flaw size and the flaw size after n cycles. A reliability assessment can be based on flaw growth if the deterministic initial flaw size a_o is replaced by a distribution

$$F(a_o) = Pr\{\text{Initial flaw size} \leqslant a_o\}$$

$$f(a_o) = dF/da_o \qquad (24)$$

A density function $g(a_n)$ for the distribution of flaw size after n fatigue cycles is then derived by solving Eq 23 for a_o and substituting into

$$g(a_n) = f[a_o(a_n)] \cdot \left| \frac{da_o}{da_n} \right| \equiv g_n(a) \qquad (25)$$

Assumptions for $F(a_o)$ have been based in the past on inspections of in-service aircraft. More recently, data have been obtained from NDI programs (for example, the B-1). When Eq 25 has been integrated, either analytically or numerically, calculations can be made for the probability that a given structure contains a crack longer than some critical size, a_{cr}, as $1 - G_n(a_{cr})$ after n fatigue cycles. The results of these calculations can be used in turn to set safe inspection intervals. This type of procedure was followed in the F-111 reliability analysis mentioned earlier [42], but with more complex fatigue loading history corresponding to several typical F-111 mission profiles. Redundancy did not enter into the analysis, since the F-111 was not designed as a fail-safe structure. The Air Force is also conducting more general studies of the statistical flaw growth concept and its possible direct impact on design criteria [16]. The requirement for large amounts of experimental data presents an obstacle to the wider application of statistical flaw growth. Each new configuration requires experiments because of the sensitivity of the da/dn equation to load history, geometric stress concentrators, corrosive environments, etc. Numerous examples will be found in the work of Schjive [10].

The second concept [48,49] avoids the difficulties of characterizing flaw growth directly by treating fatigue from a residual strength viewpoint. The general nature of flaw growth rate is used to formulate a "wear-out" equation for residual strength as a function of time or fatigue cycles. The wear-out law can be used, in the same manner as the crack growth rate equation, to predict the probability distribution for residual strength of a material at various stages of its fatigue life, given the distribution function for strength of the virgin material. Numerous experiments are still required, but this approach possesses the advantages that strength plays a central role throughout, and that an experimental strength data base is perhaps somewhat more objective than an experimental flaw size data base. Also, the wear-out approach is more satisfying for application to redundant reliability analysis in that it provides a direct picture of the increasing variability of the strength of an aging structure due to flaw growth. The wear-out concept seems to be of practical value for brittle materials, such as composites, since their static strength and flaw growth behavior appear to be directly related. However, wear-out may not be applicable to ductile alloys, for which static strength is a function of metallurgical characteristics as well as flaw distribution.

We conclude this section with a comparison of two possible procedures for calculating the failure probability of a structure. Suppose that the structure is subjected to random applied loading from a single source, characterized by a probability density function $f_A(s)$. Suppose further that variability of the components results in strength distribution functions $F_{WL}(s)$ (weak-link) and $F_R(s)$ (redundant), which we assume to be known, based on virgin material strength. A "safe" design will be such that no more than the lower tails of F_{WL} and F_R overlap the upper tail of f_A, as shown in Fig. 10. A failure probability calculation of the form

$$P_F = \int_0^\infty F_R(s)f_A(s)ds \cong \int_0^\infty F_{WL}(s)f_A(s)ds \tag{26}$$

then provides an assessment of operational unreliability due to unexpected overloads, that is, loads which are greater than the design ultimate load, but which still have a finite probability of occurrence. Proof of the accuracy of the approximation in Eq 26 by Shinozuka et al was cited earlier [31]. However, it is apparent that the number calculated from Eq 26 does not provide a complete assessment of the safety of a structure, when increasing variability due to aging is considered. We therefore propose the following type of procedure as a supplement to Eq 26. Let $F_R(s, t)$ represent the redundant structural strength distribution after time t; calculate from $f_A(s)$ and load application frequency data a largest load s_t which occurs (say) on an average of once during the elapsed time t. Then $F_R(s_t, t)$ is a measure of the unreliability of the structure due to aging. Figure 11 illustrates schematically the construction of an unreliability curve for the structure by crossplotting. The lower tail of such an unreliability curve will probably have the greatest significance for management decisions concerning fleet operations or retirement. Hence, the redundant strength distribution F_R is preferred for the unreliability calculation because lower tail values, where F_{WL} is too conservative, are required. Shinozuka has aptly characterized procedures of this type as solutions of "under-strength" problems.

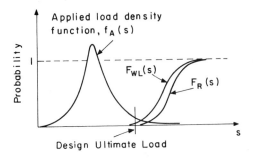

FIG. 10—*Applied load and strength statistics for a "safe" design.*

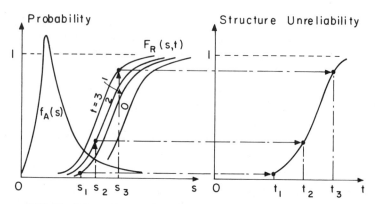

FIG. 11—*Schematic crossplot technique for structure unreliability curve.*

Conclusions

Modern structural reliability assessment methods and their antecedents have been reviewed, with primary emphasis on the mathematical analysis techniques. The classical weak-link and fiber bundle theories have appeared as the two extremes for statistical models of structural systems. While weak-link theory is useful for assessment of overload effects, fiber bundle theory is too specialized for application to engineering structures. A generalization of fiber bundle theory for redundant structures has been presented in a form permitting *"k* out of *n"* assessments which are capable of automated computation for failure probabilities between the two extremes. It has been proposed that the generalized bundle theory can play a useful role in the assessment of structural unreliability caused by wearout. Review of some typical aircraft design criteria and recent experience with aircraft structural failures has indicated the need to bring reliability assessment methods to bear on criteria and specifications at an earlier stage in the design cycle. We expect that this activity will take the form of comparative assessment of a small number of competing designs, rather than general, automated optimizing schemes. We also suspect that mathematical reliability will never enter directly into design criteria, due to a fundamental philospohical conflict between the imprecise probabilistic view of nature and the legislative need for absolute precision. However, the comparative assessment role is important in itself; we cite as an analogy the ARDC Standard Atmosphere, in which "fly-off competitions" are held daily on the computers of every major aerospace manufacturer, but in which no aircraft has ever flown.

Acknowledgments

The new analytical work presented in this paper was sponsored in part by the Air Force Materials Laboratory, in part by the Air Force Aeronautical Systems Division in conjunction with the Air Force Flight Dynamics Laboratory, and in part by the General Dynamics Corporation. The authors wish to express their appreciation to C. F. Tiffany (USAF Aeronautical Systems Division), for taking time out of a busy schedule to review the manuscript of this paper and for providing several valuable suggestions for revisions. We also wish to thank A. W. Davis (USAF Materials Laboratory), D. J. Wilkins, and M. E. Waddoups (General Dynamics), Profs. M. Shinozuka and R. Vaicaitas (Columbia University), and our colleague Prof. J. W. Mar, all of whom contributed to the reliability analysis development with enthusiasm and many helpful technical suggestions.

References

[1] Steinman, D. B. and Watson, S. W., *Bridges and Their Builders*, Dover Publications, Inc., New York, 1957.

[2] Straub, Hans, *A History of Civil Engineering*, MIT Press, Massachusetts Institute of Technology, Cambridge, Mass., 1964.

[3] Timoshenko, S. P., *History of Strength of Materials*, McGraw-Hill, New York, 1953.

[4] Chapelle, H. I., *The History of American Sailing Ships*, W. W. Norton & Co., Inc., New York, 1935.

[5] Crowninshield, B. B., *Fore-and-Afters*, Houghton Mifflin Co., Boston, Mass., 1940.

[6] LeScal, Yves, *The Great Days of the Cape Horners*, New American Library, New York, 1967.

[7] Weibull, W., "A Statistical Theory of Strength of Materials," *Proceedings of the Royal Academy of English Scientists*, No. 15, 1939.

[8] Palmgren, A., "Die Lebensdauer von Kugellager," *Z.V.D.I.*, Vol. 68, 1924, pp. 339–341.

[9] Miner, M. A., *Journal of Applied Mechanics*, Vol. 12, 1945, pp. A159–A164.

[10] Schjive, J., "The Accumulation of Fatigue Damage in Aircraft Materials and Structures," Paper No. 3, *Proceedings*, AGARD Conference No. 118, Symposium on Random Load Fatigue, Lyngby, Denmark, 13 April 1972.

[11] ASME Boiler and Pressure Vessel Code, Section III: Nuclear Power Plant Components, 1971 (to be revised in 1974).

[12] Report of Advisory Committee on Reactor Safeguards to the Atomic Energy Commission, Jan. 1974.

[13] Cornell, C. A., "A Probability-Based Structural Code," Paper No. 66–85, *Journal*, American Concrete Institute, Dec. 1969.

[14] Bouton, I. et al, "An Evaluation of Quantitative Structural Design Criteria by Statistical Methods," AFFDL-TR-67-107, Air Force Flight Dynamics Laboratory, Wright-Patterson AFB, Ohio, 1967.

[15] Brown, Colin, "Remarks on a Study of a 'New' Procedure for the Statistical Evaluation of Design Criteria," Technical Report No. 62, Institute for the Study of Fatigue and Reliability, Columbia University, New York, March 1969.

[16] Eckvall, J. C. et al, "Engineering Criteria and Analysis Methodology for the Appraisal of Potential Fracture Resistant Primary Aircraft Structure," AFFDL-TR-72-80, Air Force Flight Dynamics Laboratory, Wright-Patterson Air Force Base, Ohio, Sept. 1972.

[17] Whittaker, I. C. and Besuner, P. M., "A Reliability Analysis Approach to Fatigue Life Variability of Aircraft Structures," AFML-TR-69-65, Air Force Materials Laboratory, Wright-Patterson Air Force Base, Ohio, April 1969.

[18] Breiman, Leo, *Statistics With a View Toward Applications*, Houghton Mifflin Co., Boston, Mass., 1973.

[19] Barlow, R. E. and Proschan, F., *Mathematical Theory of Reliability,* Wiley, New York, 1967.

[20] Bien, D. D., "Optimum Allocation of Redundancy Among Subsystems Connected in Series," NASA TN D-7164, National Aeronautics and Space Administration, March 1973.

[21] Daniels, H. E., "The Statistical Theory of the Strength of Bundles of Threads," *Proceedings of the Royal Society,* Series A, Vol. 183, No. A995, 1945.

[22] Waddoups, M. E., General Dynamics Corp., Fort Worth, Tex., private communication.

[23] Orringer, O., "Failure Probability Calculations for Redundant Assemblies," Summary Technical Note to Air Force Materials Laboratory, Aeroelastic and Structures Research Laboratory, Massachusetts Institute of Technology, Cambridge, Mass., 16 July 1973.

[24] Rosen, B. W., "Tensile Strength of Fibrous Composites," *Journal,* American Institute of Aeronautics and Astronautics, Vol. 2, 1964.

[25] Hedgepeth, J. M., "Stress Concentrations in Filamentry Structures," NASA TN D-882, National Aeronautics and Space Administration, May 1961.

[26] Zender, G. and Deaton, J. W., "Strength of Filamentary Sheets with One or More Fibers Broken," NASA TN-D-1609, National Aeronautics and Space Administration, March 1963.

[27] Lin, Y. K., *Probabilistic Theory of Structural Dynamics,* McGraw-Hill, New York, 1967.

[28] Dailey, C. C., "Preliminary Environmental Requirements for Mission A Experiments," letter from NASA/MSFC HEAO Experiments Office to experiment developers, 2 June 1972.

[29] AEC Regulatory Guide, Atomic Energy Commission, Sections 1.29, 1.60, 1.61, 1973.

[30] Vaicaitas, R. and Shinozuka, M., "Digital Generation of Forces to be Applied to Structural Models in Large Scale Experiments," Modern Analysis, Inc., Ridgewood, N.J., March 1974.

[31] Shinozuka, M., Yao, J. T. P., and Nishimura, A., "A Note on the Reliability of Redundant Structures," Technical Report No. 27, Institute for the Study of Fatigue and Reliability, Columbia University, New York, Nov. 1965.

[32] Moses, F. and Kinser, D. E., "Optimum Structural Design with Failure Probability Constraints," *Journal,* American Institute of Aeronautics and Astronautics Vol. 5, No. 6, June 1967.

[33] Mau, S. T., "Optimum Design of Structures with a Minimum Expected Cost Criterion," Technical Report No. 340, Cornell University, Department of Structural Engineering, Ithaca, N.Y., 1971.

[34] Schmit, L. A., "Structural Design by Systematic Synthesis," *Proceedings,* 2nd Conference on Electronic Computation, American Society of Civil Engineers, Pittsburgh, Pa., Sept. 1960.

[35] Sved, G. and Ginos, Z., *International Journal of Mechanical Sciences,* Vol. 10, 1968, pp. 803–805.

[36] Peterson, R. M., "Reliability Analysis of Redundant Structural Assemblies," SM Thesis, Department of Aeronautics and Astronautics, Massachusetts Institute of Technology, Cambridge, Mass., June 1973.

[37] Seppanen, Kari, SM Thesis, Department of Aeronautics and Astronautics, Massachusetts Institute of Technology, Cambridge, Mass., June 1974.

[38] Orringer, O., "Strength Statistics of Engineering Components: A Preliminary Investigation," Summary Technical Note to Air Force Materials Laboratory, Aeroelastic and Structures Research Laboratory, Massachusetts Institute of Technology, Cambridge, Mass., 24 July 1973.

[39] Orringer, O. and McCarthy, J. F., "Eighth Progress Report Covering Period 1 November–15 December 1973," Aeroelastic and Structures Research Laboratory, Massachusetts Institute of Technology, Cambridge, Mass., Contract F33615-70-C-1131, 20 Dec. 1973.

[40] Ashley, Holt et al, "Report of the USAF Scientific Advisory Board Ad Hoc Committee on the F-111 on Lessons Learned from the F-111 Structural Experience," 26 Oct. 1971.

[41] McCarthy, J. F. et al, "Report of the USAF Scientific Advisory Board C-5 Advisory Group," April 1973.

[42] Maske, E. B., "F-111A/E/D/F Risk Assessment Sensitivity Analysis," General Dynamics Corp., Fort Worth, Tex., presentation to USAF Scientific Advisory Board, 25 June 1971.

[43] Final Report of the C-5 Independent Structural Review Team, Report No. LG 72 ER 0067, Lockheed-Georgia Co., Marietta, Ga., March 1973.

[44] McCarthy, J. F., et al, "Report of the B-52D Structural Assessment Group," USAF Aeronautical Systems Division, ASD/ENF, Wright-Patterson Air Force Base, Ohio, Aug. 1973. (Title UNCLASSIFIED, Report SECRET.)

[45] Haviland, G. P., "Final Report of Ad Hoc Group Review of C/KC-135 Structural Integrity Program," USAF Aeronautical Systems Division, ASD/ENF, Wright-Patterson Air Force Base, Ohio, 20 June 1973 (supplemental report 22 Aug. 1973).

[46] Clark, J. R., et al, "First Report of the F-4 Structures Committee," Division Advisory Group, USAF Aeronautical Systems Division, Wright-Patterson Air Force Base, Ohio, March 1973.

[47] Campbell, J. E. et al, "Damage Tolerant Design Handbook," Metals and Ceramics Information Center, Battelle Columbus Laboratories, Columbus, Ohio, Dec. 1972.

[48] Halpin, J. C., Jerina, K. L., and Johnson, T. A. in *Analysis of the Test Methods for High Modulus Fibers and Composites, ASTM STP 521,* American Society for Testing and Materials, 1973, pp. 5–64.

[49] Waddoups, M. E., "Fracture of Composites—A Design Viewpoint," General Dynamics Corp., Fort Worth, Tex., presentation to NASA Research and Technology Advisory Council, 23 May 1973.

Statistics and Accelerated Characterization

R. E. Maxwell,[1] R. H. Toland,[2] and C. W. Johnson[1]

Probabilistic Design of Composite Structures*

REFERENCE: Maxwell, R. E., Toland, R. H., and Johnson, C. W., "**Probabilistic Design of Composite Structures,**" *Composite Reliability, ASTM STP 580,* American Society for Testing and Materials, 1975, pp. 35–53.

ABSTRACT: The method of statistical trials (Monte Carlo simulation) in combination with a sensitivity analysis by variance separation is presented as an efficient design and analysis system for each specific mode of failure. The method has several advantages: (1) it provides a realistic reliability prediction for each failure mode of a composite structure; (2) it determines the material, geometrical, and manufacturing variables which have a significant role upon the structure's reliability with respect to each failure mode; and (3) it determines which material, geometrical, and manufacturing variables should be controlled in order to manufacture the structure at minimum product assurance costs. Application is made to the graphite-epoxy truss tubes of NASA's applications technology satellite.

KEY WORDS: composite materials, reliability, composite structures, simulation, variance separation, significance, probability distribution functions, optimum design

The purpose of this paper is to demonstrate a design system that provides a tool to design reliability into a structure as well as to realistically assess the reliability of the design with respect to a given failure mode at any point in its development. The system has been applied as a design and as an analysis tool for many problems, one of which is presented herein.

The mathematical design assessment techniques used in the paper are the method of statistical trials, hereinafter called Monte Carlo simulation (MCS), in combination with a sensitivity analysis by variance separation (VS). The MCS method has been widely used in many different areas, particularly in the area of general risk analysis. However, the application of the MCS method in conjunction with the VS technique for design application is considered to be relatively new. In this paper, the MCS/VS

*Work performed under Fairchild Industries Contract No. SC-71-6.
[1] Group supervisor of reliability engineering and lead engineer, respectively, Hercules Incorporated, Magna, Utah 84044.
[2] Assistant professor of mechanics, Drexel University, Philadelphia, Pa. 19104.

technique is applied to the design and manufacture of a composite structure, NASA's application technology satellite (ATS) graphite-epoxy truss. The MCS/VS method was applied to this composite structure's development, manufacture, and test programs, but certain aspects of the problem have been altered herein to better illustrate the system of design. The paper addresses the analysis of each single failure mode for the structure, but a reference and a brief discussion of how the individual analyses can be combined to form a reliability analysis of the structure with respect to many failure modes is given in the section on the use of MCS/VS.

Design System

Figure 1 is a highly summarized flow diagram of how a design engineer can use the MCS/VS technique on prime modes of failure to iteratively predict (from inception to conclusion) the inherent reliability of a composite structure with respect to each of the prime failure modes. The designer begins with a design concept which consists of geometry, materials, manufacturing process, and verification tests, and a concept which is thought to satisfy the intent of the application of the composite structure. Also, during the concept phase, the designer obtains a set of geometrical tolerances for the planned manufacturing process; assembles preliminary data from initial laboratory testing, handbooks, or prospective material vendors on material properties; and develops the design reliability models of the failure mode parameters which incorporate the manufacturing geometrical tolerance variables, mission objective variables (temperatures, primary-secondary loads), and material properties.

Initial probability distributions are formulated for all variables which appear in the design reliability model of each failure mode. The initial distributions of the variables are usually little more than probable ranges of the variables because test data and other specific information may not be available during the early phase of the program.

The design reliability models and preliminary probability distributions of the variables are then analyzed by the MCS/VS computer program. The output from the MCS/VS program provides a preliminary estimate of reliability for the failure mode and a sensitivity analysis of the design reliability model's variables with respect to the failure mode.

The preliminary estimate of reliability and the sensitivity analysis provide the designer with quantitative information to make decisions. If the preliminary estimate of reliability does not meet the apportioned reliability requirement for the failure mode, then the nominal value of the failure mode parameter must be shifted by changing the nominal values of the model's variables or by reducing the probable ranges of the variables on both. Since nominal values of material variables are difficult to change,

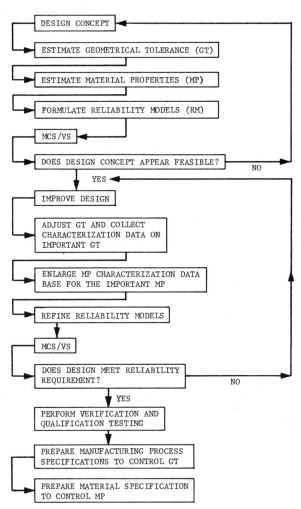

FIG. 1—*Typical composite structural design-and-reliability assessment system flow using MCS/VS.*

one may have to select another material which has the necessary nominal value, and if the nominal values of the geometrical tolerance need to be shifted, then the manufacturing equipment may have to be modified. Using the same or different variations on the model's variables, the designer can assure different nominal values for the material and manufacturing variables to obtain an a priori idea of the effect on the failure mode's predicted reliability which would result if such changes were made. These simulated effects should be used as a guide for alternate materials and to initiate planning for possible manufacturing process changes.

As soon as material and manufacturing nominals are relatively firm, then the sensitivity analysis is used to determine the scope of the material's testing program. The sensitivity analysis of the MCS/VS technique provides a quantitative ranking of the variables of the model as to their ability to cause variation in the failure-mode parameter. If a material variable (its nominal value and variational envelope) is less dominant than other material variables, then minimal or possibly no further testing effort should be completed. The material and manufacturing variables which are responsible for the majority of the variation should be the main focus of the testing program and proofing of the manufacturing process.

As the material testing programs and process proofing evolves, experimental data on variables of importance should be collected, analyzed, and assembled into probability distributions which quantify the amount and type of variation to be expected during production of the structure. The MCS/VS technique should be used iteratively and frequently during the evolution of the design to assess the effects of newly acquired data.

When the design is relatively mature, the MCS/VS technique can be used as part of the information which is required to formulate verification and qualification testing of the structure, and the resulting test data of the manufactured structure can be correlated with the refined analytical reliability design models. Throughout this design system, the MCS/VS technique has been used as an aid to help quantify the inherent reliability of the structural design and to provide the designer with quantitative information as to which variables of the design play a significant role in its inherent reliability. The MCS/VS technique will probably never replace development testing of the device, but development testing of the structure can be minimized through application of this method.

Reliability Prediction by MCS

A general description of the method is given in this section, followed by an application example.

If y (failure-mode parameter) is a known function of the independent random variables X_1, X_2, ..., X_n (material, geometrical, and manufacturing variables), that is, if

$$y = f(X_1, \ldots, X_n) = f(X)$$

where the probability distributions of the X_i's are either known or approximated, then the MCS technique can be used to generate the probability distribution of y, and VS can be used to determine the percentage of variation in y which is caused by each X_i. The probability distribution of y can then be used to calculate the probability of y being within a given interval, and the sensitivity analysis by VS can be used to determine which of the X_i's are the most important for causing variation in y.

The probability distribution of y can be obtained by purely analytical methods (such as integration); however, this is usually a difficult analysis task. MCS is a computer-numerical method which circumvents the analytical difficulty by generating a histogram (frequency plot) of the probability distribution of y. Construction of the histogram proceeds as follows:

1. A value of each X_i is selected at random according to its probability distribution.

2. $y = f(X)$ is evaluated at the set of X_i's which have been randomly selected, and this gives a value for y corresponding to the randomly selected values for the X_i's.

3. This process is repeated on a digital computer many times, and a frequency histogram of the y's is then calculated which approximates the probability distribution of y. Some practical methods have been developed to determine when a sufficient number of replications have been performed, but these methods are not the subject of this paper.

Sensitivity Analysis by VS

To determine the percentage of variation in y which is caused by the X_i's, one can use purely analytical methods such as differentiation; however, this is time-consuming and prone to error because of the symbolic complexity. This complexity can be eliminated by use of VS, which, like MCS, is also a computer-numerical method. The VS numerical procedure to complete the sensitivity analysis is as follows:

1. It is initially assumed that y can be represented as a multiple linear function of the x_i's, that is, y is modeled as

$$y \approx c + \sum_{i=1}^{n} b_i X_i$$

where c and the b_i's are unknown. The randomly selected X_i's together with the functional value of y at these X_i's (generated by the MCS procedure) are then used in a multiple linear regression (least squares) to facilitate calculation of these coefficients.

2. During the calculation of the MCS histogram, the standard deviation of $y(\sigma_y)$ is calculated and the standard deviations of each $X_i(\sigma_i)$ are also computed.

3. The coefficients b_i found in Step 1 together with the standard deviations of σ_y and σ_i of Step 2 are then used in the following formula to determine the percent of variation (PV) in y which is caused by each X_i, that is

$$PV(X_i) = 100 b_i^2 \frac{\sigma_i^2}{\sigma_y^2} \qquad (1 \leqslant i \leqslant n)$$

The assumption that y can be represented as a multiple linear function of the X_i's can be assessed by the statistical parameters which are calculated in conjunction with a multiple regression. In most cases these statistics indicate that y can be represented as a multiple linear function because the neighborhood of linear approximation is defined by the variational envelopes of the X_i's, and these envelopes are usually small enough that a linear approximation suffices. The design model y is almost always a nonlinear function of the X_i's, but over these relatively small variational envelopes the multiple linear approximation is an accurate predictor for y. Hence, if the statistics of the multiple regression indicate that y can be locally approximated by a multiple linear function, and since the X_i's are independent random variables, the formula of Step 3 for the variance separation is immediate.

Comparison of the MCS/VS Technique with Similar Methods

The MCS technique for this paper has been applied to the difference between the applied and allowable loads. This application of the MCS technique is a generalization of the requirements-versus-capability (R//C) technique. The R//C technique, as developed by General Electric [2],[3] gives a reliability prediction by calculating the probability that the capability will exceed the requirement. To formulate the solution to a prediction problem by the R//C technique, models of the requirement function $R(x)$ and the capability function $C(z)$ have to be formulated. The prediction is then effected by calculating the probability that the requirement exceeds the capability.

The mathematical framework provided by the concepts of the R//C technique is an elegant solution to the general problem of prediction. Hercules experience with the GE Tempo computer code has been good; however, many prediction problems were found where the GE Tempo code had difficulty, that is, whenever the R or C functions were the solutions of nonlinear equations. Since it was essential to have the ability to solve the full continuum of prediction problems, the MCS generalization solves the difficult problems, it also solves the simple ones; hence, the MCS implementation of the R//C ideas has replaced the original GE Tempo method of prediction.

Many of the prediction concepts of the R//C technique and the MCS implementation of it are given in a paper by Broding et al [3]. The basic idea of this paper is that the safety factor, the ratio of the allowable to the applied loads, is a random variable. Hence, the R//C technique uses the difference (R-C) to obtain the prediction, whereas Broding uses the ratio of R to C. Thus, the combination of the MCS generaliza-

---

[3]The italic numbers in brackets refer to the list of references appended to this paper.

tion of the R//C technique and the random-variable concept of the safety factor by Broding are equivalent in terms of fundamental ideas.

Hercules experience with the ratio (R/C) has shown that it (generally speaking) produces probability distributions which are skewed, whereas the use of the difference (R-C) for these same cases will usually produce a more symmetric, near normally distributed, probability distribution. In Hercules written and verbal communications with management and customers, communication is greatly facilitated whenever the normal distribution can be made applicable to the problems, as many of these interested people are not familiar with all the intricacies of statistics, and their interest and understanding is essential to implement design changes and to demonstrate compliance to contract requirements.

The GE Tempo implementation of the R//C technique does not include a direct or simultaneous method for performing sensitivity studies, whereas, the MCS implementation of the R//C technique does perform a sensitivity analysis in parallel with the reliability prediction by the aforementioned VS technique.

The previously mentioned paper by Broding gives a method (linear-perturbation) to perform sensitivity analyses. This method expands the safety factor as a Taylor series involving the linear and second-degree terms. If only the linear terms of the safety factor are considered, the linear-perturbation method gives the following sensitivity function

$$\sigma_{SF}^2 = \sum_{j=1}^{n} \left(\frac{\partial SF}{\partial x_j} \right)^2 \sigma_{x_i^2}$$

where the partial derivatives $\{ \partial SF / \partial x_j \}$ are evaluated at the mean values of the x_j's. The VS technique uses a similar method except that the difference (R-C) is used instead of the ratio (R/C), the partial derivatives are numerically approximated by a multiple regression analysis which runs in parallel with the prediction calculations, and the parameter of the sensitivity analysis is the percent of variance of the dependent variable instead of units of variance.

The VS technique also uses the statistics of the multiple regression analysis as a criterion to measure the validity of the sensitivity analysis, whereas Broding uses no such criterion. Such a criterion is essential. For example, if the multiple regression were significant and if the square of the multiple correlation coefficient (r^2) were 0.99, than 99 percent of the functional variation of (R-C) is reproduced by the multiple linear approximation, and thus only 1 percent of the variance of (R-C) cannot be allocated to the independent variables. If instead r^2 were 0.01, then this would indicate that the sensitivity analysis is worthless, and that the variational envelopes of the dependent variables must be reduced or that several analyses must be performed within the variational envelopes.

In many cases, the probability distributions of R and C are approximately normal; hence, the distribution of (R-C) is also normal, but if one uses the ratio (R/C) of normal distributions, this is a Cauchy distribution, and it has no standard deviation or mean. Thus, the difference (R-C) is the most generally applicable function for reliability prediction and sensitivity analysis.

Use of MCS/VS

The primary use of the MCS/VS technique by Hercules has been to approximate critical and highly specialized failure rates and to determine the independent variables of the critical failure modes which are responsible for the majority of the risk. The approximate failure rates are then used in Fault Tree-type logical models of the various top-line contract requirements which the manufactured hardware must exceed or meet. Evaluation of the Fault Tree then gives the reliability of the structure with respect to all of the failure modes contained within the tree.

The Fault Tree approach has been used extensively in the analysis of risk for atomic reactors *[4]*. This approach is also applicable to general reliability problems. It is a systematic method to analyze complex and realistic situations which involve many failure modes. The Fault Tree model, when numerically evaluated, gives a top-line reliability prediction, and it also organizes the many seemingly unrelated failure modes. The main function of this paper is to show how one may realistically determine various specialized failure rates which have to be quantified in order to numerically evaluate the Fault Tree.

Hercules' problems in applying the MCS/VS technique have been to find models which mirror the multifarious physical situations with sufficient accuracy to give reliability predictions in which one can have a great deal of confidence. In some cases, Hercules is still looking for accurate predictors; however, not a great deal of time has been spent lamenting about all the problems that cannot be solved to Hercules' satisfaction. When forced to work a failure mode which has only a hammer-and-tong type of predictor, Hercules performs the analysis, applies the appropriate written and verbal curses, and spends the majority of their time on problems which have solutions. This general approach to reliability analysis of complicated structures emphasizes those areas where there is a considerable vacuum between theory and practice. It stimulates research for better predictors, and simultaneously makes information available in which one can have confidence to help formulate policies and make decisions on the design, development, and manufacture of the product.

Some of the analysis work on composite structures requires the use of finite-element (FE) computer models, and a single FE computer run can take from a few seconds to a few hours. Since the MCS/VS technique requires 5000 to 10 000 functional evaluations, it should be clear that an MCS/VS analysis which would directly involve so many FE evaluations could not be economically justified in an industrial environment. If the model requires very much computer evaluation time, then it may be necessary to substitute an approximate model which, though less precise, can be more quickly evaluated by the computer. In such a case, an approximate model should be found in order for the MCS/VS scheme to be efficient and cost effective. Although the synthesis of approximate models is beyond the scope of this paper, good success, in such cases as this, has been achieved by using the FE computer programs to generate the observations from which a quickly evaluated "empirical model" is constructed. The procedure for doing this will not be illustrated here, but will be published in a forthcoming paper [5].

The MCS/VS techniques can be applied to an infinity of other similar problems from many fields, but a typical system for using it to develop a composite structural design is given in Fig. 1. In order to illustrate this design-and-reliability assessment system, an application to a composite structural design problem is provided in the following section.

One should note that the technique provides a method to quantitatively design inherent reliability into the structure so that the design contains, at its inception, the inherent reliability which tests of the particular device verify.

Composite Structure Example—The ATS Truss

NASA's application technology satellite (ATS) models F&G incorporate lightweight 15-ft graphite epoxy tubes in the truss support structure. This structure was designed and manufactured by Hercules Incorporated for Fairchild Industries. Hercules applied the MCS/VS method to the design analyses, manufacturing, quality control, and testing of the graphite-epoxy tubes. The example described herein is only one major aspect of the entire design and test program. The objective of this effort was to design and manufacture graphite-epoxy tubes with a 0.99 reliability under a column stability criterion. The failure mode which is addressed, therefore, is column buckling under a compressive load.

The example is constructed as follows:

1. Define system model, density of the load (P), and probability distribution of the X_i's (design variables or independent variables).

2. Calculate initial reliability estimate (via MSC/VS) and determine (via VS) the most significant (control parameters) X_i's which are causing the variation in P_{cr}, the critical tube buckling load.

3. Model control parameters or better characterize the probability

distribution of the important design reliability control parameters, or both.

4. Calculate an improved reliability prediction and determine the new control parameters from the refined models and improved characterizations of the X_i's.

The ATS satellite and truss are depicted in Fig. 2, and the model for column stability is shown in Fig. 3. The influences of the upper bridge

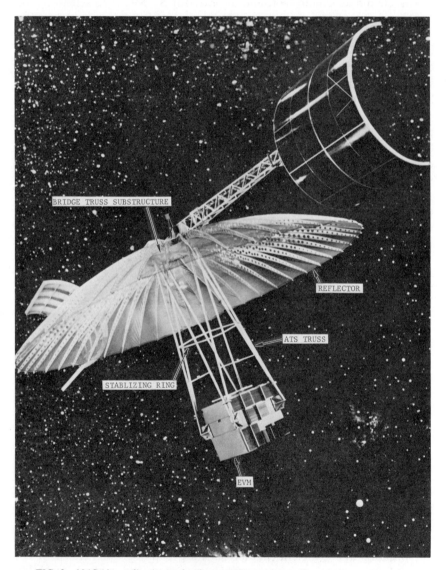

FIG. 2—*NASA's application technology satellite with graphite-epoxy support truss.*

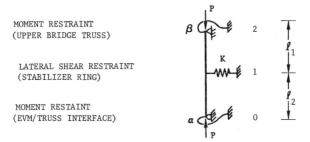

FIG. 3—*Truss tube configuration used in critical load,* P_{cr}, *analytical model.*

truss substructure, stabilizing ring, and column lower support are modeled as elastic restraints β, K, and α, respectively. These random variables and the random variable EI (the tube bending rigidity) are the X_i's for this problem where $(P_{cr} - P)$, the difference between critical and applied loads, is the dependent random variable; P_{cr} is given by

$$P_{cr} = f(\beta, K, \alpha, EI)$$

A derivation of the function f is given in the Appendix, and the analytical approach is by the transfer matrix method which is given in Ref *1*.

The preliminary reliability analysis and control parameter determination used the probability distribution for the X_i's as shown in Table 1.

TABLE 1—*Probability distributions for preliminary assessment of reliability.*

Random Variable	Distribution
α	$U(10^6, 10^8)$
K	$U(300, 700)$
β	$U(10^3, 10^5)$
EI	$T(10.5 \times 10^6, 13.43 \times 10^6, 16.7 \times 10^6)$
P	$U(17200, 17800)$

Notes:
Units are pounds, inches, and radians.
"U(a, b)" means uniformly distributed from a to b.
"T(a, b, c)" means triangularly distributed from a to c with median value at b.
"N(μ, σ)" means normally distributed with mean μ and standard deviation σ.

The preliminary analysis resulted in the histogram for $(P_{cr} - P)$ shown in Fig. 4, and the sensitivity analysis by VS of $(P_{cr} - P)$ is given in Table 2.

Figure 4 shows the predicted reliability to be 1.0-0.0796 = 0.9204 < 0.99, and the reliability requirement cannot be met if the X_i's are allowed

```
HISTOGRAM - MONTE CARLO SIMULATION

INITIAL TRUSS PROBABILITY OF FAILURE

RANDOM          SUMMED   DENSITY
VARIABLE        DENSITY  FUNCTION
-2786.496
-2650.902       0.00031  0.00031  +
-2375.715       0.00145  0.00114  ++
-2100.528       0.00386  0.00242  +++
-1825.341       0.00712  0.00326  ++++
-1550.153       0.01044  0.00332  ++++
-1274.966       0.01692  0.00648  +++++++
-999.7788       0.02647  0.00955  +++++++++++
-724.5916       0.03989  0.01343  +++++++++++++++
-449.4043       0.05629  0.01640  +++++++++++++++++
-174.2172       0.07701  0.02072  +++++++++++++++++++++++
100.9701        0.10149  0.02448  +++++++++++++++++++++++++++
376.1572        0.13303  0.03154  +++++++++++++++++++++++++++++++++++
651.3445        0.17017  0.03714  ++++++++++++++++++++++++++++++++++++++++++
926.5317        0.21203  0.04186  +++++++++++++++++++++++++++++++++++++++++++++++
1201.719        0.25992  0.04789  ++++++++++++++++++++++++++++++++++++++++++++++++++++++
1476.906        0.30531  0.04538  +++++++++++++++++++++++++++++++++++++++++++++++++++
1752.094        0.35466  0.04936  ++++++++++++++++++++++++++++++++++++++++++++++++++++++
2027.281        0.40551  0.05084  +++++++++++++++++++++++++++++++++++++++++++++++++++++++++
2302.468        0.45755  0.05205  ++++++++++++++++++++++++++++++++++++++++++++++++++++++++++
2577.655        0.50874  0.05119  +++++++++++++++++++++++++++++++++++++++++++++++++++++++++
2852.843        0.55348  0.04973  +++++++++++++++++++++++++++++++++++++++++++++++++++++
3128.030        0.61160  0.05312  +++++++++++++++++++++++++++++++++++++++++++++++++++++++++++
3403.217        0.66201  0.05040  ++++++++++++++++++++++++++++++++++++++++++++++++++++++++
3678.404        0.70752  0.04552  ++++++++++++++++++++++++++++++++++++++++++++++++++++
3953.592        0.75280  0.04527  +++++++++++++++++++++++++++++++++++++++++++++++++++
4228.777        0.79242  0.03963  +++++++++++++++++++++++++++++++++++++++++++++
4503.961        0.82808  0.03566  ++++++++++++++++++++++++++++++++++++++++
4779.145        0.86180  0.03372  +++++++++++++++++++++++++++++++++++++
5054.328        0.89133  0.02953  +++++++++++++++++++++++++++++++++
5329.512        0.91712  0.02580  +++++++++++++++++++++++++++++
5604.695        0.93597  0.01885  ++++++++++++++++++++
5879.879        0.95217  0.01619  +++++++++++++++++++
6155.063        0.96472  0.01255  ++++++++++++++
6430.246        0.97562  0.01090  ++++++++++++
6705.430        0.98402  0.00839  +++++++++
6980.613        0.98965  0.00563  ++++++
7255.797        0.99323  0.00358  ++++
7530.980        0.99570  0.00247  +++
7806.164        0.99767  0.00197  +++
8081.348        0.99853  0.00086  ++
8356.531        0.99891  0.00038  +
8631.715        0.99924  0.00033  +
8906.898        0.99980  0.00057  ++
9182.082        0.99992  0.00012  +
9457.266        1.00000  0.00007  +
9594.859
MEAN=XB =     2710.40        XB+3S =    8541.52       XB-3S =   -3120.71
STANDARD DEVIATION=S =    1943.71       RANGE =    12383.4
% NEGATIVE     7.9600 FROM EXTRAPOLATED NORMAL   0.81591D-01 CV(%)   71.713
TOTAL SAMPLE SIZE =   10000
CHI-SQUARE FOR NORMALITY =   96.2119            POS =    1.00000
CORRELATION WITH NORMAL DISTRIBUTION =   0.992813
% OF VARIATION EXPLAINED BY NORMAL DIST =   98.56779
```

FIG. 4—*Monte Carlo simulation, initial truss probability of failure.*

TABLE 2—*Sensitivity analysis—percent variation in* (P_{cr} − *P*)
caused by the X_i's.

Random Variable	% Variation in (P_{cr} − P)
α	0.0
K	39.4
β	12.9
EI	47.0
P	0.7

to vary as shown in Table 1. Hence, the variational envelopes of the X_i's must be reduced. One would certainly not waste his time and money trying to produce a smaller variational envelope for α or P, as they cause essentially no variation in $(P_{cr}-P)$. The important variables are EI, K, and β. Since α and P, considering their present variational envelopes, do not cause a significant amount of variation in $(P_{cr}-P)$, one should write their procurement, acceptance, manufacturing, and inspection documents to assure that α and P stay within the assumed variational envelopes.

In terms of cost and schedule, it was decided to obtain more experimental data to better quantify the probability distribution of K and to develop a model of EI in terms of the manufacturing and material variables which cause its variation.

Each tube was manufactured as shown in Fig. 5. The innermost ply is hoop wound with high modulus (HM) graphite-epoxy, the next eleven plies are wound with axially oriented HM graphite-epoxy, and the outermost ply is hoop-wound S-glass epoxy.

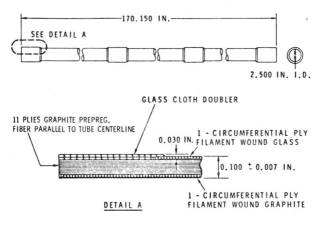

FIG. 5—*Graphite composite tube.*

$$EI = \frac{\pi}{8} D_M{}^3 (A_{11} A_{12}{}^2 / A_{22})$$

where

$D_M = D_I + h$, mean diameter,
$h = \Sigma k\, t^{(k)}$, tube thickness, and
$D_I = 2.50$ in., inside diameter.

The in-plane stiffnesses A_{11}, A_{12}, and A_{22} were computed as outlined in

Ref *6* from the lamina elastic constants and the fabrication variables $t^{(k)}$ and $\theta^{(k)}$, the kth ply thickness and orientation, respectively.

An MCS/VS analysis of *EI* was performed using this model. The probability distributions used for the independent variables are given in Table 3.

The histogram for *EI* is shown in Fig. 6, and it shows *EI* to be approximately normal with mean 14.29 × 10⁶ psi and standard deviation 0.44 × 10⁶ psi. The percent of variation in *EI* caused by the X_i's of its model is given in Table 4.

```
HISTOGRAM - MONTE CARLO SIMULATION

EI SIMULATION

 RANDOM          SUMMED  DENSITY
 VARIABLE        DENSITY FUNCTION
0.12674115 08
0.1271117E 08 0.00023 0.00023 +
0.1278530E 08 0.00030 0.00007 +
0.1285942E 08 0.00063 0.00033 +
0.1293355E 08 0.00092 0.00029 +
0.1300767E 08 0.00159 0.00067 +
0.1308180E 08 0.00256 0.00096 ++
0.1315593E 08 0.00455 0.00199 ++
0.1323005E 08 0.00892 0.00437 ++++
0.1330418E 08 0.01556 0.00664 ++++++
0.1337830E 08 0.02360 0.00803 +++++++
0.1345243E 08 0.03497 0.01138 +++++++++
0.1352656E 08 0.05107 0.01610 +++++++++++++
0.1360068E 08 0.07104 0.01997 ++++++++++++++++
0.1367481E 08 0.09909 0.02806 +++++++++++++++++++++
0.1374893E 08 0.13393 0.03484 +++++++++++++++++++++++++
0.1382306E 08 0.17357 0.03964 +++++++++++++++++++++++++++++
0.1389719E 08 0.21972 0.04616 ++++++++++++++++++++++++++++++++++
0.1397131E 08 0.27334 0.05361 ++++++++++++++++++++++++++++++++++++++
0.1404544E 08 0.32790 0.05456 +++++++++++++++++++++++++++++++++++++++
0.1411956E 08 0.39114 0.06324 +++++++++++++++++++++++++++++++++++++++++++++
0.1419369E 08 0.45320 0.06206 ++++++++++++++++++++++++++++++++++++++++++++
0.1426782E 08 0.51693 0.06373 ++++++++++++++++++++++++++++++++++++++++++++++
0.1434194E 08 0.58539 0.06646 ++++++++++++++++++++++++++++++++++++++++++++++++
0.1441607E 08 0.65022 0.06483 +++++++++++++++++++++++++++++++++++++++++++++
0.1449019E 08 0.70758 0.05737 +++++++++++++++++++++++++++++++++++++++++
0.1456432E 08 0.76050 0.05292 ++++++++++++++++++++++++++++++++++++++
0.1463845E 08 0.80711 0.04661 +++++++++++++++++++++++++++++++++
0.1471257E 08 0.84749 0.04038 +++++++++++++++++++++++++++++
0.1478670E 08 0.88408 0.03660 +++++++++++++++++++++++++++
0.1486082E 08 0.91325 0.02917 +++++++++++++++++++++
0.1493495E 08 0.93700 0.02375 +++++++++++++++++
0.1500908E 08 0.95408 0.01708 +++++++++++++
0.1508320E 08 0.96869 0.01461 +++++++++++
0.1515733E 08 0.97912 0.01043 ++++++++
0.1523145E 08 0.98586 0.00674 ++++++
0.1530558E 08 0.99125 0.00539 +++++
0.1537971E 08 0.99502 0.00377 ++++
0.1545383E 08 0.99744 0.00242 +++
0.1552796E 08 0.99863 0.00119 ++
0.1560208E 08 0.99887 0.00023 +
0.1567621E 08 0.99928 0.00041 +
0.1575034E 08 0.99945 0.00017 +
0.1582446E 08 0.99971 0.00026 +
0.1589859E 08 0.99993 0.00023 +
0.1597271E 08 1.00000 0.00007 +
0.1600978E 08
MEAN=XB =  0.142855D 08      XB+3S =  0.156186E 08      XB-3S =  0.129524E 08
STANDARD DEVIATION=S =   444370.            RANGE =  0.333567E 07
% NEGATIVE    0.0    FROM EXTRAPOLATED NORMAL  0.0              CV(%)  3.1106
TOTAL SAMPLE SIZE =  10000
CHI-SQUARE FOR NORMALITY =   33.2889            POS =    0.40156
CORRELATION WITH NORMAL DISTRIBUTION =  0.998499
% OF VARIATION EXPLAINED BY NORMAL DIST =   99.69997
```

FIG. 6—*Monte Carlo simulation,* EI *simulation.*

TABLE 3—*Probability densities for* EI *analysis.*

Random Variable			Distribution
Ply thickness	{	$t^{(1)}$ $t^{(k)}, k = 2,\ldots,12$ $t^{(13)}$	U(0.005, 0.0065) U(0.0075, 0.0085) U(0.005, 0.0065)
Ply angular orientation errors	{	$\Delta\theta^{(1)}$ $\Delta\theta^{(k)}, K = 2,\ldots,12$ $\Delta\theta^{(13)}$	U(−1°, +1°) U(−2°, +2°) U(−1°, +1°)
Elastic moduli for HM graphite-epoxy	{	E_{11}gr E_{22}gr E_{12}gr	N(23.3 × 10⁶, 0.5 × 10⁶) N(0.95 × 10⁶, 0.05 × 10⁶) U(0.26, 0.30)
Elastic moduli for S-glass epoxy	{	E_{11}gl E_{22}gl E_{12}gl	N(9.0 × 10⁶, 0.3 × 10⁶) N(2.0 × 10⁶, 0.1 × 10⁶) U(0.26, 0.30)

NOTE—Units are degrees, pounds, and inches.

From Table 4, it is apparent that if one wishes to control EI, then the axial graphite ply thickness and the graphite E_{11} modulus must be carefully controlled.

Using the improved distributions for EI and K, an MCS/VS analysis of (P_{cr}-P) was done where the distributions of the random variables involved are given in Table 5.

The histogram for (P_{cr}-P) is given in Fig. 7, and one notes that the

TABLE 4—*Sensitivity analysis—percent variation in* EI *caused by its random variables.*

Random Variable	Percent Variation in EI
$t^{(1)}$	0.1
$\sum_{k=2}^{12} t^{(k)}$	54.0
$t^{(13)}$	0.1
$\Delta\theta^{(1)}$	≈0.0
$\Delta\theta^{(k)}, k = 2, \ldots, 12$	≈0.0
$\Delta\theta^{(13)}$	≈0.0
E_{11}gr	45.8
E_{22}gr	≈0.0
ν_{12}gr	≈0.0
E_{11}gr	≈0.0
E_{22}gl	≈0.0
ν_{12}gl	≈0.0

```
HISTOGRAM - MONTE CARLO SIMULATION

FINAL TRUSS PROBABILITY OF FAILURE

RANDOM          SUMMED   DENSITY
VARIABLE        DENSITY  FUNCTION
-483.0703
-401.6852        0.00012 0.00012 +
-238.9171        0.00049 0.00038 +
-76.14838        0.00098 0.00049 +
 86.62036        0.00184 0.00087 ++
249.3891         0.00440 0.00256 +++
412.1577         0.00739 0.00299 ++++
574.9263         0.01315 0.00576 +++++++
737.6948         0.02026 0.00711 +++++++
900.4634         0.03102 0.01076 ++++++++++++
1063.232         0.04625 0.01523 +++++++++++++++
1226.000         0.06451 0.01826 +++++++++++++++++++
1388.769         0.08582 0.02132 ++++++++++++++++++++++
1551.538         0.11023 0.02440 +++++++++++++++++++++++++++
1714.306         0.14320 0.03297 +++++++++++++++++++++++++++++++++++
1877.075         0.17926 0.03607 +++++++++++++++++++++++++++++++++++++++
2039.843         0.21825 0.03899 +++++++++++++++++++++++++++++++++++++++++++
2202.612         0.25953 0.04128 +++++++++++++++++++++++++++++++++++++++++++++
2365.380         0.30815 0.04861 +++++++++++++++++++++++++++++++++++++++++++++++++++
2528.149         0.35720 0.04906 +++++++++++++++++++++++++++++++++++++++++++++++++++++
2690.917         0.40653 0.04933 +++++++++++++++++++++++++++++++++++++++++++++++++++++
2853.686         0.45925 0.05272 ++++++++++++++++++++++++++++++++++++++++++++++++++++++++
3016.455         0.51563 0.05638 ++++++++++++++++++++++++++++++++++++++++++++++++++++++++++++
3179.223         0.56854 0.05290 +++++++++++++++++++++++++++++++++++++++++++++++++++++++
3341.992         0.62175 0.05321 +++++++++++++++++++++++++++++++++++++++++++++++++++++++
3504.760         0.67422 0.05247 ++++++++++++++++++++++++++++++++++++++++++++++++++++++
3667.529         0.72287 0.04865 +++++++++++++++++++++++++++++++++++++++++++++++++++
3830.297         0.76619 0.04332 +++++++++++++++++++++++++++++++++++++++++++++++
3993.066         0.80573 0.03953 +++++++++++++++++++++++++++++++++++++++++
4155.832         0.84406 0.03833 +++++++++++++++++++++++++++++++++++++++
4318.602         0.87732 0.03326 ++++++++++++++++++++++++++++++++++
4481.367         0.90686 0.02954 +++++++++++++++++++++++++++++++
4644.133         0.93209 0.02523 +++++++++++++++++++++++++++
4806.898         0.95253 0.02044 ++++++++++++++++++++++
4969.664         0.96613 0.01360 ++++++++++++++
5132.430         0.97726 0.01114 +++++++++++
5295.195         0.98637 0.00911 +++++++++
5457.961         0.99187 0.00550 ++++++
5620.727         0.99605 0.00418 +++++
5783.492         0.99781 0.00176 +++
5946.258         0.99881 0.00099 ++
6109.023         0.99934 0.00053 +
6271.789         0.99973 0.00040 +
6434.555         0.99986 0.00013 +
6597.320         0.99998 0.00013 +
6760.086         1.00000 0.00001 +
6841.469
MEAN=XB =    3045.68         XB+3S =   6406.62      XB-3S =  -315.263
STANDARD DEVIATION=S =    1120.31        RANGE =    7324.54
% NEGATIVE     0.0800 FROM EXTRAPOLATED NORMAL  0.32780D-02 CV(%)   36.784
TOTAL SAMPLE SIZE =    10000
CHI-SQUARE FOR NORMALITY =    114.695        POS =    1.00000
CORRELATION WITH NORMAL DISTRIBUTION =  0.994347
% OF VARIATION EXPLAINED BY NORMAL DIST =   98.87265
```

FIG. 7—*Monte Carlo simulation, final truss probability of failure.*

reliability requirement for the tube is met if the models used are valid and the distributions assumed for the X_i's are correct. The sensitivity analysis of $(P_{cr}-P)$ for this final analysis is given in Table 6.

One may wonder why the proportions of these percentages are so different from those of Table 2. The reason for this is that the total variation of $(P_{cr}-P)$ was reduced by making the variational envelopes of K and EI smaller, whereas the variations in α and P are the same as before. The decrease in total variation was essential as the reliability

TABLE 5—*Distribution for the random variables used in the final*
(P_{cr} − P) analysis.

Random Variable	Distribution
α	$U(1.0 \times 10^6, 100.0 \times 10^6)$
K	$U(350.0, 550.0)$
β	$U(1.0 \times 10^3, 100.0 \times 10^3)$
EI	$N(14.2855 \times 10^6, 0.444337 \times 10^6)$
P	$U(17200.0, 17800.0)$

NOTE: Units are pounds, inches, and radians.

TABLE 6—*Sensitivity analysis—percent variation in (P_{cr} − P).*

Random Variable	Percent Variation Caused in ($P_{cr} - P$)
α	≈ 0.0
K	44.5
β	38.3
EI	14.8
P	2.4

requirement of 0.99 had to be met. Thus, the latter sensitivity analysis brings all of the mature or final design parameters into focus, and it also provides a quantitative ranking of the design variables with respect to their relative importance. One must realize, however, that these variables are important so long as the less-dominant variables stay within their variational envelopes. Hence, at this point the procurement, acceptance, manufacturing, and inspection documents can be finalized.

There are many other ways in which this program could have been conducted; however, they would have resulted in a higher program cost as this design system sequentially minimizes cost by focusing the attention on those design parameters which would produce an unreliable device. It forces a continuous dialogue between many departments, and it does this through an impersonal media (analysis and data). It also continuously points at those areas which could be troublesome and requires that they be fixed, and thus at the end of the research-and-development phase the design review is only a formal audit, instead of a major task.

Discussion

This presentation was modified slightly from the actual case history to better illustrate the example. The applied loads distribution, *P*, was "worked up" to dramatize the reliability predictions of the concept design and the mature designs. The actual truss tubes had a reliability of 99.99 percent or higher from a proof-test acceptance criterion.

Conclusions

Monte Carlo simulation in combination with a sensitivity analysis is demonstrated to be an efficient method for (1) determining the reliability of each failure mode for a composite structure, (2) developing a concept design into a mature design which yields minimum cost for a given reliability, and (3) specifying tolerance and material properties to maintain the desired reliability for a minimum inspection and testing cost.

APPENDIX

The analytical model for the critical load, P_{cr} (Fig. 3), is the matrix transfer method described in Ref 1. The state vectors at zero and 2 defining the force and kinematic boundary conditions are related as follows

$$Z_2{}^L = \bar{L}_2 \bar{L}_1 Z_0{}^R$$

where L_1 and L_2 are the transfer matrices relating the state vectors at 0 to 1 and 1 to 2, respectively. The boundary conditions for this problem are $Z_2{}^L$ and $Z_0{}^R$ defined as

$$Z_0{}^R = \begin{bmatrix} 0 \\ \psi_0 \\ \alpha\psi_0 \\ V_0{}^R \end{bmatrix} ; \quad Z_2{}^L = \begin{bmatrix} 0 \\ \psi_2 \\ -\beta\psi_2 \\ V_2{}^L \end{bmatrix}$$

The entries are, from top to bottom: deflection; rotation; moment, as a product of moment restraint and rotation; and shear. The intermediate shear restraint at 1 is included in the transfer matrix $\bar{L}_1$.

The transfer matrices $\bar{L}_1$ and $\bar{L}_2$ for the example problem are

$$\bar{L}_1 = \begin{bmatrix} 0 & \dfrac{l_1 \sin\gamma_1}{\gamma_1} & \dfrac{l_1{}^2}{EI_1}\dfrac{1-\cos\gamma_1}{\gamma_1{}^2} & \dfrac{l_1{}^3}{EI_1}\dfrac{\gamma_1 \sin\gamma_1}{\gamma_1{}^3} & 0 \\ 0 & \cos\gamma_1 & \dfrac{l_1}{EI_1}\dfrac{\sin\gamma_1}{\gamma_1} & \dfrac{l_1{}^2}{EI_1}\dfrac{1-\cos\gamma_1}{\gamma_1{}^2} & 0 \\ 0 & \dfrac{-Pl_1 \sin\gamma_1}{\gamma_1} & \cos\gamma_1 & \dfrac{l_1 \sin\gamma_1}{\gamma_1} & 0 \\ 0 & 0 & 0 & 1 & -K \end{bmatrix}$$

$$
\bar{L}_2 = \begin{bmatrix}
1 & \dfrac{l_2 \sin \gamma_2}{\gamma_2} & \dfrac{l_2{}^2}{EI_2}\dfrac{1 - \cos \gamma_2}{\gamma_2{}^2} & \dfrac{l_2{}^3}{EI_2}\dfrac{\gamma_2 - \sin \gamma_2}{\gamma_2{}^3} \\[3mm]
0 & \cos \gamma_2 & \dfrac{l_2}{EI_2}\dfrac{\sin \gamma_2}{\gamma_2} & \dfrac{l_2{}^2}{EI_2}\dfrac{1 - \cos \gamma_2}{\gamma_2{}^2} \\[3mm]
0 & \dfrac{-Pl_2 \sin \gamma_2}{\gamma_2} & \cos \gamma_2 & \dfrac{l_2 \sin \gamma_2}{\gamma_2} \\[3mm]
0 & 0 & 0 & 1
\end{bmatrix}
$$

where

$$
\gamma_i = l_i \sqrt{\frac{P}{EI_i}} \quad i = 1, 2
$$

Performing the indicated matrix multiplication and incorporating the boundary conditions, one finds two equations of the form

$$
C_1 \psi_0{}^L + C_2 V_0{}^L = 0
$$

and

$$
C_3 \psi_0{}^L + C_4 V_0{}^L = 0
$$

The lowest nontrivial root of the determinental equation

$$
\Delta = \begin{vmatrix} C_1 & C_2 \\ C_3 & C_4 \end{vmatrix} = 0
$$

gives the desired critical buckling load, P_{cr}. This model was thoroughly checked against known critical loads for similar column stability problems found in standard reference texts.

References

[1] Pestel, E. C. and Leckie, F. A., *Matrix Methods in Elastomechanics,* McGraw-Hill, New York, 1963.
[2] Herrman, C. R., Ingram, G. E., and Welker, E. L., *An Application of the Requirement vs Capability Analysis to Estimating Design Reliability of Solid Rocket Motors,* NASA Contract Number NAS-7-556, Tempo, General Electric Company, Santa Barbara, Calif., July 1968.
[3] Broding, W. C., Diederich, F. W., and Parker, P. S., *Journal of Spacecraft,* Vol. No. 1, Jan. 1964, pp. 56–61.
[4] *An Assessment of Accident Risks in U.S. Commercial Nuclear Power Plants,* WASH-1400, U.S. Atomic Energy Commission, Aug. 1974. (Copies available from the National Technical Information Service, Springfield, Va. 22151.)
[5] Johnson, C. W., Maxwell, R. E., and Allred, L. G., "Empirical Reliability Models of Complex Structures," to be published in the *Proceedings* of the 1975 Annual Reliability and Maintainability Symposium, Jan. 1975.
[6] Ashton, J. E., Halpin, J. C., and Petit, P. H., *Primer on Composite Materials Analysis,* Technometric Publishing Corp., Stamford, Conn.

E. M. Lenoe[1] and D. Neal[1]

Structural Integrity Assessment of Filament-Wound Components

REFERENCE: Lenoe, E. M. and Neal, D., "Structural Integrity Assessment of Filament-Wound Components," *Composite Reliability, ASTM STP 580,* American Society for Testing and Materials, 1975, pp. 54–76.

ABSTRACT: This paper summarizes the results of a structural integrity assessment of filament-wound glass-epoxy cylinders and rocket motor cases under conditions of dynamic fracture due to internal pressure loadings of the order of 10-ms duration. Experiments were completed on four types of fiber glass configurations; straight cylinders of various angle ply orientations, tapered cylinders, and two bonded rocket motor case designs were evaluated. A brief review is provided of techniques to assess failure rates, and these elementary reliability techniques are used to establish the relative effects of variability in design pressure and burst pressure capacity. Type II and Type III extreme value and normal distributions are utilized. Polynominal approximations for normal distribution and graphical estimates as well as a transform method are used effectively in determining failure rates for nonnormal functional representation. Furthermore, the merit of several different design concepts, as well as the reliability growth achieved with improved manufacturing techniques, is quantified in terms of the estimated probability of component failure. Failure rates are shown to be more sensitive to design pressure variations than the conventional safety-factor approach. Finally, while the reliability methodology described in the paper is sufficient for preliminary design purposes, failure mode assessment via posttest examination and high-speed photographic observations suggests the necessity for further improvements in composite analysis procedures.

KEY WORDS: composite materials, filament winding, explosive tests, dynamic strength, structures, probability distribution functions, statistical analysis

Adequate design of structures with reliability criteria requires knowledge of pertinent probability distributions of loads, and material properties, as well as knowledge of the effects of environmental deterioration. If variability in the particular controlling influence cannot be ignored, then uncertainty must be dealt with explicitly during the design and analysis process. It must not be construed that composites currently have low

[1] Chief, Mechanics of Materials, and research mathematician, respectively, Army Materials and Mechanics Research Center, Watertown, Mass. 02172.

reliability; on the contrary, examination of available facts suggests composite structures are usually designed quite conservatively. The importance of the following discussion is not so much to increase the actual reliability of composite structures but rather to improve the overall efficiency of design and analysis with such materials. In the past generation, in order to account for the probabilistic nature of materials and load environments, the design philosophy termed "structural reliability" has emerged [1-20].[2] The approach combines statistical theories and conventional stress analysis into a more rational design process. Generally speaking, although the approach has been well documented since the early 1940's, awareness and utilization of structural reliability concepts are limited to a rather small number of practitioners. In part, this is due to the lack of statistical data on properties for materials of interest and the relative complexity of the more elegant treatments. Thus one of the main objectives of this paper is to present several easily applied methods to account for variabilities of strengths and loads in a typical filament-wound composite.

Elementary Reliability Estimates

The elementary reliability equation, that is, the conditional numerical probability that the component will perform without failure, is formally stated as

$$R = \int_{-\infty}^{\infty} \left[\int_{m}^{\infty} S(s)ds \right] L(m)dm \tag{1}$$

where the probability density distributions of strength and design pressure are $S(s)$ and $L(m)$, respectively.

Suppose we assume that the strengths and design pressures are normally distributed. Let

$\overline{S}, \overline{L}$ = mean values of strength and design pressures
δ_S, δ_L = their standard deviations

and

$$N = S - L$$
$$\overline{N} = \overline{S} - \overline{L}$$
$$\delta_N = \sqrt{\delta_S^2 + \delta_L^2}$$

Then

$$\text{Reliability} = R = \frac{1}{\delta_N \sqrt{2\pi}} \int_{0}^{\infty} \exp^{-1/2} \left[\frac{N - \overline{N}}{\delta_N} \right]^2 dN \tag{2}$$

This integral can be closely approximated by the expression [21]

[2] The italic numbers in brackets refer to the list of references appended to this paper.

$$R(X) = 1 - \frac{1}{2}(1 + d_1 X + d_2 X^2 + d_3 X^3 + d_4 X^4 + d_5 X^5 + d_6 X^6)^{-16}$$

$$+ \varepsilon(X) \qquad (3)$$

$$|\varepsilon(X)| < 1.5 \times 10^{-7}$$

and where

$$d_1 = 0.049867347 \qquad d_4 = 0.0000380636$$
$$d_2 = 0.0211410061 \qquad d_5 = 0.0000488906$$
$$d_3 = 0.0032776263 \qquad d_6 = 0.0000053830$$

$$X = N/S_N$$

Thus the reliability $R(X)$, or the probability of survival, is rather simply computed via Eq 3. Provided then, that data are available which are truly representative of the loads and strengths, and can be assumed normal, the component can be designed to a prescribed or desired reliability level.

Choice of the Probability Model

In most physical situations the statistical distribution function describing the properties being measured is unknown and must be determined either from limited empirical data or alternately by theoretical reasoning [2]. Use of an empirical distribution is relevant in structural reliability analysis only when the number of test replicates is sufficiently large to permit a valid distinction between various possible distributions within the range of observations. Furthermore, a hundred specimens may not be sufficient to empirically determine whether or not a particular distribution is a valid fit to the data. Weibull [1,2] for instance has shown that a sampling of more than 1000 would be required to distinguish between a log normal and Weibull distribution. Oftentimes, probability distributions are fit with less than 10 data points, and with such scant information it is generally not possible to distinguish between the various distributions. Obviously the tails of the different distributions are markedly different, with subsequent effects on a normal distribution is most often justified on the grounds of expediency. The use of Eq 3, for instance, is straightforward, and if the probability density distributions of strength and applied stresses are indeed normal, the equation is a fine tool for preliminary design purposes. When the distributions are other than normal, the procedures are not greatly complicated [12,14], and in the worst instance require numerical integration procedures. In applying elementary reliability concepts, then our first concern deals with proper choice of the statistical distributions of design stresses and material strengths. If the choice is difficult, especially where data are limited, then the 'extreme value' distributions can be used effectively to obtain reliability values. These values, of course, will be more conservative then the actual reliability numbers.

Hot-Gas Burst Strengths

In this particular application, the filament-wound components were required to contain short-duration internal pressure pulses. To determine burst strength capabilities, a series of hot-gas burst tests was completed. The composite specimens were instrumented with strain gages and pressure transducers. In addition, high speed photographs of the failure events were obtained at rates ranging from 7000 to 11 000 frames per second.

Selection of sensors, instrumentation, and hot-gas generator was arrived at by reviewing pressure-time histories of actual field service of similar types of components. From representative pressure-time histories, the pressure rate, magnitude, and duration of the pressure pulse could be determined, or at least approximated. With this information, dynamic characteristics of the sensors and instrumentation required to measure the event could be specified. A schematic of a typical experiment appears in Fig. 1, whereas Fig. 2 illustrates representative strain-pressure-time response in a straight cylindrical section.

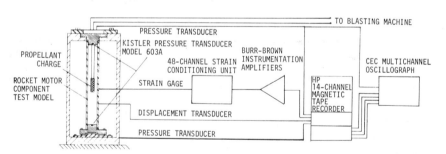

FIG. 1—*Schematic of hot-gas fixture and instrumentation.*

Four types of filament-wound components were evaluated: straight cylinders with internal diameters of 3.25 in. and nominal 0.04-in. wall thicknesses, tapered cylinders with straight inside but stepped-down outer configurations, and two types of solid propellant cases. The test pieces described in this paper were fabricated on a horizontal filament winding machine. Wetwinding techniques were used throughout the study and winding parameters were chosen to ensure uniform resin content. The reinforcement used in this study was Owens-Corning S-glass with HTS 901 glass size and the resin was EPON 815, a low-viscosity epoxy manufac-

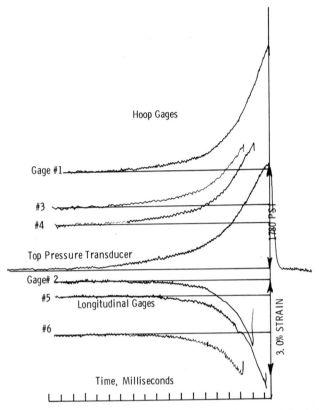

FIG. 2—*Typical pressure and strain time traces, hot-gas burst test, 60-deg helix-wrapped cylinder.*

tured by Shell. Average resin content for the composites was (17.82 percent ± 1.6 percent).[3] This epoxy was chosen after evaluation of static, dynamic, and environmental deterioration behavior of two types of glass fiber size and four resins [22].

Actual choice of materials, fiber orientations, and winding sequences has been a combined experimental and analytical procedure. For instance, comparison of pressure-strain-displacement time response with predictions based on quasistatic, orthotropic finite-element analysis suggests that further refinements are required to allow confident application of current analysis methodology. Thus the engineering procedures relied heavily on the use of hot-gas burst testing. Obviously the validity of this structural integrity assessment is directly dependent on the validity of the experimental technique. With regard to use of hot-gas burst tests, certain aspects of the loading rates are fairly closely simulated. In the cylindrical test components, the pressure-pulse simulations are quite straightforward.

[3] Mean value of resin content by weight, ± standard deviation.

A major experimental difficulty in these tests relates to the boundary conditions. The composite tubes were slip-fit on steel end plugs. Efforts were made to reduce friction effects and thereby diminish end constraint influences. Strain-gage measurements positioned throughout the specimens suggest uniform strain was indeed achieved; nonetheless, the test apparatus was only an approximation to the actual usage.

Two types of solid propellant chambers were studied—one designed for a rocket launch system (Design A) and the second intended for a recoilless rifle concept (Design B). Design A motor cases are subjected not only to internal pressure pulses but also to axial loads. In this case a steel pintle was used to throttle down the exit rocket nozzle. Thus the exact history of axial thrust and internal radial pressure may not accurately reproduce field firings. However, the peak magnitudes and pulse durations are representative.

Design B recoilless rifle propellant chambers were tested in a sealed mode, using slip-fit end plugs, and again the exact end constraint effects are a matter of concern. Regardless of these various deficiencies in simulating actual field service, the hot-gas burst experiments appear to be more severe than actual performance conditions and therefore are a conservative approach to determining component strengths.

Measured burst strength histograms are compared with several statistical models in Figs. 3 through 7. Trial procedures and standard interval

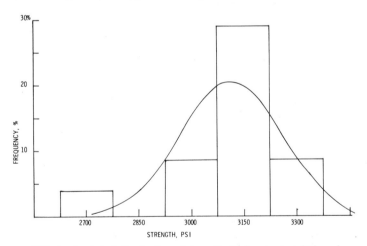

FIG. 3—*Statistical distribution of strength, Design A: straight barrels.*

selection rules were applied in attempting to present the data in the best possible way, even though the results do not uniformly conform to the Sturgis rule ($K = 1 + 3.3 \log_{10} N$) where K and N are number of intervals and data respectively. This is particularly true for Figs. 3 and 4. Difficulty is due in part to limited data. For instance, each histogram in

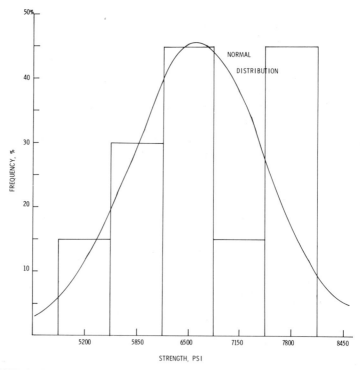

FIG. 4—*Statistical distribution of strength, Design B: tapered barrels, Section I.*

Figs. 3, 4, and 5 is based on twelve burst pressure results. On the other hand, 20 and 21 data points were used in Figs. 6 and 7 respectively. Note the differing degrees of validity of the probability distributions. We see, for instance, based on these histograms that the normal distribution is a relatively poor fit. However, on the basis of Figs. 6 and 7 the normal distribution appears reasonable for the Design B recoilless rifle chambers, whereas a two-parameter Weibull distribution seems a slightly more representative distribution for the Design A rocket motor cases.

Central Safety Factor

Usually preliminary design concepts are based on various safety factors and it is interesting to compare these with reliability estimates [12]. Therefore, normal and Weibull distributions were used to calculate probability of survival. In particular, using Eq 3 and assumed normal distributions for strength and design pressures, probability of survival or reliability estimates were completed for Designs A and B solid propellant chamber configurations. Design pressures were determined from past experience on representative recoilless rifle and rocket launcher systems using types of propellants similar to those considered for both Designs A and B.

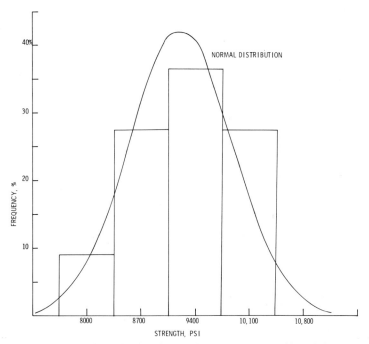

FIG. 5—*Statistical distribution of strength, Design B: tapered barrel, Section II.*

Results are presented in Fig. 8 for the normal probability density distribution for both designs. Reliability is shown as a function of coefficient of variation in the mean design pressure. Note that the lower design pressures are associated with room temperature service whereas the 7600-psi pressure is taken to be representative of potential 140 °F (60 °C) field service conditions. (Such high temperatures might result from certain storage conditions.) The central safety factor, ν_0, is also shown with

$$\nu_0 = \frac{\bar{S}(s)}{\bar{L}(m)} \qquad (4)$$

where $\bar{S}(s)$ and $\bar{L}(m)$ are mean values of the strength and design stresses respectively. It is apparent that Design A is significantly more reliable than Design B. On the horizontal axis, the estimated range of coefficient of variations in design pressures associated with two types of solid propellants is indicated. The reliability of Design B is actually substantially lower than that of Design A since the former is associated with Type II solid propellant whereas the latter utilizes Type I propellant. Thus, for assumed normal distributions, the comparative ranges in estimated probability of survival for the two systems are as given in Table 1.

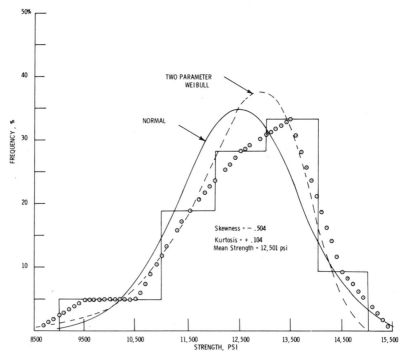

FIG. 6—*Statistical distribution of strength, filament-wound rocket motors: Design A.*

TABLE 1—*Comparison of normal probability survival estimates.*

System	Range in Probability of Survival
Design A	0.9999985 to 0.98864610
Design B	0.98467169 to 0.88779093

The limited number of hot-gas burst tests did not permit simple choice of a particular distribution. Therefore, as a matter of interest, reliability estimates were also completed for assumed Weibull probability density distributions of strength and design pressures. The computations utilized a transform method *[12]*, briefly stated as follows:

The reliability expression

$$P_s = R = \int_{-\infty}^{\infty} \left[\int_{s}^{\infty} f(m)dm \right] f(s)ds \qquad (5)$$

can be rewritten as

$$G = \int_{s}^{\infty} f(m)dm \qquad (6)$$

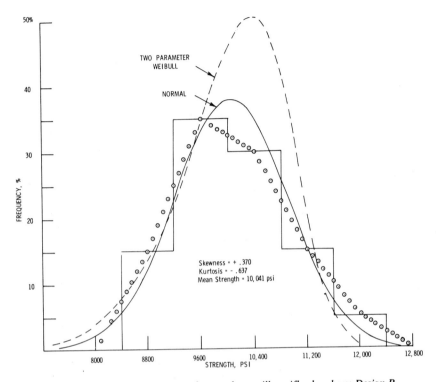

FIG. 7—*Statistical distribution of strength, recoilless rifle chambers: Design B.*

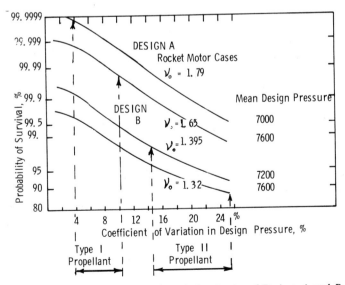

FIG. 8—*Comparison of probability of survival estimates of Designs A and B, assumed normal distributions of strength and design stress.*

and

$$F = \int_s^\infty f(s)\,ds \qquad (7)$$

then

$$R = \int_0^1 G\,dF \qquad (8)$$

where $dF = f(s)\,ds$ and $G > F$.

This method enables the evaluation of reliability for any combination of different distributions of design stress and strength, provided the partial areas F and G can be accurately found by digital computer methods based on numerical integration schemes. Probability of survival estimates, based on this formalism, appears in Fig. 9 and the relevant ranges in reliability for the different designs are given in Table 2.

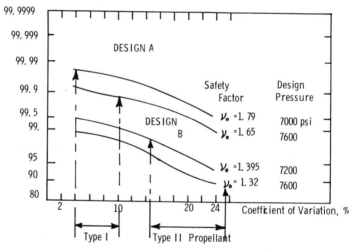

FIG. 9—*Comparison of probability of survival estimates of Designs A and B, assumed Weibull distributions of strength and design stress.*

Comparing Figs. 9 and 10, note that for the range of variability associated with Type I propellant, the Weibull reliability estimates are significantly less than those resulting from the normal distribution. However, the numerical values of probability of survival in Fig. 9 tend to converge for higher coefficients of variation in design stress. The fact of lower probability of survival in Design A is important since, recalling Fig. 6, the Weibull distribution appears slightly more realistic. Figure 7, on the other hand, suggests conformity to a normal distribution. Thus if P_s is compared using Design A Weibull versus Design B normal density function, the relative reliability of Design A is diminished.

TABLE 2—*Comparison of Weibull probability survival estimates.*

System	Range in Probability of Survival
Design A	0.99972373 to 0.99863810
Design B	0.98432785 to 0.89179612

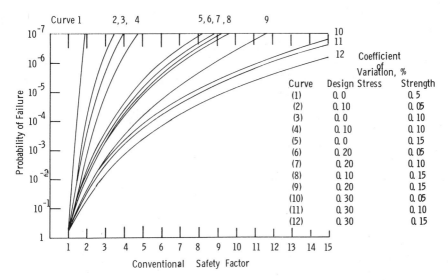

FIG. 10—*Relations between central safety factor and probability of failure for extreme-value distributions.*

In reality, it is not absolutely clear which distribution functions are appropriate for either design stresses or strength. Therefore, it is of interest to explore the most conservative extreme-value representations.

Extreme-Value Safety Factor

The normative or second-moment approach, based on Eqs 1–3, and requiring only the mean and variance distributions, has the advantage of easily fitting into conventional design procedures. However, there are other credible procedures for risk assessment [24,25]. Realistic distribution functions of relevant strength distributions and design parameters are a prerequisite to credible failure risk estimates. In general, the required statistical distributions are not obtainable due to scant information. However, Freudenthal [25] has made the important and physically germane suggestion to utilize extreme-value statistics. Implicit in this assumption is the definition of the safety factor v as the ratio between the strength and design stresses based on an extremely high (limit) design stress and an extremely low value of strength. With this concept of safety factor, the selection of probability distribution is reduced to no more than three usable functions, two for the design stresses and one for the strength.

Forms of the three distribution functions are:

For the largest extremal design stress values

$$P_1(x) = \exp[-e^{-k(x-u)}] = \exp[-e^{-y}] \tag{9}$$

$$-\infty < x < \infty \text{ and } x = u + y/k$$

or

$$P_2(x) = \exp\left[-\left(\frac{x-\varepsilon}{u-\varepsilon}\right)^{-k}\right] = \exp[-e^{-y}] \tag{10}$$

$$x \geqslant \varepsilon, u > \varepsilon \quad \text{and} \quad x = \varepsilon + u - \varepsilon)e^{y/k}$$

and for the smallest extremal strength values

$$P_3(x) = 1 - \exp\left[-\left(\frac{x-\varepsilon}{u-e}\right)^{k}\right] = 1 - \exp[-e^{y}] \tag{11}$$

$$x \geqslant \varepsilon, u > \varepsilon \quad \text{and} \quad x = \varepsilon + (u - \varepsilon)e^{y/k}$$

and the reduced variate

$$Y = -\ln[-\ln P_1(x)] = -\ln[-\ln P_2(x) = \ln\{-\ln[1 - P_3(x)]\} \tag{12}$$

The "characteristic" value $x = u$ at which $P_1(x) = P_2(x) = 1 - P_3(x) = e^{-1}$ is an indication of the location, whereas the "form parameter" K is the reciprocal of the scatter.

Probability of survival or, conversely, probability of failure estimates can now be made taking as the pertinent distribution the extreme (largest) value of the design stress and the extreme (smallest) value asymptotic strength distributions. Accepting these extreme distributions as the basis of a conservative approach, the probability functions

$$P(v) = \int_0^\infty P_1 P_3 dx \quad \text{or} \quad \int_0^\infty P_2 P_3 dx \tag{13}$$

have been calculated for different ratios of the "central" safety factor $v_0 = (\bar{S}/\bar{L})$. These functions, $P(v)$, were presented for different pairs of values of the coefficients of variation (δ_S/S), (δ_L/L) for the assumption of first $P_1(x)$ or second $P_2(x)$ asymptotic distribution of design stresses and the third $P_3(x)$ asymptotic distribution of strengths [24,25]. From those diagrams the values of the probability of failure at ordinates $v = 1.0$ can be obtained and plotted as functions of ν_0 (see Fig. 10). This figure can be used to estimate the corresponding central safety factor ν_0 and probability of failure, where now however the strength and design stress distribution are viewed as extreme values. The real-life probability of failure is obviously smaller than that estimated by this procedure since, in fact, the real probability of failure is that estimated via Eqs 5–9 multiplied by the probability of occurrence of the extreme (maximum) design stress and the extreme (minimum) strength.

An alternative method for determining extreme-value safety factors is the application of the transform method as outlined previously. Instead of using the same distributions for both stress and strength data, separate distinct distributions are used for each set of data. A Type I distribution (exponential like lower tail) is used for the stress. The strength data are also assumed to have a Type I distribution (exponential like upper tail). This method provides a more direct and accurate estimate of R than the somewhat crude graphical method as applied in the foregoing (using Fig. 10). Probability of failure estimates for Systems A and B using various methods is given in Table 3.

TABLE 3—*Comparison of safety factor and probability-based failure estimates* (P_F).

Configuration	Mean Design Pressure	Central Safety Factor	Range in P_F		
			Normal	Extreme (graphical)	Extreme[a]
Design A	7000	1.79	0.00001	0.001	0.0036
	7600	1.65	0.0017	0.011	0.0087
Design B	7200	1.40	0.016	0.065	0.0320
	7600	1.32	0.138	0.330	0.188

[a] Alternative method.

Environmental Degradation

It is well known that fiber glass epoxy composites are susceptible to environmental deterioration and, since these filament-wound components were expected to be used in rather severe tropical as well as temperate zones, it was necessary to establish potential strength loss limits. A controlled artificial environmental exposure conditioning cycle of 160 °F (71 °C) and 95 percent relative humidity was chosen. Straight cylinders of ± 60-deg orientation were exposed for up to 16 weeks in this environment and static ($\sim 1\frac{1}{2}$ min loading time to failure) hydroburst tests were conducted periodically throughout the conditioning cycle. Approximately one third of the burst strength was lost in the first six weeks and, at the end of the exposure tests, strength appeared to level off to about one half the virgin strength. Initial and final strengths are compared in Table 4.

TABLE 4—*Effects of temperature and humidity on burst pressure.*

	Burst Strength Pressures, psi	Burst Strength[a] Pressures, psi
	2015	934
	2040	997
	2040	1004
	2050	1046
	2092	1092
	2134	1103
Average	2063	1029
Standard deviation	39	58
Coefficient of variation	1.9%	5.65%

[a] Indicates artificially controlled environment.

Strength loss for this particular exposure cycle is obviously drastic. However, the probability of occurrence of 160°F (71°C) temperature is low. Nonetheless, temperatures in excess of 120°F (49°C) are definite possibilities, under field storage conditions. Both Designs A and B were to be stored in sealed containers and, furthermore, the ends of each system would be capped. The relative importance of environmental deterioration varies with the component. In Design A, for instance, the rocket motor case is nested within two telescoping composite tubes. The outermost tube obviously is most susceptible, whereas the inner tube and motor case are certainly protected, to an extent, from ultraviolet as well as humidity and thermal effects. Furthermore, the tubes burst in the deterioration studies had been finish-ground on the outer surface. Undoubtedly, the machining process exposed the glass fiber epoxy interface to more severe and rapid moisture penetration, partly due to removal of resin and partly due to minor fiber abrasion. The propellant chambers in both designs had resin-rich and nonmachined outer surfaces and would probably be more resistant to humidity.

The recoilless rifle, Design B, concept, consisting of a tapered forward barrel with integral oversized propellant chamber, is inherently more susceptible, due to direct exposure of all exterior surfaces, as compared with Design A. In order to complete a more accurate risk assessment of the system, the environmental degradation suffered by the appropriate critical component and caused by representative thermal, humidity, and ultraviolet exposures must be ascertained. This is particularly true in the propellant chamber areas, which contain an adhesive joint. Furthermore, hot-gas burst data ought to be obtained on such conditioned components. Such work must be completed in order to establish more accurate risk-of-failure estimates.

Influence of Joint Quality on Structural Integrity

During the course of the hot-gas burst testing, a number of low-strength measurements were observed. The cause of the poor performance of these rocket motor cases was discovered to be due to mold release contamination which had not been removed prior to the bonding operation. Subsequent burst tests on properly manufactured parts verified the source of difficulty. Earlier reliability estimates just discussed were based on the high-strength, high-quality parts. It is of interest to consider the entire test population to assess the influence of poor quality production methods on the failure rate. The strength sampling is shown in histogram form in Fig. 11. For expediency, normal probability density distributions were used. Results of the reliability computation appear in Fig. 12, where the reduction in reliability is obvious.

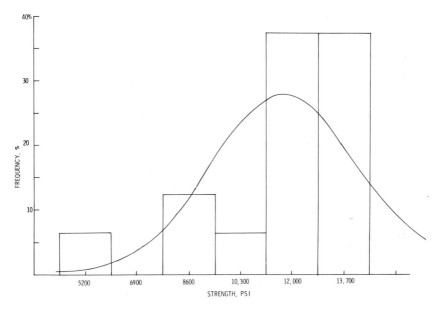

FIG. 11—*Statistical distribution of strength, Design A: rocket motors (including poor joints).*

Assessment of Analysis Capability

So far, only randomness in loads, or design pressures, $L(x)$, and strengths $S(x)$, has been taken into account in a rather simple application of reliability theories. Procedures are also available to deal with deficiencies in analytical methods [19,26]. In order to supply such methods, it is necessary to have measured strength performance as well as the design estimates. Consider the components discussed in this paper.

Strength estimates were completed based on orthotropic finite-element codes. Computer code input included five moduli (longitudinal and transverse modulus, shear modulus, and major and minor Poisson's

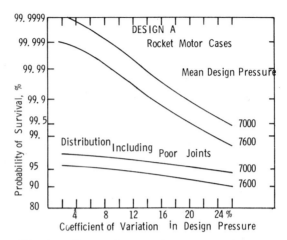

FIG. 12—*Influence of joint quality on structural integrity.*

ratios), and the five associated strength quantities (longitudinal and transverse tension and compression as shear strength). Note that different mechanical properties were used for the Design A and Design B components. The computations were completed by two design teams and their input information is given in Table 5.

TABLE 5—*Comparison of mechanical properties.*

	Strength, ksi	
Laminate Property	Design Team A	Design Team B
Longitudinal tension, σ_L	305	206
Transverse tension, σ_T	3	29
Longitudinal compression, σ_{Lc}	230	206
Transverse compression, σ_{Tc}	30	73
Shear, σ_{L_t}	5	10

Design Team A used a failure criterion of form

$$\left[\frac{\sigma_x}{\sigma_L}\right]^2 - \frac{\sigma_x \sigma_y}{\sigma_L^2}\left[\frac{\sigma_y}{\sigma_T}\right]^2 + \left[\frac{\tau_{L_t}}{\tau_{L_t}}\right]^2 \leqslant 1.0 \qquad (14)$$

where differences in tension and compression were accounted. Design Team B used the modified failure theory discussed by Chamis [27].

In addition to differences of input strength, slightly different composite moduli were also used by the two design teams. Notwithstanding these differences, we have compared experimentally observed and theoretical strength estimates in Table 6. Note that the range in predictability of

TABLE 6—*Comparison of predicted and observed.*

	Burst Pressure	
Component	Predicted	Ratio of Predicted to Observed
Design A	12 600	0.99
Design B	12 900	1.24
Tapered barrel, Section I, Design B	12 250	1.33
Tapered barrel, Section II, Design B	7 000	1.062

burst pressures was from 6 to 33 percent for Design B components, whereas Design A burst pressures were estimated within 1 percent but slightly on the nonconservative side.

Referring to Table 6, it therefore appears that the Design A rocket motor case predictions agree well with average hot-gas burst strength. On the basis of high-speed photographs, and detailed examination of fractured motor cases, this agreement is partly a fortuitous circumstance based primarily on the rather large degree of freedom to choose the moduli and strengths input to the finite-element codes. Insight into the analytical capability can be enhanced by considering predicability of failure modes. It is interesting to review the predicted sequence of failure events, proposed by Design Team A (see Fig. 13).

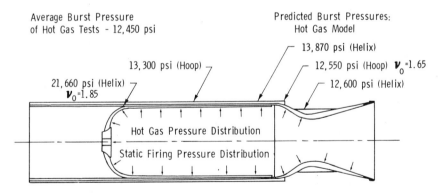

Average Burst Pressure of Hot Gas Tests - 12,450 psi

Predicted Burst Pressures: Hot Gas Model

13,870 psi (Helix)

13,300 psi (Hoop)

12,550 psi (Hoop) V_0=1.65

21,660 psi (Helix) V_0=1.85

12,600 psi (Helix)

Hot Gas Pressure Distribution

Static Firing Pressure Distribution

FIG. 13—*Predicted burst pressures, rocket motor cases.*

Based on static firing loads, the Design Team A computer code predicted initial fiber failure in the hoop layers overlapping the rear dome and in the center of the cylindrical section at pressures of 12 550 and 13 300 psi respectively. The helix layers in the case head were supposedly capable of sustaining pressures of 22 000 psi. Initial fiber failures were predicted at an internal pressure of 9000 psi in the region of the forward edge of the hoop winding in the throat. The stresses were expected to be redistributed with subsequent failure of the surrounding nozzle region at stresses of 12 600 psi.

Figure 13 also indicates conventional safety factors in the different regions. It is seen that they vary from (1.65) to (2.85). However, the actual failure modes were not as predicted. Figure 14 is of interest with regard to this failure mode assessment. These photographs are individual frames taken at speeds of 7000 frames per second. The left portion of Fig. 14 illustrates bursting not only in the predicted low-strength zone, but also near the forward dome area. Posttest examinations, (summarized in Table 7), as well as the available high-speed film strips, reveal the damage locations in the rocket motor cases. Note that the majority of cases were not extensively damaged near the nozzle transition.

Obviously it would be desireable to attempt further refined predictions, based on more accurate properties data, and then to fabricate and test to failure a range of different composite laminate orientations. In this way, the adequacy of the design and analysis methodology could be judged more effectively.

Conclusions

Let us consider the reliability of each fiber glass epoxy configuration. First of all, with regard to straight and tapered barrels, the actual design pressures were substantially lower than the measured burst pressures. Thus other criteria, such as general ruggedness, were controlling and from the burst pressure viewpoint the straight and tapered tubes were quite conservatively designed. There is potential for lighter-weight structure using the same materials, though the rather loosely defined requirement of ruggedness makes efforts at weight savings largely a matter of judgment.

As for the propellant chambers, based on the various probability distributions of loads and strengths, the Design A configuration offers higher probability of survival than Design B chambers. For instance, the failure rates ranged from 0.0017 to 0.011 for Design A and from 0.138 to 0.33 for Design B. This statement must be qualified. For instance, it is not certain that the Design B chambers subjected to hot-gas burst testing were truly representative of high-quality fabrication. There are several reasons for making this statement. In the first instance, hydrodynamic tests on supposedly similar configurations attained significantly higher burst pressures (generally 12 000 psi or greater). These larger pressures have been attributed to the use of a flexible liner during destructive testing, which apparently prevents fluid seepage into joint bond lines. This type of joint hydroburst testing therefore appears less sensitive to

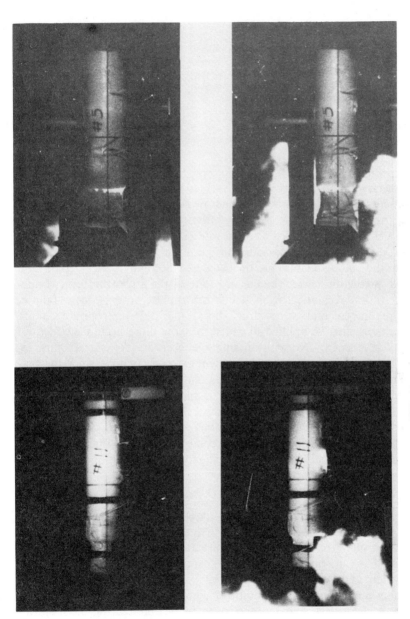

FIG. 14—*Design A, high-speed photographs.*

TABLE 7—*Major damage locations, Design A rocket motor cases.*

Specimen	Case Blown	Forward Skirt	Dome	Nozzle	Bond
1	X	X			
2					
3					X
4	X				
5	X		X	X	
6		X	X	minor	
7		X	X	X	
8			X		X
9		X	X		
10		X	X		
11		X	X		
12	X				

the presence of low-quality joints. Such is not the case in hot-gas burst experiments, particularly where no liner or flexible coatings are applied.

One major need is to obtain appropriate mechanical properties measurements, under realistic strain rates and environmental conditions and on representative composite configurations, so that realistic failure data would be available to the analyst. Secondly, the design and analysis predictions were based on state-of-the-art orthotropic finite-element codes. Analytical tools which incorporate layer-by-layer failure, nonlinear incremental stress-strain laws, and the appropriate failure theories must also be applied in order to allow more accurate structural integrity assessment. Notwithstanding the necessity for this further research, the risk estimates provided herein are conservative, since the hot-gas burst experiments are more severe than anticipated field service; thus the engineering methodology described is adequate.

Finally, in order to truly verify the reliability procedures discussed here, it would be appropriate to obtain failure rate data on production items, when these preliminary design concepts arrive at that stage. Such observations are vitally important to validate the reliability methodology.

Acknowledgments

We wish to thank R. Lamothe for supervising the hot-gas burst experiments and for developing the required instrumentation and test procedures; C. Polley for his detonics work and numerous refinements in apparatus; L. Carlson, R. Tremblay, and J. Casazza for specimen preparation and conducting of the tests; and I. Spiridigliozzi for programming the numerical computations. Finally, we are grateful to Dr. B. Halpin, A. Reppucci, and L. MacQueen for manufacturing the majority of the test items, and special thanks are expressed to Mrs. Agnes Travers for her typing skills and patience in completing this manuscript.

References

[1] Weibull, Waloddi, "A Statistical Theory of the Strength of Materials," *Ingeniors Vetenskops Akadamien-Hawdlingar,* Stockholm, No. 151, 1939, p. 1–45.

[2] Weibull, Waloddi, "The Phenomena of Rupture in Solids," *Ingeniors Vetenskops Akadamien-Hawdlingar,* Stockholm, No. 153, 1939, pp. 1–55.

[3] Epstein, B., "Statistical Aspects of Fracture Problems," *Journal of Applied Physics,* Vol. 19, 1948.

[4] Pugsley, A. G., *Journal,* Institute of Civil Engineering, Vol. 6, No. 5, March 1951.

[5] Freudenthal, A. M., Paper No. 2843, *Transactions,* American Society of Civil Engineers, Vol. 121, 1956, pp. 1337–1397.

[6] Paez, A. and Torroja, E., "La Determinacion del Coefficients de Seguridad en las Distintas Obras," Institute Technice de la Contruccion y del Cemento, Madrid, 1959.

[7] Su, H. L., *Journal,* Institute of Civil Engineering, Vol. 13, No. 3, July 1959.

[8] Brown, C. B., *Journal of Structural Division, Proceedings,* American Society of Civil Engineers, Vol. 83, No ST12, Dec. 1960.

[9] Freudenthal, "Methods of Safety Analysis of Highway Bridges," Sixth Congress, International Association for Bridge and Structural Engineering, Stockholm, 1960, pp. 655–664.

[10] Freudenthal, A. M. and Shinozuka, M., "Structural Safety Under Conditions of Ultimate Load Failure and Fatigue," WADD Technical Report 61-177, Weight Air Development Division, Oct. 1961.

[11] Daniel, I. M. and Weil, N. A., "Influence of Stress Gradient Upon Fracture of Brittle Material," ASME Paper 63-WA-228, American Society of Mechanical Engineers, Nov. 1963.

[12] Kececioglu, D. and Cormier, D., "Designing a Specified Reliability Directly into a Component," *Proceedings,* Third Annual Aerospace Reliability and Maintainability Conference, July 1964, pp. 546–565.

[13] Robinson, E. Y., "Some Theoretical and Experimental Aspects of Design With Brittle Material," University of California Report UCRL- 7729, Aug. 1964.

[14] Freudenthal, A. M., Garrelts, J. M., and Shinozuka, M., "The Analysis of Structural Safety," Columbia University Technical Report No. 12A, Contract No. NONR 266 (91), June 1965.

[15] Haugen, E. B., *Probabilistic Approaches to Design,* Wiley, New York, 1968.

[16] Bolotin, V. V., *Statistical Methods in Structural Mechanics,* Holden Day, Inc., San Francisco, 1969.

[17] De Salvo, G. J. and Stanchik, R. M., "Theory and Structural Design Applications," Astronuclear Laboratory, WANL-TME-2688, May 1970.

[18] Kececioglu, D., "Reliability Analysis of Mechanical Components and Systems," First International Conference on Structural Mechanics in Reactor Technology, Paper M ¼, Berlin, 20–24 Sept. 1971.

[19] Freudenthal, A. M. and Wong, P. Y., *Journal of Aircraft,* Vol. 7, No. 3, May–June 1970.

[20] Lenoe, E. M., "Ballistic and Static Damage Effects on Probability of Survival of Filamentary Composites," 2nd Army Solid Mechanics Symposium, Ocean City, Md., Oct. 1972.

[21] Hastings, C., Jr., *Approximation for Digital Computers,* Princeton University Press, 1955.

[22] Halpin, B. M., Lamothe, R., and Lenoe, E. M., "Dynamic and Static Failure Behavior of Filament Wound Components," Presented at 19th National Symposium and Exhibition Society for the Advancement of Materials and Process Engineering, 23–25 April 1974.

[23] Cornell, C. A., "A Normative Second Moment Reliability Theory for Structural Design," Seminar No. 6, Solid Mechanics Division, University of Waterloo, Ontario, Canada, Dec. 1969.

[24] Freudenthal, A. M., "Die Sickerheit der Baukonstruktionen," *Acta Technica Academiae Scientiarum Hungaricae,* Vol. 46, 1964, pp. 417–446.

[25] Freudenthal, A. M., "Reliability of Reactor Components and Systems Subject to Fatigue and Creep," Contact No. N00014-67-A-0214-0011, School of Engineering and Applied Science, The George Washington University, Technical Report No. 17, Jan. 1974, pp. 18–24.

[26] Benjamin, J. R., and Cornell, C. A., *Probability, Statistics, and Decisions for Civil Engineers,* McGraw-Hill, New York, 1970 pp. 83–133.

[27] Chamis, C. C., in *Composite Materials, Testing and Design, ASTM STP 460,* American Society for Testing and Materials, 1969, pp. 336–351.

S. L. Phoenix[1]

Statistical Analysis of Flaw Strength Spectra of High-Modulus Fibers

REFERENCE: Phoenix, S. L., "Statistical Analysis of Flaw Strength Spectra of High-Modulus Fibers," *Composite Reliability, ASTM STP 580,* American Society for Testing and Materials, 1975, pp. 77–89.

ABSTRACT: A new multistage tension testing procedure is developed that enables the statistical estimation of the flaw strength spectra of high-modulus fibers. The mathematical development of the procedure assumes the compound Poisson process model in distance to represent the probabilistic aspects of flaw occurrence along the fiber. The multistage procedure is applied to commercially available boron filaments, and the results are compared with those obtained on the same filaments using the conventional single-stage tension testing procedure with the Weibull distribution as the underlying model. The experimental results illustrate the dangers of fiber strength data extrapolation.

KEY WORDS: composite materials, fibers, tension tests, tensile strength, failure, flaw frequencies, statistical analysis, estimating, extrapolation

Current experimental analysis techniques for investigating the random tensile-strength character of high-modulus fibers involve several steps. First, a multiplicity of fiber specimens of fixed gage length are tension-tested, and their failure loads recorded. Second, a statistical analysis of the failure strength data is performed either by assuming a *particular* underlying probability distribution and estimating the unknown parameters, or by assuming a *general* distribution and estimating particular distribution moments and quantiles. Third, the statistical fiber strength results are interpreted in terms of random flaw occurrence and related to composite materials strength performance by an appropriate deterministic or probabilistic composite failure model. Difficulties in such experimental analysis procedures persist. The rational choice of an underlying fiber failure probability model or distribution is not a simple exercise. Fiber failures in the clamps, which are frequent at short gage lengths, are not easily accounted for in statistical terms [1].[2] Parameter estimation and hy-

[1] Senior research associate, Frabric Research Labs, An Albany International Co., Dedham, Mass. 02026.
[2] The italic numbers in brackets refer to the list of references appended to this paper.

pothesis testing procedures for the more complex probability distributions are either cumbersome or not available at all, and it is rarely clear how the estimated distribution should be used as a tool to forecast the strength performance of composites which are fabricated from such fibers. (See Ref 2 for elaboration.)

Probabilistic models associated with single-fiber tensile strength behavior have been investigated previously [2]. The compound Poisson process in distance was shown to be a particularly attractive model for representing the random aspects of the position and failure strength of various types of flaws occurring along the fiber. In fact, the popular Weibull distribution was shown to be a special case of the Poisson model applied to elementary tension testing situations. The Weibull distribution was shown to possess several substantial shortcomings, but more general realistic distributions were said to pose serious parameter estimation and data analysis problems.

This paper discusses the development and use of a new multistage tension testing procedure for high-modulus fibers that is based on the compound Poisson process model, and the multistage technique is applied to commercially available boron filaments. The results are compared with those obtained on boron filaments using the conventional single-stage procedure with the Weibull distribution as the underlying model. The dangers of fiber strength data extrapolation are discussed.

Theoretical Development

Consider the compound Poisson process as a model representation for the position and failure strength of flaws occurring along the fiber. Let $\lambda(\sigma)d\sigma$ represent the mean or average number of flaws per unit length with strength between σ and $\sigma + d\sigma$, and let $\Lambda(\sigma)$ be defined as the mean number of flaws per unit length with strength less than or equal to σ, that is

$$\Lambda(\sigma) = \int_{0}^{\sigma} \lambda(\sigma')d\sigma' \tag{1}$$

In this study $\lambda(\sigma)$ is termed the flaw strength spectrum and $\Lambda(\sigma)$ is termed the cumulative flaw strength spectrum. The primary interest is in developing an estimation technique for $\lambda(\sigma)$ and subsequently for $\Lambda(\sigma)$. The discussion of the Poisson model as given by Phoenix [2] provides the basis for the analysis here. It is pointed out that in the elementary case of simple tension of a fiber element of length L, the cumulative distribution function of fiber failure $F(\sigma; L)$ is given as

$$F(\sigma;L) = 1 - \exp\{-L\Lambda(\sigma)\}, \quad 0 \leqslant \sigma \leqslant \sigma_m \tag{2}$$

where σ_m is the maximum possible tensile strength of the fiber. The three-parameter Weibull distribution is a special case of Eq 2 with $\Lambda(\sigma)$ having the parametric form

$$\Lambda(\sigma) = \begin{cases} \left(\dfrac{\sigma - \sigma_u}{\sigma_0}\right)^m, & \sigma_u \leqslant \sigma \\ 0, & \sigma_u > \sigma \end{cases} \tag{3}$$

where $\sigma_m = \infty$; and m, σ_u, and σ_0 are characteristic constants that are usually estimated from fiber tension test data. The two-parameter Weibull distribution requires the additional restriction that $\sigma_u \equiv 0$. The analysis here will *not* require that $\Lambda(\sigma)$ have any particular power rule form such as that given by Eq 3.

Several definitions involving $\lambda(\sigma)$ and $\Lambda(\sigma)$ are necessary. Let $0 < \bar{q}_1 < \cdots < \bar{q}_k$ be a particular set of values for σ, preferably with $\bar{q}_k \geqslant \sigma_m$. Define Λ_i as

$$\Lambda_i = \begin{cases} \Lambda(\bar{q}_i) - \Lambda(\bar{q}_{i-1}), & i = 2, \cdots, k \\ \Lambda(\bar{q}_1), & i = 1 \end{cases} \tag{4}$$

It follows from Eq 1 that Λ_i is related to $\lambda(\sigma)$ by

$$\Lambda_i = \int_{\bar{q}_{i-1}}^{\bar{q}_i} \lambda(\sigma) d\sigma \tag{5}$$

for $i = 1, \cdots, k$ where $\bar{q}_0 \equiv 0$. Define

$$\lambda_i = \Lambda_i/(\bar{q}_i - \bar{q}_{i-1}) \tag{6}$$

which is essentially the average value of $\lambda(\sigma)$ in the region where $\bar{q}_{i-1} \leqslant \sigma \leqslant \bar{q}_i$.

The object of the multistage test procedure is to obtain estimates of λ_i and Λ_i for $i = 1, \cdots, k$, from which estimates of $\lambda(\sigma)$ and $\Lambda(\sigma)$ can be made. The procedure consists of k stages, where each stage is conducted in the conventional fashion except for the following modifications. The tensile stress in the gage section for stage-i fibers is increased from 0 to q_i (unless specimen failure occurs prior to $\bar{q}_i$) where $0 < \bar{q}_i < \cdots < \bar{q}_k$. For stage-$i$, the gage length is set at g_i with $g_1 \leqslant g_2 \leqslant \cdots \leqslant g_k$ being the sequence. Specimens for stage-i are derived from the surviving specimens of stage $i - 1$, that is, from the stage $i - 1$ specimens which do not fail under load $\bar{q}_{i-1}$. Let n_i be the number of specimens tested at stage-i and let the random variable $\bar{N}_i$ denote the number that survive. The n_i specimens are obtained by either shortening or subdividing the $\bar{N}_{i-1}$ surviving specimens of stage $i - 1$, subdivision being possible when $g_i + 2c \leqslant (g_{i-1}$

+ $2c)/2$, where c is the length of the fiber specimen embedded in the clamp. The process of specimen subdivision allows doubling or tripling the number of test specimens at some of the k-stages, thus compensating for the general depletion of the number of specimens at each stage that occurs because some specimens fail. The choice of $\bar{q}_i, \cdots, \bar{q}_k$ and $g_1, \cdots, g_k$ generally requires some advance knowledge of how the fiber behaves. This knowledge can be obtained by performing preliminary conventional single gage length tension tests and properly interpreting the results. The method is discussed later.

Estimation of λ_i *and* Λ_i

Let Θ_i denote the probability that a given specimen survives the loading of stage-i. From Eqs 6 and 7 of Ref 1 and from Eq 4 it is easy to show that

$$\Theta_i = \exp\left(- \bar{g}_i \Lambda_i\right) \tag{7}$$

where

$$\bar{g}_i \cong g_i + C(\bar{q}_1, \cdots, \bar{q}_i; \Lambda_1, \cdots, \Lambda_i) \tag{8}$$

Here $C(\cdot)$ is a clamp correction factor that is necessary because the clamps are not "perfect" but operate on the fiber in a manner described earlier by Phoenix and Sexsmith [1]. Except for the very short gage lengths, $C(\cdot)$ is very small and may be neglected. In fact, for the multistage procedure described here the clamp correction factors are generally much smaller and easier to compute than are those for conventional tension test procedures at comparable gage lengths. In many situations $C(\cdot)$ may be approximated by $(\bar{q}_i - \bar{q}_{i-1})/\tau$, where τ is the approximate rate of change of the tensile stress field in the fiber within the clamp but near the fiber exit point. A more detailed discussion of clamp correction factors for the multistage procedure appears in Ref 3.

It is clear that each of the n_i tests represents a Bernoulli trial with probability of survival Θ_i. The random variable $\bar{N}_i$ therefore follows a binomial distribution with parameters n_i and Θ_i. The maximum-likelihood estimator $\hat{\Theta}_i$ of Θ_i is given as (Ref 4, p. 225) $\hat{\Theta}_i = \bar{N}_i/n_i$ with mean and variance respectively as $E[\hat{\Theta}_i] = \Theta_i$ and $Var[\hat{\Theta}_i] = \Theta_i(1 - \Theta_i)/n_i$. By the central limit theorem (Ref 4, p. 121) the distribution of $\hat{\Theta}_i$ approaches the normal distribution with mean Θ_i and variance $\Theta_i(1 - \Theta_i)/n_i$ as n_i becomes large.

The estimator for Λ_i denoted $\hat{\Lambda}_i$ is based on the statistic $\hat{\Theta}_i$. Let $\hat{\Lambda}_i$ be defined as

$$\hat{\Lambda}_i = - \frac{1}{\bar{g}_i}\left\{\log\left(\frac{\bar{N}_i}{n_i}\right) + \frac{n_i - \bar{N}_i}{2n_i \bar{N}_i}\right\} \tag{9}$$

It is shown in Ref *3* that the distribution of $\hat{\Lambda}_i$ is asymptotically normal for large n_i, with the mean and variance of the limiting distribution given respectively by

$$E[\hat{\Lambda}_i] = \Lambda_i + 0(1/n_i^2) \tag{10}$$

and

$$\text{Var } [\hat{\Lambda}_i] = \frac{\exp{(\bar{g}_i \Lambda_i)} - 1}{\bar{g}_i^2 n_i} + 0(1/n_i^2) \tag{11}$$

Unfortunately, the maximum-likelihood estimator of Λ_i is biased. The second term of the right-hand side of Eq 9 is added to reduce the bias to $0(1/n_i^2)$ as indicated by Eq 10. Of course, the larger n_i is, the better $\hat{\Lambda}_i$ can be expected to perform.

The estimator of λ_i denoted $\hat{\lambda}_i$ is given by

$$\hat{\lambda}_i = \hat{\Lambda}_i/(\bar{q}_i - \bar{q}_{i-1}) \tag{12}$$

The asymptotic distribution of $\hat{\lambda}_i$ for large n_i is also normal with the mean and variance of the limiting distribution given respectively by $E[\lambda_i] = \lambda_i + 0(1/n_i^2)$ and

$$\text{Var } [\hat{\lambda}_i] = \text{Var } [\hat{\Lambda}_i]/(\bar{q}_i - \bar{q}_{i-1})^2 \tag{13}$$

It is seen that if the number of survivors of stage-i is recorded, then the estimates of Λ_i and λ_i denoted respectively by $\hat{\Lambda}_i$ and $\hat{\lambda}_i$ may be easily computed from Eqs 9 and 12. Furthermore, estimates of the variance of $\hat{\Lambda}_i$ and $\hat{\lambda}_i$, denoted as $\hat{V}[\hat{\Lambda}_i]$ and $\hat{V}[\hat{\lambda}_i]$ respectively, can be obtained from Eqs 11 and 13 by replacing the unknown value Λ_i with the estimate $\hat{\Lambda}_i$.

Estimation of $\lambda(\sigma)$ and $\Lambda(\sigma)$

A simple and useful estimator of $\lambda(\sigma)$ denoted $\tilde{\lambda}(\sigma)$ is given as

$$\tilde{\lambda}(\sigma) = \begin{cases} 0, & \sigma < 0 \\ \hat{\lambda}_i, & \bar{q}_{i-1} \leqslant \sigma < \bar{q}_i \\ \infty, & \bar{q}_k \leqslant \sigma \end{cases} \tag{14}$$

If the division sizes given by $\bar{q}_1, \cdots, \bar{q}_k$ are small so that $\lambda(\sigma)$ does not change rapidly within these divisions, then $\lambda(\sigma)$ will provide a relatively good estimate of $\lambda(\sigma)$. By Eq 1, the corresponding estimator for $\Lambda(\sigma)$ is given as

$$\tilde{\Lambda}(\sigma) = \int_0^\sigma \tilde{\lambda}(\sigma')d\sigma' \tag{15}$$

A second approach would be to assume that $\hat{\lambda}_1, \cdots, \hat{\lambda}_k$ are point estimates of $\lambda(\bar{q}_1/2)$, $\lambda([\bar{q}_1 + \bar{q}_2]/2)$, $\cdots$, $\lambda([\bar{q}_{k-1} + \bar{q}_k]/2)$. A linear parametric form of $\lambda(\sigma)$ such as a polynomial could be fitted to the point estimates by the usual regression analysis techniques. Integration of this form would also yield an estimator for $\Lambda(\sigma)$. Further discussion of this approach is given in Ref 3.

Experimental Application

Procedure and Equipment

A tension test apparatus (Fig. 1) was designed and constructed to test boron filaments at gage lengths from 0 to 24 in. One clamp assembly was fitted with precision lineal motion bearings on hardened steel shafts. The position of the other clamp assembly was adjustable in fixed increments to allow a wide selection of gage lengths. Considerable care was taken during the assembly of the apparatus to obtain the best possible alignment of the various components. Vertical slot guides, with slot widths slightly larger than the fiber diameter, were fitted to the back of each clamp region. Jaw liners of 3-mil fully annealed aluminum foil were constructed for each test specimen.

Mounting of a given specimen was proceeded by first setting the apparatus in the zero gage length configuration and then placing the specimen in the slot guides. A foil jaw liner was placed into position and the free clamp was tightened with the specimen properly positioned. The adjustable clamp assembly was then moved to the position yielding the appropriate

FIG. 1—*Tension test apparatus with boron filament in position.*

gage length and then fastened down. A second foil jaw liner was inserted and the clamp was tightened onto the specimen. Slight pretensioning of the longer specimens during final clamping was very helpful in achieving virtually perfect alignment.

Loading was applied by a cable and precision pulley system connected to a load cell attached to the crosshead of an Instron tester. Since only load magnitudes were of interest, no elongations were measured. The effective specimen strain rate was estimated to be approximately 3 percent per minute for all specimens.

Considerable time was spent perfecting the specimen mounting and handling technique. Early in the equipment development program it was discovered that when specimens which had survived a given load were subdivided, remounted and retested, they often failed to survive the given load a second time. Misalignment, which resulted in sharp bending radii in the specimens during testing, was identified as the cause. Minor equipment modifications and technique improvement eliminated this difficulty so that, during the main experiments, specimens always survived their previous survival load levels. (This is a strong indication, also, that multiple handling did not damage the specimens.) The problem is pointed out here because conventional tension test procedures, by their very nature, do not reveal misalignment problems to the extent of those revealed by the multistage procedure. It was also noted that at gage lengths of one inch or less the majority of the specimens did not fracture into multiple fragments but could be reunited at the single fracture position by returning the clamps to the no-load position. Cup and cone fractures were very frequent. These cases increased with decreasing gage length.

The multistage technique was applied to commercially available Hamilton Standard boron filament. Twenty-six continuous yards of boron filament were divided up into 36-in. specimens. The diameter of each specimen was measured in two places with a projection microscope. The average filament diameter was found to be 5.64×10^{-3} in. with a coefficient of variation of less than 0.5 percent.

Preliminary information about the behavior of $\Lambda(\sigma)$ was necessary to allow proper choices of $g_1, \cdots, g_k$ and $\overline{q}_1, \cdots, \overline{q}_k$ for the multistage experiment. For this purpose 41 four-inch specimens were randomly detached from the ends of the 36-in. specimens. The 4-in. specimens were tension-tested in the *conventional* manner at a one-inch gage length, and the empirical distribution function [5] of the results is plotted in Fig. 2. From the mean and standard deviation of the data, Weibull parameters of $\sigma_0 = 493$ ksi-in.$^{1/19}$ and $m = 19$ were obtained for the two-parameter Weibull distribution, and the associated cumulative distribution function is shown in Fig. 2 by the solid straight line. The preliminary estimate of $\Lambda(\sigma)$, denoted as $\Lambda_2(\sigma) = (\sigma/493)^{19}$, was used with Eqs 4 and 7 to choose values of $g_1, \cdots, g_k$ and $\overline{q}_1, \cdots, \overline{q}_k$ that would lead to reasonable

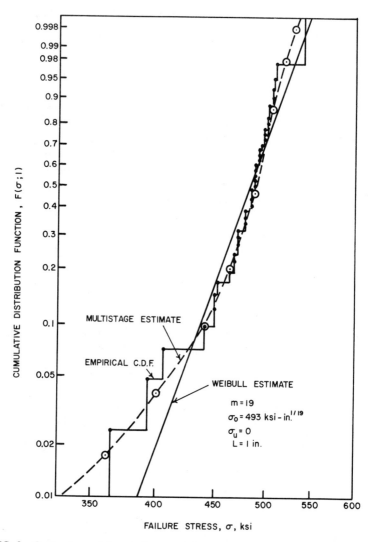

FIG. 2—*Comparison of three estimates of the cumulative distribution function of failure for one-inch gage length boron filament specimens.*

survival percentages at each stage. Of course, small values of Θ_i must be avoided or excessive specimen depletion will result. The chosen values for $\bar{q}_1, \cdots, \bar{q}_k$ and $g_1, \cdots, g_k$ are listed in Table 1.

Experimentation proceeded by shortening each of the $n_1 = 26$ original 36-in. specimens to 27 in. Each of these were mounted at a gage length of 23.8 in. and loaded to 360 ksi through three stages. The failure loads were recorded for the specimens that failed, $\bar{N}_1$, $\bar{N}_2$, and $\bar{N}_3$ were computed, and each of the surviving specimens was divided in half to

TABLE 1—*Multistage parameter estimates calculated from the boron filament experimental results.*

Stage Number	$\bar{q}_i$, ksi	g_i, in.	N_i/n_i	$\hat{\Lambda}_i$, No./in.	$\hat{\lambda}_i$, No./in./ksi	$\sqrt{\hat{V}[\hat{\lambda}_i]}$, No./in./ksi
1	120	23.8	26/26	0	0	...
2	240	23.8	24/26	3.34×10^{-3}	2.78×10^{-5}	1.98×10^{-5}
3	360	23.8	17/24	1.41×10^{-2}	1.17×10^{-4}	4.50×10^{-5}
4	400	9.8	25/32	2.50×10^{-2}	6.25×10^{-4}	2.37×10^{-4}
5	440	3.8	39/49	5.95×10^{-2}	1.49×10^{-3}	4.73×10^{-4}
6	464	1.0	58/66	1.19×10^{-1}	4.95×10^{-3}	1.80×10^{-3}
7	488	1.0	36/58	4.08×10^{-1}	1.70×10^{-2}	3.88×10^{-3}
8	504	0.50	16/33	1.34	8.38×10^{-2}	2.06×10^{-2}
9	516	0.50	5/16	1.96	1.63×10^{-1}	5.28×10^{-2}
10	528	0.50	1/5	2.06	1.72×10^{-1}	9.68×10^{-2}
11	540	0.50	0/1	∞	∞	...

form $n_4 = 2\bar{N}_3$ stage-4 specimens. Note that the first three stages were performed without changing the gage length. The remainder of the stages were conducted in a similar manner.

Results and Discussion

Values for $\hat{\Theta}_i = \bar{N}_i/n_i$ were obtained from the resulting experimental data and are listed in Table 1. The number of specimens actually tested at each stage was sometimes slightly lower than that allowed by subdivision because of occasional specimen loss or damage during dismounting or mounting. From the values of $\Theta_i = \bar{N}_i/n_i$ and $\bar{N}_i$, $i = 1, \cdots, k$, values for the $\hat{\lambda}_i$, $\hat{\Lambda}_i$, and $\hat{V}[\hat{\lambda}_i]$ were obtained using Eqs 8, 9, 11, 12, and 13 and are given in Table 1. The $C(\cdot)$ factors were determined using the methods of Ref 3.

The estimate $\tilde{\lambda}(\sigma)$ for $\lambda(\sigma)$ was computed using Eq 14, and is shown in Fig. 3 using a log-log scale. The broken lines in Fig. 3 represent $\tilde{\lambda}(\sigma) \pm \sqrt{\hat{V}[\hat{\lambda}_i]}$ for $\bar{q}_{i-1} \leq \sigma \leq \bar{q}_i$ and $i = 1, \cdots, k$, where $\sqrt{\hat{V}[\hat{\lambda}_i]}$ is an estimate of the standard deviation of $\hat{\lambda}_i$. The solid straight line is a plot of $\hat{\lambda}_2(\sigma) = d\hat{\Lambda}_2(\sigma)/d\sigma$ obtained from the preliminary two-parameter Weibull function $\Lambda_2(\sigma)$ which has parameters $m = 19$ and $\sigma_0 = 493$ ksi-in.$^{1/19}$. The preliminary one-inch gage length test data were also fitted with the three-parameter Weibull distribution, whose parameters were determined to be $m = 14$, $\sigma_0 = 371$ ksi-in.$^{1/14}$ and $\sigma_u = 120$ ksi (which was the lowest failure strength observed in the experimental program). The corresponding estimate of the Weibull function $\hat{\Lambda}_3(\sigma)$ is $\hat{\Lambda}_3(\sigma) = [(\sigma - 120)/371]^{14}$. The function $\hat{\lambda}_3(\sigma) = d\hat{\Lambda}_3(\sigma)/d\sigma$ is plotted in Fig. 4 together with the flaw strength spectrum estimate $\tilde{\lambda}(\sigma)$ obtained by the multistage procedure.

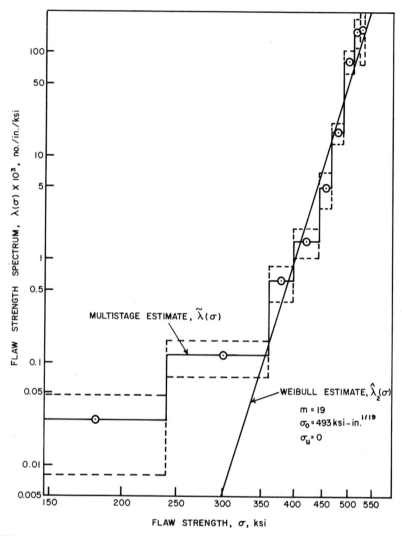

FIG. 3—*Comparison of the multistage estimate and the two-parameter Weibull estimate of the flaw strength spectrum for boron filament.*

Estimates of $\Lambda(\bar{q}_1), \cdots, \Lambda(\bar{q}_k)$ denoted $\hat{\Lambda}(\bar{q}_1), \cdots, \Lambda(\bar{q}_k)$ were obtained from the estimates $\hat{\Lambda}_1, \cdots, \hat{\Lambda}_k$ using the relation $\hat{\Lambda}(\bar{q}_i) = \Sigma_{j=1}{}^{i}\hat{\Lambda}_j$, which follows from Eq 4. Estimates of $F(q_1; 1), \cdots, F(q_k; 1)$ were computed from Eq 2 for $L = 1$ in. and these appear in Fig. 2 as circled dots. The broken line drawn through these points is then an estimate of $F(\sigma; L)$ for $L = 1$ in. obtained by the multistage procedure.

It is first observed in Fig. 2 that the multistage procedure estimate of $F(\sigma; 1)$, and the estimate of $F(\sigma; 1)$ given by the empirical cumulative

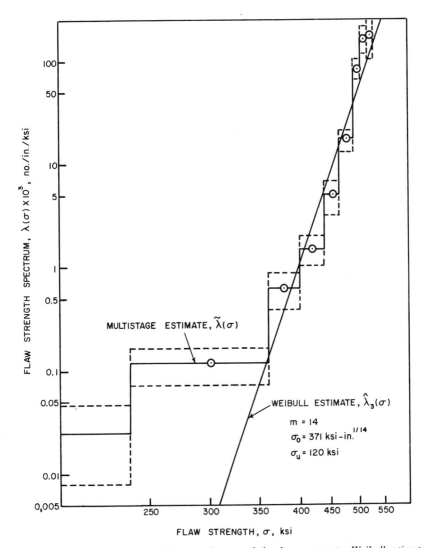

FIG. 4—*Comparison of the multistage estimate and the three-parameter Weibull estimate of the flaw strength spectrum for boron filament.*

distribution function of the preliminary 1-in. gage length tension test data, agree very closely even though the corresponding experimental procedures have been very different. This is strong evidence in support of the Poisson model. The second observation is that neither of these estimates of $F(\sigma; 1)$ forms a straight-line graph in Fig. 2. This strongly indicates that the actual 1-in. gage length cumulative distribution function $F(\sigma; 1)$ is not given by the two-parameter Weibull distribution, and furthermore that the cumulative flaw strength spectrum $\Lambda(\sigma)$ is not well represented by the two-parameter Weibull form given by Eq 3 with $\sigma_u \equiv$ 0. If $\Lambda(\sigma)$ could be well represented by the two-parameter Weibull form $\hat{\Lambda}_2(\sigma)$, then its derivative $\lambda(\sigma)$ would form a straight line in Fig. 3. Clearly the multistage estimate $\tilde{\lambda}(\sigma)$ does not form a straight line and only follows the preliminary Weibull form $\hat{\lambda}_2(\sigma)$ in the range of σ where most of the preliminary 1-in. gage length tenstion test data occur (Fig. 2).

The difficulty is that the Weibull form $\hat{\lambda}_2(\sigma)$ seriously underestimates the true frequency of flaw occurrence at low levels of σ as reflected by $\tilde{\lambda}(\sigma)$ in Fig. 3. For example, at 300 ksi, $\tilde{\lambda}(\sigma)$ estimates that there are approximately 1.5×10^{-4} flaws per unit length per ksi while $\hat{\lambda}_2(\sigma)$ estimates that there are only approximately 5×10^{-6} flaws per unit length per ksi, a value which is much lower. Similarly, $\hat{\lambda}_2(\sigma)$ appears to underestimate $\lambda(\sigma)$ as reflected by $\tilde{\lambda}(\sigma)$ in the upper range of σ in Fig. 3. In fact, $\hat{\lambda}_2(\sigma)$ appears to overestimate the flaw frequency $\lambda(\sigma)$ in the range $400 < \sigma < 500$. The preliminary data in Fig. 2 also support these trends.

From Fig. 4 it can be seen that the three-parameter Weibull estimate $\hat{\lambda}_3(\sigma)$ obtained from the preliminary tension test data also differs seriously from the multistage estimate $\tilde{\lambda}(\sigma)$ at low values of σ, possibly more so than does the two-parameter estimate $\hat{\lambda}_2(\sigma)$. Clearly no choice of σ_u between 0 and 120 ksi will alleviate the situation.

The information in Figs. 2 and 3 suggests that if the preliminary tension tests had been conducted using a 10-in. gage length for this particular boron fiber, then an estimated value of $m \cong 8$ would have been likely for the two-parameter Weibull distribution. On the other hand, if the gage length had been chosen as 0.2 in., a value of $m \cong 26$ would have been quite likely (not counting the clamp effects [1] which are likely to inflate m even further). Extrapolation of one-inch gage length tension test results to predict the behavior of other gage lengths by using the Weibull distribution appears to be a highly questionable procedure.

Conclusions

Weibull estimates, which have been calculated from high-modulus fiber tension test data of a given gage length, are frequently used in statistical theories of composite failure to represent the strength performance of fiber elements whose effective length is an order of magnitude shorter [6–8] (termed the "ineffective length" by some authors). One motivation for such extrapolation is that for some high-modulus fibers, a log average fiber strength versus log fiber gage length plot yields a near straight-line graph over a limited gage length range. It has been shown here that such extrapolation is not in general valid and may in fact be very inaccurate. The difficulty is that the Weibull estimate of $\Lambda(\sigma)$, given by Eq 3, often will not accurately represent the *true* fiber cumulative flaw strength spectrum $\Lambda(\sigma)$ over a wide range of σ, but only for the range of σ in which the data lie. For the boron fiber studied here, a gage length of one inch corresponds to a length-to-diameter ratio of approximately 180. For high-modulus graphite fibers a one-inch gage length corresponds to a length-to-diameter ratio of 2000 or more, and the extrapolation associated with the statistical theories of composite failure mentioned in the foregoing becomes even more questionable. The multistage procedure outlined here allows a very general form of the cumulative flaw strength spectrum $\Lambda(\sigma)$ for estimation purposes. Moreover, one may experimentally obtain information about $\Lambda(\sigma)$ in the particular range of σ of interest simply by adjusting g_i and $\bar{q}_i$, $i = 1, \cdots, k$ in the appropriate manner.

References

[1] Phoenix, S. L. and Sexsmith, R. G., *Journal of Composite Materials*, Vol. 6, 1972, pp. 322–337.

[2] Phoenix, S. L. in *Composite Materials: Testing and Design (Third Conference), ASTM STP 546*, American Society for Testing and Materials, pp. 130–151.

[3] Phoenix, S. L., "Probabilistic Strength Analysis of Fibers and Fiber Bundles", Ph.D. thesis and Materials Science Center Report No. 1873, Cornell University, 1972.

[4] Fraser, D.A.S., *Statistics—An Introduction*, Wiley, New York, 1958.

[5] Karlin, S., *A First Course in Stochastic Processes*, Academic Press, New York, 1968.

[6] Rosen, B. W., *Journal*, American Institute of Aeronautics and Astronautics, Vol. 2, 1964, pp. 1985–1991.

[7] Zweben, C., *Journal*, American Institute of Aeronautics and Astronautics, Vol. 6, 1968, pp. 2325–2331.

[8] Zweben, C. and Rosen, B. W., *Journal of the Mechanics and Physics of Solids*, Vol. 18, 1970, pp. 189–206.

A. P. Berens[1] and B. S. West[1]

Evaluation of an Accelerated Characterization Technique for Reliability Assessment of Adhesive Joints*

REFERENCE: Berens, A. P. and West, B. S., "**Evaluation of an Accelerated Characterization Technique for Reliability Assessment of Adhesive Joints,**" *Composite Reliability, ASTM STP 580,* American Society for Testing and Materials, 1975, pp. 90–101.

ABSTRACT: Adhesively bonded joints were failed statically and in fatigue to test the validity of a fatigue-life assessment model. The results of the tests were in agreement with both the assumptions and the predictions of the model. In particular, the failure mode was constant for all tests and the observed static strength and fatigue lives were adequately modeled by the Weibull family of distributions with constant, but different, shape parameters over the range of test conditions considered. The predicted relationship between the shape parameters as a function of an experimentally determined material property was observed. The predicted distribution of residual strength as a function of time in the fatigue environment was verified and agreement between prediction and observation for an accelerated fatigue test was obtained.

KEY WORDS: composite materials, bonded joints, fatigue tests, static tests, reliability, accelerated testing, residual strengths, adhesive bonding

This paper reports the results of an experimental program designed to test the applicability of a reliability evaluation model to the structural behavior of adhesively bonded joints. This model, developed by Halpin, Jerina, and Johnson [1],[2] is based on a structural reliability assessment methodology that has evolved as a result of developments in reliability analysis, kinetic fracture mechanics, and the introduction of the closed-loop fatigue testing machines. The essential features of the model may be summarized as follows. Fatigue failure occurs when the applied stress exceeds the residual strength of a structure. Repeated low-level stresses

*This work was sponsored by the Air Force Materials Laboratory, Wright-Patterson Air Force Base, Ohio, under Contract No. F33615-72-C-2161.
[1]University of Dayton Research Institute, Dayton, Ohio 45469.
[2]The italic numbers in brackets refer to the list of references appended to this paper.

reduce the strength, and the mechanism for this strength reduction is the growth of flaws which are inherent to all structures. Under this hypothesis, a model was developed which yields the distribution of strength as a function of time in the testing environment. The model is a function of the statistical parameters of the initial strength distribution and the fatigue life distribution, the slope of the flaw growth rate equation, a material constant, and the maximum applied stress in the fatigue spectrum. Further, by analogy with the methods of viscoelastic analysis [2], the statistical parameters of the strength and time-to-failure distributions are modeled by well-defined, shift-factor type relationships when the tests are performed under varying conditions of stress and temperature environments. The shift-factor relationships are derived from static tests and are applied to fatigue tests, thus allowing the fatigue tests to be performed in an accelerating environment.

To validate this model as an engineering tool in the fatigue-life assessment of quasi-brittle adhesives, specimens were statically tested at various combinations of temperature and loading rate and fatigue-tested at several levels of constant-amplitude load at room temperature. The resulting data were then analyzed to test basic assumptions and parameter relationships of the model. Using a shift factor derived from the static tests, the predicted life from an accelerated fatigue test was compared with the observed life.

Analytical Framework

The derivation of the fatigue-life methodology under consideration is presented in Ref 1, but in order to establish notation and to specify the equations of interest in this study, the following summary of the analytical framework is presented. Given that the strength of a structure is a function of the size of the maximum flaw, the strength at time t under a loading environment is derived as

$$F(t)^{2(r-1)} = F(0)^{2(r-1)} - (r - 1) \, AF_{max}^{2r} t \qquad (1)$$

where

$F(t)$ = strength at time t,
r = slope of crack growth rate equation, a material constant,
A = material constant, and
F_{max} = maximum applied stress in fatigue spectrum.

This equation implies that strength at time t is a deterministic function of the initial static strength. Variability is introduced by assuming that the initial static strengths have a Weibull distribution with constant shape parameter, α_0, and scale parameter, $\hat{F}(0)$. Using Eq 1 and the Weibull distribution of initial strengths

$$P[F(t) > F] = \exp - \left[\frac{F^{2(r-1)} + (r-1) AF_{max}^{2r}t}{F(0)^{2(r-1)}} \right] \alpha_f \qquad (2)$$

where $\alpha_f = \alpha_o/2(r-1)$. Since fatigue failure occurs when the applied stress exceeds the strength, the probability of survival to time t is $P[F(t) > F_{max}]$. For $F_{max} \ll \hat{F}(0)$, Eq 2 can be approximated by

$$P[F)t) > F_{max}] = P[t_f > t] = \exp[-t/\hat{t}_f] \alpha_f \qquad (3)$$

where

$$\hat{t}_f = \frac{\hat{F}(0)^{2(r-1)}}{(r-1) AF_{max}^{2r}} \qquad (4)$$

[For the data on this study, $r \approx 5$ and the maximum ratio of $F_{max}/\hat{F}(0) = 0.615$, which resulted in a maximum error of 2 percent in the fatigue-life distribution by dropping the $F_{max}/\hat{F}(0)^{2(r-1)}$ term.] By estimating $\hat{t}_f$ from fatigue tests for a given stress history, Eq 2 can be used to generate the distribution of strengths after the structures have been exposed to the environment for a time t. Further, from Eq 4

$$\hat{t}_f F_{max}^{2r} = \frac{\hat{F}(0)^{2(r-1)}}{(r-1)A} = B \qquad (5)$$

where B is a constant. Hence, a plot of log F_{max} versus log $\hat{t}_f$ is linear with slope $-\frac{1}{2}r$.

Equation 3 implies that, for a fixed mode of failure, the shape parameter of the time to fatigue failure distribution is independent of history, load, or environmental and side effects. The fatigue-life shape parameter is functionally related only to the static-strength shape parameter, α_0, and the material constant, r. The scale parameter, however, is dependent on the environmental conditions and it is shown that if fatigue tests are conducted at different temperatures

$$\hat{t}_f(T_i) = \hat{t}_f(T_0)/a_T \qquad (6)$$

where $\hat{t}_f(T_i)$ and $\hat{t}_f(T_0)$ are the characteristic fatigue lives at temperatures T_i and T_0, respectively, and a_T is the shift factor. If the static tests are performed by applying a constant loading rate history, $F(t) = Vt$, it is shown that the breaking strengths, F_b, have a Weibull distribution

$$P[F_b > F] = \exp - [F/\hat{F}_b]^{\alpha_0} \qquad (7)$$

where

$$\hat{F}_b = [B' (2r + 1) V]^{1/2r+1} \tag{8}$$

$$\alpha_0 = 2r + 1 \tag{9}$$

and B' is dependent on thermal and other environmental effects. Since $\hat{F}_b = V\hat{t}_b$, Eq 8 can be written in the form

$$\hat{t}_b \hat{F}_b{}^{2r} = B' (2r + 1) \tag{10}$$

Thus, a plot of log $\hat{F}_b$ versus log $\hat{t}_b$ is linear with slope $- \frac{1}{2}r$ and is parallel to the corresponding plot for fatigue lives, Eq 5. To shift the static time to break curve from temperature i to reference temperature R, assume $a_T = B'_i/B'_R$. Then, taking the ratio of $\hat{F}_{bi}$ to $\hat{F}_{bR}$ as expressed in Eq 8 yields

$$\log a_T = \alpha_0 \log \left[\frac{\hat{F}_{bi}}{\hat{F}_{bR}} \right] - \log [V_{ij}/V_R] \tag{11}$$

where V_{ij} represents loading rate j at temperature i [3]. The shift factors are then applied to the characteristic lives from fatigue tests to permit accelerated testing to locate the fatigue curve on the log F_{max} versus log $\hat{t}/a_T$ plot. Since the model indicates the slope of this curve is $- \frac{1}{2}r$, the fatigue curve at usage temperature is thus established.

The objectives of the test program can now be stated in terms of the assumptions and predicted relationships of the model. These were:

1. To the extent possible, check the applicability of the Weibull distribution.

2. Test the constancy of the Weibull shape parameter for static tests and fatigue tests.

3. Evaluate the relationships between α_0, α_f, and r.

4. Evaluate the predicted distribution of strengths as a function of time in loading environment.

5. Compare the slope of the log F_{max} versus log $\hat{t}/a_T$ curves with $- \frac{1}{2}r$.

6. Evaluate shift factors from static tests by performing an accelerated fatigue test and comparing observed results with the predicted.

7. Evaluate constancy of failure mode in the adhesively bonded joint.

A more complete description of the program on which this paper is based is presented in Ref 4.

Experimental Procedure

The test specimen configuration shown in Fig. 1 was selected for

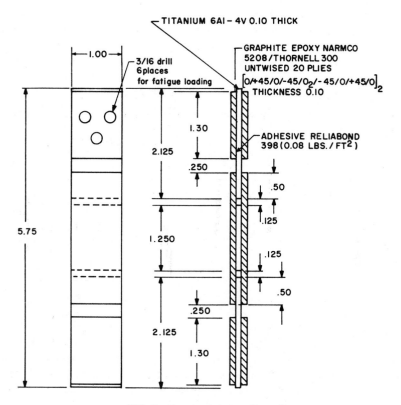

FIG. 1—*Test specimen configuration.*

achieving the objectives of the research effort reported herein. This configuration was arrived at through an experimental design study which investigated strength and failure mode as a function of adherend stiffness and configuration. The resulting specimen exhibited a cohesive failure in the adhesive layer forming the bonded joint. The Reliabond 398 adhesive system was selected because it is a brittle adhesive system and therefore should be compatible with the assumptions made in the structural behavior model.

The test specimens were fabricated in panels 9.5 in. wide by 5.75 in. long. Three panels were made during each cure cycle. The specimens were cured 60 min at 350°F (177°C) at a pressure of 30 psig following a heat-up rate of 6°F per minute. A total of eight specimens was cut from each panel using a diamond cutoff wheel with liquid cooling. Quality-control tests were conducted on the adherend and adhesive material used to fabricate the specimens. In addition, all adherend material was sorted and matched with respect to thickness to ensure that the bonded joint would be of constant thickness.

All fatigue and static strength testing was performed on MTS closed-loop control testing systems. Instron grips with serrated loading wedges were used for all static strength testing. Loading was achieved through the loading holes indicated in Fig. 1 for fatigue testing. High- and low-temperature testing was accomplished using an Instron Environmental Chamber. Specimens were soaked for 60 min at temperature prior to testing at temperature. Specimens were allocated for testing using a quasi-random selection procedure and were stored in a controlled laboratory environment from completion of fabrication to start of testing.

Test Results

Ten specimens were statically loaded to failure at each combination of five temperatures, $T = -40$, 73, 150, 250, and 300°F (-40, 23, 66, 121, and 149°C), and three loading rates, $V = 120$, 1200, and 12 000 lb/min. Ten specimens were also failed at $T = 200$°F (93°C) and $V = 1200$ lb/min. For each of the sixteen sets of data, the maximum likelihood estimates of the shape and scale parameter were calculated, and these summary statistics are presented in Table 1. To test the equality of the shape parameters, 90 percent confidence limits were determined for each shape parameter [5]. Nonoverlapping confidence intervals indicate a significant difference at the 90 percent level of confidence. All confidence intervals were overlapping except for the highest $\alpha_0[\alpha_0 = 22.06$ at $T = 250$°F (121°C), $V = 120]$ with the two lowest [$\alpha_0 = 8.01$ at $T = -40$°F

TABLE 1—*Weibull parameter estimates for static tests.*

Temperature, °F	Loading Rate, lb/min	Specimen Size	Scale Parameter, $\hat{F}(0)$, psi	Shape Parameter, α_0
-40	120	10	5165	8.01
	1 200	10	5756	11.37
	12 000	10	5638	13.87
73	120	10	5057	12.32
	1 200	10	4955	8.44
	12 000	10	5145	14.41
150	120	10	4449	11.37
	1 200	10	4510	8.88
	12 000	10	4624	14.26
200	1 200	10	3949	12.98
250	120	10	2840	22.06
	1 200	10	3143	13.68
	12 000	10	3486	16.01
300	120	10	1693	10.95
	1 200	10	2148	9.08
	12 000	10	2879	16.51

$(-40\,^{\circ}\mathrm{C})$, $V = 120$ and $\alpha_0 = 8.44$ at $T - 73\,^{\circ}\mathrm{F}$ $(23\,^{\circ}\mathrm{C})$, $V = 1200]$. Since the highest α_0 was the only significantly different value, it was concluded that this value was due to chance and that these data indicate a constant shape parameter for static strengths.

Constant-amplitude fatigue tests were conducted with $R = 0.1$ at $T = 73\,^{\circ}\mathrm{F}$ $(23\,^{\circ}\mathrm{C})$ for seven levels of maximum load, $F_{\max} = 3100$, 2900, 2700, 2500, 2350, 2150, and 2000 lb, and at $T = 200\,^{\circ}\mathrm{F}$ $(93\,^{\circ}\mathrm{C})$ at $F_{\max} = 2000$ lb. All failed specimens were examined for constancy of failure mode and were found to exhibit a cohesive failure in the adhesive layer for both the static strength and fatigue tests. In three sets of tests, $T = 73\,^{\circ}\mathrm{F}$ $(23\,^{\circ}\mathrm{C})$ and $F_{\max} = 2500$, 2150, and 2000 lb, runouts were observed which were an order of magnitude or greater than the characteristic life of the remaining specimens in the set. Although no assignable cause could be found for these long lives, they were considered indicative that the distribution of fatigue lives may be bimodal. Since primary interest in the practical problem is in the distribution of the shorter lives, the runouts were eliminated in the analysis of the fatigue data. The maximum-likelihood estimates of the shape and scale parameters for the fatigue data are presented in Table 2. The equality of the fatigue shape parameters was selected was tested by 90 percent confidence intervals with

TABLE 2—*Weibull parameter estimates for fatigue tests.*

Temperature, °F	Max Load, lb	Specimen Size	Scale Parameter, $\hat{t}$, min	Shape Parameter, α_f
73	3100	10	53.3	2.62
73	2900	10	140	2.22
73	2700	10	124	1.99
73	2500	9	1020	1.43
73	2350	6	777	0.92
73	2150	8	485	1.56
73	2000	9	2870	0.69
200	2000	15	367	1.34

inconclusive results. The middle six values were not significantly different, but the highest α_f was significantly greater than the three lowest and the lowest value was significantly less then the three highest. Further, there was a distinct decreasing trend in α_f with increasing characteristic life. Nevertheless, a constant α_f was assumed for the remaining analysis, ascribing the observed differences to chance.

Since each data set in either the static or fatigue tests contains few data points, a test of the Weibull distribution function for each set would not be meaningful. Given a constant shape parameter, however, dividing each data point by its respective scale parameter, yields data sets of 160 points for the static tests and 77 points for the fatigue tests. Further, the transformed data should have a scale parameter of unity and shape parameters of α_0 and α_f. When this transformation was performed, the unbiased maximum-likelihood estimates of the shape parameters were $\alpha_0 = 11.23$ and $\alpha_f = 1.26$ with scale parameters of 1.001 and 1.076 for the static and fatigue data, respectively. The unbiased average shape parameters of the individual data sets were $\bar{\alpha}_0 = 10.96$ and $\bar{\alpha}_f = 1.37$, which are in agreement with the standardized parameter estimates. The observed cumulative distribution of the transformed data points and their Weibull fits are presented in Fig. 2. The differences between the theoretical and observed distributions are not significant and it is concluded that the Weibull distribution is an acceptable model for both the static strength and fatigue life data.

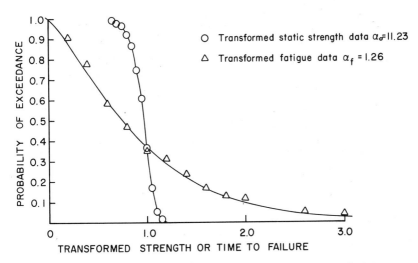

FIG. 2—*Transformed static strength and time to fatigue failure distributions.*

The fatigue characteristic lives are erratic in that a consistent increase in characteristic life was not obtained for decreasing maximum load. No assignable cause could be determined for this effect. Nevertheless, a least-squares fit was obtained for the log F_{max} versus log $\hat{t}$ plot (which is shown later) and the slope of this line was -0.101, which according to Eq 5 implies an r value of about 5. This is in agreement with the value of r obtained from α_0 by means of Eq 9 and either of the α_0 estimates. Further, $r = 5$ implies by Eq 2 that $\alpha_f = 1.37$, which agrees with observed estimates of α_f. Therefore, in further analyses it was assumed that $r = 5$, $\alpha_0 = 11$, and $\alpha_f = 1.37$.

Strength as a Function of Time in Fatigue Environment

Equation 2 provides a model for the distribution of strength as a function of time in the fatigue environment. The applicability of this aspect of the model was tested [6] by exposing specimens to the fatigue environment for a period of time and statically determining the strength of the unfailed specimens. Since the present program was directed primarily to an investigation of the shift-factor aspects of the model, that approach was not used. Since each specimen contained two adhesive joints, however, the strength of the second joint at the time of failure of the first joint provides a definite indication of the validity of Eq 2.

Since each specimen consists of two joints, the static strength of a specimen can be considered as the minimum of two Weibull random variables which also has a Weibull distribution with a smaller characteristic strength. To determine the characteristic strength of the individual joints, the strength of the second (unfailed) joint of the specimens statically tested at $T = 73\,°F$ ($23\,°C$) was determined. Since no loading rate effect was observed at this temperature, all 60 of the joint strengths were pooled and the maximum-likelihood estimate of the scale parameter of these data was determined to be 5540 lb. Since this value is greater than the predicted value (5380 lb) from the minimum of two Weibull random variables as obtained from the specimen tests, it was concluded that loading the stronger joint to the level of first joint failure did not effect the second joint, and the scale parameter of all joints at $T = 73\,°F$ ($23\,°C$) was taken as 5540 lb.

According to Eq 4, the quantity $\hat{F}(0)^{2(r-1)}/(r-1)\,AF_{max}^{2r}$ of Eq 2 can be estimated by t_f obtained from the fatigue environment. To estimate t_{f1} for a larger static strength characteristic life and the same fatigue environment, the ratio of the characteristic lifetimes yields

$$\hat{t}_{f1} = \hat{t}_{fR}\left[\frac{\hat{F}_1(0)}{\hat{F}_R(0)}\right]^{2(r-1)} \tag{12}$$

where $\hat{t}_{fR}$ and $\hat{F}_R(0)$ are the scale parameters of the fatigue lives and static strengths for reference conditions, and $\hat{F}_1(0)$ is the increased scale parameter of the static strengths.

The undamaged second joints of the fatigue tests run at $T = 73\,°F$ ($23\,°C$) and $F_{max} = 3100, 2900, 2700, 2500,$ and 2000 lb were statically tested to failure. Using Eqs 12 and 2, predicted 10th, 50th, and 90th percentiles of the strength distributions for these values of F_{max} were determined as a function of time. Transforming the time scale by the median life at each F_{max} level within a data set permitted the five sets of data to be presented on a single plot with less than a 2 percent error in the transformed time scale. Figure 3 presents the predicted percentiles of the strength distributions and the

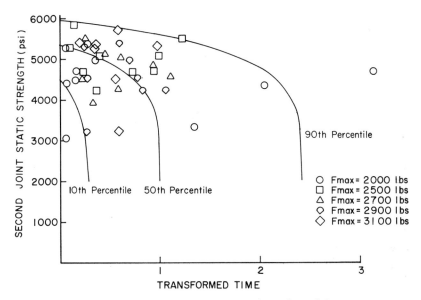

FIG. 3—*Static strength as a function of transformed time.*

observed static strength of the 42 undamaged joints. The observed strengths are reasonably scattered with respect to the predicted percentiles with 25 points above the median and 17 below. Since these joints were actually the stronger of two with the assumed characteristic life, they were expected to have more points above the median line. Further, since the failure times were determined from the weaker of two joints, the high density at the shorter times was also expected. The results presented in this figure are taken as supportive evidence that the model for predicting strength as a function of time in fatigue environment is applicable to the adhesive joints of this study.

Shift Factors for Accelerated Testing

The objective in the determination of the shift factors from the static tests is to determine the amount of translation of log $\hat{t}_b$ required to account for the change in strength due to temperature and loading rate. Equation 11 provides an analytical approach to determination of this shift factor and was applied to the static data with reference conditions taken as $T_R = 73\,°F$ (23 °C) and $V_R = 120$ lb/min. The individual logarithm of the shift factors and a curve through their average value are shown in Fig. 4. The separation of the individual log a_T values is due to the difference between the actual and assumed slopes of the log $\hat{F}_b$ versus log $\hat{t}_b$ curves. Note that selecting $V_R = 1200$ or 12 000 lb/min simply increases the log a_T values by 1 or 2, respectively, and does not change

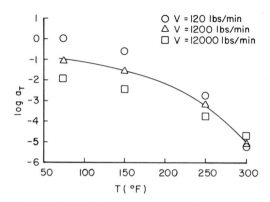

FIG. 4—*Shift factors as a function of temperature.*

the shape of the log a_T versus T curve. Using the average log a_T values for each temperature, the resultant log $\hat{F}$ versus log $\hat{t}/a_T$ relationship is presented in Fig. 5.

To test the applicability of the shift factors to fatigue lives, an accelerated fatigue test was performed at a temperature of 200 °F (93 °C) with F_{max} = 2000 lb and R = 0.1. The shifted fatigue life from this test was compared with the results of the fatigue tests performed at the reference temperature. This comparison is presented in Fig. 6, which is a plot of log F_{max} versus log $\hat{t}/a_T$ where log a_T = −1.00 for T = 73 °F (23 °C) and log a_T = −2.18 for T = 200 °F (93 °C). The straight line shown on this graph is the least-squares line through the room-temperature data and the slope of this line agrees with the predicted slope of −½r = −0.10. As can be seen from Fig. 6, the shifted $\hat{t}$ value for the accelerated tests agrees well with the predicted value. Therefore, the analytical framework of the model yielded and acceptable agreement between theory and data for this one accelerated test.

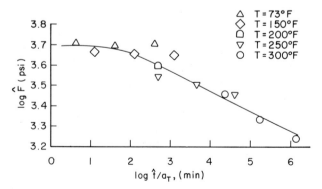

FIG. 5—*Characteristic strength as a function of transformed time to break.*

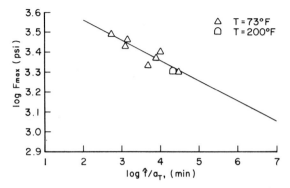

FIG. 6—*Maximum load as a function of transformed life.*

Conclusions

The objective of this study was to experimentally verify a fatigue-life assessment methodology for a brittle adhesively bonded joint. The particular aspects of the model that could be verified in the study and the conclusions drawn are as follows. Both static strength and fatigue lives are satisfactorily described by the Weibull family of distributions, and the mode of failure was constant for all tests. The shape parameter of the static strength distribution can be considered a constant for the range of temperatures and loading rates considered. Although the fatigue tests displayed anomalies, for practical engineering purposes their shape parameters could also be considered constant and the theoretical relationships with the shape parameter of static tests agreed with observed values. The predicted relationship of residual strength as a function of time in the fatigue environment was verified. Finally, on the basis of one test, agreement was observed between prediction and observation of an accelerated fatigue test result.

References

[1] Halpin, J. C., Jerina, K. L., and Johnson, T. A. in *Analysis of the Test Methods for High Modulus Fibers and Composites, ASTM STP 521,* American Society for Testing and Materials, 1973, pp. 5–64.
[2] Tsai, S. W., Halpin, J. C., and Pagano, N. J., *Composite Materials Workshop,* Technomic Publishing Co., Inc., Standford, Conn., 1968.
[3] Halpin, J. C., "Structural Reliability Characterization of Advanced Composites," *Proceedings* of the Colloquium on Structural Reliability, Department of Mechanical Engineering, Carnegie-Mellon University, Pittsburgh, Pa., 1972.
[4] Berens, A. P., Johnson, P. E., and West, B. S., "Experimental Evaluation of a Reliability Assessment Model for Adhesively Bonded Joints," AFML-TR-74-120, Air Force Materials Laboratory, Dayton, Ohio, 1974.
[5] Thoman, D. R., Bain, L. J., and Antle, C. E., *Technometrics,* Vol. 2, No. 3, Aug. 1969, pp. 445–460.
[6] Wolff, R. V. and Lemon, G. H., "Reliability Prediction for Adhesive Bonds," Technical Report AFML-TR-72-121, Air Force Materials Laboratory, Dayton, Ohio, 1972.

Applications

D. L. Reed[1] and J. R. Eisenmann[1]

Reliability Aspects of a Composite Bolted Scarf Joint

REFERENCE: Reed, D. L. and Eisenmann, J. R. "**Reliability Aspects of a Composite Bolted Scarf Joint,**" *Composite Reliability, ASTM STP 580,* American Society for Testing and Materials, 1975, pp. 105–118.

ABSTRACT: A wing splice representative of a next-generation transport aircraft requires an extended fatigue life and the capability of disassembly and reassembly. The design, fabrication, static test, and fatigue test of both tension and compression graphite-epoxy candidates for such a splice was the objective of the research program reported here. A single-scarf bolted joint was selected as the design concept.

Test specimens were designed and fabricated to represent an upper surface and a lower surface panel containing the splice. The load spectrum was a flight-by-flight random load history including ground-air-ground loads.

The results of the fatigue testing indicate that, for this type of joint, the inherent fatigue resistance of the laminate is reflected in the joint behavior, and consequently the rate of damage accumulation is very slow under realistic fatigue loadings.

KEY WORDS: composite materials, composites, laminates, bolted joints, strength, wearout, tension fatigue tests, compression fatigue tests, structures, reliability, random loads

The objective of this paper is to document a demonstration of the long service capacity of composite materials for a piece of flight-critical hardware—a wing skin splice. The program required the design of a tension and compression splice, fabrication of typical test specimens, development of a realistic fatigue history, construction of a test laboratory setup to apply the static and fatigue loadings, and an experimental program to test the splice specimens.

---

[1] Senior structures engineer, General Dynamics, Fort Worth Division, Fort Worth, Tex. 76101.

Splice Elements

An initial requirement that the splice be capable of disassembly and re-assembly immediately placed the splice in the bolted-joint category. The spanwise splice was assumed to take place within a single rib-to-rib bay of a transport wing with sandwich construction skins on both the upper and lower wing surfaces. Thus, test specimens had to be representative of the joint region and also simulate the transition from sandwich skins to the solid laminate in the splice region. A constant-thickness panel was designed with the overall thickness determined from the splice requirements.

A single-scarf bolted joint was selected as the design concept for this study. Test specimens were designed and fabricated to represent an upper surface and a lower surface of a composite transport wing. The test specimens simulate a spanwise strip of unit width which contains one row of bolts. Figure 1 is a line sketch of a typical splice element.

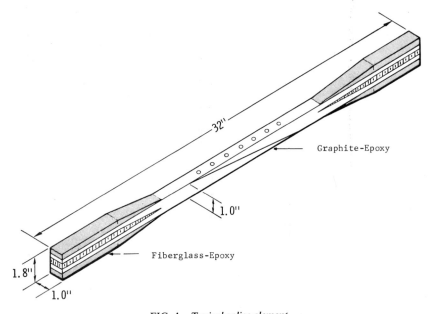

FIG. 1—*Typical splice element.*

Specimen Design

The material selected for the test specimens was T300/5208 graphite-epoxy and the thickness of the test specimens was full scale. The mating pieces of the wing panel test specimens were joined at a machined-scarf interface by mechanical fasteners which were countersunk on the aerodynamic surface. Strain matching techniques were used to assure equal load distribution among the fasteners. This required that the laminate be tailored to arrive at the required modulus at each bolt location. Thus the percent of 0-deg layers in the laminate varies from one end of the scarf to the other. The strength design of the laminate at each bolt location was based on a fracture model. The applicability of classical fracture mechanics to the loaded or unloaded hole problem was developed by Waddoups et al [1][2] and justified by Manning and Lemon [2]. The splice design was based on static considerations only. The design limit and ultimate loads were 15 000 lb/in. and 22 500 lb/in., respectively.

The resulting test specimens for the compression surface were 1.238 in. thick (225 plies), 33 in. long, and 1 in. wide with five ¼-in. bolts on 1.0-in. centers along the scarf. The tension test specimens were 1.070 in. thick (195 plies), 34 in. long, and 1 in. wide with seven ¼-in. bolts along the scarf. Twenty compression and 20 tension splice specimens were fabricated. Figure 2 is a photograph of the tension and compression splice specimens.

Load History

To obtain as much realism as possible in developing the fatigue load history, a flight-by-flight random load sequence was generated. For a transport aircraft, the primary source of alternating load is the response of the structure to gust loads. The gust load-exceedance curve which was used to develop the load history for this study is shown in Fig. 3. In the procedure used, the loads within each flight were generated as a random sequence and differ from flight to flight while retaining the exceedance curve for the entire load history. The simulated life contained 30 000 two-hour accelerated flights.

A factor which cannot be neglected in a realistic fatigue history is the aircraft landings. These ground-air-ground (GAG) loads cause reversals which are significant factors in the fatigue life of most structures [3]. GAG load reversals were included in the fatigue spectrum. Thus, for 30 000 flights per life, a one-lifetime load history contains 30 000 deterministic GAG load reversals.

A computer program described in Ref 4 was used to generate a one-lifetime load history. This loading history contained approximately 448 780 loads and was stored on magnetic tape for use in the test laboratory. One test lifetime of loading required approximately 18 test hours. Figure 3 contains a plot of one flight of random loads.

Experimental Program

Static and fatigue testing was performed in a closed-loop testing system using a set of five test frames designed and fabricated for these tests. The

---

[2] The italic numbers in brackets refer to the list of references appended to this paper.

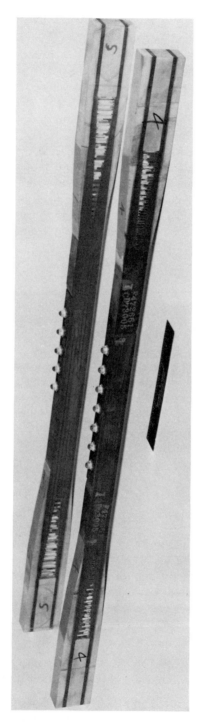

FIG. 2—*Tension and compression joint specimens.*

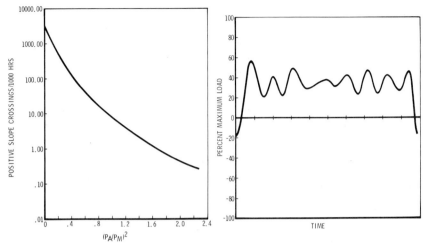

FIG. 3—*Random load simulation.*

loads were introduced into the specimen through fiber glass end tabs, which were bolted between serrated steel plates.

The closed-loop testing system was controlled by a command signal sent to a servo-controlled hydraulic ram located below the specimen in each of the test frames. The command signal was generated by a Varian 620i computer in the test laboratory. The computer was fed information from the magnetic tape containing the random load history. A load cell was located above the test specimen and provided the feedback load signal to complete the loop.

Static Tests

Of the 20 tension splice specimens and 20 compression splice specimens, five specimens from each set were allocated for static testing. End-grip problems and system malfunctions reduced the number of usable test points to three each for tension and compression. Static and fatigue test results are presented in Table 1 for tension and compression tests. The α and β in this table are Weibull shape and scale parameters, respectively.

A typical static failure of a tension splice specimen is depicted in Fig. 4. Load versus relative movement between the two halves of the splice was monitored with a clip gage. In general the curves were linear until failure occurred. If the particular specimen did not fail catastrophically at the first nonlinear point in the curve, the point of nonlinearity was called failure. None of the compression specimens failed catastrophically. However, upon inspection of the specimens, cracks and bearing-type damage was observed.

Fatigue Tests

In an effort to cause fatigue failures within a reasonable test time, the

TABLE 1—*Splice test results.*

Initial Static Strength, lb		Residual Strength, lb, at 4.0 Lifetimes Magnification Factor = 1.3636	Fatigue Failure (Lifetimes) Magnification Factor = 1.7727	
		Tension		
22 500		21 600	0.465	
23 000	$\alpha_0 = 60$	22 300	0.625	$\alpha_f = 3.10$
23 200	$\beta_0 = 23100$	23 800	0.670	$\beta_f = 0.835$
			0.854	
			1.107	
		Compression		
22 400		21 200	0.254	
22 600	$\alpha_0 = 109$	21 800	0.460	$\alpha_f = 2.67$
22 800	$\beta_0 = 22700$	22 000	0.530	$\beta_f = 0.568$
		22 700	0.603	
			0.633	

maximum load in the fatigue spectrum was scaled up to 80 percent of the design static ultimate load, or 18 000 lb. The limit load level was reduced from 15 000 to 13 200 lb to allow for a 12 percent of gross weight fuel burn at mid-flight. Thus under the scaled-up loading spectrum, the maximum load level was 1.3636 times limit load. This load level was reached six times per simulated aircraft lifetime. This scale-up factor is a multiplier for all loads in the history. The GAG load level reversal for this spectrum was 3600 lb.

Under this scaled-up loading spectrum, five tension splice specimens and five compression splice specimens were loaded to the four-lifetime level. By this point in life, two tension specimens and one compression specimen had been lost due to system malfunctions. The remaining specimens were tested for residual strength, and the results are given in Table 1. These data show that four lifetimes of random fatigue under the magnified spectrum had a very small effect on the mean static strength of the splice element.

At this point in the fatigue test program, the magnification factor was raised by 30 percent to 1.7727 and the spectrum truncated at 80 percent of ultimate. This truncation resulted in the 18 000 lb load being reached approximately 150 times per lifetime. The GAG load level reversal for this truncated spectrum was 4680 lb. A load-time trace of the 1.3636 and 1.7727 magnification factor spectra, illustrating the severity of the magnified spectrum and the GAG load reversals, is shown in Fig. 5.

Five tension splice specimens were installed and loaded with the truncated random load spectrum. Two specimens failed catastrophically at 0.465 and 0.670 lifetimes. A tension fatigue failure is shown in Fig. 6. A third specimen test was stopped when the test monitor heard one of the bolts snap. Upon

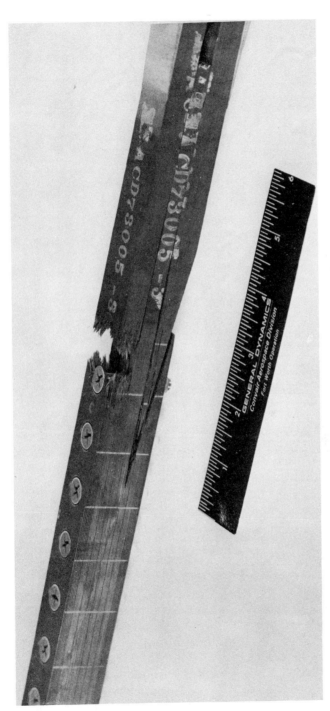

FIG. 4—*Static tension failure close-up.*

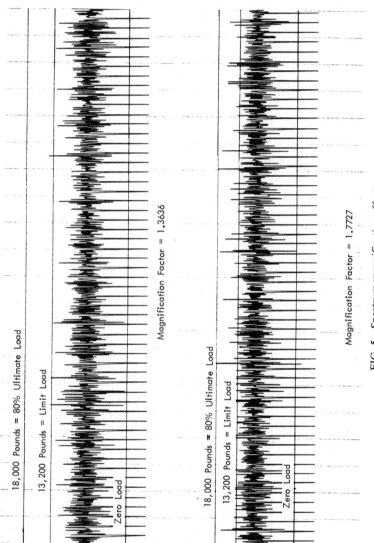

FIG. 5—*Spectrum magnification effects.*

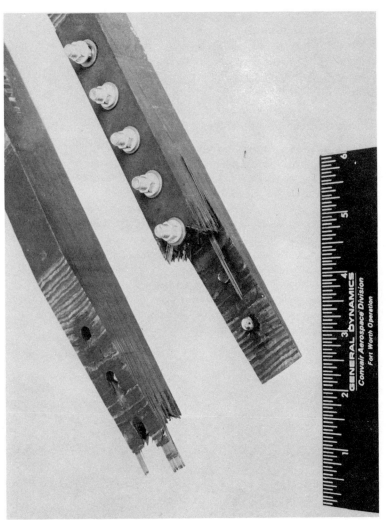

FIG. 6—*Tension fatigue failure at 0.465 lifetimes.*

inspection, it was found that two bolts were broken and fatigue damage was present in all bolt holes. The two broken bolt holes were elongated by 10 percent. This specimen had reached 0.854 lifetimes and, based upon the inspection, the test was terminated. Figure 7 is an X-ray radiograph of the holes near the thin end of the splice; viewed from the inner surfaces of the splice, the extent of the fatigue damage is clearly evident. This newly developed nondestructive evaluation method is described in Ref 5.

The failure mechanism thus appears to be bearing damage resulting in displacement of the two pieces of the splice, which results in bolt failures due to bending. The results obtained for the five tension fatigue specimens are given in Table 1, and the fatigue failure of the specimens was based on a first-bolt failure criterion.

Five compression splice specimens were also tested under the 1.7727 magnification factor spectrum. Similar test results were obtained with re-

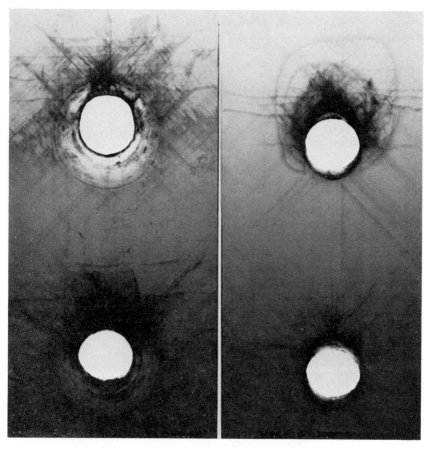

FIG. 7—Tension fatigue damage at 0.854 lifetimes.

spect to the first-bolt breakage, and the fatigue failure data are also presented in Table 1.

Analysis of Test Data

The wearout model of Ref 6 and 7 was used as a means of analyzing and extrapolating the data presented in Table 1. This wearout model relates the residual strength and fatigue lifetime distributions through a kinetic fracture hypothesis that was based on the assumptions that all materials in a structure contain preexisting flaws and that failure occurs from the growth to final failure of these flaws. These flaws were assumed to grow in a deterministic manner depending upon the material state and its environmental history. A discussion of the input parameters for this model follows.

The static strength distribution parameter α_0 is probably large (tension = 60, compression = 109) because of the small number of test points. The laminate static strength α_0 for fiber-controlled graphite laminates is approximately 30. Thus, it was decided to use $\alpha_0 = 30$ as a conservative estimate for both tension and compression data sets. Next, the α_f of the fatigue failures (tension = 3.10, compression = 2.67) was very close, so a data pooling technique was used to determine an α_f for the combined tension and compression data. In this technique, each of the five tension fatigue failure data points is divided by the β_f for its particular set and likewise for the compression data. This technique results in ten data points from which to estimate an α_f and yields an α_f of 3.36.

The next parameter required by the wearout model is the crack growth rate exponent, r

$$r = \frac{\alpha_0}{2\alpha_f} + 1 = \frac{30}{(2)\,(3.36)} + 1$$

$$r = 5.46$$

This r value is indicative of resin cracking advance rates and is similar to that observed in bonded joints. The static fracture data show filament-dominated results (large α_0); hence the joint specimens show a combination-type failure.

With these basic input data (α_0, β_0, and r), the model can be used to fit both residual strength and fatigue failure data. Figure 8 contains the wearout model plot for the tension data. A similar plot was obtained from the compression data.

The wearout model can also be used to predict the effects of load level changes through the use of the load magnification parameter A_1

$$\beta_{fA_1} = \beta_{fref}(A_1)^{-2r}$$

where β_{fref} represents the $A_1 = 1$ or no load magnification.

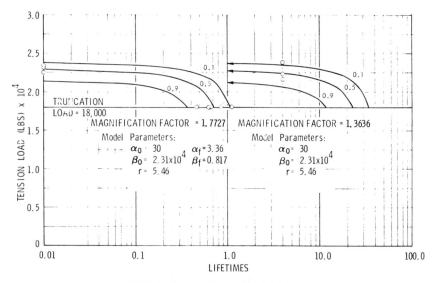

FIG. 8—*Wing splice tension joint data.*

For the tension data set

$$A_1 = 1.7727, \beta_{fA_1} = 0.835, r = 5.46$$

thus

$$\beta_{fref} = 0.835/(1.7727)^{-10.92} = 433 \text{ lifetimes}$$

Therefore, under the limit load (peak load) tension fatigue spectrum, the wearout model would predict a fatigue life scale parameter of 433 lifetimes. For the compression data set, the wearout model would predict a fatigue life scale parameter of 295 lifetimes under the limit-load (peak load) compression fatigue spectrum. Thus, the long life characteristics of composite laminates have been transferred to the splice concept.

Discussion

The β_f of the reference spectrum was predicted by the wearout model to be 433 lifetimes for the tension splice. Now, assuming that the α_f would translate to this spectrum, one can calculate the point at which one lifetime falls in the distribution as follows

$$P = \exp\left[-\left(\frac{X}{\beta}\right)^{\alpha}\right] = \exp\left[-\left(\frac{1}{433}\right)^{3.36}\right]$$

or

$$P_{ele} = 0.999\ 999\ 998\ 6$$

Now, since this detail (one line of bolts in the total wing splice) must be repeated approximately 60 times (60-in.-chord transport wing)

$$P_{splice} = P_{ele}^{60} = 0.999\ 999\ 916$$

Thus, the probability of survival of the total wing splice at one lifetime under the initial limit load spectrum is quite high.

Another aspect of the test results reveals the relationship between limit and ultimate design stress or load levels. Since the load magnification factor of 1.3636 only raised the peak load to 18 000 lb and did not truncate any loads, let us assume, for the moment, that 18 000 lb is the design limit load level. Now, since the splice was designed to an ultimate load of 22 500 lb, the factor of safety relating limit and ultimate load becomes

$$\text{factor of safety} = \frac{22500}{18000} = 1.25$$

For the 1.3636 magnification factor curves in Fig. 8, it may be observed that the splice element has an adequate fatigue life (>10 lifetimes) and at 1.0 lifetime the residual strength lines are essentially flat. This line of reasoning leads one to the conclusion that a 1.5 factor of safety (a carryover from metallic design) may be too large for this splice element. A more realistic approach would be to set this overload factor as the load ratio derived from a once-per-fleet lifetime gust.

The discussion could also be viewed from the overload design procedure outlined in Ref 8. Again referring to the 1.3636 magnification factor curves of Fig. 8, the tension splice specimen has a 0.9 probability of survival of an overload of 21 000 lb or 93 percent of ultimate at 1.0 lifetime. With residual strength data and fatigue lifetime data at two or more levels, the entire design procedure as outlined in Ref 8 could be implemented.

Conclusions

We have established the feasibility of an all composite-to-composite wing splice in an advanced transport loading environment. This was done with a small number of data points and, while a complete detail overload and fatigue life design would require a larger data set, this research firmly establishes an effective structural design concept and a revised design/ evaluation strategy. We very economically developed the preliminary design data set by relating our results to a large data base and thus were able to greatly extend our conclusions.

We are currently fabricating two large wing panels (one tension and one compression) which will be fatigue-tested. The panels contain 12 rows of bolts and will serve to demonstrate the shift of statistics due to complexity.

Acknowledgments

The research program described herein was funded under a contract with NASA-LRC. C. C. Poe was the NASA contract monitor, and the contract number was NAS1-11974.

References

[1] Waddoups, M. E., Eisenmann, J. R., and Kaminski, B. E., *Journal of Composite Materials*, Vol. 5, Oct. 1971.

[2] Manning, S. D. and Lemon, G. H., *Study of Structural Criteria for Composite Airframes*, AFFDL-TR-73-4, Vol. 1, April 1973.

[3] Naumann, E. C., *Evaluation of the Influence of Load Randomization and of Ground-Air-Ground Cycles on Fatigue Life*, NASA TN D-1584, National Aeronautics and Space Administration, Washington, D.C., Oct. 1964.

[4] Wilkins, D. J., Wolff, R. V., Shinozuka, M., and Cox, E. F., *Fatigue of Composite Materials*, ASTM STP 569, American Society for Testing and Materials, 1975, pp. 307-322.

[5] Chang, F. H., Couchman, J. C., Eisenmann, J. R., and Yee, B. G. W. in this symposium, pp. 176-190.

[6] Halpin, J. C., Waddoups, M. E., and Johnson, T. A., *International Journal of Fracture Mechanics*, Vol. 8, 1972, pp. 465-468.

[7] Halpin, J. C., Jerina, K. L., and Johnson, T. A. in *Analysis of the Test Methods for High Modulus Fibers and Composites*, ASTM STP 521, American Society for Testing and Materials, 1973, pp. 5-64.

[8] Eisenmann, J. R., Kaminski, B. E., Reed, D. L., and Wilkins, D. J., *Journal of Composite Materials*, Vol. 7, No. 3., July 1973.

W. J. Renton[1] and J. R. Vinson[1]

Shear Property Measurements of Adhesives in Composite Material Bonded Joints

REFERENCE: Renton, W. J. and Vinson, J. R., "**Shear Property Measurements of Adhesives in Composite Material Bonded Joints,**" *Composite Reliability, ASTM STP 580,* American Society for Testing and Materials, 1975, pp. 119–132.

ABSTRACT: A test specimen has been designed and procedures developed for determining the effective shear modulus, shear proportional limit, and ultimate shear strength for adhesive materials used in bonded lap joints between adherends of either metals or composite materials. By utilizing adhesives in their joint geometry, effects of errors from using bulk property data are avoided. Surface interaction phenomena between adhesive and adherend, surface roughness effects, etc. are automatically included.

Test data to date are presented for adherends of 1002 S-glass uniply and angleply construction, and Hysol EA951 adhesive. Effects of adhesive thickness and joint length are also presented.

KEY WORDS: composite materials, adhesive bonding, bonded joints, adhesives

It has been the usual practice to utilize the bulk mechanical properties of adhesives in the analysis and design of bonded joints between structural components of either metal or composite materials. More recently a torsion ring test specimen has been used to obtain shear properties.[2] The use of bulk properties for the adhesive can be erroneous because the adhesive system in most structural joints is in the order of thousandths of an inch in thickness, and could have significantly different properties than the bulk adhesive. The effects of "scaling" have been observed in many materials and configurations.

---

[1] Research associate and chairman, respectively, Department of Mechanical and Aerospace Engineering, University of Delaware, Newark, Del. 19711.

[2] Hughes, Edward J. and Rutherford, John L., "Study of Micromechanical Properties of Adhesive Bonded Joints," Technical Report 3744, Aerospace Research Center, General Precision Systems, Inc., Little Falls, N.J., Aug. 1968.

The use of a cylindrical torsion ring test specimen can provide shear properties of an adhesive of typical bonded joint thickness, but great care in loading is required to ensure a pure torque only. Additionally, the cost per test item is quite high.

An alternative approach is presented herein for the measurement of the shear properties of an adhesive for use in structural joints. In lap joints the state of stress in the adhesive is a combination of both transverse shear and transverse normal (tensile and compressive) stresses. The complexities of the stress field, the surface interactions between adhesive and adherends, possible diffusion between differing material systems, and other effects suggest obtaining "effective" shear properties from test specimens that are the actual lap joint configuration as far as the adhesive is concerned.

The work presented herein presents research performed to date on the development of the test specimen, the instrumentation, test data obtained using one promising adhesive material, and the correlation of the test results.

Obtaining the adhesive effective shear modulus from this test provides data readily usable in the various methods of analysis in use today for determining stresses and deformations in both the adhesive and adherends of bonded joints.[3] Further, the trends associated with cogent variables such as lap length, adhesive thickness, surface roughness, ply orientation, temperature, and strain rate for various adhesive systems can be obtained through these standardized tests. In this paper we examine the influence of lap length, ply orientation, and adhesive thickness for one adhesive.

Shear Test

Specimen Theory and Test Equipment

The test specimen developed is shown in Fig. 1. It consists of two 0.50-

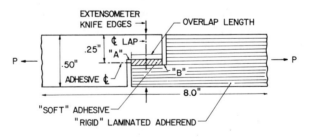

FIG. 1—*Shear property test piece.*

[3] Renton, W. J. and Vinson, J. R., "The Analysis and Design of Composite Material Bonded Joints Under Static and Fatigue Loadings," Air Force Office of Scientific Research, Report No. 1760-72, Aug. 1973.

in.-thick laminates of 1002 S-glass bonded together with the adhesive whose properties are desired. The specimen width is 1.00 in., and the overall length is 8 in. The test specimen is placed in the jaws of a standard tension tester wherein the resultant of the applied load is in line with the adhesive joint.

Theoretically, the only load path between the two adherends of the specimen is the "shear" transfer that takes place across the adhesive. As shown by a free-body analysis of the specimen (Fig. 2), however, a small moment is prevalent along the overlap length. Moreover, the discontinuity

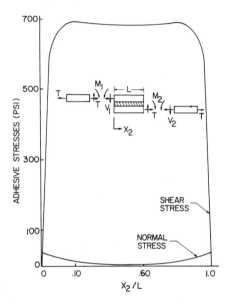

FIG. 2—*Adhesive stresses versus overlap length.*

of the specimen at the overlap ends gives rise to stress concentrations at these ends. Collectively, these two secondary effects can be effectively minimized by proper design of the specimen such that a uniform shear stress is prevalent along most of the overlap region and the peak normal stresses are minimal at the ends of the overlap. This design requirement should exist over the load range for which the shear modulus and proportional limit are to be measured. Figure 2 displays a typical adhesive stress distribution for a properly designed specimen.

Because the material comprising the thick adherends is relatively stiff, they are assumed to be rigid bodies when compared with the thin, relatively flexible adhesive material. Hence, if in the lap joint region one mounts a zero-length extensometer, as shown in Figs. 1 and 3, one can measure the deformation of the adhesive quite accurately, thereby determining the effective shear modulus and proportional limit of the adhesive.

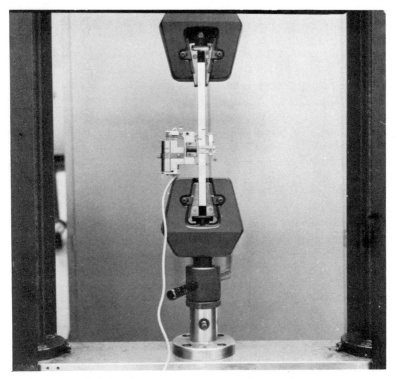

FIG. 3—*Extensometer mounted on shear specimen.*

The tensile load causing the deformation is measured by a load cell in the standard tension tester. The only limitation of the test is that the adhesive should be relatively "soft" compared with the stiff adherend material.

In all tests to date, an Instron Model TT-DM testing machine has been used. A Tinius-Olsen Model S1 LVDT (modified so that the knife edges are directly opposite each other) has been used in conjunction with a high-gain signal conditioner to gather deformation data, and a Moseley Model 7001A, X-Y recorder has been used to record load-deformation data continuously. The adhesive thickness is measured using a Zeiss optical microscope with ×80 magnification. Several measurements along the joint are made of the adhesive thickness and the values averaged.

Test Procedure

The test procedure is as follows:

1. Place the specimen in the grips of the Instron test machine, making sure that it is properly aligned.

2. Attach the LVDT knife edges at the centerline of the overlap length as shown in Fig. 1.

3. Select load and deformation scales. In this series of tests with the Hysol EA951 adhesive, a 2-kip load scale and a deformation magnification accurate to 25.0×10^{-6} in. has been used.

4. Load the specimen, recording load and deformation data. Also, measure the temperature and relative humidity.

From experience to date, care must be exercised to ensure that the extensometer knife edges are horizontal, that one is operating in the linear range of the LVDT, and that its accuracy is of 25×10^{-6} in. or better.

Analysis of Data

The effective shear modulus is calculated from a load deformation curve, such as that given in Fig. 4. A schematic illustrating the kinematical measurement of the adhesive deformation is shown in Fig. 5. The effective shear modulus is calculated using the initial slope of the load-deformation curve. The equation used assumes that the shear stress is

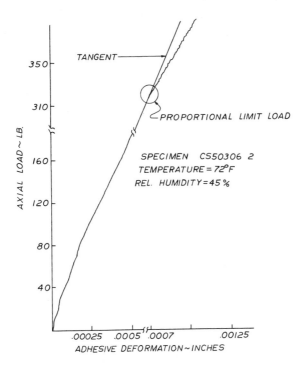

FIG. 4—*Adhesive shear load deformation data.*

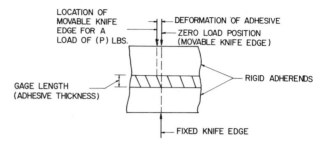

FIG. 5—*Schematic of the kinematics to measure the adhesive displacement.*

equal to the applied load divided by the surface area of the adhesive. Thus

$$\overline{G} = \frac{Pt}{\delta WL}$$ (1)

where

$\overline{G}$ = effective shear modulus, psi,
P = load, lb,
δ = adhesive deformation corresponding to load at P, lb, (in.),
t = adhesive thickness, in.,
W = width of specimen (nominally 1 in.), in., and
L = overlap length of test specimen, in.

Also, the proportional limit load is determined from Fig. 4 by observing at what load level the load-deformation curve becomes nonlinear.

Experimental Results

Failure Observations

A summary of the tests to date is given in Tables 1, 2 and 3. In each case the adhesive was Hysol EA951. Table 1 provides results for adherends laid up in a +45/0/−45/0 repeated pattern, while Table 2 provides results for all 0-deg (uniply) laminas. Each adherend was designed to have two nominal lap lengths, 0.30 and 0.60 in., and two nominal adhesive thicknesses, 0.0025 and 0.010 in.

The types of failure experienced were primarily either cohesive or adhesive. The former refers to a break within the adhesive thickness, resulting in a layer of adhesive material remaining on both adherend surfaces. The latter refers to a failure at the interface between the adhesive and one of the adherends. One set of angle-ply specimens (0.60 in. overlap, 0.003 in. thickness), however, did fail in the 45-deg ply of the adherend closest to the adhesive while another set of angle-ply specimens (0.60 in. overlap

TABLE 1—*Summary of shear specimen test results.*

Specimen No.	Adhesive Thickness, in.	Overlap, in.	Width, in.	Effective Shear Modulus, psi	Type of Failure
XCS50310-1	0.0111	0.297	0.996	. . .	System malfunction
-2	0.0108	0.290	0.998	7990	Adhesive
-3	0.0096	0.278	1.010	9110	Adhesive
XCS50610-1	0.0093	0.602	1.005	10053	Primarily adhesive
-2	0.0130	0.604	0.995	7443	Primarily adhesive ply adjacent to adhesive showed degradation
-3	0.0127	0.604	1.005	9200	Primarily adhesive
XCS50302-1	0.0034	0.300	1.004	3110	Cohesive
-2	0.0031	0.280	0.991	3927	Cohesive
-3	0.0040	0.302	1.006	3850	Cohesive
XCS50602-1	0.0034	0.600	1.016	1586	Resin[a]
-2	0.0031	0.615	1.000	1453	Resin[a]
-3	0.0034	0.615	1.001	1769	Resin[a]

[a]1002 S-glass adherend fibers cut at points "A" and "B" of Fig. 1.
45/0/−45/0 adherends.
EA951 film.

TABLE 2—*Summary of shear specimen test results.*

Specimen No.	Adhesive Thickness, in.	Overlap, in.	Width, in.	Effective Shear Modulus, psi	Type of Failure
CS50304-1	0.0034	0.310	0.998	5 659	Cohesive
-2	0.0034	0.325	1.000	6 156	Cohesive
-3	0.0037	0.295	1.005	4 236	Cohesive[a]
CS50306-1	0.0093	0.283	0.994	17 107	Adhesive[a]
-2	0.0136	0.290	1.000	20 187	Adhesive
-3	0.0087	0.296	1.015	12 800	Adhesive[a]
CS50606-1	0.0087	0.600	1.012	2 700	Adhesive[a]
-2	0.0077	0.594	0.992	6 036	Adhesive
-3	0.0080	0.596	1.005	5 119	Adhesive
CS50604-1	0.0034	0.600	1.005	2 485	Cohesive
-2	0.0031	0.600	0.997	3 311	Cohesive
-3	0.0031	0.602	1.000	2 270	Cohesive[a]

[a]1002 S-glass adherends slightly overcut at points "A" and "B" of Fig. 1.
All 0-deg adherends.
EA951 film.

TABLE 3—*Summary of shear specimen test results.*

Specimen No.	Crosshead Rate, in./min	Adhesive Thickness, in.	Overlap, in.	Width, in.	[a]Effective Shear Modulus, psi	Type of Failure
T350-3-1	0.005	0.0092	0.326	1.000	17 400	Cohesive
T350-3-3	0.005	0.0084	0.295	1.001	18 500	Cohesive
T350-3-5	0.050	0.0090	0.303	1.002	20 900	Cohesive
T350-3-2	0.050	0.0079	0.295	1.001	21 800	Cohesive

[a]Each value is an average of three tests.
7075-T6 adherends.
EA951 film.

and 0.010 in. thickness) showed signs of initial resin deterioration in the 45-deg ply adjacent to the adhesive.

Analysis of Results

Several parameters were analyzed with the limited test data available in order that their effect could be determined on the effective shear modulus, proportional limit load, and ultimate shear strength of the adhesive in the lap joint configuration. Figures 6 and 7 indicate the effect of the Hysol EA951 adhesive thickness on the effective shear modulus for joint lengths of 0.30 and 0.60 in. respectively. Plotted are the results for both the uniply and the angle-ply construction described previously. Limits of two standard deviations and correlation of data using standard regression analysis procedures are also shown.

Based on the data available, the results show a trend of increasing

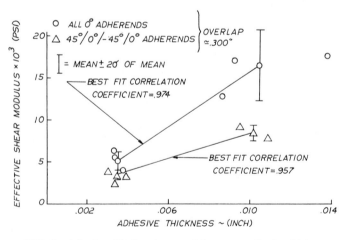

FIG. 6—*Adhesive effective shear modulus versus adhesive thickness.*

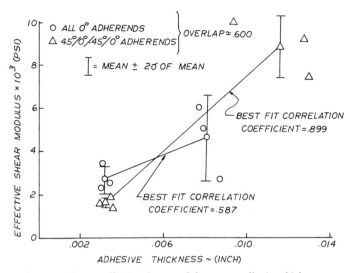

FIG. 7—*Adhesive effective shear modulus versus adhesive thickness.*

effective shear modulus for increased adhesive thickness. A possible explanation for this is that flaws are more critical in a thinner adhesive, decreasing in importance as the adhesive layer thickens.

The effects of ply orientation are also clearly seen in Figs. 6 and 7.

Figures 8 and 9 show the influence of the joint length on the effective adhesive shear modulus for two different adhesive thicknesses. The decrease in effective shear modulus with increased joint length is seen clearly in most of the data. More data are needed before definite conclusions can be made, however. Also note that in Fig. 9 the data points marked "A" all failed in the ply nearest to the joint rather than in the adhesive itself; this was due to the fibers at points "A" and "B" in Fig. 1 inadvertently being cut when the joint was fabricated. This effectively altered the joint gage length and geometry with the result that the resin was the primary shear transfer element. Hence, these data are thought to be invalid for comparison with the other data insofar as establishing trends are concerned.

No discernible influence by the parameters studied on the proportional limit load and the ultimate shear strength was observed. For EA951 the mean proportional limit load was 330 lb while the ultimate shear strength was 4300 psi, for a crosshead rate of 0.02 in./min.

Figure 10 shows a typical load-deformation curve for the adhesive employed in this series of tests. Results show that the EA951 adhesive is very ductile, and the shape of the curve suggests that one can model the material as an elastic, perfectly plastic material to analytically study the behavior of joints utilizing this type of adhesive. This will be elaborated on in a subsequent paper.

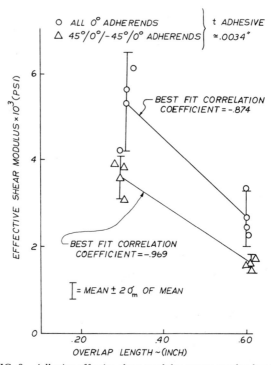

FIG. 8—*Adhesive effective shear modulus versus overlap length.*

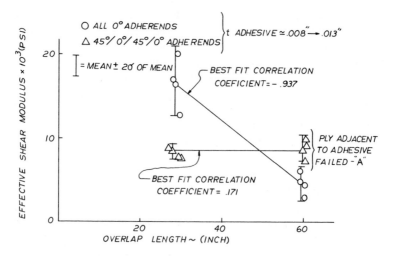

FIG. 9—*Adhesive effective shear modulus versus overlap length.*

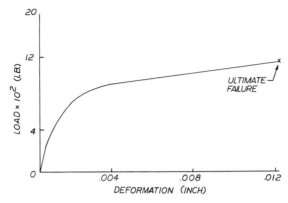

FIG. 10—*EA951 adhesive shear load deformation curve.*

Discussion

Concern was expressed over the possibility that shear deformation in the adherends, or that significant variation in shear strain along the lap joint, was prejudicing the results. Therefore, a grid was carefully marked on one test specimen (Fig. 11). The specimen was then filmed during loading, and the results are shown in Fig. 11 through 14. The results of the filming clearly showed no measurable change of angle in the grid lines of the adherends even to the ultimate load of the adhesive, indicating negligible transverse shear deformation and the high rigidity of the adherends compared with the adhesive. Moreover, the filming showed that the shear strain in the

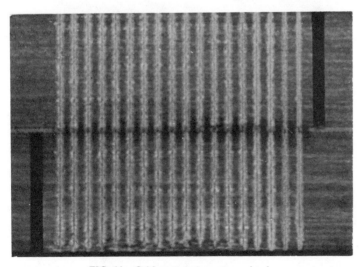

FIG. 11—*Grid on test piece at zero load.*

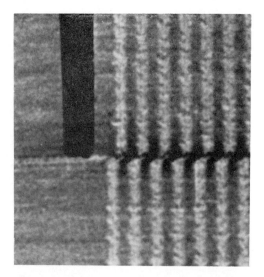

FIG. 12—*Shear strain at left end of adhesive joint.*

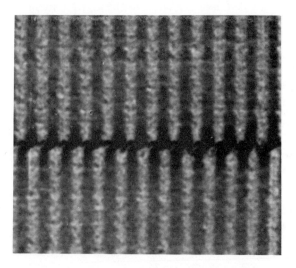

FIG. 13—*Shear strain at center of adhesive joint.*

adhesive was uniform, as seen by the angle of the grid lines remaining uniform along the length of the joint except, of course, at the ends.

Scatter in the data as evidenced by inspection of Tables 1 and 2 was also of concern. Two items, however, should be pointed out. First, the shear modulus results of Rutherford[2], using the torsion ring shear test, consistently show scatter comparable to that evidenced in this report. Perhaps this is an imperfection one must tolerate when using an average adhesive thickness.

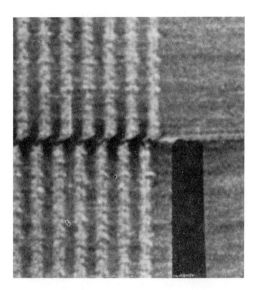

FIG. 14—*Shear strain at right end of adhesive joint*

Second, as noted in Tables 1 and 2, several specimens were overcut at locations "A" and "B" in Fig. 1. The result is that the geometry of the joint is effectively altered. The severed plys in the overlap area are called upon to transfer the load across the joint and they effectively lengthen the gage length and result in the adhesive not being loaded in the desired manner. This problem can be eliminated by precise machining of laminated adherend test specimens. Table 3 is included to confirm the consistency one can expect in the test results when the problem of severed plys is eliminated.

Conclusions

A test specimen has been designed and a reliable test procedure developed for obtaining the effective shear modulus, proportional limit load, and ultimate shear strength of adhesive materials for bonded joints. Use is made of the actual joint configuration rather than obtaining bulk properties or utilizing tests employing torsional loads. The test specimen configuration and test procedure are reliable and are suggested for wider usage. Such information is essential in order to analyze the stresses that occur in bonded joints, employing comprehensive analytical methods (see footnote 3) which account for the elastic properties of the adhesive material as well as those of the adherend materials.

From the tests conducted to date, it was found that the ply orientation of the adherend had a modest effect upon the effective shear modulus of the adhesive; the joint length was inversely proportional to the effective shear modulus; and the effective shear modulus increased proportionally with adhesive thickness over the range of thicknesses tested. No influence by these parameters on the proportional limit load or ultimate shear strength was discernible.

Acknowledgment

This research was sponsored by the Air Force Office of Scientific Research under Grant 1760-72; William J. Walker, Project Manager.

N. P. Freund[1]

Measurement of Thermal and Mechanical Properties of Graphite-Epoxy Composites for Precision Applications

REFERENCE: Freund, N. P., **"Measurement of Thermal and Mechanical Properties of Graphite-Epoxy Composites for Precision Applications,"** *Composite Reliability, ASTM STP 580,* American Society for Testing and Materials, 1975, pp. 133–145.

ABSTRACT: Results are reported on an investigation to evaluate the usefulness of selected graphite-epoxy composite structures for applications requiring precision tolerancing and dimensional control. GY-70/X-904 laminate composites in the double symmetric design $(0/\pm45/90)_2$, were tested, as well as a honey-comb design having two singly symmetric GY-70/X-904 faceplates bonded to an aluminum core.

Measurements were made to evaluate the coefficient of thermal expansion and its directional variations at 0, 45, and 90 deg to the outermost fiber orientation. Additional measurements of the coefficient included variations normal to the surface. Nondestructive testing employing holography was conducted to determine microcreep behavior.

Optical processing methods were investigated and mirrors with three types of reflector surfaces were fabricated. Environmental testing, including thermal cycling, thermal stability, humidity/vacuum effects, and temporal stability, was done on mirrors representing the various processing methods.

Data, discussion of results, and recommendations for applicable areas are given for the specific material and design types tested.

KEY WORDS: composite materials, mechanical properties, environmental tests, mirrors, thermal expansion, nondestructive tests, honeycomb structures

The light weight, high stiffness, and achievable near-zero coefficient of thermal expansion (CTE) of graphite-epoxy *[1]*[2] composite material has made it an attractive candidate material for aerospace applications, including radiation shields and vehicle skins. More recently it has been recommended for

[1] Engineer, Metrology Department, Electro-Optical Manufacturing Division, The Perkin-Elmer Corp., Norwalk, Conn. 06856.
[2] The italic numbers in brackets refer to the list of references appended to this paper.

applications requiring precision dimensional control and stability, such as metering rods in optical systems, high-performance antennas, and optical mirrors.

This study was conducted [2] to ascertain the applicability of selected graphite-epoxy advanced composite materials to dimensionally stable systems and structures. In particular, GY-70/X-904 [1] laminate composites in the doubly symmetric design $(0/\pm45/90)_{2s}{}^1$ and a honeycomb design having two singly symmetric GY-70/X-904 faceplates bonded to an aluminum core were investigated to determine their feasibility for use as optical and structural components for optical systems.

To accomplish the objective, laminate and honeycomb composites were evaluated relative to their coefficient of thermal expansion (CTE) and its directional variation, microyielding, microcreep and anelastic behavior, optical fabricability characteristics, thermal and temporal stability, and humidity/vacuum effects.

Data, results, and recommendations are given.

Materials

The test material, manufactured by General Dynamics/Convair under a related program [3], is an ultrahigh-modulus graphite-epoxy system composed of GY-70 (graphite fibers manufactured by Celanese Corp.) and X-904 epoxy resin manufactured by Fiberite Corp. The specimens supplied by GD/Convair consist of pseudo-isotropic layups with the symmetric configuration $(0/\pm45/90)_s{}^1$. Material selection was made by GD/Convair based on their test results and observations. Thirty flat, 150-mm-diameter solid laminate specimens with the doubly symmetric configuration $(0/\pm45/90)_{2s}$ (16 ply), 2.5 mm thick, and thirty flat, 150-mm-diameter aluminum honeycomb structures with singly symmetric configuration $(0/\pm45/90)_s$, 14.5 mm thick, were supplied for optical fabrication and testing.

CTE Measurements

CTE measurements were made with a Vacuum Interferometric Dilatometer, described by Goggin and Raquin [4] of Perkin-Elmer, over the temperature range -18 to $66\,°C$ (-0.4 to $151\,°F$). With this instrument, the specimens are used as the etalon spacer in a Fizeau interference cavity.

Changes in specimen length, caused by expansion or contraction, result in a translation of a straight-lined interference fringe pattern. By monitoring this fringe displacement, a change in length can be measured to high precision. Accuracies of $\pm1 \times 10^{-8}/\,°C$ in expansion coefficients have been achieved with low-expansion materials.

Measurements are made along three principal directions and perpendicular (normal) to the plane of both specimen types:

(*a*) Zero deg, that is, parallel to the outermost fiber orientation,
(*b*) 45 deg to the outermost fiber orientation, and
(*c*) 90 deg to the outermost fiber orientation.

Since the specimens under study have fiber orientation (0/ ±45/90), the measurement directions just described will give a good representation of expansion homogeneity in the composite. Two test panels of nominal size, 25 by 100 mm, were fabricated for each fiber orientation (at 0, 45, and 90 deg to the 100-mm gage length). Solid laminate material was tested in pairs; honeycomb panels were tested individually. The results of these measurements are:

1. For solid laminate material and fiber orientation along the gage length (0-deg orientation), the range of values is +0.06 deg to +0.12 ppm/°C. For fiber orientation at 45-deg to the gage length, the values range from +0.03 to +0.06 ppm/°C. Data obtained for 90-deg orientation of the outermost fibers were in the range from +0.06 to +0.15 ppm/°C. Values measured perpendicular to the surface are approximately 100 times greater than those obtained for the zero orientation.

2. Data obtained for the honeycomb material is higher in value than solid laminate and, for the outermost fiber orientation at zero degrees, has a range +0.24 to +0.41 ppm/°C for one specimen, and a range +0.31 to +0.34 ppm/°C for the other specimen (at 0-deg orientation). Data for the other fiber orientations of honeycomb fell within the same range of values for each of the respective specimens. Measurements taken normal to the surface have a range +9.42 to +11.51 ppm/°C.

The homogeneity of expansion in the plane of the layup is good and within 0.06 ppm/°C for laminate material and within 0.11 ppm/°C for the honeycomb. A dimensional change was observed in all specimens upon being placed in vacuum. This may in part be due to the evaporation of moisture in the specimens. Testing was done only after the test specimen had been in vacuum for 16 or more hours.

Micromechanical Measurements

Micromechanical property measurements of graphite-epoxy specimens were made by means of a three-point bend test. Circular specimens of 150 mm diameter were held in a vertical position by means of spring clips positioned over the point supports. The mechanical loading was applied to the rear of the specimen by means of a lever system.

The magnitude and spatial extent of a deformation produced by an applied load was obtained through holographic interferometry [5-7]. With holographic interferometry (experimental arrangement shown in Fig. 1), no surface modification to produce mirrorlike surfaces must be made to the test material; testing may be done on the material in its "as-received" condition. In regular visible-light interferometry, the object sur-

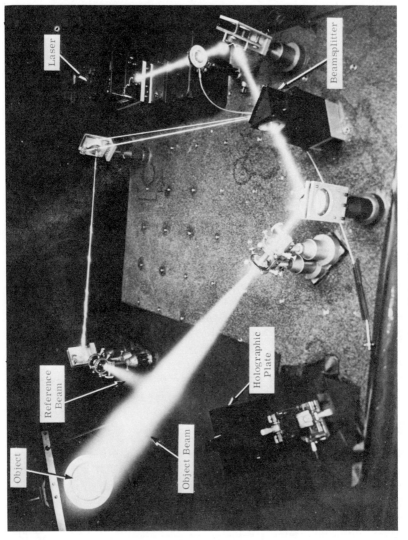

FIG. 1—*Holographic test facility.*

face (a mirror) is compared with a reference surface (an optical reference flat in the case of a flat mirror). In holographic interferometry, the object and the image of the object (reconstruction), recorded on the photographic plate, and viewed as superimposed. The reconstruction of the object behaves as a reference surface.

Any change in the object was seen as an interference pattern (a comparison of the deformed object and the undeformed reconstruction of the object). When a deformation has occurred, the magnitude of the deformation can be calculated from the resulting interference fringe pattern in a similar manner, as is done with more conventional interferometric techniques.

Microcreep/Anelastic Behavior Studies

Microcreep behavior is determined from measurements taken before and after load application over extended time intervals. Testing was done, in the manner described in the foregoing, on two 150-mm-diameter solid laminate specimens and two honeycomb structures. The solid laminate specimens were loaded to a tensile stress level of 350 kg/cm²; the honeycomb specimens were loaded to the nominal stress levels of 900 and 1400 kg/cm², respectively.

Interferograms were taken after approximately 23 and 70 h, and the deformations measured. Any plastic deformation immediately discernable after removal of the load indicated microcreep or anelastic effects or both. To separate anelastic effects from microcreep behavior, observations were continued for several days after load removal. Observations of the materials indicated an anelastic response (elastic aftereffect) upon load removal; the honeycomb material tended toward its strainfree state (complete recovery) whereas the solid laminate material tended toward a permanent deformation (incomplete recovery).

Information on homogeneity (uniformity of stress distribution) was obtained from the shape of the holographic interference pattern during microcreep testing. The symmetry of the interference pattern indicated that the particular specimen is pseudo-isotropic. (An isotropic material will have a similar symmetric interference pattern when tested in the way described in the foregoing.)

Structural defects in the composite layup, such as areas of weakness, are observed as departures from the symmetry of the interference pattern. Under load, weak areas would deform more than other areas of the specimen surface. This results in a distortion of the observed fringe pattern (which is a measure of surface deformation).

Distortions in the interference fringe pattern were observed during microcreep testing of the solid laminate disks. These distortions are indicative of structural anomalies in the specimens (distortions continued to be observed after unloading). It is believed that the nonuniform stress distribution caused by structural anomalies resulted in a nonuniform relaxation of the specimen since relaxation rate is related to stress load. No such distortions were observed in microcreep testing of honeycomb material.

Optical Fabricability Studies

The epoxy-based materials are generally not readily amenable to conventional optical processing due to cold flow and low mechanical hardness properties of the epoxy. In addition, high-smoothness surfaces are not reasonable if the optical surface cuts into the matrix and intersects a filament winding. In the specimens supplied by GD/Convair, a thin layer of free epoxy, approximately 0.125 mm thick, shields the fibers from the external surface. This free epoxy surface was ground flat using optical grinding techniques in preparation for the following surfacing methods:

1. Bonding of sheet glass onto composite material.
2. Surface replication from an optical master.
3. Direct polishing of a replication.

Although initial investigations explored both solid laminate and honeycomb structures, the most successful mirror specimens were made with the honeycomb material.

Bonding of Sheet Glass onto Composite

Mirror samples were fabricated with two available thicknesses of sheet glass (0.125 and 0.6 mm). The thickness of the glass faceplates was kept to a minimum in order to preserve as many of the characteristics of the composite honeycomb structure as possible, that is, to keep the glass variables to a minimum. Mirrors fabricated with 0.125-mm-thickness glass were flat within one wavelength ($\lambda = 632.8 \times 10^{-9}$m). The surface flatness attainable with the thicker glass (0.6 mm) was within $\lambda/4$ (158 $\times$ 10^{-9}m). Other mirrors made with this method employed the thicker glass due to easier fabricability and higher-precision surfaces (the thin glass fractured easily during processing).

Surface Replication

Replication [8,9] is an optical process whereby a master pattern is reproduced without going through time-consuming and costly optical processing for each specimen. The process consists of coating a glass master (in this case, an optical plane flat within ½ wavelength) with a vacuum-deposited silver coating. This is followed by a deposition of silicon monoxide and a rather heavy coating of aluminum. The aluminum forms the reflective surface while the silicon monoxide provides abrasion and corrosion resistance. The silver acts as a parting agent during the removal of the replicated surface and master flat. Any residual silver on the replication is easily washed off with concentrated nitric acid.

Honeycomb specimens (150 mm diameter) were used as substrates for the replicating process, employing Shell Epon 815 and Curing Agent A as the replicating medium. A quantity of the epoxy resin is poured onto the prepared glass master. The substrate is then contacted with the epoxy. The weight of the substrate (no other force is used) produces a slow, even flow of epoxy from the center of the sample toward the edge.

Various curing times and temperatures were tried with the best results occurring at room temperature and a curing time of approximately 72 h. The surface flatness achieved for this curing cycle was 790×10^{-9} m (1.25 wavelengths of light). Some deformation in separating the master from the specimen was noticed and has an approximate magnitude of 475.0×10^{-9} m (0.75 wavelength).

While it is acknowledged that Epon 815 has a glass transition temperature above room temperature (60 to 80°C) (140 to 176°F), curing at room temperature is commonly done with this resin and curing agent combination. According to the manufacturer (Shell Chemical Company), this combination is subject to additional hardening upon subsequent heating. (The resin did not become rubbery or tacky in nature in later tests.)

Specimens cured at elevated temperatures [40°C (104°F) for 24 h] produced replicated surfaces with the substrate undulations "printed through"; that is, the fiber structure of the composite material could be seen on the replicated surface. The highly irregular surface was not measurable with visible-light interferometry.

Polishing of the Replication

A variation of the replication technique is to polish the replicated surface. The specimen was prepared in the same way as the replication. After the epoxy medium cured [at 70°C (158°F) for 24 h], the specimen was optically polished. It was hoped that the polishing of the epoxy would enhance the surface quality but, due to the soft nature of the resin, sleeks and scratches were introduced during optical processing. The surface flatness of mirrors produced by this method was approximately 2.2×10^{-6} m (3.5 wavelengths). Mirrors fabricated this way were, in general, inferior to mirrors made by the replication process and glass surfacing method.

Environmental Testing

The mirrors produced by the methods mentioned in the foregoing were evaluated relative to their environmental performance. In particular, the response to humidity/vacuum cycling, thermal stability testing, thermal cycling, and temporal stability evaluation for each mirror type was investigated.

Humidity/Vacuum Testing

Humidity/vacuum cycling consisted of placing the test mirrors into a chamber at 90 percent relative humidity at 49 °C (120 °F) for 24 h (MIL-C-675A), followed by one and five cycles (each of 24-h duration) of vacuum drying at 10^{-5} torr. Interferograms of the specimen mirror surface were taken before and after each sequence in the series. These interferograms were subsequently analyzed to give surface geometry changes, if any, due to humidity effect and subsequent drying. Figure 2 gives the history of one specimen (specimen with glass faceplate). Interferograms show the deviation from flatness (the curvature and spacing of the interference fringes are a measure of this deviation; for example, fringes are straight and equally spaced for a flat surface) through its manufacture, humidity, and vacuum testing.

The change in surface flatness before and after optical coating, as seen in Fig. 2a and b, may be attributed to the effect of the optical coating process (that is, vacuum drying). Figure 2b and c show the temporal changes from post-optical coating to initiation of humidity testing (a time period of 20 days). The recovery of surface geometry after humidity/vacuum testing to the configuration just after optical coating seems to indicate an elastic response by the composite material to humidity effects.

The epoxy surface specimens (replication and polished replicating medium) show a more substantial loss of geometry (which was expected) due to humidity effects and hardly any recovery after vacuum drying.

Thermal Testing

Thermal tests conducted on the test mirrors were of two types: (a) thermal cycling from room temperature to -200 °C (-328 °F) with interferograms taken before and after testing, and (b) thermal stability evaluation (in vacuum at 10^{-2} torr) in the range -73 to $+121$ °C (-99 to 250 °F) with continuous monitoring of the surface.

Observations from these tests have indicated the following response: (1) Thermal cycling from room temperature to -200 °C (-328 °F) at the rate of 24 °C/h caused severe fracturing in the glass surface mirror. Since testing was done before and after cycling, the exact temperature at which fracturing occurred was not determined. (2) Epoxy-surfaced mirrors became highly irregular after cycling, and interferometric analysis was not possible. (3) Interferometric monitoring of glass surface mirrors above 50 °C (122 °F) and below 4 °C (39 °F) was not possible because of the large deviation from flatness (high interference fringe count). It was observed from testing performed during fabrication that these mirrors failed

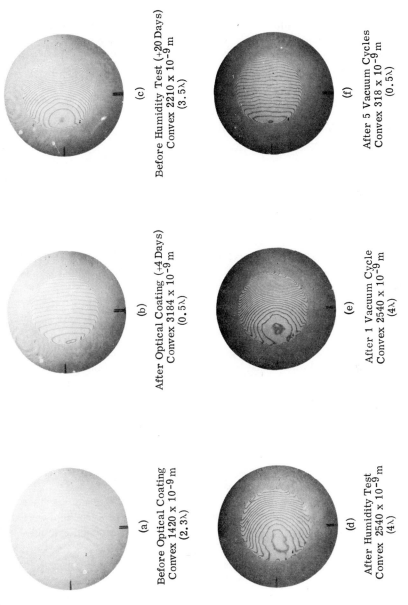

(a)
Before Optical Coating
Convex 1420 x 10^{-9} m
(2.3λ)

(b)
After Optical Coating (+4 Days)
Convex 3184 x 10^{-9} m
(0.5λ)

(c)
Before Humidity Test (+20 Days)
Convex 2210 x 10^{-9} m
(3.5λ)

(d)
After Humidity Test
Convex 2540 x 10^{-9} m
(4λ)

(e)
After 1 Vacuum Cycle
Convex 2540 x 10^{-9} m
(4λ)

(f)
After 5 Vacuum Cycles
Convex 318 x 10^{-9} m
(0.5λ)

FIG. 2—*Humidity/vacuum testing—history of specimen thin-glass faceplate.*

(surface became highly irregular and did not return to the pretest configuration) above the heat distortion temperature of the bonding medium [approximately 66 °C (151 °F)]. Below 4 °C (39 °F), surface deviations again became too large for interferometric analysis. Exposure to −73 °C (−99 °F) caused mirror failure (did not return to original configuration).

Mirrors, where evaluation was possible, have exhibited a range of thermal sensitivities which are listed in Table 1. Trends are difficult to determine due to the complex interaction between composite substrate and reflector surface.

TABLE 1—*Thermal sensitivity of evaluated mirrors.*

Specimen	Deviation, nm/ °C
Honeycomb, polished epoxy surface	23 (0.017λ/ °C)
Honeycomb, glass faceplate surface	75 (0.067λ/ °C)
for range 68 °F (20 °C) to 124 °F (50 °C)	75 (0.067λ/ °C)

In an attempt to evaluate the effect of a second faceplate (on the side opposite to the reflector surface) on thermal performance, a mirror was prepared by bonding a 6-mm-thick ultralow-expansion glass (ULE; CTE = 0.03×10^{-6}/deg C) to a 150-mm-diameter honeycomb flat. The specimen was tested with one faceplate and with two faceplates over the same temperature range of 25 to 45 °C (77 to 113 °F). Figure 3 shows the improvement effected by the second faceplate. The thermal sensitivity of this specimen after bonding is less than 4 nm/ °C (0.006λ/ °C). This construction was the only candidate that came near to being qualified as a usable optical construction.

Temporal Stability Evaluation

Temporal changes in surface geometry, with several test mirrors (glass faceplate and replication) maintained at ambient conditions, were interferometrically monitored at monthly intervals for eight months. Surface fluctuations over the testing period for the glass surface specimen were within one wavelength of light (632.8 nm). The replicated specimen exhibited greater fluctuations over the testing period (approximately 2.54×10^{-6} m). In addition, the surface became more irregular (irregularity being indicated by a high-frequency ripple in the fringe pattern during the summer months, these evaluations occurring from May to December), increasing in surface roughness from less than 25 nm in May to approximately 150 nm in September. The roughness decreased once more to less than 25 nm by December. The observed changes in surface roughness seen in the repli-

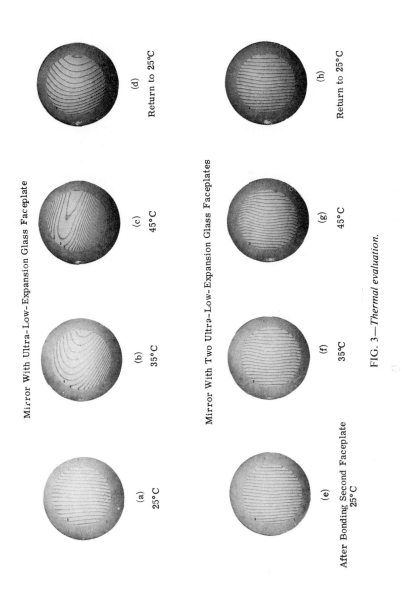

Mirror With Ultra-Low-Expansion Glass Faceplate

(a) 25°C

(b) 35°C

(c) 45°C

(d) Return to 25°C

Mirror With Two Ultra-Low-Expansion Glass Faceplates

After Bonding Second Faceplate 25°C

(e)

(f) 35°C

(g) 45°C

(h) Return to 25°C

FIG. 3—*Thermal evaluation.*

cated specimen are caused, in part, by the fluctuations of humidity and temperature of the ambient surroundings of the laboratory.

Conclusions

The measurement phases of this program dealt with composite material selected by GD/Convair from observations and measurements on a variety of materials. Material was tested in its "as-received" condition and also after optical processing; that is, mirrors were fabricated on some composite material specimens. While it is acknowledged that only a small sampling of the many different types of composite materials, designs, and structures were evaluated here, trends have been observed consistently which will determine the usefulness of these materials in specific applications.

The utility of graphite-epoxy composites can be discussed relative to three different classes of aerospace applications:

1. Load-bearing structures requiring noncritical dimensional stability.

2. Moderate dimensional stability, for example, antennas and some metering structures.

3. Highly critical dimensional applications, for example, mirrors and passive high-performance metering structures.

In the area of noncritical load-bearing structures, graphite-epoxy composites appear suitable in almost every category. The one area of concern is the continued outgassing of volatiles in the epoxy, and the possible condensation of these products onto sensitive optical, thermal, and electronic components. This is of particular concern in optical sensor applications, where the performance of low-scatter mirror surfaces must be maintained. The low expansion and mechanical properties of graphite-epoxy composites are insignificant in importance as the material is primarily used for its attractive stiffness-to-weight behavior.

In applications where good thermal dimensional stability is required, in addition to high strength and stiffness-to-weight properties, the feasibility for use of the eight-ply composite laminates tested is marginal. The honeycomb material, in conjunction with proper design considerations, may meet these additional thermal stability requirements. More extensive testing is required, however, to verify performance for any specific application. Larger specimens and discrete components should be analyzed.

For components requiring close dimensional tolerancing and stability, for example, mirrors and optical bench components, composite material requires further development. The structural properties of the materials studied in this program are significantly better than alternative material choices and, therefore, warrant further development to improve stability characteristics.

A major portion of this program has been the determination of material properties of planar (or essentially planar) structural elements. While these properties are useful for mirror structures, they are not typical of most structural applications.

At the present time, information does not exist to ascertain the stability of nonplanar structures, for example, trusses or tubular members. Any in-depth investigation should include evaluation of all candidate composite material in larger specimen sizes than in the foregoing investigation, and in different structural configurations. Testing is necessary to determine the CTE on trusses and tubes, and the changes in length in vacuum. Specimen length changes (seen as a shift in the interferometric fringe pattern) were noticed after operating vacuum had been reached. These changes are beyond the shift in the interferometric fringe pattern expected due to air removal. In addition, mechanical properties of the various configurations should be investigated as a function of the environment.

Acknowledgment

The author wishes to express his sincere thanks to Homer Lincoln and Hubert Geyselaers for their effort in the experimental work in this study, and to Bill Goggin, Roger Paquin, and Al Slomba for their technical guidance.

References

[1] Nomenclature used in the *Advanced Composites Design Guide,* Jan. 1973, 3rd ed. (Rockwell International Corp.) under Air Force Contract No. F33615-71-C-1362.

[2] Air Force Contract No. F33615-72-C-2033.

[3] Air Force Contract No. F33615-72-C-1388.

[4] Goggin, W. R., and Paquin, R. A., *Image Technology,* Vol. 13, No. 6, 1971.

[5] Sollid, J., *Applied Optics,* Vol. 8, No. 8, 1969.

[6] Boone, P., and Verbiest, R., *Optica Acta,* Vol. 16, No. 5, 1969.

[7] Haines, K. A., and Hildebrand, B. P., *Applied Optics,* Vol. 5, No. 4, 1966.

[8] Haas, G., and Erbe, W. W., *Journal of the Optical Society of America,* Vol. 44, No. 9, 1954.

[9] Bradford, A. P., Erbe, W. W., and Haas, G., *Journal of the Optical Society of America,* Vol. 49, No. 10, 1959.

L. W. Masters[1] and T. W. Reichard[1]

Evaluation of Adhesive-Bonded Joints in Housing Components of Glass Fiber-Reinforced Polyester Laminate

REFERENCE: Masters, L. W. and Reichard, T. W., "Evaluation of Adhesive-Bonded Joints in Housing Components of Glass Fiber-Reinforced Polyester Laminate," *Composite Reliability, ASTM STP 580,* American Society for Testing and Materials, 1975, pp. 146–156.

ABSTRACT: A series of tests was performed on sandwich panel housing components made with glass fiber-reinforced polyester (FRP) laminates. Specifically, long- and short-term tests were performed to evaluate the adhesive bonds between the FRP laminate facings and cores of the panels. Specimens of two different FRP laminates were analyzed and their bonding characteristics with two different adhesives were studied. The test data show that the bond strength was significantly affected by the laminate formulation, adhesive formulation, adhesive thickness, sustained loading, and temperature.

KEY WORDS: adhesive bonding, aging tests (materials), composite materials, glass fibers, housing system, laminates, reinforced plastics, sustained loading, tensile strength, shear strength

An essential phase of the Department of Housing and Urban Development's "Operation Breakthrough" Program was an evaluation of the structural adequacy of each proposed housing system. The system considered here (Fig. 1) employed roof and wall sandwich panels constructed from laminated sheets of polyester reinforced with chopped strands of glass fiber (FRP). The basic panel consisted of an FRP sheet (facing) bonded to each side of a corrugated FRP sheet (core) with a polyester adhesive.

The structural evaluation included a consideration of the transfer of

---

[1] Research chemist and research physicist, respectively, Structures, Materials and Safety Division, Center for Building Technology, Institute for Applied Technology, National Bureau of Standards, Washington, D.C. 20234.

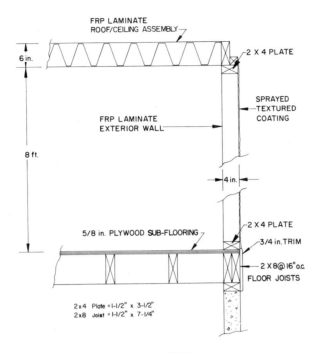

FIG. 1—*Typical section for the FRP laminate housing system.*

stresses through and from the thin FRP sheets into other structural components. To investigate this behavior, tests[2] were performed on wall and roof panels as well as on typical adhesive bonded connections. Tests on the wall and roof panels indicated that the tested panels would be satisfactory for the proposed application if the long-term performance of the adhesive bonds was satisfactory.[2] This report describes the short- and long-term tests of the structural bonds between the FRP facings and cores.

Originally, the panels were fabricated with a polyester adhesive for bonding the core and the facings and used an FRP laminate formulation (Formulation 1) which yielded dense laminates with smooth surfaces. Later, a different FRP laminate formulation (Formulation 2) was used in fabricating the panels, and the adhesive used for bonding the core and facings was changed from the polyester to an epoxy material. The new formulation resulted in laminates which were porous and had glass fibers exposed on the surface. The studies described in this paper were conducted on specimens cut from panels bonded with the two different adhesives and fabricated with the two different FRP laminate formula-

[2] Reichard, T. W., Green, W. E., Jr., Cattaneo, L. E., and Masters, L. W., "Structural Tests on Housing Components of Glass Fiber Reinforced Polyester Laminate," NBSIR 73-188, National Bureau of Standards, Washington, D.C., April 1973.

tions. Table 1 summarizes the adhesive bond tests that were performed in the study.

Test Samples and Specimens

All specimens were cut from sample sandwich panels fabricated by the housing systems producer. Panels fabricated with Formulation 1 FRP were chosen by the producer, while those fabricated with Formulation 2 FRP were chosen by a government quality-control inspector.

TABLE 1—*Summary of adhesive bond tests performed.*

Tests Performed to Determine	Formulation 1 Polyester Adhesive	Laminates Epoxy Adhesive	Formulation 2 Polyester Adhesive	Laminates Epoxy Adhesive
Effect of elevated temperature on short term strength[a]	yes	no	yes[c]	yes[c]
Effect of adhesive thickness on short term strength[a]	yes	no	no	no
Effect of ASTM C 481[d] on strength[a]	yes[b]	no	yes[c]	yes[c]
Effect of sustained loading	yes[b]	no	no	yes[c]
Effect of water submersion at 160°F (71.1°C) on strength[a]	no	no	no	yes[c]

[a] Strength measured by tensile shear tests.
[b] Group B, C, D adhesive thickness specimens only.
[c] Group B adhesive thickness specimens only.
[d] ASTM Test for Laboratory Aging of Sandwich Constructions (C 481-62).

Specimens approximately ½ in. (1.27 cm) wide and 7 in. (17.78 cm) long, which were used to measure bond strength, were cut from the bonded areas of sandwich panels. Notches were cut in the specimens as shown in Fig. 2 to provide lap-type, tensile shear specimens with a bond area of 0.50 in.² (3.23 cm²) at the lap.

Specimens of the FRP laminates for chemical analysis were cut from nonbonded areas of the sandwich panels.

Tests and Results

Bond Strength Between the Polyester Adhesive and the FRP Laminate Made with Formulation 1

The lap joint specimens were tested in tensile shear to determine the effects of: (1) temperature, (2) adhesive thickness, (3) accelerated laboratory aging, and (4) sustained loading on the bond strength between the polyester adhesive and the FRP laminates. In the tests to evaluate the effects of temperature, adhesive thickness, and accelerated laboratory

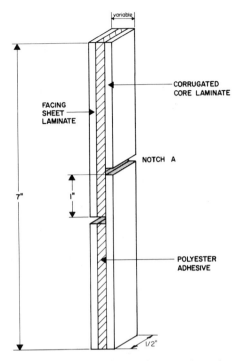

FIG. 2—*Adhesive bond specimen with notch.*

aging, specimens were tested in triplicate. A minimum of two specimens was used for each sustained loading point.

The polyester adhesive thickness at the bond area of the lap joint in various specimens varied from 0.01 to 0.20 in. (0.25 to 5.0 mm). In order to evaluate the adhesive bond, the specimens were grouped in the following way: Group A, adhesive thickness less than 0.04 in. (1.0 mm); Group B, 0.04 to 0.08 in. (1.0 to 2.0 mm); Group C, 0.08 to 0.12 in. (2.0 to 3.0 mm); and Group D, 0.12 to 0.20 in. (3.0 to 5.0 mm). The highest percentage of specimens was in Group B.

Figure 3 illustrates the effect of temperature on the polyester adhesive bond strength. Each plotted point represents the mean and one standard deviation of three values. All failures were at the bond between the adhesive and the FRP laminate. The standard deviations of the various points ranged from 7 to 17 percent of the mean. The bond strength decreased significantly with increasing temperature. The bond strength at 180°F (82.2°C) averaged only about 25 percent of the strength at 73°F (22.8°C). Figure 3 also indicates the effect of adhesive thickness on bond strength. The adhesive bond strength decreased significantly with increasing adhesive thickness. For example, at 73°F (22.8°C) the mean and standard deviation of the bond strength of Group A specimens was 700 ±

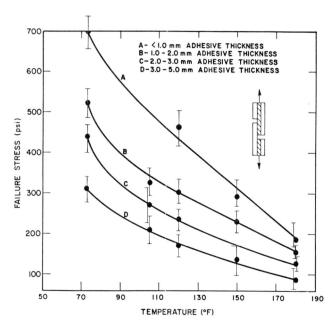

FIG. 3—*Effect of temperature on polyester adhesive bond strength using Formulation 1 laminates.*

81 psi [(4.826 ± 0.558) × 10^6 N/m²], while that for Group D specimens was 308 ± 42 psi [(2.123 ± 0.290) × 10^6 N/m²]. At 180°F (82.2°C), the mean and standard deviation of the bond strength of Group A specimens was 186 ± 25 psi [(1.282 ± 0.172) × 10^6 N/m²] while that for Group D specimens was 88 ± 20 psi [(6.067 ± 1.380) × 10^5 N/m²].

Table 2 contains a comparison of average bond strength values for Groups B, C, and D obtained with and without laboratory aging by ASTM Method C 481, Cycle A.[2] The laboratory aging procedure included cycles of water soaking, steam spraying, heating, and freezing. The comparison in Table 1 indicates that the accelerated aging did not significantly affect the bond strength for these specimens.

Figure 4 shows a plot of sustained stress versus time to failure at 150°F (65.5°C) for Group B specimens. One specimen loaded at 60 psi (4.136 × 10^5 N/m²) failed at 296 h and one specimen loaded at 50 psi (3.447 × 10^5 N/m²) failed at 728 h. The other two specimens at each of these loads exhibited no failure at 3000 and 3500 h, respectively. Extrapolation of the curve of Fig. 4 to 10 000 h yielded an endurance limit of 60 psi (4.136 × 10^5 N/m²), which was approximately 11 percent of the short-term bond strength of Group B at room temperature.

Thus, temperature, adhesive thickness, and sustained loading had substantial effects on the polyester adhesive bond strength.

TABLE 2—Comparison of polyester adhesive bond strength[a] with and without laboratory aging[b] using laminate Formulation 1 Specimen.

Group B (1.0 to 2.0 mm)[c]			Group C (2.0 to 3.0 mm)[c]			Group D (3.0 to 5.0 mm)[c]		
Temperature, °F (°C)	Max Load Without Aging, psi	Max Load With Aging, psi	Temperature, °F (°C)	Max Load Without Aging, psi	Max Load With Aging, psi	Temperature, °F (°C)	Max Load Without Aging, psi	Max Load With Aging, psi
73 (22.8)	526 ± 51	494 ± 52	73 (22.8)	406 ± 45	362 ± 43	73 (22.8)	308 ± 42	316 ± 35
105 (40.6)	324 ± 32	372 ± 40	105 (40.6)	268 ± 34	304 ± 25	105 (40.6)	208 ± 24	208 ± 25
120 (48.9)	312 ± 46	264 ± 31	120 (48.9)	236 ± 18	260 ± 20			
150 (65.5)	230 ± 32	192 ± 23	150 (65.5)	134 ± 24	162 ± 19			
180 (82.2)	152 ± 8	124 ± 26	180 (82.2)	124 ± 26	134 ± 22			

[a] Strength values in psi are the averages of three specimens.
[b] Aged by ASTM Method C 481.
[c] Range of adhesive thickness.

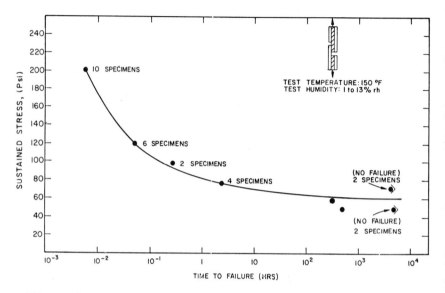

FIG. 4—*Effect of sustained load magnitude on time to failure for Group B thickness polyester adhesive bonds to Formulation 1 laminates.*

Bond Strength Between the Polyester Adhesive and the FRP Laminate Made with Formulation 2

Studies were conducted to measure the bond strength developed between the polyester adhesive and the laminates fabricated with laminate Formulation 2 to determine: (1) if the bond strength developed was dependent upon the composition of the laminate, and (2) if moisture penetration through the porous laminate would result in more rapid degradation of the bond than was observed with the nonporous laminate.

All failures of specimens made with the polyester adhesive and Formulation 2 laminates during tensile shear tests were bond failure of the adhesive to the laminate.

Figure 5 shows a plot of the tensile shear strength at various temperatures of the polyester adhesive bond with both laminates using Group B thickness specimens. Each point represents the mean of three values and the ranges on the figures are the standard deviations. The strength of the laminate Formulation 2 bonds was about two third's that of the bonds with laminate Formulation 1. Thus, the laminate formulation had a significant effect on the bond strength.

On the other hand, the percent loss of bond strength during aging using ASTM Method C 481-62, Cycle A, was not substantially different in the two cases. The laboratory aging results indicated that the bond to the porous

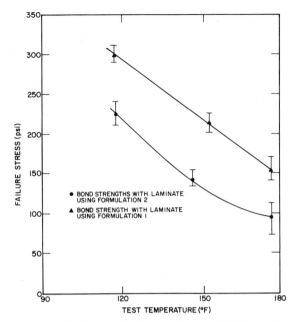

FIG. 5—*Comparison of polyester adhesive bond strength between Group B specimens fabricated with laminate Formulations 1 and 2.*

laminate (Formulation 2) would not degrade more rapidly than the bond to the nonporous laminate (Formulation 1).

Bond Strength Between the Epoxy Adhesive and the FRP Laminate Made with Formulation 2

Lap joint specimens were tested in tensile shear to determine the effects of (1) temperature, (2) moisture, (3) accelerated laboratory aging, and (4) sustained loading, on the bond strength between the epoxy adhesive and the laminate fabricated with laminate Formulation 2. The test specimens were grouped according to adhesive thickness as described earlier, and Group B adhesive thickness specimens were used for the tests.

Specimens were tested in triplicate at 73, 90, 120, 150 and 180°F (22.8, 32.2, 48.9, 65.5 and 82.2°C) to determine the effect of temperature on the short-term bond strength. Specimens tested at 73 and 90°F (22.8 and 32.2°C) failed by a separation of the fibers within the FRP laminate. The mean and standard deviation of the failure stress of these specimens was 520 ± 74 psi [(3.585 ± 0.510) × 10^6 N/m²] at 73°F (22.8°C) and 511 ± 58 psi [(3.523 ± 0.400) × 10^6 N/m²] at 90°F (32.2°C). Specimens tested at 120, 150 and 180°F (48.9, 65.5, and 82.2°C) failed by a cohesive separation within the epoxy adhesive. The mean and standard deviation of the failure stress decreased from 455 ± 51 psi [(3.137 ± 0.352) × 10^6

N/m²] at 120°F (48.9°C) to 320 ± 31 psi [(2.206 ± 0.214) × 10⁶ N/m²] at 180°F (82.2°C). Thus, increasing the temperature from 120 to 180°F (48.9 to 82.2°C) resulted in approximately a 30 percent decrease in failure stress.

Specimens were exposed for as long as 56 days in 160°F (71.1°C) water and tested in triplicate at 160°F (71.1°C) to evaluate the effect of continuous exposure to high-moisture and high-temperature conditions on the failure stress. Figure 6 shows a plot of the data. All specimens failed by a cohesive separation within the epoxy adhesive. The failure stress decreased approximately 41 percent, from 225 ± 20 psi [(1.551 ± 0.138) × 10⁶ N/m²] to 133 ± 16 psi [(9.169 ± 1.103) × 10⁵ N/m²], after 56 days.

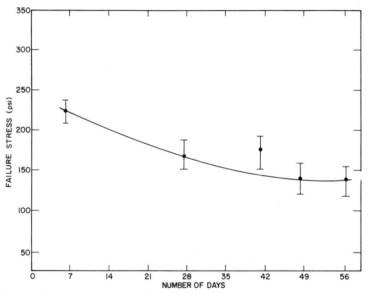

FIG. 6—*Failure stress of epoxy adhesive-bonded, laminate Formulation 2 specimens after aging in 160°F (71°C) water.*

Specimens were also subjected to accelerated laboratory aging by ASTM Method C 481, Cycle A, and tested at 160°F (71.1°C) following the aging. Five specimens which were not subjected to the aging procedure yielded an average failure stress standard deviation of 337 ± 91 psi [(2.323 ± 0.627) × 10⁶ N/m²] at 160°F (71.1°C). Seven specimens which were subjected to the aging procedure yielded an average failure stress of 288 ± 48 psi [(1.985 ± 0.331) × 10⁶ N/m²]. The specimens failed by a cohesive separation within the epoxy. The failure stress decreased approximately 14.5 percent as a result of the aging.

Sustained loading of specimens at 150°F (65.5°C) yielded an estimated endurance limit at 10 000 h of 85 psi (5.860 × 10⁵ N/m²), which was approximately 16 percent of the short-term failure stress at 73°F (22.8°C). The failure mode of the specimens changed from a separation of the fibers within the FRP laminate to cohesive failure within the epoxy adhesive, with increasing temperature and with increased time of laboratory aging.

Thus, test temperature, prolonged exposure to high-moisture and high-temperature conditions, and sustained loading were shown to significantly reduce the failure stress of the epoxy bonded specimens.

Chemical Analysis of Laminates Fabricated by Formulations 1 and 2

Specimens of the laminate materials were analyzed in triplicate to determine the percentage by weight of: (1) combustibles at 1112°F [600°C], (2) filler, and (3) glass fibers. Specimens were weighed in tared crucibles and ashed at 1112°F (600°C) for 3 h. After ashing, weighings were taken to determine the weight of combustibles. The glass fibers were then separated from the filler by either dissolving the filler or by sieving. The glass fibers were then weighed. When the filler was dissolved chemically, its weight was obtained by difference, but, in the sieving method, the filler was weighed directly.

The mean and standard deviation of the content by weight of the laminate using Formulation 1 was 31.8 ± 0.9 percent combustibles, 15.1 ± 0.7 percent glass fibers, and 53.1 ± 1.5 percent filler. Formulation 2 laminates contained 29.1 ± 0.8 percent combustibles, 23.0 ± 0.6 percent glass fibers, and 47.9 ± 1.0 percent filler.

The percentage by weight of combustibles was used as a measure of the polyester resin content in the laminates since the absorbed water in the specimens, which would also be expelled as a combustible, was shown to be negligible. The data showed that the polyester resin content in the laminates did not differ greatly between the two formulations. The percent glass fibers differed appreciably in the two formations with Formation 1 laminates containing 15.1 weight percent and Formation 2 laminates containing 23.0 weight percent glass fibers. Another difference between the two skins was the chemical composition of the filler. The filler in the laminates of Formulation 1 was finely ground calcium carbonate; that in Formulation 2 laminates was a relatively coarse sand (SiO₂). One further difference observed between the laminate formulations was that the glass fibers in the first laminate formulation were fine and were usually individually dispersed, while the fibers in Formulation 2 laminates were bound together in clumps which restricted the fiber direction randomness.

Conclusions

The adhesive bond strength tests using the two different laminate formulations showed that laminates of Formulation 1 yielded polyester adhesive bonds approximately 50 percent higher in shear strength than laminates of Formulation 2. This difference is believed to be due to the difference in the surfaces of the two laminates since Formulation 1 yielded dense, nonporous laminates with smooth bonding surfaces, while Formulation 2 yielded porous laminates in which glass fibers were exposed on the laminate surface. The differences between the composition of the two laminates was the percent glass fibers by weight, the type of filler used, and the coarseness of the glass fibers.

Adhesive thickness was shown to be an important factor for the polyester adhesive bonded to Formulation 1 laminates.

Temperature and sustained loading were shown to have substantial effects on the bond strengths (or failure stresses in cases where bond failure was not achieved) of both adhesives and both laminates tested.

Specimens of Formulation 2 laminates bonded with the polyester adhesive failed at 225 ± 15 psi [(1.551 ± 0.103) × 10^6 N/m²] at 120°F (48.9°C), and at 95 ± 15 psi [(6.549 ± 1.034 × 10^5 N/m²] at 180°F (82.2°C). Specimens of Formulation 2 laminates bonded with the epoxy adhesive failed at 455 ± 51 psi [(3.137 ± 0.352 × 10^6 N/m²] at 120°F (48.9°C), and at 320 ± 31 psi [(2.206 ± 0.214 × 10^6 N/m²] at 180°F (82.2°C). The decrease in bond strength (or failure stress in the case of the epoxy specimens) from 120°F (48.9°C) to 180°F (82.2°C) was about 58 percent for the polyester bonded specimens and about 30 percent for the epoxy bonded specimens. Thus, the tensile shear test results of un-aged specimens showed the strength of polyester bonded specimens to be less than that of epoxy bonded specimens. The results of these tests also showed the strength of polyester bonded specimens to be affected by elevated temperature more than that of the epoxy specimens. It was not possible in this test series, however, to compare the *actual* bond strengths of the two adhesives because of the different failure modes obtained.

No significant difference was observed between the performance of the epoxy and polyester bonded specimens with Formulation 2 laminates following exposure to the cyclic aging of ASTM Method C 481.

Nondestructive Testing

R. D. Adams,[1] *D. Walton,*[1] *J. E. Flitcroft,*[1] *and D. Short*[2]

Vibration Testing as a Nondestructive Test Tool for Composite Materials

REFERENCE: Adams, R. D., Walton, D., Flitcroft, J. E., and Short, D.,
"Vibration Testing as a Nondestructive Test Tool for Composite Materials,"
Composite Reliability, ASTM STP 580, American Society for Testing and Materials, 1975, pp. 159–175.

ABSTRACT: Certain failures, such as resin bound shear cracks in fiber-reinforced materials, give rise to little change in ultrasonic attenuation or radiographic transmission but can result in significant reductions in material properties. A vibration technique is being evaluated as a nondestructive test tool under such conditions. The work described forms the first part of this evaluation program and concerns unidirectional carbon and glass fiber reinforced plastic subjected to static and dynamic torsional loading. The results and techniques will eventually be applied to complex composite structures.

In the static torsion test program, 'good,' void-free specimens failed at shear stresses of between 52 and 60 MN/m^2 (carbon fiber) and between 56 and 62 MN/m^2 (glass fiber) in a very brittle manner. The cracks thus generated led to substantial changes in the dynamic (vibration) test data. Specimens containing voids failed at lower shear stresses and less catastrophically.

In torsional fatigue, all failures occurred by the propagation of resin-bound shear cracks at shear stresses below the static strength of the material. The dynamic (vibration) test parameters showed permanent and progressive changes due to the accumulation of fatigue damage. Crack development was observed visually in the glass fiber specimens and broadly related to the changes in the dynamic properties.

KEY WORDS: composite materials, carbon fibers, glass fibers, reinforced plastics, nondestructive tests, vibration tests, crack propagation, static tests, torsional fatigue

Based on the evidence of an earlier test investigation[3] an extensive program has been planned for the evaluation of a vibration method as a nondestructive test tool for filamentary reinforced composite materials.

[1] Reader and research assistants, respectively, Department of Mechanical Engineering, University of Bristol, Bristol, U.K.

[2] Senior lecturer, School of Engineering Science, Plymouth Polytechnic, Plymouth, U.K.

[3] Adams, R. D., Flitcroft, J. E., Hancox, N. L., and Reynolds, W. N., *Journal of Composite Materials,* Vol. 7, 1973, p. 68.

The first part of this program involves correlating the measured dynamic (vibration) test parameters with crack development and material deterioration for various modes of failure. The second stage involves integrating these principles and data into investigations involving more complex composite structures.

It is recognized that, in fiber-reinforced materials, failures occur due to filament fracture, matrix crazing and cracking, delamination, or by some combination of these fracture modes. Failure in any mode will have an influence upon subsequent material behavior and upon the vibration response of the component, which will have to be characterized by experimentation and analysis. The work reported here deals exclusively with matrix shear cracks induced by torsional loading (static and fatigue) of unidirectional composite material. Such cracks are particularly important since they give little change in ultrasonic attenuation or radiographic transmission,[4] which are standard nondestructive tests.

(It should be noted in this work that the unit of damping used is the specific damping capacity [SDC], for which the symbol is ψ. It is defined as $\psi = \Delta W/W$ where ΔW is the energy dissipated during a stress cycle and W is the maximum stored energy. In all cases, it is to be understood that 'carbon fiber' means 'carbon fiber reinforced plastic' [and similarly for 'glass fiber'].)

Procedure

Materials and Specimen Manufacture

All the specimens were produced from unidirectional carbon fiber/epoxy (Grafil HT-S/DX210) or glass fiber/epoxy (E-glass/DX210) preimpregnated material supplied by Rotorway (Marine) Ltd. Nominally, the fiber loading of the carbon fiber and the glass fiber specimens was respectively 50 percent and 60 percent. Two methods were used to produce a 12.7-mm-square billet of unidirectional material.

Initial Manufacturing Method—All the early specimens were produced by cutting and stacking rectangular strips of 'prepreg' material and heating the stack in a mold between platens for 2 h at 170°C (338°F). The specimens were subsequently postcured for 3 h at 170°C (338°F). Most of the specimens produced in this manner contained many small voids which were evenly distributed and which gave the glass specimen optical opacity and a low interlaminar shear strength (53 to 60 MN/m²).

The bars, 200 mm long and 12.7 mm square in section, were then ground to 10 mm diameter over a central gage length of 150 mm. All the specimens were visually examined prior to testing and all the carbon

[4] Reynolds, W. N., Non-Destructive Test Centre, Atomic Energy Research Establishment, Harwell, U.K., private communication, 1972.

fiber specimens were radiographed at the Atomic Energy Research Establishment, Harwell, U.K.

Vacuum Precure Method—In order to eliminate or reduce the multiple small voids, the pre-preg stack was precured in a vacuum to remove entrapped air and volatiles. The specimens were subsequently pressed to size between heated platens for 1 h at 165 °C (329 °F) and postcured as before. This method produced translucent glass fiber specimens which contained a few isolated defects, usually long, thin needle-like bubbles. The interlaminar shear strength was also improved, typically being 88 to 90 MN m^{-2}.

These bars were then machined and examined as in the foregoing.

Test Apparatus

Torsion Pendulum—A torsion pendulum[5] was used to monitor the vibrational characteristics of the specimens at various stages during the test. The rig could be run as a simple or compound pendulum at resonance to enable direct evaluation of the longitudinal shear modulus (G_{LT}) and damping (ψ_{LT}).

Static Torsion Machine—All the tests were carried out on an autographic torsion machine. The autographic outputs were provided by a direct drive from the main motor to an *X-t* chart recorder and from a calibrated strain-gaged load cell torque signal. In some of the later tests, strain was more directly monitored using a capacitive transducer driven from the specimen grips. Also in the latter part of the test program, acoustic emission equipment was used in an attempt to detect the early stages of material deterioration. The system consisted of a PZT-5H barium titanate crystal mounted on the specimen, its output being fed into a charge amplifier and a variable cutoff frequency high-pass filter and, finally, to a digital event counter.

Torsional Fatigue Machine—Fatigue loading was performed on a deflection-controlled fatigue machine driven at constant speed. Load readings were taken periodically using a calibrated load cell in series with the specimen via a telescope/mirror system. During fatigue loading, air cooling was provided to keep the specimen surface temperatures to an acceptable level.

Test Procedure

Static Tests—The initial part of the test program was aimed at incrementally loading carbon fiber specimens up to and beyond failure in torsion and monitoring the dynamic characteristics of the material at each

[5] Adams, R. D., Fox, M. A. O., Flood, R. J. L., Friend, R. J., and Hewitt, R. L., *Journal of Composite Materials,* Vol. 3, 1969, p. 594.

stage. Because the dynamic properties varied with time after test ('recovery'), the vibration tests were repeated at timed intervals after each static loading increment. Some work with cyclic loading and different strain rates was also carried out.

Finally, a similar series of tests was performed on a batch of glass fiber specimens.

Fatigue Tests—Once loading levels were established, specimens were removed from the fatigue machine at various stages during their life and their dynamic characteristics evaluated on the torsion pendulum. Again, because of a recovery phenomenon, the tests were repeated at various times after the fatigue test.

The crack development in the glass fiber specimens was visually monitored during the fatigue test and, where possible, the initiation site noted. With the carbon fiber specimens, similar procedures were not possible but dye penetrant tests were performed once significant cracking had occurred. Since the fatigue test machine was deflection controlled, the resulting loss in stiffness due to crack growth led to a reduction in the applied load range.

Discussion of Experimental Results

Static Torsion Investigation

Visual and Radiographic Evidence—The many evenly distributed small voids which caused opacity in the original glass fiber specimens were also present in the early carbon fiber specimens as illustrated in Fig. 1. The results of the visual inspection for the 'void-free' glass fiber specimens tested in this program are summarized in Table 1, together with the radiographic features for carbon fiber specimens of both types. Most of the defects were thin, needle-like bubbles which generally grouped between the original prepreg planes.

Static Torsion Behavior and Failure Characteristics—The behavior of specimens under monotonic torsional loading is typified by Fig. 2. On loading the initial material, which contained voids, several minor load decreases occurred before final failure. These load reductions were accompanied by audible cracking, which suggested that irreversible damage was being accumulated. As shown by Table 1, final failure occurred at 51 and 42 MN/m² (Nadai corrected values) which was accompanied by load reductions of 25 and 27 percent respectively. In general, failure was by the propagation of multiple longitudinal shear cracks along the length of the specimen. Since the defects were so numerous and so broadly distributed, no single defect could be identified as the initiation site.

On loading the 'vacuum precure' specimens, no minor load decreases

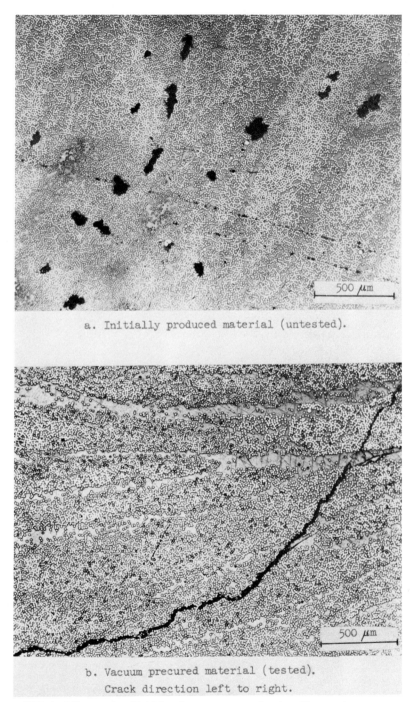

a. Initially produced material (untested).

b. Vacuum precured material (tested).
Crack direction left to right.

FIG. 1—*Micrographs of initial and vacuum-precured carbon fiber specimens.*

TABLE 1—*Static test data.*

Specimen No.	Shear Stress[a] at Failure, MN/m²	Load Decrease at Failure, %	Initial Dynamic Properties		Final Dynamic Properties		Remarks—Visual Radiographic Microscopic and Failure Details	
			ψ_{LT}, %	G_{LT} GN/m²	ψ_{LT}, %	G_{LT} GN/m²		
101	51.0	25.0	6.1	3.73	16.0	3.45	Many small defects evenly distributed throughout specimen.	⎫ Initial carbon fiber specimens, $V_f = 0.5$
102	42.0	27.0	5.2	3.57	19.0	3.24	Many small defects evenly distributed throughout specimen.	⎭
225	59.0	42.2	7.9	3.30	28.8	2.18	A few isolated needle-type defects, maximum length 30 mm.	⎫ Vacuum precure carbon fiber specimens, $V_f = 0.5$
223	53.4	47.2	6.6	3.27	21.0	2.22	Several low-aspect-ratio bubbles.	
229	60.3	catastrophic	5.9	3.22	…	…	Several low-aspect-ratio bubbles, one larger defect 23 mm long.—Catastrophic failure.	
237	52.1	catastrophic	7.3	3.13	…	…	Several needle-type defects—one on the surface, 20 mm long, 1.5 mm deep. Catastrophic failure occurred through plane of bubbles.	
227	53.8	39.5	6.1	3.44	19.2	3.05	A few isolated defects, maximum length 46 mm.	⎭

276	56.0	30	6.6	4.91	13.5	4.37	A region of many small subsurface needle-type defects through which final crack passes.	
289	58.0	41.4	6.7	4.6	17.7	3.87	One long (50 mm) subsurface defect through which final fracture passes.	Vacuum precure glass fiber specimens, $V_f = 0.6$
295	58.3	43.2	6.9	4.46	17.5	3.76	Some evidence of fiber swirl. No defects.	
299	62.5	48.6	7.0	5.69	27.8	4.62	Rolled specimen. One 20-mm-long surface defect through which final fracture passed.	

[a] All shear stress values Nadai-corrected.
[b] Dynamic values quoted at a shear stress of 0.6 MN/m^2.

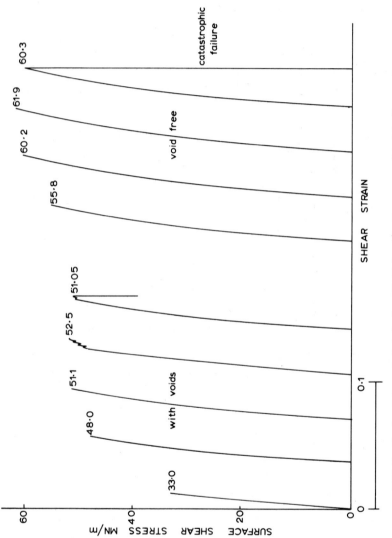

FIG. 2—*Torsional stress-strain behavior of initial and vacuum-precured carbon fiber specimens.*

were sustained prior to the rapid, and sometimes catastrophic, growth of a single longitudinal shear crack. Even using sensitive acoustic emission equipment, no warning of imminent failure was recorded. The surface stress at fracture was 52.1 to 60.3 MN/m^2 for the carbon fiber specimens and 56.0 to 62.5 MN/m^2 for the glass fiber specimens. Thus, it can be seen that the shear strength of the void-free vacuum precure material is higher than that of the earlier batch. Failure was accompanied by a load reduction of between 30.0 and 48.6 percent, which suggested that more severe crack development had occurred than with the initial material. In most cases where the crack path could be examined, it passed through the isolated defects recorded from the visual and radiographic investigation, suggesting that these defects behaved as effective crack-initiation sites.

A common feature for the failure of material produced by the two techniques was that the failure load was often lower than the maximum to which the specimen had been previously subjected without obvious signs of damage. This could be a strain limit effect brought about by the 'permanent' set incurred on the previous loading.

Since there is no accepted standard strain rate for torsion tests on composite materials, a series of variable strain rate tests was carried out on a carbon fiber specimen up to 60 percent of the expected failure load. In these tests, the initial slope modulus increased by approximately six percent when the strain rate was increased from 0.0025 to 0.2355 min^{-1}. At approximately 50 percent of the expected failure load, this increase had risen to 15 percent.

Correlation Between Dynamic Properties and Loading History—In general, there appears to be no simple correlation between the initial dynamic properties (shear modulus and specific damping capacity) and the voidage of the specimens. This is because although the damping arises mainly from the resin content the absence of resin leads to voids and defects which also contribute to the damping. Similarly, there appears to be no direct correlation between the fracture strength and the initial dynamic parameters.

After loading in torsion, the dynamic shear modulus decreased and the damping increased. If the applied load was insufficient to cause irreversible damage, nearly all of these changes would be recovered after a rest period. Usually, about 50 percent of the change would be recovered within one to two hours, but often changes were still taking place after 24 h. Once damage had been incurred at high static loads, there were large irrecoverable changes in the dynamic parameters. This process is clearly illustrated in Fig. 3 for specimens produced by both manufacturing processes. The changes incurred with the void-free vacuum precure specimens are greater than those for the other material because the cracking induced is more severe.

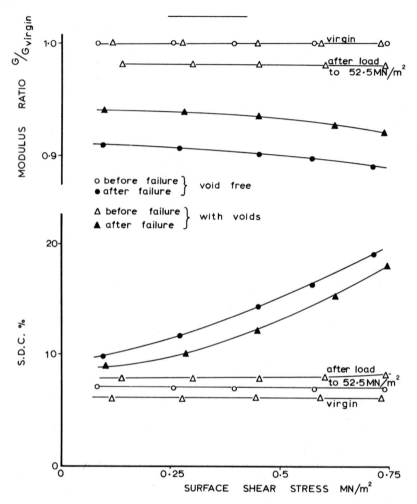

FIG. 3—*Effect of static torsional loading on the damping and dynamic modulus of carbon fiber material.*

Fatigue Investigation

Initial Visual and Radiographical Evidence—All the glass fiber specimens produced by the vacuum precure method were translucent and had a lower void content compared with the original batch, although some isolated defects were usually present as described in Table 2. Most of the defects were thin, needle-like bubbles which formed as clusters between the planes of prepreg, although some low-aspect-ratio bubbles were also present. Of the carbon fiber specimens tested, only two (Nos. 286 and 281) contained serious surface defects and these also appeared to be very narrow, almost needle-like in appearance. Specimen 286 had the largest of these defects, this being 60 mm long and up to 1 mm wide.

TABLE 2—Fatigue data.

Specimen No.	Cyclic Shear Stress, MN/m²	(psi)	Initial Dynamic Properties		Fatigue Life at		Remarks, Initial Defects and Final Failure
			ψ_{LT}, %	G_{LT} GN/m²	10% increase in ψ_{LT}	2% decrease in G_{LT}	
290	68.2	(9900)	9.8	5.00	2 100	1 800	Crack developed from subsurface needle-type defect.
271	55.9	(8120)	9.1	4.98	19 000	13 700	Crack developed from subsurface needle-type defect.
291	53.0	(7700)	9.4	5.10	33 000	34 000	64-mm-long needle defect. Crack did not initially grow from this.
294	50.2	(7280)	9.25	5.00	>3.5 × 10⁵	>3.5 × 10⁵	Crack initiated from the radius at end of gage length.

Vacuum precure glass fiber specimens, $V_f = 0.6$

286	60.7	(8810)	7.89	3.352	43 200	47 500	One long (59 mm) surface defect. Crack did *not* develop from this.
281	57.7	(8380)	9.81	3.221	137 000	138 000	One long defect from which failure finally occurred.
285	55.5	(8060)	7.48	3.084	89 500	92 000	Some minor X-ray defects.
284	52.5	(7620)	8.27	3.032	580 000	690 000	
287	50.0	(7260)	7.30	3.172	400 000	600 000	
282	46.5	(6750)	8.80	2.890	>6.3 × 10⁶	>6.3 × 10⁶	

Vacuum precure carbon fiber specimens, $V_f = 0.5$

Radiographic results were obtained for the carbon fiber specimens in their square form at the Atomic Energy Research Establishment and the results are summarized in Table 2. Only three of the specimens tested showed significant defects and Specimens 286 and 281 contained the most serious faults. The major surface defect of Specimen 286 showed up as an internal, thin cylindrical bubble probably caused by entrained air or volatiles during manufacture. Note that in this case the final crack line did not pass through this defect although it could have developed from other smaller defects.

Crack Development During Fatigue—At the stress levels investigated, the main mode of failure is by single or multiple shear crack propagation. In two specimens, an alternative type of failure occurred, namely, a short circumferential delamination caused by misalignment.

For the glass fiber specimens, crack development could be directly observed and often followed a similar pattern:

(*a*) Whitening of a small area of the subsurface defect.

(*b*) Radial crack propagation to the specimen surface.

(*c*) If the stress was high enough, the crack propagated longitudinally.

(*d*) If the fatigue process continued long after the crack was formed, the faces of the crack appeared to darken.

Not all the glass fiber specimens, however, failed from obvious defects; for example, Specimen 291 contained a 64-mm-long needle-type defect but initial crack growth started from another site. In general, the low-aspect-ratio bubbles did not initiate fatigue cracks, and in one case the crack deviated to avoid such a bubble.

For the optically opaque glass fiber specimens, failure occurred by general material degradation and multiple cracking and not by the propagation of a single major shear crack. The degradation was generally accompanied by heat generation and local discoloration of the specimen. In general, the fatigue life was appreciably lower than for the 'good' specimens [for example, at a cyclic shear stress ($\Delta\tau$) of 30 MN/m^2, the fatigue life (N_f) is less than 10^6 cycles].

The first visual indication of crack development in carbon fiber specimens was a fine white deposit of powdered resin along the line of the crack. In general, crack growth was rapid and great difficulty was experienced in trying to detect the early stages of crack development. Of the two specimens which exhibited severe surface defects, only in one case did this lead to failure (Specimen 281). Neither specimen appeared to suffer from a reduced fatigue life as a direct consequence of these defects; indeed Specimen 281 had a longer than expected life but this does not mean that the other failures did not arise from manufacturing defects.

Once a significant crack had developed, bending occurred during the fatigue loading so that the later stages of crack development may not be representative of purely torsional fatigue loading.

Correlation Between Dynamic Properties and Fatigue Damage—In general, the dynamic modulus reduced with the number of cycles of fatigue loading and the specific damping capacity increased. Early in the fatigue life of the specimens some of these changes were recoverable by a rest period. Later in life, when significant crack growth had occurred, large irrecoverable changes took place in the dynamic parameters.

Comparing the virgin dynamic properties for the optically opaque and clear glass fiber specimens, it appears that no single dynamic test parameter characterizes the specimen type although in general a specimen with a relatively high damping and dynamic shear modulus was void-free and optically homogeneous and translucent.

Recovery can occur after fatigue cycling due to the relaxation of local high stresses by creep strain of the matrix, by a reduction in temperature at local hot spots, or by relaxation of a 'permanent set' and hence shear stresses at the fiber/resin interface. Of these three mechanisms, stress relaxation is probably the most important since air cooling is provided to limit temperature rises and little permanent set is built up in bidirectional loading about a zero mean stress.

From these preliminary results, it appears that:

(*a*) The recovery rate appears to be independent of the preceding number of fatigue cycles.

(*b*) The recovery rate increased by increasing the fatigue stress range.

For the greater part of the test program, the influence of recovery was reduced by measuring dynamic properties at a constant time period after the fatigue test (usually one hour). For each specimen, values of the specific damping capacity and dynamic shear modulus were correlated with the dynamic shear stress at various stages during the fatigue life (Fig. 4). Initially, the damping and dynamic shear modulus values were independent of the dynamic shear stress. As the fatigue test continued, dependence of the damping and modulus on the shear stress first appears at high amplitudes. The greater the damage sustained by the material, the lower is the stress level at which the damping and modulus become stress-dependent and the higher the damping and the lower the modulus at any given shear stress.

If a common value of dynamic shear stress is chosen, it is then possible to correlate changes in damping, shear modulus, and crack length (glass fiber only) with the number of cycles (Fig. 5). It is shown in Fig. 5 that a rapid increase in damping occurs when rapid crack growth is observed, suggesting a relationship between these parameters. Further work will be required (probably using linear elastic fracture mechanics) before such a relationship can be investigated thoroughly.

If failure criteria are defined in terms of changes in the specific damping capacity and shear modulus values, it is possible to form an overall correlation of the conventional *S-N* type (Fig. 6). In the present

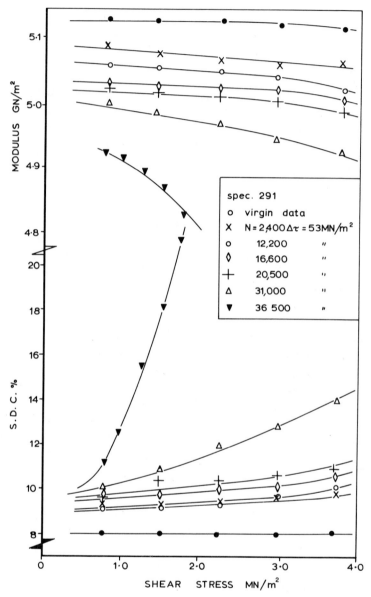

FIG. 4—*Effect of torsional fatigue cycling on the damping and dynamic modulus of glass fiber specimen No. 291.*

investigation, a 10 percent increase in damping and a 2 percent decrease in modulus have been used to define failure. Note that, using this technique, deterioration has been detected before large losses in stiffness have occurred. On the basis of Fig. 6, the carbon fiber specimens

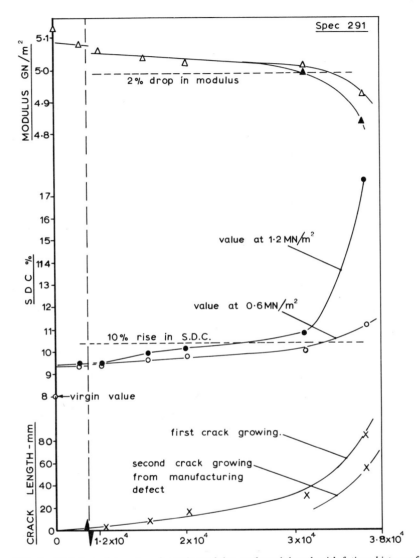

FIG. 5—*Variation of damping, dynamic modulus, and crack length with fatigue history of glass fiber specimen No. 291.*

appear to have marginally better fatigue characteristics than the glass fiber specimens. A second interesting feature shown by Fig. 6 is that the carbon fiber Specimens 281, 284, and 282 had longer than expected lives, and examination of Table 2 shows that these specimens also had higher than average values of initial specific damping capacity.

The influence on the dynamic properties of the ingress of dye penetrant into the shear cracks was also examined. The shear modulus falls due to

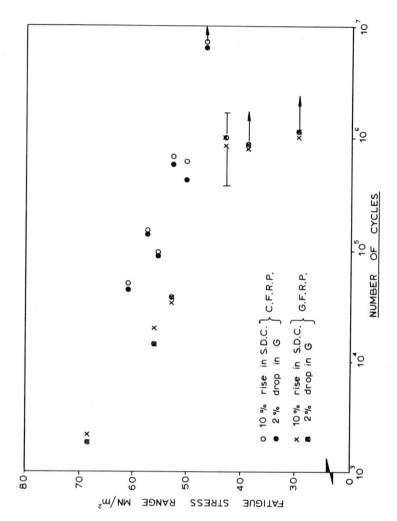

FIG. 6—*Overall torsional fatigue data for glass and carbon fiber specimens.*

lubrication of the crack surfaces, and the damping increases because of increased slipping on these surfaces, together with a certain amount of viscous friction.

Conclusions

From the static torsion investigation on unidirectional carbon and glass fiber reinforced plastics, it was found that failure depends critically on the quality of the material (that is, voidage). Good-quality material, containing only a few voids, fails by the rapid growth of a single longitudinal shear crack without prior warning by load reduction or acoustic emission. Material containing many evenly distributed small voids fails at a lower load and in a more progressive manner by the development of multiple shear cracks.

Under torsional fatigue loading, it was found that good-quality material fails by the development of resin-bound shear cracks at cyclic stresses below the static shear strength of similar material. Poor-quality specimens failed prematurely at low stresses and without discrete crack propagation. Fatigue cracks may or may not be initiated by manufacturing flaws, but the fatigue life does not appear to be significantly reduced by the presence of a few large defects. Once visual crack initiation has occurred (in glass fiber specimens) subsequent crack growth is rapid.

The nondestructive test method used (the vibration technique) was able to detect material deterioration due to shear cracks produced by both static and cyclic loading. Where progressive cracking occurred, the dynamic shear modulus and damping capacity showed permanent and progressive changes. The vibration method sensed material deterioration via damping changes prior to large reductions in material stiffness. Before irreversible damage was incurred, the changes in the dynamic properties could be wholly recovered by a sufficient rest period. There appears to be no simple correlation between the virgin dynamic properties and either the voidage or the load-bearing capacity. Dye-penetrant testing leads to significant irreversible changes in damping and modulus and cannot therefore be used in combination with the vibration technique.

Acknowledgments

The authors wish to acknowledge the Science Research Council and the United Kingdom Atomic Energy Authority for their financial support for this work.

F. H. Chang,[1] J. C. Couchman,[1] J. R. Eisenmann,[1] and B. G. W. Yee[1]

Application of a Special X-Ray Nondestructive Testing Technique for Monitoring Damage Zone Growth in Composite Laminates

REFERENCE: Chang, F. H., Couchman, J. C., Eisenmann, J. R., and Yee, B. G. W., "**Application of a Special X-Ray Nondestructive Testing Technique for Monitoring Damage Zone Growth in Composite Laminates,**" *Composite Reliability, ASTM STP 580,* American Society for Testing and Materials, 1975, pp. 176–190.

ABSTRACT: A modified X-ray nondestructive testing technique was used to study matrix cracks parallel to fibers and delaminations between plies in graphite-epoxy composite material. A tetrabromoethane (TBE) opaque additive applied at the source of the damage zones enhanced the flaw image.

Center-slit specimens were fabricated from Modmor II/Narmco 5208 graphite-epoxy laminates with three different ply orientations. Tensile ramp and sawtooth cyclic loadings at different levels were applied to these specimens. Periodic X-ray monitoring was conducted to observe the initiation and growth of cracks and delaminations at the slit tips. The initiation of damage zones appeared as fiber separation in the ±45-deg directions tangent to the semicircular periphery of the cutout tips. As the load level was increased, this fiber separation continued while fiber separation at other locations also appeared.

Delamination first occurred at approximately the same time as fiber separation. The delaminated area was found to surround the most severe fiber separation region and grew in size as the load level was increased.

Limited test results indicated a slow and an accelerated damage growth rate during ramp loading. For cyclic loading the majority of growth occurred on the first load cycle. Subsequent cyclic loading to the same level contributed little additional growth in the majority cases.

KEY WORDS: composite materials, nondestructive tests, cracking (fracture), crack propagation, damage detection, tension tests, stress concentration, radiography, opaque additive, failure, fatigue

[1] Senior research scientist, project research scientist, senior structures engineer, and group design engineer, respectively, General Dynamics, Fort Worth, Tex. 76101.

Localized failures and damage zone growth in fiber-reinforced composite laminates have been topics of interest to structural designers and non-destructive testing (NDT) engineers. Studies in these areas reported in the literature [1-5][2] are generally limited to idealized theory, real-time surface damage study, or postfracture evaluation. Several examples of previous investigations are listed in Table 1.

TABLE 1—*Previous work on failure studies in composites.*

Authors	Studies Performed
Daniel [1]	two-dimensional dynamic photoelastic study of crack growth in idealized fiber-reinforced models
Cruse and Stout [2]	study of fracture surfaces in graphite-epoxy laminated specimens by using a scanning electron microscope
Mandell, Wang, and McGarry [3]	studied local damage near a stress singularity in graphite-epoxy laminates by (1) optical microscopy using a fluorescent dye and (2) using a scanning electron microscope
Marcus and Stinchcomb [4]	made measurements of fatigue damage around a circular hole in boron-epoxy plates under tensile load
Sedor and Watterson [5]	studied fatigue failure of E-glass-epoxy composites under low-cycle compressive loads using photomicroscopy

A need exists for the real-time monitoring of the damage zone growth in composite materials at increasing load levels. It is also desirable to correlate a failure mechanism with the level and mode of loading. The authors have undertaken these studies using a special X-ray NDT technique. The X-ray technique consists of the introduction of an opaque additive into discontinuities in the composite laminates so that the flaw growth could be monitored by periodic X-ray photography. Results of the application of this technique on graphite-epoxy composite tension specimens of three different ply orientations under ramp and cyclic loading are presented in this paper.

Experimental Setup and Procedures

Specimens

Center-slit specimens were fabricated from Modmor II/Narmco 5208 graphite-epoxy laminates with orientations of $[0/ \pm 45]_{2s}$,[3] $[0/ \pm 45/90]_{2s}$, and $[\pm 45]_{3s}$. These laminates were chosen to exhibit fiber failure and linear and nonlinear matrix failures, respectively. All specimens were 2.50 in. wide, 24.0 in. long, containing a 1.00-in.-long center slit. The center slit was machined ultrasonically to a width of 0.012 in. with a tip radius of

[2] The italic numbers in brackets refer to the list of references appended to this paper.
[3] The laminate orientation code represents the following fiber orientation layers: 0, +45, −45, −45, +45, 0, 0, +45, −45, −45, +45, 0. The other two codes are similar.

approximately 0.006 in. The 0-deg direction was chosen to be the long axis of the specimen and the 90-deg direction was parallel to the long axis slit. The identification of the damage line directions will be based on this set of coordinates. A photograph of the test equipment with the specimen mounted is shown in Fig. 1.

FIG. 1—*Experimental setup for modified X-ray and AEM monitoring of advanced composite specimens.*

Equipment

An Instron testing machine with a load capacity of 10 000 lb was used in all the tests. The radiographic energy source was a 110-kV Picker portable X-ray unit. This X-ray unit had a 0.25-mm beryllium window with a 5-mA rating. The X-ray head was located at a distance of 30 in. from the specimen. A lead shield with a 3 by 5-in. opening was mounted on the Instron tester to limit the X-ray radiation to the immediate area surrounding the center slit on each specimen.

Kodak type M industrial X-ray film was used. A film-transport mechanism was fabricated to advance a continuous 200-ft roll of film. A film guide positioned the 70-mm-wide film behind the slit area of the composite specimen. The film-advancing time for each frame was 14 s. The exposure time for each X-ray record was 16 s. The maximum recording speed of 2 frames per minute was found to be quite sufficient for the translation speed of the crosshead during the loading process. The exposed film was processed by a Kodak automatic film processor. Average processing time for a 20-ft length of film was 45 min.

The conventional X-ray technique is not suitable for the detection of delaminations in graphite-epoxy or carbon-epoxy composites due to the fact that carbon has a low attenuation coefficient for X-ray. Small differences in attenuation caused by planar delaminations and voids are indistinguishable on X-ray records. In the experimental work described in this paper on opaque additive, tetrabromoethane (TBE), was used to enhance the image of the delaminations and voids in the composite materials. This additive was found to have no deleterious effect on the matrix and fibers in the composites. When applied to the area surrounding the slit, the liquid additive entered the opening in the damage zone by capillary action. When the testing time exceeded 2 h, it was necessary to reapply the TBE to compensate for evaporation loss.

Test Procedures

A crosshead speed of 0.002 in./min was used for all the ramp loading tests. This corresponded to a loading speed of approximately 40 lb/min for all the specimens. An X-ray exposure was made at each 50- or 100-lb interval. Occasionally, extra exposures were made at closer intervals when specimen fracture noises intensified.

Load levels and R factors for the cyclic fatigue tests were determined from the results of the ramp-loading tests. Generally, three load ranges—low, medium, and high stress levels—were used for the fatigue tests. The load level was increased from zero to the maximum level for the first range at the slowest crosshead speed. It was then cycled 20 times in this range. A speed of 0.01 in./min was used for some cyclic fatigue tests in order to minimize testing time. In these fatigue tests, the Instron testing machine was adjusted to cycle between desired load levels as sensed by the load cell. The loading rate during these fatigue tests was essentially linear.

X-ray exposure was made each time the load reached the maximum level. At the end of 20 cycles, the load was increased to the maximum level in the next range at the slowest crosshead speed. It was again cycled 20 times at a higher crosshead speed with an exposure taken at the maximum level for each cycle. At the end of the last cyclic range, the crosshead speed was reduced to the minimum and the specimen stressed to failure at this speed.

Experimental Results

Experimental results are presented in the form of photographic sequences of damage zones and plots of the damage length as a function of stress level. Representative sequences of damage zone growth under ramp loading for specimens with three-ply orientations are shown in Figs. 2, 3, and 4.

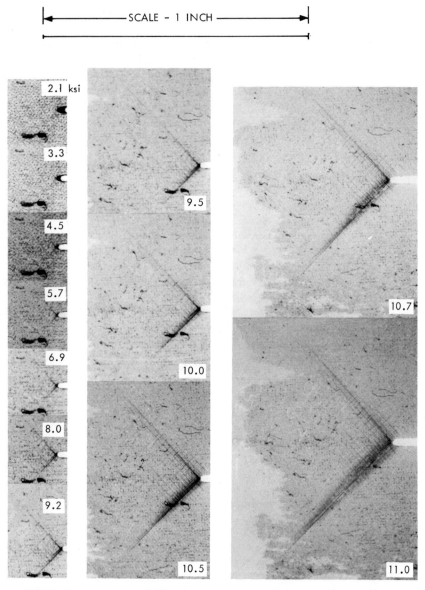

FIG. 2—*Representative sequence of damage zone growth for a [±45]₃ₛ specimen.*

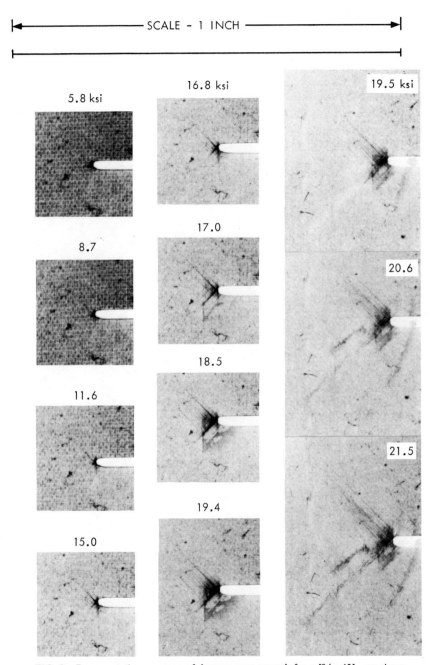

FIG. 3—*Representative sequence of damage zone growth for a [0/ ±45]*$_{2s}$ *specimen.*

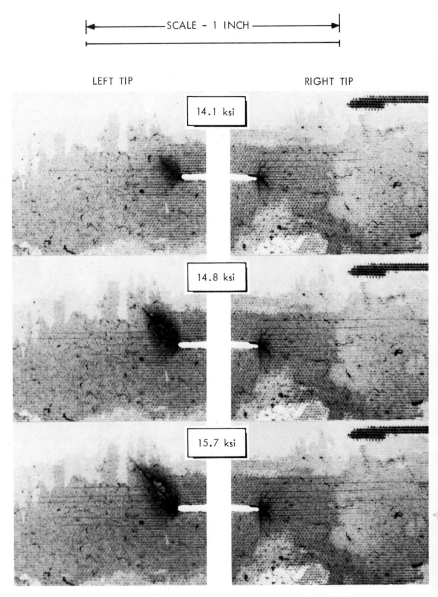

FIG. 4—*Representative sequence of damage zone growth for a [0/ ± 45/90]₂ₛ specimen.*

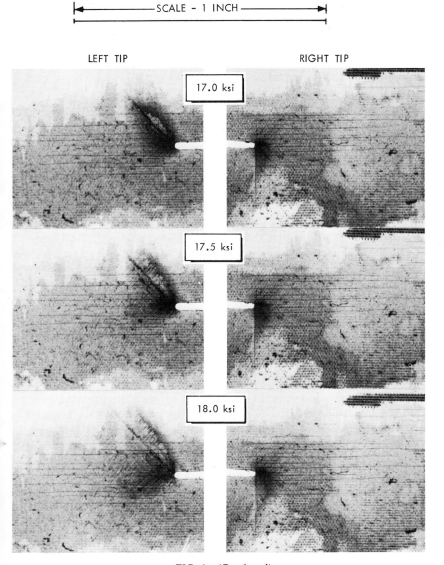

FIG. 4—*(Continued)*

Dark areas in these figures indicate damage zones where TBE has permeated into the voids. Delaminations between the composite layers can be distinguished from the crazing and matrix failure along the fiber directions. As the delaminations increased in size due to increasing load, the shadow areas extended correspondingly. When the delaminated area extended too far and the opaque additive had not been replenished, the central portion of the dark area appeared light. The periphery of the delamination area can be identified by the smudged dark contour line. The propagation of these delamination fronts is most evident in Figs. 3 and 4.

A typical plot of damage lengths along fiber directions under ramp loading is shown in Fig. 5 for a specimen with ply orientation of $[\pm 45]_{3s}$. The lengths of the damage lines were measured from enlargements of X-ray records. A 0.01-in. damage line started at 0.3 ksi (based on the gross area of the specimen) in the -135-deg direction. The growth rate of this line was almost negligible until a stress level of 3.3 ksi was reached. Damage lines in the other three directions then became visible. All the damage lines increased in length at a slow rate until the stress reached approximately 6 ksi. Starting from this stress level, the lines increased in length at a much faster rate.

The growth curves of damage lines under ramp loading for specimens with other ply orientations followed a similar pattern as shown in Fig. 5. Lengths of the damage lines increased slowly at first as the stress increased. As a critical stress level was reached, the growth started to accelerate. The approximate critical stress levels for specimens with ply orientation of $[\pm 45]_{3s}$, $[0/\pm 45]_{2s}$, and $[0/\pm 45/90]_{2s}$ were 6, 19, and 15 ksi, respectively.

Damage line growths along fiber directions under cyclic loading are exemplified by the plots in Fig. 6 for a specimen with ply orientation of $[\pm 45]_{3s}$. This specimen was loaded in four cyclic load ranges with the same R-factor of 0.5. The maximum stress levels for these ranges were 1.2, 2.4, 4.8, and 9.6 ksi. No damage lines could be observed in the first stress range. Short damage lines in the directions of $\pm 45-$deg were observed in the second range (1.2 to 2.4 ksi). These lines remained short and no growth could be detected during the 20 cycles of tensile loading. In the third range (2.4 to 4.8 ksi), damage lines were observed in all fiber directions. The length of these lines also remained essentially unchanged throughout the cyclic loading. In the fourth range (4.8 to 9.6 ksi), considerable damage line growth occurred in all fiber directions. The ultimate failure stress level for this specimen was 10.8 ksi. A similar pattern in the damage line growth was observed during cyclic loadings for specimens with other ply orientations.

Discussion

A common feature among the damage growth curves for all the test specimens under ramp loading appears to be a nonlinear growth rate. At low stress level, the damage lines increased in length at a slow rate. The existence

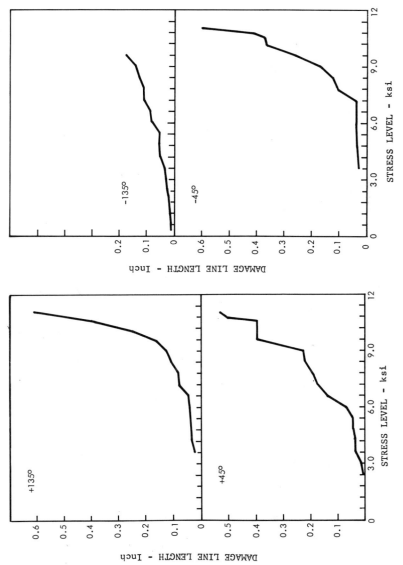

FIG 5—Damage line growth for a [±45]₃ₛ specimen under ramp loading.

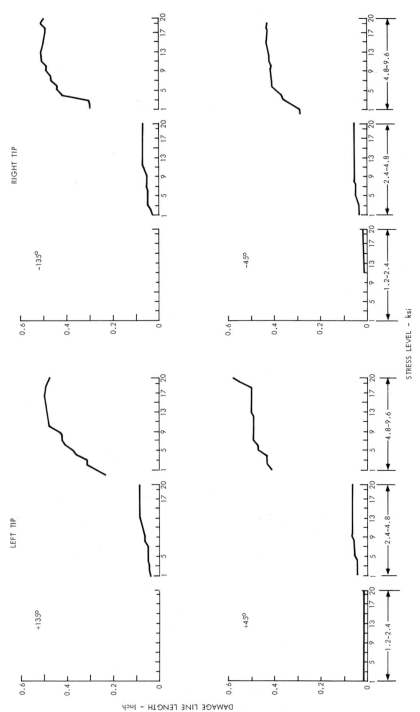

FIG. 6—*Damage line growth for a [±45]₃ₛ specimen under cyclic loading.*

of short damage lines prior to load application did not affect the damage zone growth appreciably. As the loading reached a stress level characteristic of the ply orientation of the specimen, the damage growth rate started to accelerate. The physical changes that occurred around the discontinuity at this characteristic stress level can be observed in Fig. 3. Two consecutive frames of X-ray records at 16.8 and 17.0-ksi stress levels indicated that the damage line in the +135−deg direction increased rapidly in length and width within a short period of time. A new damage line in the +180−deg direction appeared at 17.0 ksi, simultaneously initiating a delamination area to the right of the line. Two subsequent X-ray records at 19.4 and 19.5 ksi in the same figure indicated a similar massive delamination and rapid damage line growth. It seems plausible that the rate of damage growth under ramp loading is a function of the amount of damages present near the discontinuity. Fiber fracture, matrix failure, and ply delamination are coupled in the failure mechanism of the composite specimens.

A statistical analysis was conducted on the damage growth data obtained from a specimen with ply orientation of $[0/\pm45/90]_{2s}$. Figure 7a shows the medians of the lengths of damage lines at progressively increasing load levels. The upper and lower bars represent the maximum and minimum length respectively. A dip in the curve can be discerned in the neighborhood of 13.6 ksi. This dip was observed in the damage line growth curves in practically every direction. The log-normal plot of all the damage line lengths is shown in Fig. 7b with the stress level as a parameter. This figure indicates that the size distributions at lower stress levels are log-normal while those at higher stress levels appear to deviate from a simple log-normal distribution. In Fig. 7c, damage lines at the highest stress level (18.0 ksi) were separated into two categories of long and short lines. The size distributions were then plotted separately for the ±90− and ±45 − deg directions. It can be seen that the size distributions of the damage lines for the high stress level have changed in composition. The single log-normal distribution of crack lengths at low stress levels developed into two distinctly different log-normal distributions at the characteristic stress level. This observation indicates that different failure mechanisms were involved in damage line initiation and catastrophic growth.

Another observation as the specimen loadings reached their respective characteristic stress level was that audible fracture noises were emitted. Acoustic emission monitoring has been conducted in separate tests on several specimens with the three types of ply-orientations, using a special spatial filtering technique with amplitude distribution analysis [6]. Emitted stress waves were observed with extraordinarily large amplitude near the characteristic stress levels. The association of these large-amplitude acoustic emissions with the massive delaminations and acceleration of damage line growth remains to be confirmed by future tests in which X-ray and acoustic emission monitoring are conducted simultaneously. It is reasonable to believe,

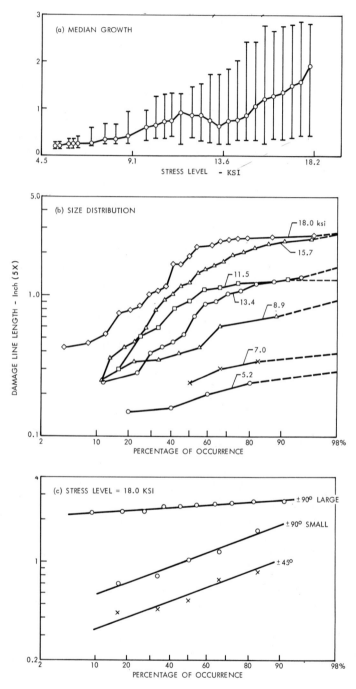

FIG. 7—*Damage line size distribution for a [0/ ±45/90]₂ₛ specimen.*

however, that the onset of accelerated damage growth could be identified with the acoustic emissions with extraordinary amplitude. Results of previous acoustic emission monitoring work and of future tests with simultaneous acoustic emission and X-ray monitoring will be covered in a separate paper.

Conclusion

From the damage zone growth data obtained on graphite-epoxy composite specimens with three laminate configurations, the concept of a nonlinear growth rate seems plausible. The slow growth rate in the low-stress region was separated from the accelerated growth rate in the high-stress region by a characteristic stress level. The failure mechanism near this characteristic stress level appears to be massive ply delaminations, fiber fracture, and matrix failure occurring in a short time period.

Low-cycle fatigue loading at low-stress level was found to cause small damage growth. The existence of short damage lines prior to load application did not affect the history of damage growth appreciably. At high stress levels in the cyclic tests, the majority of damage growth occurred in the earlier cycles.

It has been established that the modified X-ray technique using TBE as an opaque additive can assess damage zone growth surrounding discontinuities in fibrous composite laminates. The method is efficient and can be economically applied in real time for stress concentration studies in composites. This technique may be used simultaneously with an acoustic emission monitoring technique for residual serviceability evaluation of composite components.

Acknowledgments

The authors wish to express their gratitude to W. Shelton of Air Force Materials Laboratory for suggesting the use of TBE as an opaque additive and to M. E. Waddoups for many helpful suggestions and discussions. The help of A. D. Crowe in conducting the experiments is gratefully acknowledged. This study was supported by an independent research and development program of General Dynamics.

References

[1] Daniel, I. M., *Journal of Composite Materials,* Vol. 4, April 1970, p. 178.
[2] Cruse, T. A. and Stout, M. G., *Journal of Composite Materials,* Vol. 7, April 1973, p. 272.
[3] Mandell, J. F., Wang, S. S., and McGarry, F. J., "Fracture of Graphite Fiber Reinforced Composites," Technical Report AFML-TR-73-142, Air Force Materials Laboratory, Dayton, Ohio, 1973.
[4] Marcus, L. A. and Stinchcomb, W. W., "Measurement of Fatigue Damage in Composite Materials," paper submitted at 1973 Fall Meeting of the Society for Experimental Stress Analysis at Indianapolis, Ind.

[5] Sedor, G. and Watterson, R. K., "Low Cycle Compressive Fatigue Failure of E Glass-Epoxy Composites," ASRL TR 162-2, Air Force Office of Scientific Research, Arlington, Va., 1972.

[6] Chang, F. H. and McCauley, B. O., "Acoustic Emission Monitoring of 2219 Aluminum Weldment Specimens Under Static Loadings," General Dynamics Engineering Report, ERR-FW-1445, Oct., 1973.

M. A. Hamstad[1] and T. T. Chiao[1]

Acoustic Emission from Stress Rupture and Fatigue of an Organic Fiber Composite*

REFERENCE: Hamstad, M. A. and Chiao, T. T., "Acoustic Emission from Stress Rupture and Fatigue of an Organic Fiber Composite," *Composite Reliability, ASTM STP 580,* American Society for Testing and Materials, 1975, pp. 191–201.

ABSTRACT: A series of tests was carried out to determine the scatter in acoustic emission data gathered during stress rupture and fatigue testing of a simple fiber-reinforced epoxy composite. Single-end organic fiber-epoxy strands were monitored for acoustic emission during tension tests to failure, stress rupture tests, and dynamic fatigue tests. During the stress rupture and fatigue tests, the plots of summation of acoustic emission counts versus time were found to resemble metal creep curves in that primary, secondary, and tertiary regions could be distinguished. Because of a significant amount of scatter, only a limited correlation can be made between the slope of the summation of acoustic emission in the steady-state region and the specimen life during stress rupture and fatigue testing. In addition, flawed specimens were easily sorted out during the tension tests. These results indicate that acoustic emission data gathered during composite fatigue and stress rupture testing might be useful for life prediction.

KEY WORDS: composite materials, acoustics, emission, fiber composites, fatigue test, creep rupture tests

Acoustic emission (AE) refers to the small-amplitude transient elastic waves that are generated by rapid releases of energy within a material [1].[2] In the past few years, AE records have been shown to be very useful in the microstructural interpretation of pressure testing of filament wound vessels. For example, AE has been shown to be sensitive to winding pattern changes, different fibers, different matrix materials, and both winding and artifically induced flaws [2,3].

As far as we are aware, previous studies of the AE generated during

---

*This work was performed under the auspices of the U.S. Atomic Energy Commission.

[1] Mechanical engineer and chemist, respectively, Lawrence Livermore Laboratory, University of California, Livermore, Calif. 94550.

[2] The italic numbers in brackets refer to the list of references appended to this paper.

stress rupture (that is, time under sustained loading) and dynamic fatigue of fiber-epoxy composites are quite limited [4-6]. Only a few specimens were tested in each of these studies, and hence the scatter that occurs in the AE from such tests was not determined. The object of our research was to examine many specimens to determine the amount of scatter in AE data, and to continue to assess the usefulness of AE data gathered during such tests. Because AE data give microscopic information, they may have great significance in the development of theoretical models for the phenomenon of stress rupture and fatigue of fiber-epoxy composites.

Procedure

Specimen Preparation

A spool of single-end organic fiber (Kevlar 49 with 285 filaments[3] was dried in a vaccum oven at 82 °C (180 °F) for a minimum of 24 h. Then approximately one layer was stripped from the outside and discarded. The single-end fiber was impregnated with Union Carbide ERL 2258/ZZL 0820 (100/30) epoxy and wound by a vacuum filament winding process [7] into strand specimens. The specimens were gelled at 93 °C (200 °F) for 3 h and cured at 163 °C (325 °F) for 2 h on the steel winding frame. Using a previously successful technique, specimens with a 13-cm gage length were bonded to mechanical clamps with room-temperature-cure epoxy adhesives [7]. The tensile strength, stress-strain behavior, and stress-rupture behavior of such strands of organic fiber are well documented in Ref 8. The average fiber volume was about 72 percent. The rationale behind the use of these simple-composite specimens was two-fold. First, many specimens could be tested because they were very inexpensive, and second, since the specimens were very simple, it was expected that the AE response would be easier to interpret than with more complicated composite specimens.

Acoustic Emission Equipment

Commercial AE equipment and transducers were used to monitor the AE during the tests. A piezoelectric AE transducer[4] was coupled to one of the mechanical specimen grips using a viscous resin and tape. As is shown in Fig. 1, a second dummy transducer was coupled to the opposite side of the grip so that the grip with transducers remained with its center of gravity in the line of the strand. The AE signal was processed through a preamplifier, a filter (set to pass 100 to 300 KHz), and a power amplifier. In

---

[3] Reference to a company or product name does not imply approval or recommendation of the product by the University of California or the U.S. Atomic Energy Commission to the exclusion of others that may be suitable.

[4] Dunegan-Endevco—S 14OB radial resonant mode at about 140 kHz.

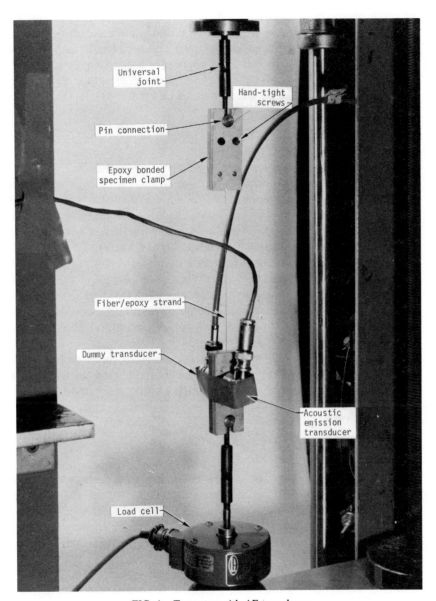

FIG. 1—*Test setup with AE transducers.*

total, the system provided some 80 to 90 dB of electronic gain[5] as needed. The acoustic signal was presented visually in two ways. First, the signal was displayed on an oscilloscope as a function of time. In addition, a count was made of the number of times that the amplitude of the acoustic signal exceeded a voltage bias (nominally set at 1 V). The cumulative total of counts was recorded on an X-Y plotter as a function of load, time, or number of fatigue cycles.[6] In addition, during the fatigue tests a voltage control gate was used which disabled the counter during a certain portion of the load cycle.

Test Conditions

All specimens were tested at room temperature [about 22°C (72°F)] in a modified commercial testing machine. The strand clamp system was suspended between self-aligning universal joints, one of which was connected to a load cell. First, a series of strands was tested to failure using a constant crosshead rate of 0.5 cm/min. Next, a series of strands was cycled between approximately 88 percent and 12 percent of their average failure load at 10 Hz in a sinusoidal mode until each failed. Finally, a series of strands was brought to a deadweight load of approximately 88 percent of their average failure load. This deadweight loading was accomplished by lowering at a constant rate the crosshead on which the deadweight was supported. It took less than 10 s to load the strands in this manner. The strands then remained under load until failure occurred.

During each test, the AE was monitored. The relatively high load levels for the fatigue and stress rupture tests were chosen so that the testing time for each specimen would be relatively short—on the order of 4 h or less.

Experimental Work

Tension Tests

Figure 2 shows the results of typical tension tests with organic fiber strands. This figure shows the band within which the sum of AE versus the load fell for 14 specimens, the actual curves for two of these specimens, and the actual curves for two flawed specimens. Figure 2 also shows a typical strain-versus-load curve during a strand tension test. The average tensile strength based on the 16 specimens tested here was 3710 MPa (538 ksi). Figure 3 shows the sum of AE versus load for a typical tension strand test as well as the same data for two specimens which were unknowingly flawed during attachment of the AE transducers. All tension tests were carried out at an electronic gain of 80 dB.

[5] Gains were set using a test oscillator at 150 kHz and an rms meter.
[6] When excited by an incident stress wave, the AE transducer rings at a characteristic frequency. Thus, a single AE event normally gives several counts.

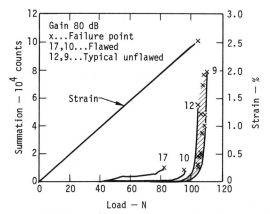

FIG. 2—*Summation of AE for organic fiber-epoxy strand tension tests, and typical strain versus load for strand tension test.*

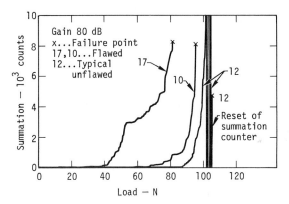

FIG. 3—*AE of flawed and unflawed organic fiber-epoxy strand specimens.*

Fatigue Tests

Two difficulties were encountered during the fatigue tests. First, a large share of the specimens failed at the clamps in spite of a number of modifications in the adhesive joint design. Second, at the same point in each load cycle, extraneous AE was often generated in the adhesive bond of the joint. Visual observation indicated that this AE often came from rubbing of particles of the adhesive that had broken loose from the adhesive but still remained bonded to the strand. This latter difficulty was largely overcome by using the voltage control gate to ignore all the AE generated at loads below 75 percent of the average tensile failure load. In tests where there was no adhesive-generated AE, it was verified that the slope of the summation of AE versus number of test cycles did not significantly change when the voltage control gate was set to 50 percent of the average tensile failure load. Attempts to eliminate adhesive AE generation by using different adhesives were not successful.

The results of ten fatigue tests are shown in Fig. 4. This figure shows the summation of AE as a function of the number of test cycles. All of these specimens failed properly in the gage length.

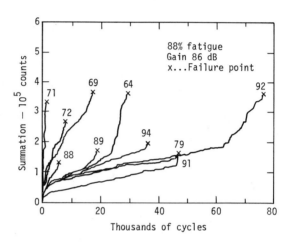

FIG. 4—*Summation of AE above 75 percent of tensile failure load during fatigue tests versus number of cycles. Specimen numbers shown.*

Stress Rupture Tests

The results of 19 stress rupture tests are shown in Fig. 5. Here the summation of AE is shown as a function of time. All of these tests were at 80-dB electronic gain.

Discussion

The discussion and interpretation of the results are based on the premise that the large majority of the AE generated during these tests is associated with fiber filament failure.[7] The basis for this assumption has been more fully discussed previously [2,3]. Briefly, the filament failure stresses are on the order of 50 times the resin failure or the interfacial debonding stresses. Thus, the energy released by the latter two mechansims in the form of stress waves is expected to be much lower than that released by filament failure. The result is that AE electronic gains, which allow the experimenter to

[7] Machine noises were assumed to have insignificant influence on the AE data because: (*a*) the electronic gains used were 85 db or less; (*b*) the universal joints provided attenuation of such noises; and (*c*) machine noise characteristically occurs at all loads, while our data have major portions of the loading time with no AE sensed.

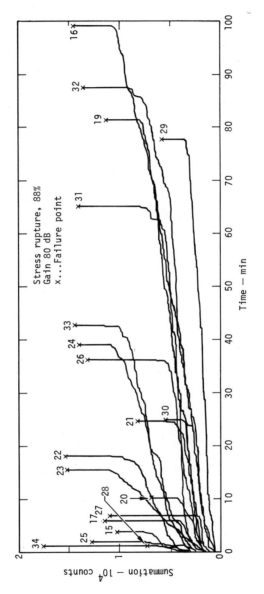

FIG. 5—AE counts during stress rupture of organic fiber-epoxy strands.

conveniently process the stress waves generated by filament failures, are too small to provide the amplification necessary to process the majority of stress waves generated by the two matrix-related damage mechanisms.

The strand tension tests with AE were performed first to provide a background to help in the interpretation of the stress rupture and fatigue AE data. These tests indicate that strand specimens which fail (because of handling-induced flaws) at loads below the lowest strength associated with the typical distribution of strength of the organic fiber are easily distinguished at low loads by the AE data. For example, the AE data in Fig. 3 for Specimen 17 indicated by the substantial early AE at about 40 percent of the average strand tensile strength that this specimen was flawed. As is shown, the specimen failed at about 78 percent of the average strand strength. This result shows that AE testing has promise as a nondestructive test technique for fiber composites.

As Fig. 2 shows, even for these very simple composite specimens, one cannot use summation of AE to pick out the strong and the weak specimens within the typical distribution of strand strengths. We suggest that successful sorting of strengths by summation of AE would only work if failure in the strand took place as a result of filaments progressively breaking at only one location along the length of the fiber. The most likely situation is that this type of mechanism is occurring at several locations in each strand and that the number of locations is not a constant from strand to strand. This situation results in the total AE counts-to-failure during a tension test changing radically from strand to strand as shown by the scatter in Fig. 2.

The AE data gathered during the stress rupture and fatigue tests have a number of similarities. In both cases, the summation of AE as a function of time or the number of cycles resembles metallic creep curves in that primary, secondary (or steady state), and tertiary regions can be distinguished. During the first few minutes of testing, filament breakage occurs at a decreasing rate until, averaged over a period time, an approximately steady rate of breakage occurs. Just prior to failure, the rate of breakage progressively increases, giving an AE warning of impending failure. Figures 4 and 5 show that there is some correlation between the life of the specimen and the slope of the steady-state summation of AE. The specimens with less slope tend to last longer. The exceptions to this tendency are probably related to the differences in the number of locations along the length of each strand where filaments are progressively breaking. This phenomenon again leads to scatter.[8]

The fact that the steady-state region exists indicates that AE may be a useful tool for the study of the effect of different environments on the

---

[8] The scatter in the stress rupture data is not reduced by eliminating the few specimens that failed at the grips.

stress rupture or fatigue life of these organic fiber composites. For example, during the steady-state region, the environment could be changed while noting whether or not the slope of the AE curve changed. An increase in slope would indicate a more detrimental environment. Using this technique would allow a relatively rapid screening of many different environments because the experimenter would not have to wait for specimens to fail to see if their stress rupture behavior had been degraded or improved.

Typically, the AE data gave a warning of impending failure during the dynamic fatigue tests at approximately 85 to 98 percent of the fatigue life. The AE data also gave a warning of impending failure during the stress rupture tests. Figure 5 illustrates that the warning was usually on the order of 1 to 4 min. The fact that AE gives clear indication of impending failure implies that AE could be used as a tool to enable the experimenter to stop a test just prior to failure so that other inspection techniques could be used to study the test-generated flaws.

It is of interest to point out that the total number of AE counts at failure was on the average significantly higher for the tension tests than for the stress rupture tests. For example, most of the stress rupture specimens had approximately 10 000 or less counts (at 80 dB) just prior to failure, while most of the tension specimens had approximately 20 000 to 80 000 counts (at 80 dB) at failure. This implies that the filament breakage was not as extensive in the stress rupture specimens as in the tension specimens. This phenomenon is to be expected in stress rupture because of the stress level dependence of the stress rupture mechanism in the organic fiber [8]. Thus, with increased time at load during the stress rupture tests, progressive damage occurs at fewer locations along the length of the specimen.

A comparison of the stress rupture data of Fig. 5 with the AE obtained during a stress rupture test of an S-glass-epoxy pressure bottle is shown in Fig. 6 (taken from Ref 4). This comparison shows that data in both cases are similar, which implies that one could expect more complicated filament-wound organic fiber-epoxy pressure vessels to result in AE data very similar to Fig. 5.

Conclusions

1. For tension, fatigue, and stress rupture tests, the AE data showed a good deal of scatter for macroscopically identical specimens and tests.

2. During stress rupture and fatigue tests of the organic fiber-epoxy strands, the summation of AE versus time curves was found to resemble that of metal creep curves. These curves gave an AE warning of impending failure.

3. As a result of scatter, only a limited correlation can be made between the slope of the steady-state region of the AE curve and specimen life.

4. The existence of the steady-state region implies that AE may prove

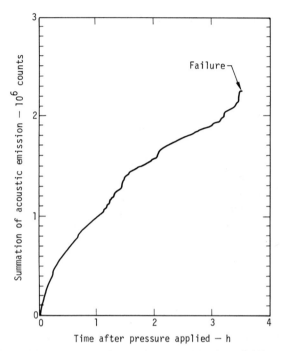

FIG. 6—*S-glass-epoxy pressure vessel stress rupture summation of AE versus time at 83 percent of expected failure pressure (85 dB) (taken from Ref 4).*

useful in studies of the effect of different environments on the stress rupture and fatigue life of organic fiber composites.

5. Based on the results of these tests, AE data should be obtained from many fatigue tests of more complicated organic fiber composite specimens in order to determine if scatter precludes life prediction.

Acknowledgment

The contributions of R. G. Patterson and L. E. Trent to this project are gratefully acknowledged.

References

[1] Liptai, R. G., Harris, D. O., and Tatro, C. A., in *Acoustic Emission, ASTM STP 505,* American Society for Testing and Materials, 1972, p. 336.
[2] Hamstad, M. A., "Acoustic Emission from Filament-Wound Pressure Bottles," *Proceedings,* Fourth National Technical Conference, Society of Aerospace Materials and Process Engineering, Palo Alto, Calif., Oct. 1972.
[3] Hamstad, M. A. and Chiao, T. T., *Journal of Composite Materials,* Vol. 7, July 1973, p. 320.
[4] Liptai, R. G., in *Composite Materials: Testing and Design (Second Conference), ASTM STP 497,* American Society for Testing and Materials, 1972 pp. 285–298.

[5] Hoggatt, J. T., "Development of Cryogenic PRD-49-I Filament-Wound Tanks," NASA Report CR-120835, National Aeronautics and Space Administration, Washington, D.C., Dec. 1971.

[6] Kim, H. C., Rippen Neto, A. P., and Stephens, R. W. B., *Nature Physical Science,* Vol. 237, May 1972, p. 78.

[7] Chiao, T. T. and Moore, R. L., *Quarterly,* Society of Aerospace Materials and Process Engineering, Vol. 3, No. 3, April 1972, p. 28.

[8] Chiao, T. T., Wells, J. E., Moore, R. L., and Hamstad, M. A. in *Composite Materials: Testing and Design (Third Conference), ASTM STP 546,* American Society for Testing and Materials, 1973, pp. 209–224.

E. G. Henneke II[1] and H. W. Herring[2]

Spectrum Analysis of Acoustic Emissions from Boron-Aluminum Composites

REFERENCE: Henneke, E. G., II, and Herring, H. W., "**Spectrum Analysis of Acoustic Emissions from Boron-Aluminum Composites,**" *Composite Reliability, ASTM STP 580,* American Society for Testing and Materials, 1975, pp. 202–214.

ABSTRACT: Acoustic emissions were monitored from unidirectional tension specimens of boron-aluminum composites. It is shown that a sudden increase in count rate presages final failure. This sudden increase, however, occurs at a variable point relative to final failure load. Spectrum analysis in the range to 1 to 100 kHz was performed on the emissions with the result that no immediately obvious recognition pattern exists to distinguish between types of failure mechanisms. Thus, it is suggested that either acoustic emissions cannot be used to distinguish different failure modes in boron-aluminum composites in the frequency range studied or else the specimens used here had only one failure mode operating with sufficient energy release to be detected. The spectrum analysis did show, however, that the acoustic emissions had frequency components much higher than the frequencies for the fundamental modes of natural vibration of the specimen.

KEY WORDS: acoustics, emission, composite materials, spectrum analysis, failure modes

The present work was undertaken to determine what utility the study of acoustic emissions might have in determining modes and mechanisms of failure in boron-aluminum filamentary composites. Several papers [1–5][3] have appeared in the literature suggesting that signature analysis of the emitted stress waves might yield valuable information on the energy releasing mechanisms and, hence, might further knowledge of the underlying modes of failure. Also, preliminary work by one of the present authors (HWH) has suggested that emissions from metal-matrix tension specimens had distinctly different spectra at different loads. For these reasons, par-

[1] Associate professor of engineering science and mechanics, Virginia Polytechnic Institute and State University, Blacksburg, Va. 24061.
[2] Office of the Administrator, National Aeronautics and Space Administration Headquarters, Washington, D.C.
[3] The italic numbers in brackets refer to the list of references appended to this paper.

ticular interest was placed in obtaining signature analysis of the acoustic emissions. In addition, it was felt that the use of emissions for event counting would aid in identifying the role played by the cumulative or noncumulative fracture mechanism [6] in the rupture of the material used here.

The several papers suggesting signature analysis which have appeared in the literature and were just cited have, with one exception (Ref 4), used accelerometers or semiconductor strain gages as transducers. The sole exception recorded emissions from fiber-glass reinforced plastics via a microphone. Takehana and Kimpara [4] noted that, while acoustic emissions from metals are generally in a higher frequency range (several hundred kHz to several hundred MHz), emissions from composites are audible and hence could be detected by a suitable condenser microphone. They performed spectral analysis measurements in the frequency range of 300 Hz to 11 kHz. This frequency range is particularly susceptible to influence from the fundamental natural frequency modes for the specimen. Other authors [5], have also worked in this frequency range when studying composites. In the present case, it was decided to use a condenser microphone with as wide a frequency band as could be obtained. There are commercially available wideband microphones that have very flat, broad-band frequency response. They do not have the disadvantage displayed by accelerometers and piezoelectric AE transducers of having self-resonances in the frequency range of interest. Of course there are many disadvantages associated with the use of a microphone such as relative insensitivity, as compared with accelerometers, and susceptibility to background noise. For boron-aluminum, however, the emissions are sufficiently intense to be picked up by the microphone over and above relatively large levels of ambient noise.

The work is described in two sections. The first details the experimental instrumentation and procedure while the second describes the results.

Experimental Procedure

Tension Tests

Tension specimens of 8-ply unidirectional boron-aluminum composite were pulled by a Baldwin-Lima-Hamilton, 120-kip capacity tension machine at a strain rate of approximately 1.1×10^{-3} min^{-1}. The specimens, nominally 1.27 by 0.15 by 30.5 cm, were standard coupon specimens with the fibers aligned parallel to the tension axis and with fiber-glass tabs bonded to the ends. The tabs were approximately 6.35 cm long, giving a specimen gage length of 17.8 cm. Several specimens 33.02 cm long (gage length 20.3 cm) were also tested. Two different bonding agents were employed to bond the fiber-glass tabs to the composites: (1) A room-temperature curing contact cement was used in the first group of specimens. This proved inadequate in that the bonds would "pop" during the tension test and become separated from the specimen. The four pops that occurred in these tests were easily distinguishable from acoustic emissions and were removed from the acoustic emission (AE) data. This debonding, however, was not detrimental to the tension test as failures were found to occur in the gage length and not in the grips. Also, as will be pointed out later, the loud pops emitted by the debonding tabs had a fortuitous use in the spectrum analysis. (2) A high-temperature curing adhesive, HT-424 [curing temperature 340 to 350°F], was used for the second group. This proved to be a more adequate bonding agent since no debonding was observed in any of the tests with these specimens.

The specimens were gripped by standard wedge grips in the tension machine. While the gripping arrangement may be inadequate for acoustic emission tests of metal specimens, it proved to be quite suitable for the study of composites. The emissions from composites are energetic and distinct since they arise from sharp, discontinuous local disturbances such as fiber breakage, debonding, or delamination. To assure the validity of this, a steel bar with no fiber-glass tabs and an aluminum bar with fiber-glass end tabs were pulled to load values consistent with those required to rupture the composite specimens. No audible nor significant number of emissions occurred in either case, showing that the emissions obtained in the tests reported herein were coming from neither the load train-gripping system nor the deformation of the fiber-glass end tabs in the wedge grips.

Acoustic Emission Tests

The acoustic emissions emanating from the tension coupons were monitored by the instrumentation shown schematically in Fig. 1. The microphone employed in this study (B&K, 1/8-in. condenser microphone, Type 4138) was placed a distance of 0.02 in. away from the center of the speci-

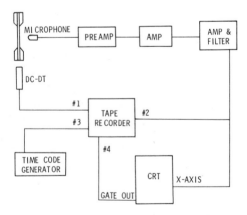

FIG. 1—*Schematic of instrumentation setup.*

men. The frequency response calibration curve for this microphone, as provided by the manufacturer, was perfectly flat for the frequency range 5.5 Hz to 160 kHz. This particular type of microphone also has a high sensitivity. Although the sensitivity is less than that of piezoelectric transducers, preliminary tests which were run on several specimens with an accelerometer, together with the microphone, showed no significant difference in the response of the two types of pickups for emissions from boron-aluminum composites. The reasons for using the microphone instead of the accelerometer were, as previously noted, because of the wide-band width of the microphone and the desire for spectral analysis unencumbered by self-excited frequencies of the accelerometer.

The signal from the mcirophone was preamplified by a B&K Type 2618 preamplifier and delivered to a B&K Measuring Amplifier, Type 2608 (2Hz to 200 kHz). This amplifier was calibrated by standard procedures to measure absolute noise levels and was set to respond to sound pulses with levels between 70 and 90 dB at the microphone, a sonic range which included all but the weakest emissions. The signal was further conditioned and amplified 20 dB by an Ithaco Type 453 amplifier-filter before being delivered to the tape recorder. The amplifier-filter was set to high-pass frequencies above 1000 Hz. This amplifier set the upper frequency range for the entire system to 100 kHz. The total system amplification was estimated to be approximately 60 to 70 dB. This is 20 to 30 dB less than amplifications normally reported in the literature for monitoring acoustic emissions from metals. For composites, the amplification used here is sufficient since, as noted earlier, acoustic emissions from filamentary reinforced composites are highly energetic.

The AE signals were simultaneously recorded by direct electronics on an Ampex PR-500 tape recorder at 30 in./s (frequency response 100 Hz to 150 kHz) and monitored on an oscilloscope. During preliminary tests, an appropriate trigger level for the scope was determined so that only sound pulses above the constant ambient noise levels would trigger the scope. Tests were conducted at night so that the background ambient noises from fans, air conditioners, etc. would be constant. The sweep of the scope was set also during these preliminary tests so that one emission would either die out by the end of the sweep or reach voltage levels low enough that the scope would not be triggered again by the same emission. The square gate pulse, corresponding to the sweep time, was taken from the scope and also recorded on tape to allow convenient counting of the emission events. To check the correspondence between the square gate pulse and the emission event, several tapes were played into a dual-channel oscillograph. The correspondence between the two was within 10 percent, the major discrepancy occurring very late in the tests when the emissions became very energetic shortly before rupture. This leads to multiple firing of the scope by the same emission event. The acoustic emission data were analyzed in two ways: (1) the total number of emission events occurring up to a given load value was recorded, and (2) spectrum analysis of individual emissions at various loads was obtained. The spectrum analysis was performed by a real-time analyzer, Spectral Dynamics Model SD301C, operating on transient mode. This analyzer can capture a single acoustic emission pulse, store it in memory, and read out the relative amplitude of the frequency components present in the pulse. The maximum frequency range of this real-time analyzer is 50 khz. The recorded emissions on tape were played back into the analyzer at half the recorded speed, however, making the effective frequency range 100 khz.

Natural-Frequency Tests

The natural frequencies of the various fundamental vibrational modes of the coupon specimens were measured by a Magnetest Elastomat Type FM-500, an instrument designed for the rapid measurement of dynamic moduli of elasticity in the frequency range 600 Hz to 25 khz. While this particular instrument was designed to determine the natural frequencies of a free-free cylindrical bar, its test fixtures were modified for use in this testing program to allow for the determination of the natural modes of a fixed-fixed specimen in the grips of the tension machine. That the specimen was indeed vibrating in a resonant condition could be easily determined in the audible range by the application of a stethoscope.

The frequency range (0.6 to 25 khz) for the natural vibrational modes measured in this study was limited by the instrumentation. This range, however, covered the fundamental frequency of all modes of vibration and the third- to sixth-order harmonic for all modes except the longitudinal (see Table 2). In general, an impulsive load (such as a localized release of stress energy causing an acoustic emission) will drive only the lower-order harmonics (see, for example, Thornton [7]), since the higher-order harmonics are more rapidly attenuated. Thus the frequency range used to determine the natural frequencies of the specimens in this study was deemed sufficient to determine which of the frequency components of the AE pulses could be accounted for by induced ringing of the specimen. The results reported indicate the validity of this conclusion.

Results and Discussion

Mechanical Properties

The results of the tension tests on the boron-aluminum coupon specimens are listed in Table 1. The stress-strain curves for all of the specimens tested (except for the two not loaded to failure) had at least three distinct slopes as shown in the table. The knees of the curves cannot generally be located precisely and, hence, are not reported here. Their location is quite arbitrary,

TABLE 1—*Mechanical properties.*

Run No.	Specimen No.	E_1, 10^4MPa	E_2, 10^4MPa	E_3, 10^4MPa	E_4, 10^4MPa	E_5, 10^4MPa	σ_{ult} 10^3MPa	ε_{ult} %
1	5-9	19.7	18.4	17.8	...	...	1.276	0.6925
2	1	19.7	18.0	17.2	...	...	1.489	0.8282
3	2	20.0	17.9	17.8	17.0	...	1.471	0.8167
4	3	19.7	17.8	17.2	...	...	1.412	0.7932
5	4	19.5	17.6	17.0	...	...	1.441	0.8185
6	5	19.7	17.7	15.4	...	...	1.502	0.8371
8	7	19.2	18.5	17.8	15.9	...	1.428	0.7751
9	9	21.7	18.3	17.7	16.8	...	1.418	0.7789
10	10	20.1	18.2	17.8	16.3	...	1.460	0.8008
11	11	20.4	18.2	17.2	...	...	1.467	0.8077
12	12	19.7	18.4	...	...	...	not loaded to failure	
13	13	19.6	17.9	...	...	...	not loaded to failure	
16	14	21.0	17.1	17.7	...	...	1.391	0.7665
17	19	21.0	18.5	17.6	...	...	1.464	0.7926
18	20	21.8	17.9	17.3	...	...	1.428	0.7957
19	15	21.4	18.4	17.2	...	...	1.483	0.8072
20	16	20.8	18.3	17.6	...	...	1.444	0.7917
21	21	21.4	18.8	18.1	...	...	1.380	0.7303
22	22	21.0	18.3	17.4	...	...	1.240	0.6873
23	23	20.1	17.9	17.2	...	...	1.234	0.6917
24	24	22.2	18.5	17.8	...	...	1.470	0.7985
25	25	22.4	18.9	17.9	...	...	1.302	0.7048
26	26	22.3	18.4	17.7	16.8	...	1.534	0.8473
27	4-11	21.0	18.2	17.9	16.9	...	1.317	0.7341
28	27	22.4	18.2	17.3	16.4	13.2	1.321	0.7525
Average		20.7	18.2	17.4	16.5	13.2	1.407	0.7760

depending upon where one decides to break the curve when connecting the data points. The different values of Young's moduli are quite distinct, however, and can be delineated. Six specimens had a fourth distinct slope and one had five slope values. As seen in the table, the average values of the three slopes are 20.7 × 10⁴ MPa (30.0 Msi), 18.2 × 10⁴ MPa (26.4 Msi), and 17.4 × 10⁴ MPa (25.3 Msi). The actual values for ultimate stress and strain are slightly higher than given in the table. Data for the values shown here were recorded by the centralized computer facility which, except for Runs 1 through 8, took a record at two-second intervals toward the end of the test. Runs 1 through 8 recorded data every ten seconds. The average ultimate stress and strain values so recorded were 1407 Mpa (204.1 ksi) and 0.7760 percent, respectively, as shown.

Acoustic Emission Events

The total accumulated events occurring up to a given value of load have been plotted for 23 of the runs shown in Table 1. For one reason or another, the missing runs had unrecorded data. Typical curves of the results obtained are shown in Fig. 2. The data shown in Fig. 2 were chosen so that Runs 19 and 3 effectively bound the curves for all the other tests. Thus, Fig. 2 also shows the degree of reproducibility of the results. While Fig. 2 exhibits the data as continuous curves for convenience and ease in presentation, it must be realized that such data are highly discontinuous since they come at different times. The data are more realistically plotted as a histogram as shown for typical runs in Fig. 3. The AE events generally accumulate at a relatively steady rate until shortly before failure. Then there is an increasingly rapid rate of emission up to final fracture. This effect is much more dramatically displayed on the monitoring oscilloscope than as indicated by the figures. This sudden rise in rate occurred as early as 5560 N (1250 lb) below the ultimate load to as late as 222 N (50 lb) below the ultimate load. By far the majority of specimens (15) displayed the sudden increase in emission rate by 1779 N (400 lb) or more newtons before the ultimate load. The acoustic emissions evidently indicate that these specimens failed by a combination of cumulative and noncumulative fracture modes, a result consistent with one reported earlier [6].

As a further check on the physical interpretation of the AE events recorded in this study, four specimens were slowly chemically etched to re-

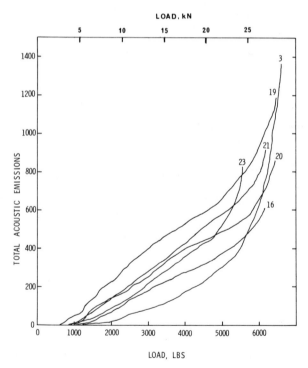

FIG. 2—*Total acoustic emission counts for several typical tests.*

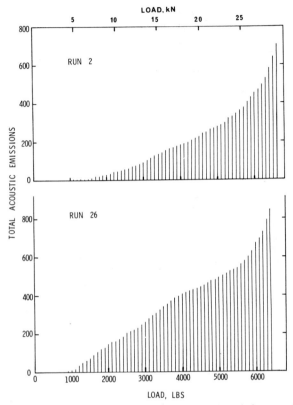

FIG. 3—*Histogram representation of total acoustic emission counts.*

move the matrix from the chemically inert fibers. The four specimens used were as received, tested to a 15 570 N (3500 lb) load, tested to a 24 465 N (5500 lb) load, and tested to rupture. The number of filament breaks observed in these specimens was, except for the ruptured specimen, very close to the number of recorded emission events. For the ruptured specimen, there was a very large number of fragmented filaments. This effect has been observed previously [6], and has been accounted for by the sudden propagation of large energy wave at the instant of fracture. Hence, the number of breaks would not be expected to be in a one-to-one correspondence with AE events in this case.

Spectrum Analysis of Acoustic Emissions

The major emphasis of the present test program was placed upon obtaining signature analysis of the acoustic emissions from the boron-aluminum composite. In particular, it was desired to determine whether or not different but distinctive spectra would be displayed by emissions corresponding to different localized failure processes such as fiber fracture, debonding, or delamination. Because of the limitations imposed by available instrumentation, the only type of signature analysis which was performed was spectrum analysis.

Typical spectra are presented in Figs. 4*a* through 4*f*, which show the relative amplitudes of each frequency component present in individual pulses taken at the indicated loads. As can be seen in Figs. 4*c*–4*f*, there is no

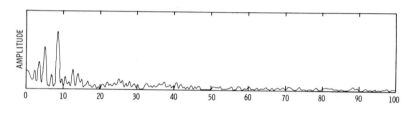

FREQUENCY, kHz

FIG. 4*a—Spectrum from tab debonding [Run 20, load 8896 N (2000 lb)].*

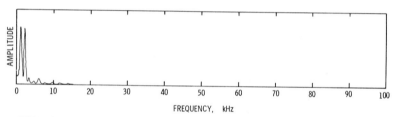

FREQUENCY, kHz

FIG. 4*b—Spectrum from hit with rubber hose [Run 16, load 4448 N (1000 lb)].*

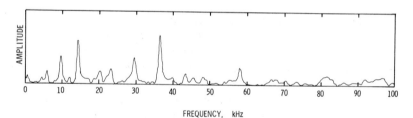

FREQUENCY, kHz

FIG. 4*c—Spectrum from high-level AE pulse [Run 20, load 13345 N (3000 lb)].*

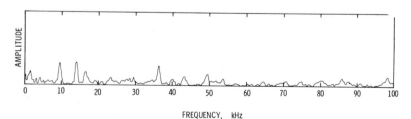

FREQUENCY, kHz

FIG. 4*d—Spectrum from low-level AE pulse [Run 20, load 13345 N (3000 lb)].*

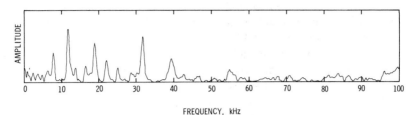

FIG. 4e—*Spectrum from AE pulse [Run 20, load 5337 N (1200 lb)].*

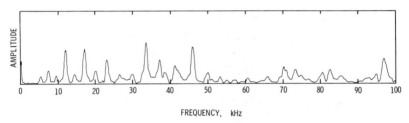

FIG. 4f—*Spectrum from AE pulse [Run 20, load 28024 N (6300 lb)].*

immediately discernible pattern to the spectra for the acoustic emissions. A few statements, however, can be made concerning some aspects of the behavior of the spectra. First, it does appear that the spectra carry certain information concerning the source of the sound. As can be seen in Figs. **4a** and **4b**, the spectra associated with tab debonding, which is a highly energetic event, and with a low-energy, external impulse (applied in this case by softly striking the specimen with a rubber hose) are composed of mainly low-frequency components, less than 25 kHz. These low frequencies are in the range of the low-order harmonics of natural vibration modes of the specimen. As will be discussed in the next section, there is strong reason to believe that these low frequencies are indeed the natural ringing of the specimen due to impulsive loads. On the other hand, *all* the spectra associated with the acoustic emissions caused by some internal stress-releasing mechanism have high-frequency components (>25 kHz) in addition to the low-frequency components. The energy of the acoustic emissions studied during this work varied over the range of very low energies comparable to the rubber hose strikes to the very high energies contained in tab debonding. This energy was measured in effect by noting the trigger level required to operate the spectrum analyzer. Typical spectra for high- and low-level pulses are given in Figs. **4c** and **4d**. As can be seen, there is no obvious distinction between the two as far as their spectra are concerned.

Second, there appears to be some consistent change in certain specific frequency components for different values of load. For example, in Fig. **4e** there is a relatively large component present at approximately 40 kHz. This was present for all acoustic emission spectra below a load of 8896 N (2000 lb). This component gradually decayed in relative amplitude with increasing load while a second one at 45 kHz increased, as can be seen in Fig. 4*f*. At high load levels, however, not all pulses contained this 45-kHz component. (One event out of ten studied did not have this component for this particular specimen.) This statement is presently somewhat loose as it is based upon only one specimen. Other runs have different frequencies present than those noted here. Further analysis is required to determine what meaningful pattern is present, if any.

Natural Frequencies of Vibration

The natural frequencies of vibration in the range 0.6 to 25 kHz were measured experimentally by an Elastomat, as discussed earlier. The experimental results are listed in Table 2. For comparison purposes, the frequency components which were present in the spectrum obtained by striking a specimen externally are also listed in the table. Both of these measurements were taken with a load of 4448 N (1000 lb) applied to the specimen. It is believed that some of the higher-frequency resonanting conditions determined by the Elastomat are artifacts of the system and do not actually denote a natural mode of the specimen.

Theoretical calculations were also made using the standard expressions

TABLE 2—*Natural frequencies.*

Experimental, kHz	Spectrum Analysis, kHz	Theoretical Bar, kHz	Theoretical Plate, kHz
0.72	1.1	0.31—1st T⊥	1.18—1st S-S
1.45	2.0	0.87—2nd T⊥	1.91—1st A-S
2.39	4.5	1.70—3rd T⊥	4.27—1st S-A
3.39	7.7	2.67—1st T‖	6.31—2nd A-S
3.85	9.4	2.80—4th T⊥	6.51—2nd S-S
4.72	11.2	4.19—5th T⊥	9.23—1st A-A
5.24	15.7	5.85—6th T⊥	12.80—2nd S-A
7.05	18.0	7.36—2nd T‖	15.62—3rd S-S
15.74	. . .	14.43—3rd T‖	18.46—2nd A-A
16.35	. . .	20.42—1st L	. . .
17.96	. . .	23.85—4th T‖	. . .
18.98	. . .	. . .	. . .
20.75	. . .	. . .	. . .

NOTES:
 S = Symmetric plate mode,
 A = Antisymmetric plate mode,
 T⊥ = Transverse beam mode, motion perpendicular to large cross-sectional dimension,
 T‖ = Transverse beam mode, motion parallel to large cross-sectional dimension, and
 L = Longitudinal bar mode.

for natural frequencies of longitudinal, transverse, and torsional vibrations of cylindrical bars and beams. In addition, the natural frequencies for vibration of an isotropic plate with two opposite sides clamped while the other two are free were calculated. The expressions used all pertain to isotropic, homogeneous materials and are not completely accurate for the determination of natural modes of composites. They should give ball park values, however, and were used since no solution presently exists in the literature for an orthotropic plate with such boundary conditions. As can be seen, there is close agreement between many of the natural-frequency values obtained by the various means described in the foregoing. Hence, it is quite apparent that the low-frequency components in the spectrum analyses do indeed correspond to natural resonances of the specimen. The higher frequency components, however, may or may not be natural modes. The usual situation is for an impulsive load to drive only the lower-order harmonics of the natural resonances (see, for example, Thornton [7]). Hence, there is strong reason to believe that the higher-frequency components are more related to the emission source. Further work would have to be performed to determine if this indeed is the case here.

Conclusions

The study of the acoustic emissions emanating from stressed materials appears to offer a large potential in aiding the understanding of failure mechanisms. The techniques one uses for analyzing AE data from composites, however, is still open for discussion. The most easily obtained and obvious results of an AE test are event counting, count rate, or total integrated counts as a function of stress or strain in the material. In addition, it is quickly observed that for boron-aluminum composites there are distinct differences in the energy content of the emissions at all levels of stress. To go further than this will require additional work.

For boron-aluminum composites, it has been found here that the total AE counts increase at a relatively steady rate with increasing load up to a load approaching the ultimate. Then the rate of emissions suddenly begins to increase quite rapidly and continues to increase until final failure. The point at which this sudden increase begins may vary anywhere from 5337 N (1200 lb) to 222 N (50 lb) (276 MPa through 11.7 MPa) before the ultimate load. The spectra of these acoustic emissions are quite distinct and easily distinguishable from those associated with other impulsive loadings which lead to resonating states of the specimen. No consistent distinction, however, has been found in the spectrum analysis of various high-energy-level and low-energy-level emissions nor between emissions occurring at different levels. While the AE spectra are all different, no obvious pattern has been ascertained which might allow one to distinguish between different types of AE sources in the frequency range studied here.

Acknowledgments

This work was performed at the NASA-Langley Research Center under the Summer Faculty Research Program. Thanks are to be given to B. A. Stein for his efforts in behalf of the program and H. Bloxom for his technical assistance in performing the tests.

References

[1] Ono, K., Stern, R., and Long, M., Jr. in *Acoustic Emission, ASTM STP 505,* American Society for Testing and Materials, 1971, pp. 152–163.
[2] Mehan, R. L. and Mullin, J. V., *Journal of Composite Materials,* Vol. 5, April 1971, pp. 266–269.
[3] Beattie, A. G., *Proceedings,* Institute of Electrical and Electronic Engineers, U.S. Symposium, 1972, pp. 13–17.
[4] Takehana, M. and Kimpara, I., *Proceedings,* International Conference on the Mechanical Behavior of Metals, Vol. 5, Society of Materials Science, Tokyo, Japan, 1972, pp. 156–167.
[5] Mullin, J. V. and Mehan, R. L., *Journal of Testing and Evaluation,* Vol. 1, May, 1973, pp. 215–219.
[6] Herring, H. W., Lytton, J. L., and Steele, J. H., Jr., *Metallurgical Transactions,* Vol. 4, March, 1973, pp. 807–817.
[7] Thornton, D. L., *Mechanics Applied to Vibrations and Balancing,* Wiley, New York, 1940, pp. 270–274.

J. L. Rose[1] *and W. Shelton*[2]

Damage Analysis in Composite Materials

REFERENCE: Rose, J. L. and Shelton, W., **"Damage Analysis in Composite Materials,"** *Composite Reliability, ASTM STP 580,* American Society for Testing and Materials, 1975, pp. 215–226.

ABSTRACT: Two nondestructive evaluation test methods, radiography and ultrasonics, are examined for potential use in composite material characterization programs for composite structures subjected to either fatigue damage, foreign object damage, or environmental degradation. The principal goal of the work is to introduce semiquantitative test methods for measuring the size of damage zones and for defining the characteristic flaws within the zone with emphasis being placed on developing test techniques, test philosophies, and discussions on various signal processing procedures. Sample test results are presented along with a description of selected computer simulation signal processing studies.

KEY WORDS: composite materials, damage, degradation, nondestructive tests, tests, radiography, ultrasonics

The values and procedures of employing such nondestructive evaluation (NDE) procedures as tetrabromoethane (TBE) impregnation in radiographic inspections and transform analysis in ultrasonic processing are discussed for their potential use in studying damage characteristics in composite materials.

Basic elements of NDE test philosophy should be considered before proceeding with the technical details of the paper. The first item considers aspects of flaw characterization analysis, that of determining flaw type, shape, size, orientation, and location within a composite structure. The second problem is related to mechanics and the evaluation of the effects of the specific flaws on system and material performance. In other words, if a particular flaw is allowed to exist in the structure, will the flaw continue to grow beyond bound until failure occurs or will some flaw arrest mechanism occur in the structure? Will the flawed structure be able to resist foreign object damage, further cyclic loading, a saline cyclic environ-

---

[1] Associate professor of mechanical engineering, Drexel University, Philadelphia, Pa. 19104.
[2] Materials engineer, Air Force Materials Laboratory, Dayton, Ohio 45433.

ment, etc.? These problems can be studied by incorporating NDE procedures into the experimental testing programs being carried out in laboratory programs today. By selecting various fiber angles in a multi-ply structure, it is a well-known fact that the strength of a particular component can be adjusted to meet some particular design criterion. The relationship between flaw characteristics in the multi-ply structure and performance of the composite, however, is a fact not well understood at all. It is to this particular problem that NDE can play an important role in advancing the state of the art in composite material mechanics and analysis. These and similar topics considered in the composite challenge to NDE are discussed in a paper by Rose [1].[3] Emphasis in the paper is placed on discussing various test techniques and signal processing procedures and philosophies.

As indicated in the paper by Owston [2], nondestructive testing procedures are quite capable of detecting such flaws as porosity, resin-rich areas, large areas of delamination, and discrete cracking or extensive microcracking of the matrix and fiber. These features are detectable but not easily distinguished from one another. One purpose of this paper is therefore to introduce flaw characterization concepts that can be used to distinguish one flaw type from another. Suitable composite layups and design criteria can then be specified by the designer for resisting damage growth and degradation in a structure.

Several papers associated with ultrasonic analysis that are useful in this study have already been published. For example, work by Smith [3] describes a procedure for measuring wave speeds and elastic constant values in a composite. The work by Rose et al [4] presents an early attempt to understand the wave profile analysis and mode conversion problem associated with composite structures. The problem of ultrasonic wave interaction with specially shaped flaws and photoelastic composite models has been studied from a dynamic photoelastic point of view by Rose, Mortimer, and Chou [5]. In a paper by Rose, Carson, and Leidel [6], such flaw characterization procedures as signal shape and arrival time analysis, "C" scan testing, and frequency analysis have been discussed. Work on spectral analysis is presented by Whaley and Cook [7], and Gericke [8]. Much more work in data acquisition analysis and wave mechanics is necessary if we are to realize the fullest potential of ultrasonics in flaw characterization analysis.

Signal Processing Considerations

High-speed data acquisition and analysis are required to realize the fullest potential of nondestructive evaluation in composite materials research and analysis. A basic signal processing system is outlined in Fig. 1. Items listed

---

[3] The italic numbers in brackets refer to the list of references appended to this paper.

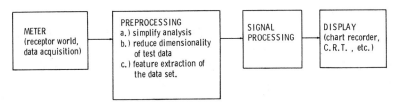

FIG. 1—*A basic signal processing system.*

in the figure are applicable to such optical measuring systems as radiographic TBE or amplitude time displays in ultrasonics. Preprocessing techniques, some of which are outlined by Rose and Meyer [9], can be developed by a large number of methods, from curve-fitting procedures to integral transform analysis. A large number of preprocessing techniques could be utilized once efficient instrumentation techniques and software routines are developed. It is not always feasible to record and store all of the data contained in an ultrasonic signal. It is also not possible to employ every possible data reduction procedure that may provide information characteristic of the particular flaw being studied. It is possible, however, to establish various preprocessing or transform techniques that provide certain feature extraction characteristics of the ultrasonic signal. The ultrasonic test data, when transformed to some new domain, may display features that are ordinarily missed in time-domain analysis. Preprocessing procedures, besides emphasizing certain features of the test data, also reduce the dimensionality of the total data set. For example, in Fourier transform analysis, only the Fourier coefficients have to be recorded.

Radiographic Technique

A newly developed NDE technique was demonstrated and resulted in a significant improvement for the radiographic evaluation of nonmetallic composites. This technique utilizes an X-ray opaque compound, tetrabromoethane, which is applied to the surface of the material prior to radiography. The technique is capable of detecting surface-connected defects and is very effective for use with porous materials. Since the compound can penetrate porous materials, defects appear as high film density areas on the radiographic film and can be readily detected.

The objective of the impregnation radiographic technique is to get the maximum amount of information from the test specimen into the radiograph. The approach is to impregnate the material with a solution of a higher atomic (Z) number compound; then the differential absorption of X-rays would improve the contrast on the resultant radiograph, and greater resolution of the structure of the material is obtained. The compound 1,1,2,2-tetrabromoethane was used for evaluation. Sample materials used were porous. The impregnation procedure involves four basic steps: (1) preparation of the specimen by removal of moisture and surface contamination; (2) the specimen is then soaked or sponged with the TBE solution for a period of time sufficient to allow penetration into cracks or pores; (3) X-raying the impregnated specimen; and (4) removal of the impregnant from the specimen.

Ultrasonic Technique

The feasibility of employing an ultrasonic spectroscopy technique for characterizing the "damage zone" was found to work quite well. Standard ultrasonic pulse echo techniques are not always applicable for thin test specimens because of the superposition effects of the front surface and intermediate or flaw echoes. Various transform signal preprocessing procedures, on the other hand, work quite well regardless of any pulse superposition or pulse dispersion or attenuation that occurs in the material. This spectroscopy approach appears promising as a preprocessing procedure since it provides significant feature extraction parameters as well as providing reduction in the dimensionality of the test data. A major problem with this approach, however, is the difficulty of specimen alignment and a lack of suitable high-speed data acquisition and signal processing instrumentation. Faster data analysis routines are certainly required. A detailed explanation of the spectroscopy experimental procedure is outlined in Ref *10*.

Test Results

Specimens considered for this study included standard tension-type coupons of fiberglass-epoxy and graphite-epoxy with simulated mechanical damage in the form of drilled centered holes. Each specimen was fatigue-cycled and the growth of defects monitored by the radiographic TBE and the ultrasonic techniques. This was accomplished by inspection of each specimen at designated intervals during the cycling tests. The radiographic test results are shown in Figs. 2, 3, and 4. Figures 2 through 4 are prints of radiographs showing the capability of the radiographic TBE technique for monitoring the initial damage due to machining and then the additional damage caused by the fatigue cycling of the materials. To illustrate the frequency signature approach in flaw characterization, typical ultrasonic tests conducted on a graphite-epoxy specimen with a 10-MHz Aerotech, ¼-in.-diameter beam and water-immersion technique are shown in Fig. 5 over a range of 0 to 20 MHz. The entire front surface and back surface echoes were gated in a pulse echo mode for Fourier transform analysis. Although the transducer characteristics are not ideal for this study (broader band over a wider frequency range), it is readily shown that substantial differences in the spectrum enable us to define the damage zone quite well. The radiographic and ultrasonic techniques produced similar damage zones for each specimen.

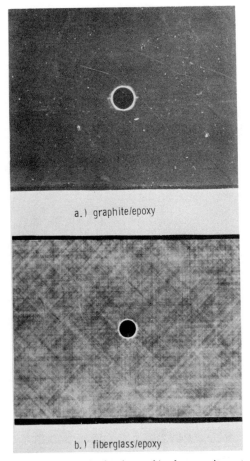

FIG. 2—*Radiographic reference results for the machined composite material test specimens.*

Preprocessing Suggestions

The photographs produced by the radiographic TBE process are certainly adequate for data analysis of the damage zone areas in the composite structures. In order to characterize flaws, however, that are not open to a surface (that is, internal cracking, porosity, etc.), it is desirable to supplement the damage zone details with ultrasonic inspection.

Suitable ultrasonic testing and characterization are rather tedious and time-consuming but do appear however to be quite useful as a research aid in composite materials testing programs. With use of proper analog-to-digital equipment and use of a minicomputer, reliable damage zone details can be mapped and characterized within a composite structure. Although much work in developing the required software is needed, several useful concepts worthy of consideration are outlined in the following paragraphs.

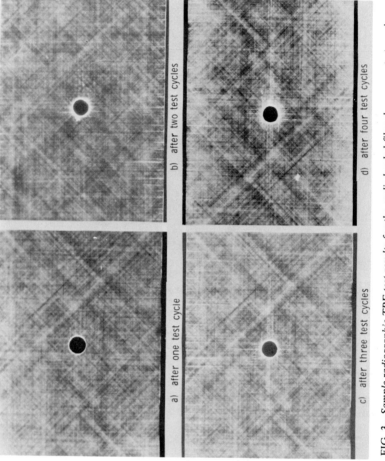

FIG. 3—Sample radiographic TBE test results for the cyclic loaded fiberglass-epoxy test specimen.

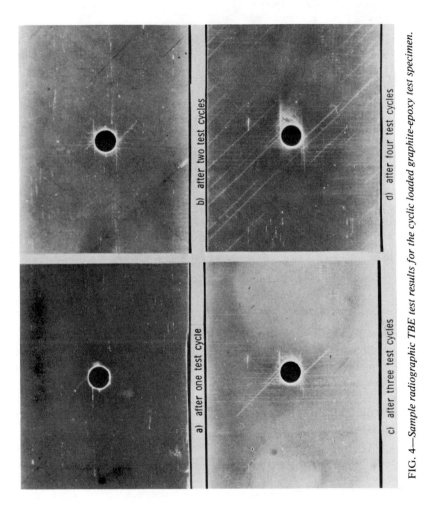

FIG. 4—*Sample radiographic TBE test results for the cyclic loaded graphite-epoxy test specimen.*

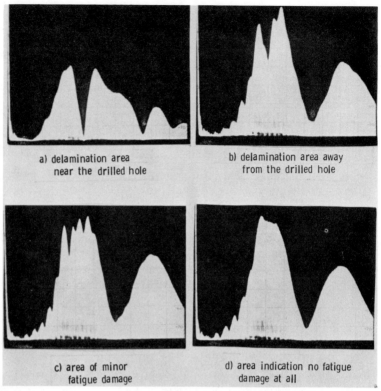

a) delamination area
near the drilled hole

b) delamination area away
from the drilled hole

c) area of minor
fatigue damage

d) area indication no fatigue
damage at all

FIG. 5—*Sample ultrasonic spectroscopy test results for the cyclic loaded graphite-epoxy test specimen.*

One method of signal analysis that is widely used today is the Fourier transformation. It is electronically implemented through the use of an analog spectrum analyzer. This device displays the power spectral density of the input time function. This representation, however, only offers one piece of smoothed information which is devoid of phase content and imposes limitations on theoretical studies useful in ultrasonic analysis. For instance, one cannot recover or "build" the original time function by inverse transformation since the phase angle is lost. Another disadvantage of this technique is the lack of variable options. That is, one cannot leave all parameters unchanged and vary only one (for instance, echo pulse width or pulse echo spacing). Figure 6 shows several computer-processed (FFT algorithm) Fourier transforms as well as several theoretical thickness measuring problems. Other signal processing concepts are discussed in the following paragraphs. A paper by Mast and Rose [11] illustrates various signature techniques of transform magnitude and phase analysis in flaw characterization. Conceptual extensions of the work in Ref 11 are outlined in the following.

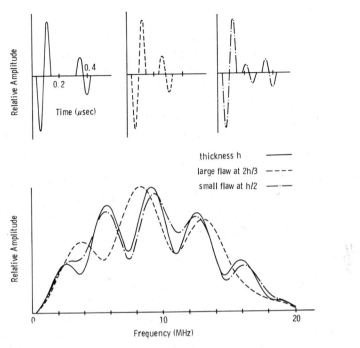

thickness h   ———
large flaw at 2h/3 — — — —
small flaw at h/2   —·—·—

FIG. 6—*Results for selected ultrasonic response functions from a composite material.*

Double Transform and Transform Difference Concepts

The FFT algorithm *[12]*, permitting one to bypass the analog method, provides more information about the time signals. All inputs and variables are now supplied by the programmer, with real-time signals as motivation for specific mathematical models. This routine calculates the real and imaginary parts of the Fourier transform, which are, in effect, the Fourier *a* and *b* coefficients of the time function. From these coefficients, the phase angle and amplitude of the transform may be calculated. The theorist now has more information at his disposal. Instead of one smoothed-out piece of information, he has therefore two pieces retaining phase information lost in the analog technique.

The information yield of the FFT algorithm, in conjunction with the concept of the Stieltjes transform (iterated Laplace transform), has led to two types of iterated Fourier transforms. The first type involves transforming the input time function, computing its power spectral density, and transforming the resulting density. Physically, this would be the effect of connecting two spectrum analyzers in tandem. Software routines could be developed that provide damage zone information as related to either the 1st or 2nd transform difference.

Computer-Processed, Double Fourier Phase-Angle Approach

The second type of iterated transform takes advantage of having both the *a* and *b* Fourier coefficients. These coefficients are now used to construct a new complex frequency function. This function is transformed, yielding a new *a* coefficient *A*, and a new *b* coefficient *B*. The "double" power density and the "double" phase angle are now computed. It has been found that the double power density computed from the *A* and *B* coefficients is the original time function amplified, rectified, and time reversed. It was of no value for the particular models studied in this work, but warrants further investigation using more complex models. The double phase angle, on the other hand, showed significant changes with respect to subtle variations in the original function. Although the power spectral density does not indicate any substantial change, the double phase angle did reveal rather significant differences and is worthy of further study.

Other Integral Transform Procedures

Related transforms that utilize the Fourier transform procedures often provide significant signal characterization. FFT in unison with the theoretical relations given in the *Bateman Manuscript Project [13]* facilitates investigation of the following transforms: Laplace, Mellin, and Hankel. Other transform signatures are outlined by Mast and Rose *[11]*.

Series Decomposition Concepts

Fourier series analysis has been widely used in signal analysis. It represents the decomposition of an arbitrary function into a sum of plane waves. In the theoretical fashion of the preceding discussion it might be noted that there exist series and transforms that decompose a function into sums of orthogonal polynomials and into sums of spherical waves *[14]*. These approaches might also prove useful in ultrasonic signal interpretation and processing.

Linear Systems Modeling for Computer Processing

An additional concept worthy of further study at the present time was introduced by Seydel and Frederick *[15]*. They modeled the transducer/test specimen situation as a linear system. Their inputs to this system were the digitized power spectrum of the echo return from a point source and the power spectrum of the echo return of an unknown target plus a phase reference function. The second "phase-tagged"[4] spectrum was divided point by point by the first spectrum. The result was then inverse-transformed to yield a new time function characteristic of the test specimen.

---

[4]Quotes ours (the authors').

Using this system idea as motivation, but doing things mathematically rather than through analog instrumentation, one can reconstruct a test specimen time model using FFT alone. Since FFT retains phase information, there is no need for "phase-tagging." The forward and inverse transformations can be carried out by FFT, leaving only the point-by-point spectral division and the plot routine external to the FFT subroutine. Studies along this line of approach are presently being investigated.

Concluding Remarks

The nondestructive evaluation procedures presented in this work can be used to study materials and mechanics problems of composite material fatigue damage, foreign object damage, and saline cycling degradation. Accurate evaluations of the damage growth in cyclic fatigue allow us to grasp such concepts as crack arrest mechanisms in composite materials, optimization procedures for angle-ply layups, and the effects of various processing flaws or in-service environments on material performance. The experimental techniques also allow us to evaluate the extent of damage in a composite structure. Optimization procedures for such items as impact resistance as a function of angle-ply layup can therefore be assisted with radiographic and ultrasonic test procedures. Various signal processing concepts have been introduced for analyzing the echo separation, superposition, and dispersion problems of ultrasonic wave interaction within a composite material.

A number of experimental test techniques and philosophies have been studied for the purpose of understanding the failure modes and mechanics of composite materials. As a result of these efforts, a number of fundamental, significant advances have been made. For example, sample results indicate that flaws within a composite are formed adjacent to such mechanical flaws as drilled holes. The flaws are often termed as a "damage zone." The damage zone is defined as a region containing local crack crazing and delaminations. This damage zone appears to be the dominant characteristic dimension of interest in the analysis of composite fracture. The challenge is to develop nondestructive tests that can determine the size of the damage zone and to define the characteristic nature of flaws within the zone.

Acknowledgments

This work is partially supported by the Air Force Office of Scientific Research, Arlington, Va. under grant number AFOSR-73-2480 A. Thanks are also given to Michael Avioli of Drexel and Phil Mast of the Naval Research Laboratory for their interest and technical discussions.

References

[1] Rose, J. L., "The Composite Challenge for NDE," *Proceedings,* National Materials Advisory Board Workshop, Feb. 1974.

[2] Owston, C. N., *British Journal of Nondestructive Testing,* Jan. 1973, pp. 2–11.

[3] Smith, R. E., *Journal of Applied Physics,* Vol. 43, No. 6, June 1972.

[4] Rose, J. L., Wang, A. S. D., and Deska, E., *Journal of Composite Materials,* Vol. 8, Oct. 1974.

[5] Rose, J. L., Mortimer, R. W., and Chou, P. C., *Materials Evaluation,* Vol. 30, No. 11,

[6] Rose, J. L., Carson, J. M., and Leidel, D. J. in *Analysis of the Test Methods for High Modulus Fibers and Composites, ASTM STP 521,* American Society for Testing and Materials, 1973, pp. 311–325.

[7] Whaley, H. L. and Cook, K. V., *Materials Evaluation,* March 1970.

[8] Gericke, O. R., *Journal of the Acoustical Society of America,* Vol. 35, March 1963.

[9] Rose, J. L. and Meyer, P. A., *British Journal of Nondestructive Testing,* Vol. 16, No. 4, July 1974, pp. 97–106.

[10] Rose, J. L. and Raisch, J. W., *Materials Evaluation,* Vol. 39, Dec. 1974.

[11] Mast, P. W. and Rose, J. L., "Signature Techniques for Defect Characterization" *Proceedings,* IEEE Ultrasonics Symposium, Milwaukee, Wis., Nov. 1974.

[12] Brighan, E. Oran, *The Fast Fourier Transform,* Prentice-Hall Inc., Englewood Cliffs, N.J., 1974.

[13] "Tables of Integral Transforms," *Bateman Manuscript Project,* Vol. 1, p. 4; Vol. 2, p. 213, McGraw-Hill, New York, 1954.

[14] John, Fritz, "Planes Waves and Spherical Means Applied to Parital Differential Equations," *Interscience,* New York, 1955.

[15] Seydel, J. A., and Frederick, J. R., *Materials Evaluation,* Vol. 31, Nov. 1973, pp. 223–228.

Environment

T. R. Guess[1] and B. L. Butler[1]

Optimization of the Thermal Shock Resistance of Carbon-Carbon Composites*

REFERENCE: Guess, T. R. and Butler, B. L., **"Optimization of the Thermal Shock Resistance of Carbon-Carbon Composites,"** *Composite Reliability, ASTM STP 580,* American Society for Testing and Materials, 1975, pp. 229–246.

ABSTRACT: A three-dimensional rule of mixtures model was developed to calculate the room-temperature thermal and mechanical properties of carbon-carbon composites whose constituents have anisotropic properties. The model was used, along with the properties of different carbon fibers and pyrocarbon matrices, to determine the fiber-matrix combination, constituent volume fractions, and constituent orientations that maximize expected composite thermal shock resistance of heat shields. The results indicate that a composite having a low volume fraction of high-modulus carbon fibers, arranged in a 3D array, and coated with anisotropic, heat-treated pyrocarbon matrix, will have the maximum thermal shock resistance. Confidence in the model was established by good agreement between model predictions and experimental data on actual carbon-carbon composites.

KEY WORDS: carbon, composite materials, thermal shock, mechanical properties, carbon fibers, pyrocarbon matrix, models, reentry materials

Among the many graphites and composites that are being developed and evaluated as nosetip and heat-shield materials for reentry vehicles are carbon fiber/carbon matrix composites *[1–5]*.[2] Two of these composites, CVD/Felt (fibrous carbon felt substrate with a chemical vapor deposited (CVD) pyrocarbon matrix) and CVD/FW (helical-wound carbon fiber substrate with a CVD pyrocarbon matrix), have been successfully fabricated and flown as heat shields and are considered state-of-the-art materials. However, improved materials will be required to survive the thermal shock associated with more severe reentry conditions.

*This work was supported by the United States Atomic Energy Commission.
[1] Staff member, Composite Research and Development Department, Sandia Laboratories, Albuquerque, N. Mex. 87115.
[2] The italic numbers in brackets refer to the list of references appended to this paper.

The thermal and mechanical properties of a composite can be tailored within limits imposed by the properties, volume fractions, and orientations of the individual constituents in the composite. Wide ranges of properties are available in commercial carbon (graphite) fibers and the CVD pyrocarbon matrices [6]. For future material development, it would be helpful to have a method of selecting the proper fiber-matrix combination to use and then to optimize their volume fractions and orientations to maximize the thermal shock resistance of the composite.

A qualitative method used to compare the thermal shock resistance of isotropic materials, subjected to a temperature gradient, is the so-called thermal shock factor (TSF)

$$\text{TSF} = \frac{K\sigma}{\alpha E} \tag{1}$$

where K is the thermal conductivity (W/mK), σ the ultimate tensile strength (kN/m^2), α the coefficient of thermal expansion (CTE) ($m/m/K$), and E the modulus of elasticity (GN/m^2). Those materials exhibiting the highest numerical values of TSF are usually more resistant to fracture from thermal shock. Because carbon-carbon composites are anisotropic, the applicability of Eq 1 for ranking them as to their thermal shock resistance is debatable. However, we feel that Eq 1 can be used as the preliminary step in evaluating carbon-carbon composites if the thermal and mechanical properties of the composite are properly selected. Heat shields are generally modeled as thin-walled axisymmetric shells. For the present study it is assumed the heat shield is subjected to uniform (independent of longitudinal or circumferential position) heat flux that produces a temperature gradient through the shell thickness (radial direction). Therefore, K must be the radial-direction thermal conductivity and σ, E, and α must be in-plane properties, that is, in the longitudinal or circumferential direction.

The purposes of this paper are (1) to develop a micromechanics model for determining average room-temperature properties of carbon-carbon composites having anisotropic constituents; (2) to utilize the model for selecting the proper fiber-matrix combination from among available constituents; and (3) to optimize their volume fractions so that the calculated TSF of the resulting carbon-carbon composite is maximized.

Composite Model

The model consists of a unit cell of filaments and matrix oriented in three orthogonal directions as schematically illustrated in Fig. 1a, where the x-y plane is assumed to be the plane of the heat shield and z is the radial direction. A three-dimensional (3D) model was chosen so that the

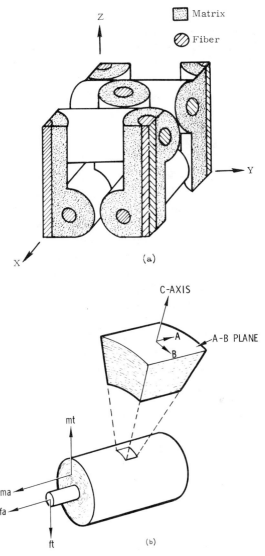

FIG. 1—*Schematics of* (a) *the 3D orthogonal unit cell and* (b) *a carbon fiber coated with CVD pyrocarbon matrix. The matrix crystallographic orientation and the axial,* a, *and transverse,* t, *directions of both fiber,* f, *and matrix,* m, *are designated.*

effect of having fibers and matrix oriented in the radial direction could be evaluated.

The average properties of the 3D composite will be approximated by extending basic micromechanics concepts and equations for a two-component unidirectional composite to the more complex 3D model. The approach will be, first, to list the equations for the axial and transverse properties of a two-component composite; secondly, to indicate whether the two components are physically in a parallel or series arrangement; and, finally, to derive the expression for the average property of the 3D composite using the basic equations and the physical arrangement of each constituent in the 3D unit cell.

Definitions of the nomenclature are needed for clarity. The total volume of the unit cell in Fig. 1a is

$$V = V_{fx} + V_{mx} + V_{fy} + V_{my} + V_{fz} + V_{mz} + V_p = 1.0 \qquad (2)$$

where V is the volume fraction; f and m denote fiber and matrix, respectively; x, y, and z denote the axial orientation of the constituent in the x-direction, y-direction, and z-direction, respectively; and p denotes porosity. Thus V_{fx} is the volume fraction of fiber oriented in the x-direction, V_p is the total volume fraction of pores, etc.

Since carbon fibers and CVD pyrocarbon matrices are anisotropic, the properties are designated in such a way as to denote whether it is an axial or transverse property and to denote the orientation of the constituent as shown in Fig. 1b. For example, the axial modulus of the matrix deposited on the x-oriented fiber is designated E_{ma}^{x}. Likewise, the transverse thermal conductivity of the fiber oriented in the z-direction is designated K_{ft}^{z}. The superscript denotes the orientation of the fiber or matrix, and subscripts a and t denote the axial and transverse directions, respectively.

Thermal Conductivity, K

The average radial (z-direction) thermal conductivity K of the composite is needed for the TSF calculation. The axial conductivity of a two-component filamentary composite is given by the micromechanics expression [7,8]

$$K_a = \frac{1}{V_f + V_m} (K_{fa}V_f + K_{ma}V_m) \qquad (3)$$

and the transverse conductivity [8] is given by

$$K_t = \frac{(V_f + V_m)}{\dfrac{V_f}{K_{ft}} + \dfrac{V_m}{K_{mt}}} \qquad (4)$$

Note that Eq 3 applies for a parallel arrangement of the components and Eq 4 for a series arrangement, as shown in Fig. 2a and b, respectively.

The radial conductivity K of the 3D composite unit cell is given by an analysis of the schematic in Fig. 2c, which shows the physical arrange-

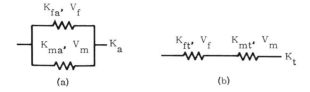

(a)   (b)

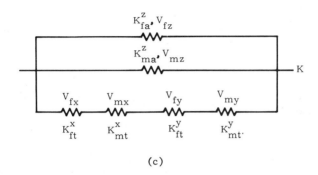

(c)

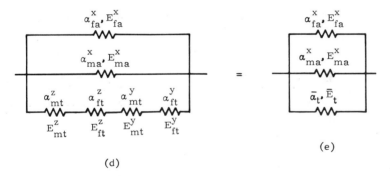

(d)   (e)

FIG. 2—(a) *Parallel and* (b) *series arrangement of constituents for a two-component composite.* (c) *Network illustrating the physical arrangement of constituents affecting the radial thermal conductivity of a 3D composite.* (d) *Physical arrangement of constituents affecting in-plane (x-direction) CTE of the 3D model.* (e) *An equivalent network for composite CTE.*

ment of all the constituents. The particular constituent represented by each element of the schematic is denoted by the property and its volume fraction. The physical arrangement of Fig. 2c was constructed from an examination of Fig. 1a which revealed that the z-direction heat conduction paths are through three parallel elements: (1) the z-oriented fiber, (2) the z-oriented matrix, and (3) the element consisting of a series arrangement of the x- and y-oriented fibers and matrices.

Using expanded forms of Eqs 3 and 4, to allow for more than two components

$$K = \frac{1}{V} \left[K_{fa}{}^z V_{fz} + K_{ma}{}^z V_{mz} \right.$$

$$\left. + \frac{(V_{fx} + V_{mx} + V_{fy} + V_{my})}{\dfrac{V_{fx}}{K_{ft}{}^x} + \dfrac{V_{mx}}{K_{mt}{}^x} + \dfrac{V_{fy}}{K_{ft}{}^y} + \dfrac{V_{my}}{K_{mt}{}^y}} (V_{fx} + V_{mx} + V_{fy} + V_{my}) \right] \quad (5)$$

From Eq 1, $V = 1.0$; thus Eq 5 becomes

$$K = K_{fa}{}^z V_{fz} + K_{ma}{}^z V_{mz} + \frac{(V_{fx} + V_{mx} + V_{fy} + V_{my})^2}{\dfrac{V_{fx}}{K_{ft}{}^x} + \dfrac{V_{mx}}{K_{mt}{}^x} + \dfrac{V_{fy}}{K_{ft}{}^y} + \dfrac{V_{my}}{K_{mt}{}^y}} \quad (6)$$

Equation 6 expresses the average radial conductivity of the 3D composite unit cell in terms of the constituent properties, volume fractions, and orientations. Note that if $V_{fz} = V_{mz} = 0$, Eq 6 can be used to calculate the radial (z-direction) conductivity of a 2D crossplied composite.

Modulus, E

The in-plane modulus, E (in the x-direction or the y-direction), of the 3D model is derived in the same manner as described for the conductivity. The axial modulus of a two-component composite (parallel arrangement) is given by *[9]*

$$E_a = \frac{1}{(V_f + V_m)} (E_{fa} V_f + E_{ma} V_m) \quad (7)$$

and the transverse modulus of the same composite (series arrangement) is approximated by *[10]*

$$E_t = \frac{V_f + V_m}{\dfrac{V_f}{E_{ft}} + \dfrac{V_m}{E_{mt}}} \quad (8)$$

Note that Eqs 7 and 8 are the same as Eqs 3 and 4 except that E replaces K. Also, a schematic of the physical arrangement for E in the x-direction would be the same as Fig. 2c if the z and x subscripts were interchanged and E replaced K. Therefore E is given by replacing K with E and interchanging z and x in Eq 6; that is

$$E = E_{fa}{}^x V_{fx} + E_{ma}{}^x V_{mx} + \frac{(V_{fz} + V_{mz} + V_{fy} + V_{my})^2}{\dfrac{V_{fz}}{E_{ft}{}^z} + \dfrac{V_{mz}}{E_{mt}{}^z} + \dfrac{V_{fy}}{E_{ft}{}^y} + \dfrac{V_{my}}{E_{mt}{}^y}} \qquad (9)$$

An expression of composite modulus in the y-direction can be obtained by interchanging x and y in Eq 9. It should be noted that for carbon-carbon composites E_{fa} is taken to be the modulus of an unimpregnated strand instead of the actual fiber modulus [11].

Coefficient of Thermal Expansion, α

The micromechanics expression for the coefficient of thermal expansion (CTE) in the axial direction (parallel arrangement) of a 2D filamentary composite is given by [12]

$$\alpha_a = \frac{E_{fa} V_f \alpha_{fa} + E_{ma} V_m \alpha_{ma}}{E_{fa} V_f + E_{ma} V_m} \qquad (10)$$

and the CTE in the transverse direction (series arrangement) is [12]

$$\alpha_t = \frac{1}{(V_f + V_m)} (1 + \nu_f) V_f \alpha_{ft} + (1 + \nu_m) V_m \alpha_{mt} - (\nu_f V_f + \nu_m V_m) \alpha_a \qquad (11)$$

where ν is Poisson's ratio. Because the Poisson's ratios of graphite fibers and the CVD carbon matrix are not available, the assumption is made that $\nu \ll 1$, and Eq 11 reduces to

$$\alpha_t = \frac{1}{(V_f + V_m)} (\alpha_{ft} V_f + \alpha_{mt} V_m) \qquad (12)$$

The in-plane CTE of the composite α in the x-direction can be obtained from an analysis of the schematic in Fig. 2d, which is replaced by its equivalent in Fig. 2e to help visualize the solution.

Using Eq 12 for the effective transverse CTE of a series arrangement

$$\bar{\alpha}_t = \frac{(\alpha_{ft}{}^z V_{fz} + \alpha_{mt}{}^z V_{mz} + \alpha_{ft}{}^y V_{fy} + \alpha_{mt}{}^y V_{my})}{(V_{fz} + V_{mz} + V_{fy} + V_{my})} \qquad (13)$$

and, using Eq 8, the effective transverse modulus of a series arrangement is

$$\overline{E}_t = \frac{(V_{fz} + V_{mz} + V_{fy} + V_{my})}{\dfrac{V_{fz}}{E_{ft}{}^z} + \dfrac{V_{mz}}{E_{mt}{}^z} + \dfrac{V_{fy}}{E_{ft}{}^y} + \dfrac{V_{my}}{E_{mt}{}^y}} \tag{14}$$

Therefore, from Fig. 2e and Eq 10, the composite CTE in the x-direction becomes

$$\alpha = \frac{E_{fa}{}^x V_{fx}\alpha_{fa}{}^x + E_{ma}{}^x V_{mx}\alpha_{ma}{}^x + \overline{E}_t\overline{\alpha}_t(V_{fz} + V_{mz} + V_{fy} + V_{my})}{E_{fa}{}^x V_{fx} + E_{ma}{}^x V_{mx} + \overline{E}_t(V_{fz} + V_{mz} + V_{fy} + V_{my})} \tag{15}$$

where $\overline{\alpha}_t$ and $\overline{E}_t$ are given by Eqs 13 and 14, respectively. The composite CTE in the y-direction can be obtained by interchanging x and y in Eq 15.

Strength, σ

A lower bound on the in-plane tensile strength of the composite in the x-direction is approximated by

$$\sigma_x = (E_{fa}{}^x V_{fx} + E_{ma}{}^x V_{ma})\varepsilon_{ult} \tag{16}$$

Equation 16 results from the assumption that only the fiber-matrix combination oriented parallel to the load direction (x-axis in this example) supports load at failure. That is, the fiber-matrix combinations normal to the x-axis have failed prior to the ultimate strain (ε_{ult}) and do not contribute significantly to the ultimate strength. These assumptions are thought reasonable because of the low (<0.1 percent) strain to failure of carbon-carbon lamina loaded transverse to the filaments, whereas ε_{ult} of many carbon-carbon composites loaded parallel to the fibers is in the range of 0.3 to 0.5 percent [13]. Therefore, for the purposes of estimating strengths by Eq 16, it is assumed that $\varepsilon_{ult} = 0.3$ percent for all cases regardless of the constituents or their volume fractions.

Note that the assumption of constant strain to failure for calculating strength in Eq 16 does not imply that the σ/E ratio from Eq 1 is a constant. As defined by Eq 9, E is the initial elastic modulus and has contributions from the constituents oriented normal to the load direction but, as discussed previously, the effective modulus in Eq 16 depends only on the fiber/matrix combination in the load direction.

Fiber and Matrix Properties

Data on four fibers covering the range of properties available in carbon fibers and two pyrocarbon matrices in the as-deposited and heat-treated (graphitized) conditions were utilized in this study, Table 1. The four fibers were Carborundum Company's CY2-5 and Union Carbide's Thornel 16, Thornel 25, and Thornel 50 (Th-16, Th-25 and Th-50, respec-

TABLE 1—*Mechanical and thermal properties of carbon fibers and pyrocarbon matrices.*

	Fibers				
Property	CY2-5	Th-16	Th-25	Th-50	Source
$K_{fa}{}^a$ (W/mK)	25	42	88	122	Ref *15*, p. 10
K_{ft} (*W/mK*)	12.6	12.6	12.6	12.6	isotropic value
$E_{fa}{}^b$ (GN/m^2)	27.6	75.9	152	200	Ref *11*, p. 11
E_{ft} (GN/m^2)	10.4	10.4	10.4	10.4	isotropic value
$\alpha_{fa}{}^c$ (m/m/K)	3.9×10^{-6}	2.4×10^{-6}	1.0×10^{-6}	0.54×10^{-6}	Ref *16*
α_{ft} (m/m/K)	4×10^{-6}	6×10^{-6}	9×10^{-6}	12×10^{-6}	Ref *17*, p. 48

	Matrix				
	Rough Laminar		Isotropic		
Property	AD^d	HT^d	AD	HT	Source
a-b Plane					
K_{ma} (W/mK)	398	994^e	180	450	Ref *18*, Fig. 1
E_{ma} (GN/m^2)	34.5	34.5	27.6	26.2	Refs *14, 19*
α_{ma} (m/m/K)	1.5×10^{-6}	1.2×10^{-6}	3×10^{-6}	2.3×10^{-6}	Ref *14*, p. 26
c-Direction					
K_{mt} (W/mK)	2.3	4.6	5.1	23	Refs *14, 20*
E_{mt} (GN/m^2)	10.4	9.0	10.4	9.0	estimate
α_{mt} (m/m/K)	4×10^{-6}	4×10^{-6}	4×10^{-6}	4×10^{-6}	Ref *16*

[a] All conductivities are room-temperature values.
[b] Fiber axial moduli are values for unimpregnated strands; see Ref *11*.
[c] Secant value: 300 to 1500 K.
[d] AD and HT denote as-deposited and heat-treated (3270 K) conditions, respectively.
[e] K_{ma} (HT) = 2.5 K_{ma} (AD); estimated from CVD/Felt data, Ref *14*.

tively) and the two matrices were the rough laminar and isotropic[3] CVD pyrocarbon.

Note from the data in Table 1 that if a particular fiber or matrix is selected as a constituent to use in the model, its entire set of properties must be used. That is, an individual property of a constituent is not independent. Take, for example, carbon fibers that are typically identified by their axial modulus. Not only does the modulus change when going from one fiber to another, but so do the other properties. Likewise the matrix properties are controlled by its microstructure, which in turn are controlled by deposition conditions and heat treatment *[6]*.

Results and Discussion

For the numerical phase of this study, the constituents oriented in the *x*-direction were set equivalent to those oriented in the *y*-direction because

---

[3] The terms rough laminar and isotropic are derived from the appearance of the pyrocarbon matrix under polarized light. See Ref *14* for a more complete description.

in-plane biaxial stresses are developed in a heat shield during reentry. It makes sense, when considering thermal stresses as the only loading, for the material to have identical properties in the x- and y-directions. In addition, the ratios of fiber-to-matrix volume fraction in each direction were set equivalent, that is, $V_{fx}/V_{mx} = V_{fy}/V_{my} = V_{fz}/V_{mz}$.

A simple computer program was utilized to calculate the composite properties (based on the 3D model and the constituent properties listed in Table 1) and the TSF's of many potential composites. For brevity, the following discussion will be limited to the most significant results.

Fiber-Matrix Combination

The effects of constituent properties on the TSF of a carbon-carbon composite are evident from the numerical results in Table 2. The data are for the situations of equivalent fiber volume fractions in each axis ($V_{fx} = V_{fy} = V_{fz} = 0.05$), equivalent matrix volume fractions ($V_{mx} = V_{my} = V_{mz} = 0.217$), and 20 percent porosity. Only the combination of constituents was changed. The reason for presenting results for these particular volume fractions is discussed later.

The results in Table 2 show (1) for a fixed matrix, the composite TSF increases as the fiber modulus increases; (2) for a fixed fiber, the composite TSF increases as the anisotropy of the matrix microstructure increases from isotropic to rough laminar microstructure; and (3) the composite TSF increases when the matrix is heat-treated. Thus the model indicates that a composite of high-modulus fibers and a heat-treated, rough laminar pyrocarbon matrix combination is desirable.

TABLE 2—*Fiber-matrix combinations investigated and calculated TSF (TSF for condition of* $V_{fx} = V_{fy} = V_{fz} = 0.05$; $V_{mx} = V_{my} = V_{mz} = 0.217$; *and* $V_p = 0.20$*).*

	Matrix			
	Rough Laminar		Isotropic	
Fiber	AD[a]	HT[a]	AD	HT
CY2-5 (x, y, z)	62[b]	176	23	61
Th-16 (x, y, z)	69	194	27	68
Th-25 (x, y, z)	91	250	38	100
Th-50 (x, y, z)	106	291	45	122
Th-50 (x, y) ⎱ [c] CY2-5 (z) ⎰	...	312	...	128

[a] AD and HT denote as-deposited and heat-treated (3270 K) conditions, respectively.
[b] The units of the TSF's are kW/m.
[c] The fibers used with the HT isotropic matrix to compare with the AVCO 3D material (Table 4).

Effect of Fiber Properties

A close look at the model calculations will help determine why high-modulus fibers produce composites with higher TSF's than low-modulus fibers. The effect of fiber properties on the TSF of a 3D composite is illustrated in Fig. 3, which shows TSF as a function of equivalent fiber volume fractions ($V_{fx} = V_{fy} = V_{fz}$) for composites of low-modulus fibers (CY2-5) and high-modulus fibers (Th-50). Since the same matrix is used for both composites, the difference in the curves results from differences in fiber properties.

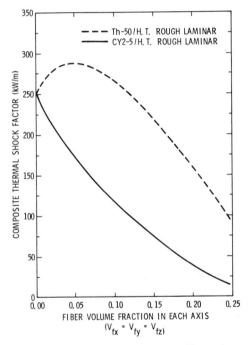

FIG. 3—*Model calculations of composite TSF versus fiber volume fraction. The composite porosity was assumed to be 20 percent.*

The fiber properties have little effect on composite conductivity, when compared with their effect on composite CTE and σ/E ratio; see Figs. 4, 5, and 6. The composite CTE is a function of both the modulus and CTE of the constituents (Eq 15). Recall that the fiber axial CTE decreases as its axial modulus increases, Table 1. Therefore, the inherent combination of high modulus and low CTE is the important fiber property that causes the TSF of the Th-50 fiber composite to be greater than the TSF of the CY2-5 composite as illustrated in Fig. 3.

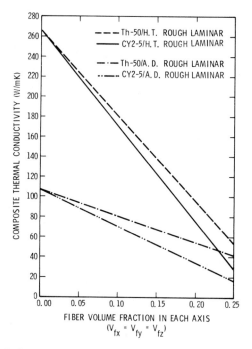

FIG. 4—*Model calculations of composite thermal conductivity versus fiber volume fraction for the case of 20 percent porosity.*

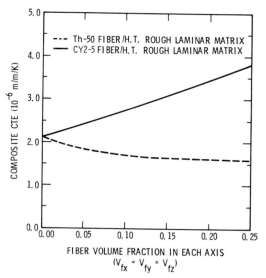

FIG. 5—*Model calculations of composite coefficient of thermal expansion versus fiber volume fraction for the case of 20 percent porosity.*

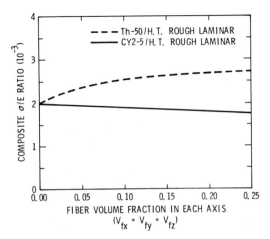

FIG. 6—*Model calculations of composite o/E ratio versus fiber volume fraction for the case of 20 percent porosity.*

Effect of Matrix Properties and Heat Treatment

It was shown that fiber properties have very little effect on composite conductivity K, Fig. 4. However, the curves in Fig. 4 show that K is a strong function of matrix microstructure and volume fraction. Regardless of the fiber-matrix combination, K decreases rapidly as the fiber volume fraction increases (or conversely, as the volume fraction of radially oriented matrix, V_{fz}, decreases). This occurs because the matrix conductivity in the *a-b* plane, K_{ma}, is much higher than the axial conductivity of the fibers, K_{fa}, Table 1, and thus controls the composite thermal conductivity. Inspection of the matrix properties presented in Table 1 reveals that K_{ma} is the only matrix property that is strongly dependent on matrix microstructure. The K_{ma} value increases as the matrix microstructure goes from isotropic to anisotropic (rough laminar) and increases even more with heat-treatment.

Optimum Volume Fractions

Once the fiber-matrix combination has been selected, optimization of the relative volume fractions and orientations is needed to maximize the potential TSF of the composite. The curves in Fig. 3 clearly indicate that low fiber volume fractions $V_{fz} = V_{fy} = V_{fz} = 0.03$ to 0.07) optimize the TSF for composites of high-modulus fibers and heat-treated, rough laminar pyrocarbon matrix.

The shape and magnitude of the curves in Fig. 3 are due to the competing effects of the composite thermal conductivity, CTE, and o/E, Figs. 4, 5, and 6, in the expression for composite TSF, Eq 1. For high-modulus fiber composites, both α and K decreases while σ/E increases with increasing fiber volume, and the competing effects produce the maximum in the TSF curve. However, in the low-modulus fiber materials, α increases while both K and σ/E decrease, and these trends cause the TSF of the composite to decrease continuously over the entire range of fiber volumes, Fig. 3.

The data presented earlier in Table 2 were for composites having low fiber volumes ($V_{fx} = V_{fy} = V_{fz} = 0.05$) because this study indicates that low fiber volume optimizes TSF values. Additional results indicate that changing V_{fz} to values greater than V_{fx} and V_{fy} did not significantly increase the composite TSF, whereas reducing V_{fz} to values less than V_{fx} and V_{fy} decreased composite TSF.

The results presented have been for the condition of fibers oriented in each of three orthogonal directions. However, a comparison can be made with a crossply 2D composite by setting $V_{fz} = V_{mz} = 0.0$ in the model. Results of TSF calculations for CY2-5 and Th-50 fibers in the heat-treated rough laminar matrix for both the 3D and 2D conditions are listed in Table 3. The calculated TSF's of the 3D composites are much greater than TSF's of the 2D composites. These comparisons clearly illustrate the importance of having fiber-matrix combinations oriented in the radial direction for the purpose of increasing composite thermal conductivity in that direction.

TABLE 3—*Comparison of calculated TSF values for the 3D orthogonal case (*$V_{fx} = V_{fy} = V_{fz}$*) and the 2D case (*$V_{fx} = V_{fy}$, $V_{fz} = 0$*). Porosity set at* $V_p = 0.20$.

	TSF (kW/m)	
Fiber Volume Fraction	CY2-5 Fibers[a]	Th-50 Fibers[a]
3D; $V_{fx} = V_{fy} = V_{fz}$[b]		
0.00	250	250
0.05	181	288
0.10	117	267
0.15	74	218
0.20	40	157
2D; $V_{fx} = V_{fy}$, $V_{fz} = 0$[c]		
0.00	5.1	5.1
0.05	4.9	7.2
0.10	4.7	9.0
0.15	4.6	10.8
0.20	4.6	12.8

[a] Case of heat-treated rough laminar matrix.
[b] $V_{fx}/V_{mx} = V_{fy}/V_{my} = V_{fz}/V_{mz}$.
[c] $V_{fx}/V_{mx} = V_{fy}/V_{my}$; $V_{mz} = 0.0$.

Comparison with Experiment

The model has been used to provide insights into the selection of the constituents and their volume fractions for maximizing the TSF of carbon-carbon composites. However, the reliability of the model must be evaluated before it can be used with confidence.

Comparisons are made with three Sandia materials: (1) CVD/FW filament-wound composite consisting of CY2-5 filaments at a ±45 deg helical angle and an isotropic CVD pyrocarbon matrix in the heat-treated condition; (2) CVD/Felt consisting of low-modulus fibers and rough laminar matrix; and (3) CVD/PAN Felt consisting of high-modulus PAN fibers and a rough laminar matrix, and with Avco Corporation's 3D cylinders consisting of high-modulus graphite fibers in the x- and y-directions and low-modulus fibers in the radial direction and a pyrolized organic matrix. These results are listed in Table 4. Note that calculations for Table 4 are made based on actual modeling of the real materials; for example, $V_{fx} = V_{fy} = V_{fz}$ does not hold except for the CVD/Felt.

It is reassuring to observe that the model correctly predicts the ranking or trends of composite TSF of all materials considered. Note that the composite having the greatest experimental TSF, the CVD/PAN Felt, has high-modulus fibers in a pseudo 3D array in low volume fractions and a heat-treated rough laminar matrix—the combination suggested by the model. The results in Table 4 also indicate that a filament-wound 2D composite (CVD/FW) considered in this study has far less potential than the 3D composites. No matrix is oriented in the radial direction of the filament-wound composites; thus composite thermal conductivity in the radial direction is greatly reduced.

A word of caution is needed at this point. A more complete thermal stress analysis, coupled with experimental data, is necessary to substantiate the results of this study in a more quantitative way. Room-temperature data were used with no attempt to incorporate the effects of temperature on the properties of the constituents. Therefore, it cannot be assumed that the TSF values at reentry temperatures will have the same relative ranking or absolute values that are calculated for room temperature. Nor can it be assumed that the actual thermal stress resistance will rank the same as the TSF. However, the 3D model presented has provided valuable insights into the important constituent variables that control the room temperature TSF of carbon-carbon composites.

Summary and Conclusions

A 3D micromechanics model was developed to predict the room-temperature thermal and mechanical properties of carbon-carbon composites. The model was used first to select the fiber-matrix combination, and

TABLE 4—Comparison of experimental and predicted room-temperature properties of four carbon-carbon composites ($N_{fx}/V_{mx} = V_{fy}/V_{my} = V_{fz}/V_{mz}$ for all calculated properties).

Type of data	K, W/mK	σ, MN/m²	E, GN/m²	α(300–1500 K), m/m/K	TSF, kW/m	Ref
CVD/FW (±45°)						
Experimental[a]	12–18	35–48	14.5–17.3	3.6×10^{-6}–4.3×10^{-6}	5.6–16.6	[3,21]
Calculated[a]	13	32	14.6	3.4	8.5	This study
CVD/Felt						
Experimental[b]	125–209	15–27	5.9–13.2	3.6–6.0	24–265	[3,21]
Calculated[b]	220	27	13.7	2.4	181	This study
AVCO 3D						
Experimental[c]	38–45	100–164	93–99	1.0–1.1	35–79	[22,23]
Calculated[c]	45	127	48	1.5	79	This study
CVD/PAN Felt						
Experimental[d]	111	21	7.2	2.3	141	[21]
Calculated[d]	168	43	18.6	1.8	216	This study
Experimental[f]	135	87[e]	15.9[e]	0.6–1.8	410–1231	[24]
Calculated[f]	202	79	29.0	1.3	423	This study

[a]CY2-5 fibers; HT isotropic matrix; $V_{fx} = V_{fy} = 0.20$; $V_{fz} = 0.0$; $V_p = 0.20$.
[b]CY2-5 fibers; HT rough laminar matrix; $V_{fx} = V_{fy} = 0.05$; $V_{fz} = 0.20$.
[c]Th-50 fibers in x- and y-directions; CY2-5 fibers in z-direction; HT isotropic matrix; $V_{fx} = V_{fy} = 0.20$; $V_{fz} = 0.15$; $V_p = 0.20$.
[d]Th-50 fibers; HT rough laminar matrix; $V_{fx} = V_{fy} = 0.033$; $V_{fz} = 0.024$; $V_p = 0.30$.
[e]Flexural rather than tensile property.
[f]Th-50 fibers; HT rough laminar matrix; $V_{fx} = 0.054$; $V_{fy} = 0.012$; $V_{fz} = 0.024$; $V_p = 0.17$; values of α, E, and α listed are the calculated x-direction properties.

secondly to optimize their volume fractions and orientations so as to maximize the composite thermal shock resistance. In addition, confidence in the model was achieved by comparing model predictions with actual experimental data. The major conclusions of this study are:

1. High-modulus carbon fibers and anisotropic, heat-treated pyrocarbon matrices are the constituents that result in increased composite TSF.

2. Once the fiber-matrix combination has been selected, low fiber volumes will maximize the TSF of composites having fibers equally oriented in the three orthogonal directions.

3. Three-dimensional carbon-carbon composites will have greater TSF's than 2D composites.

4. The model correctly predicts the TSF ranking of real materials.

References

[1] Pierson, H. O. and Smatana, J. F., "Development and Properties of Pyrolytic Carbon Felt Composites," Proceedings, 14th National Symposium of Aerospace and Process Engineers, Nov. 1968.

[2] Irwin, J. L. "Development and Evaluation of Carbon-Carbon Reentry Heat-shields," SC-DR-70-108, Sandia Laboratories report, Albuquerque, N. Mex., April 1972.

[3] Stoller, H. M. et al, "Properties of Flight-Tested CVD/Felt and CVD/FW Carbon Composites," SC-DC-71-4046, Sandia Laboratories report, Albuquerque, N. Mex., June 1971.

[4] Theis, J. D., Taylor, A. J., Rayner, R. M., and Frye, E. R., "Filament Wound Carbon/Carbon Heatshield SC-11FW-Y-12-7, A Process History," SC-DR-70-425, Sandia Laboratories report, Albuquerque, N. Mex., Dec. 1970.

[5] Stoller, H. M. and Frye, E. R., "Processing of Carbon/Carbon Composites—An Overview," SC-DC-71-3653, Sandia Laboratories report, Albuquerque, N. Mex., April 1971.

[6] Lieberman, M. L. and Pierson, H. O., "Effect of Gas Phase Conditions on Resultant Matrix Pyrocarbons in Carbon/Carbon Composites," Paper FC-12, Summary of Papers, Eleventh Biennial Conference on Carbon, Gatlinberg, Tenn., 1973.

[7] Thornburgh, J. D. and Pears, C. D., "Prediction of the Thermal Conductivity of Filled and Reinforced Plastics," ASME paper 65-WA/HT-4, American Society of Mechanical Engineers, 1965.

[8] Springer, G. S. and Tsai, S. W., Journal of Composite Materials, Vol. 1, No. 2, April 1967, p. 166.

[9] Ekvall, J. C., "Elastic Properties of Orthotropic Monofilament Laminates," ASME paper 61-Av-5, American Society of Mechanical Engineers, March 1961.

[10] Calcote, L. R., The Analysis of Laminated Composite Structures, Van Nostrand Reinhold Co., New York, 1969, p. 20.

[11] Butler, B. L., Northrop, D. A., and Guess, T. R., Journal of Adhesion, Vol. 5, 1973, pp. 1–18.

[12] Schapery, R. A., Journal of Composite Materials, Vol. 2, No. 3, July 1968, p. 380.

[13] Guess, T. R., Butler, B. L., and Theis, J. D., "An Advanced Filament-Wound Carbon Composite," SC-DR-71-0192, Sandia Laboratories report, Albuquerque, N. Mex., March 1971.

[14] Granoff, B., Pierson, H. O., Schuster, D. M., and Smatana, J. F., "The Properties of Carbon-Felt, Carbon-Matrix Composites as a Function of Processing Conditions," SC-DR-72-0337, Sandia Laboratories report, Albuquerque, N. Mex., June 1972.

[15] Stoller, H. M., Lieberman, M. L., Butler, B. L., and Theis, J. D., "Carbon Fiber Reinforced-Carbon Matrix Composites," SC-DC-72-1474, Sandia Laboratories report, Albuquerque, N. Mex., Aug. 1972.

[16] Butler, B. L. and Duliere, S. F., "Relation of Carbon Fiber Axial Thermal Expansions to Their Microstructures," SLA-73-0485, Sandia Laboratories report, Albuquerque, N. Mex., Nov. 1973.

[17] Butler, B. L. and Tidmore, J., "The Micromechanics of Modmor II—Pyrocarbon Composites," *Proceedings,* 10th Biennial Conference on Carbon, FC-31, 1971, p. 49.

[18] Kaae, J. L., *Carbon,* Vol. 9, 1971, pp. 291–299.

[19] High Temperature Materials, Inc. data sheet, 1962. Information can be obtained from Union Carbide Corporation, New York City.

[20] Bokros, J. C., "Deposition Structure and Properties of Pyrolytic Carbons," *Chemistry and Physics of Carbon,* Vol. 5, P. L. Walker, Jr., Ed., Marcel Dekker, Inc., New York, 1969.

[21] Northrop, D. A., Granoff, B., and Lieberman, M. L., Sandia Laboratories, private communications.

[22] Legg, J. K., Sanders, H. G., Engelke, W. T., and Pears, C. D., "Thermal and Mechanical Properties of Advanced Heatshield Resinous (CP) and Carbonaceous (CC) Composites," AFML-TR-72-160, Air Force Materials Laboratory, Dayton, Ohio, Vol. 1, 1972.

[23] Mullen, C. K. and Roy, P. J., "Fabrication and Properties of AVCO 3D Carbon/Carbon Cyclinder Materials," SAMPE—*Materials Review for '72,* Society of Aerospace Materials and Process Engineering, Vol. 17, p. III-A-two-1.

[24] Northrop, D. A., Pierson, H. O., and Smatana, J. F., "Development and Properties of PAN-Based Carbon Felt-Pyrolytic Carbon Composites," *Proceedings,* 11th Biennial Conference on Carbon, FC-8, 1973, p. 275.

D. H. Kaelble, [1] *P. J. Dynes,* [1] *L. W. Crane,* [1] *and L. Maus* [2]

Kinetics of Environmental Degradation in Graphite-Epoxy Laminates

REFERENCE: Kaelble, D. H., Dynes, P. J., Crane, L. W., and Maus, L., "**Kinetics of Environmental Degradation in Graphite-Epoxy Composites,**" *Composite Reliability, ASTM STP 580,* American Society for Testing and Materials, 1975, pp. 247–262.

ABSTRACT: A detailed study of the kinetics of environmental degradation in graphite-epoxy composites show a close correlation between analytical predictions and experimentally observed changes in interlaminar shear and fracture energy response under high moisture exposure conditions. Unaged composite specimens exhibit high interlaminar shear strength $\lambda_b \geq 850$ kg/cm² (12 000 psi) and relatively low fracture energy $W_b/A \cong 10$ to 20 kg cm/cm² (56 to 112 lb in./in.²). Exposure to 95 percent relative humidity or water immersion at 100°C (212°F) for times $t \geq 200$ h produces a 30 to 50 percent reduction in λ_b accompanied by a concurrent two to fivefold increase in W_b/A and acoustic energy absorption. These property changes are shown to be irreversible and directly related to cumulative moisture degradation of the fiber-matrix interfacial bond. The magnitudes of these property changes are consistent with surface energy analysis and micromechanics predictions.

KEY WORDS: composite materials, environments, degradation, interfaces, bonding, fracture strength, shear strength

This study forms part of a more general program addressed to developing a better understanding of the mechanisms of interfacial bonding and environmental stability in polymer matrix composites *[1–3].* [3] Several published studies have shown that exposure of graphite fiber reinforced epoxy or polyester composites to water immersion or water vapor at elevated temperature produces decreases in interlaminar shear strength accompanied by rising or falling values of fracture toughness *[2,4–6].* An approach to the correction of this moisture sensitivity has been suggested by Kaelble *[2,3]* based upon a modified Griffith-Irwin model for interfacial failure and a micromechanics model for fracture energy due to fiber debonding.

[1] Science Center, Rockwell International, Thousand Oaks, Calif. 91360.
[2] Tulsa Division, Rockwell International, Tulsa, Okla.
[3] The italic numbers in brackets refer to the list of references appended to this paper.

The first objective of this study is to evaluate the thermodynamic and kinetic aspects of shear strength degradation in uniaxial reinforced graphite-epoxy composites exposed to high moisture and elevated temperature. The second objective is to analyze the relationships between interlaminar shear strength, fracture energy, and acoustic response during environmental degradation.

Materials and Methods

The graphite fiber chosen as reinforcement was Hercules HTS. BP-907, a modified epoxy (Bloomingdale Division of American Cyanamide), was employed as the matrix material for Panel SC1.

Wettability measurements and surface energy analysis methods detailed in previous reports [1,2,7] were applied to define the surface tension $\gamma_{sv} = \gamma_{sv}^d + \gamma_{sv}^p$ properties for both fiber and cured epoxy resin components of the reinforced composites. Surface property data for the Hercules HTS graphite fiber are $\gamma_{sv}^p = 25.9 \pm 1.5$, $\gamma_{sv}^d = 25.7 \pm 33.3$, and $\gamma_{sv} = 51.6 \pm 2.3$ dyn/cm. For the cures epoxy resin, $\gamma_{sv}^p = 37.2 \pm 3.1$, $\gamma_{sv}^d = 8.3 \pm 2.0$, and $\gamma_{sv} = 45.5 \pm 1.2$ dynes/cm.

Measurement of interlaminar shear strengths using the standard short-beam shear test produced combinations of tensile and shear failure which indicated that this test was not useful in detailed study of environmental degradation effects. The specimen and test geometry shown in the upper portion of Fig. 1 was developed as a replacement of the short-beam shear test. The interlaminar shear strength is described by the following relation

$$\lambda_b = F_b/A_0 \tag{1}$$

where F_b is the compressional force at break and $A_0 = 0.25$ cm² is the nominal cross-sectional area of the shear plane.

Fracture energy measurements in slow crack propagation were conducted using the three-point bend specimen designed Tatersall and Tappin [9] and illustrated in the lower view of Fig. 1. The geometry of flexure loading shown in Fig. 1 generates a crack at the apex of the isosceles triangle section which propagates downward to the base of the triangle. The work of fracture per unit area W_b/A is defined as

$$\frac{W_b}{A} = \frac{1}{A_0} \int_{L=0}^{L_b} F dL \tag{2}$$

Samples were aged for varied times using 100°C (212°F) and 95 percent relative humidity vapor phase immersion over a saturated water solution of K_2SO_4 as described by Gahimer and Nieske [10]. A second group of samples was subjected to full water immersion exposure at 100°C (212°F) for

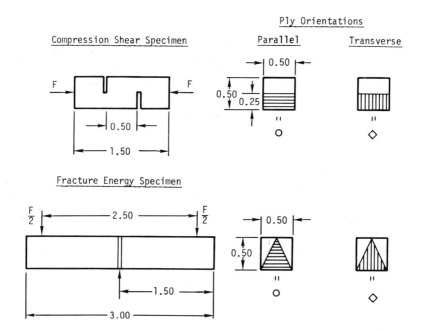

FIG. 1—*Test specimens for interlaminar shear strength (upper) and fracture energy (lower) measurement.*

varied times. Compression shear and fracture energy measurements were conducted at 23 ± 1 °C (73 °F) immediately after sample withdrawal from the high moisture environment. Constant Instron crosshead speeds of 0.02 cm/min for compression shear and 0.05 cm/min for fracture energy measurement were applied. Sample weighing immediately upon removal from the high moisture environment and subsequent to extended desiccation over anhydrous calcium sulphate permits determination of moisture content at the time of fracture testing.

Subsequent to moisture exposure, fracture testing, and desiccation for moisture determination, all samples were subjected to ultrasonic inspection using through transmission (C-scan) at 2.25 MHz. The samples were coupled via thin films of Nonaq grease (Fisher Scientific Co.) to the signal transmission and detector transducers of a Sperry Reflectoscope UM721 (Customation Industries, Inc.). The sound transmission path was vertical in the cross-sectional views shown in Fig. 1 with the wave front parallel (circle data points) or transverse (diamond data points) to the ply orientations. The longitudinal sound velocity C_L(km/s) and the acoustic absorption coefficient α_L (nepers/cm) are determined by the following standard relations

$$C_L = L/\Delta t = L/(t_2 - t_1) \tag{3}$$

$$\alpha_L = L^{-1}\ln(A_1/A_2) \qquad (4)$$

where $t_2 - t_1$ is the delay time and A_1 and A_2 are signal amplitudes. These acoustic properties reflect combined effects of moisture sorption, mechanical loading, and subsequent desiccation upon the material response.

Interlaminar Shear Strength Degradation

Surface Energy Aspects

Previous studies by us have shown that the interfacial bond between fiber and matrix under varied conditions of environmental immersion can be expressed in terms of surface energy parameters which describe (London-d) dispersion $\gamma^d = \alpha^2$ and (Keesom-p) $\gamma^p = \beta^2$ contributions to liquid-vapor $\gamma_{LV} = \gamma_{LV}{}^d + \gamma_{LV}{}^p$ or solid-vapor $\gamma_{SV} = \gamma_{SV}{}^d + \gamma_{SV}{}^p$ surface tension [7]. Since these definitions include the surface tension properties of water where $\gamma_{LV}{}^d = 21.8$ dyn/cm $\gamma_{LV}{}^p = 51.0$ dyn/cm, and $\gamma_{LV} = 72.8$ dyn/cm at 20°C (68°F), this dispersion-polar interaction model forms the basis for predictions of the degradation of bond strength when the fiber-matrix interface is transferred from air to water immersion and comes to full equilibrium with the water immersion environment [2].

Surface energy parameters required to define this three-phase model where the matrix (or adhesive) is Phase 1, the environmental immersion phase (air or water) is Phase 2, and the matrix (or adherend) is Phase 3, are represented by the following expressions [1,2]

$$\gamma_1 = \gamma_1{}^d + \gamma_1{}^p = \alpha_1{}^2 + \beta_1{}^2 \qquad (5)$$

$$\gamma_2 = \gamma_2{}^d + \gamma_2{}^p = \alpha_2{}^2 + \beta_2{}^2 \qquad (6)$$

$$\gamma_3 = \gamma_3{}^d + \gamma_3{}^p = \alpha_3{}^2 + \beta_3{}^2 \qquad (7)$$

The parameters $\alpha = (\gamma^d)^{1/2}$ and $\beta = (\gamma^p)^{1/2}$ are introduced for notational convenience. These six surface energy terms enter a detailed statement of the Griffith relation for critical stress σ_c for crack initiation under normal plane stress loading as defined by the following expression [2]

$$\sigma_c\left(\frac{\pi c}{2E}\right)^{1/2} = \gamma_G{}^{1/2} = (R^2 - R_0{}^2)^{1/2} \qquad (8)$$

where the surface energy coefficients appear in the following supplementary relations

$$R_0{}^2 = 0.25\,[(\alpha_1 - \alpha_3)^2 + (\beta_1 - \beta_3)^2] \qquad (9)$$

$$R^2 = (\alpha_2 - H)^2 + (\beta_2 - K)^2 \tag{10}$$

$$H = 0.50 (\alpha_1 + \alpha_3) \tag{11}$$

$$K = 0.50 (\beta_1 + \beta_3) \tag{12}$$

and E is Young's modulus and C is the crack length. The application of Eq 8 assumes that the change in immersion environment does not significantly influence the system modulus E or crack length C and that the significant variable is the reversible Griffith surface energy $\gamma_G = (R^2 - R_0^2)$.

Inspection of Eqs 9 through 12 shows that the modified Griffith expression of Eq 8 can be conveniently represented on a cartesian coordinate of α versus β as shown in Fig. 2 (left portion). The left view of Fig. 2 indicates the location of the α versus β points for the matrix and fiber surfaces of Panel SC1. The vectors R(air) and $R(H_2O)$ originate at H, K as defined by Eqs 11 and 12 and terminate at $\alpha = \beta = 0$ for air and $\alpha = 4.67$ (dynes/cm)$^{1/2}$ and $\beta = 7.14$ (dynes/cm)$^{1/2}$ for water, which represent the surface tension properties of these two immersion phases. The R_0 vector shown in Fig. 2 also originated at H, K and describes a circle which encloses the region where $R \leqslant R_0$, and from Eq 8 it is predicted that $\sigma_c = 0$.

The master function of $\sigma_c(\pi C/2E)^{1/2} = \gamma_G^{1/2}$ versus R shown in Fig. 2 (right portion) shows air and water immersion environments as two special cases. For panel SC1 the prediction is that $\sigma_c(H_2O)/\sigma_c(air) = 0.46$ for ratio of fiber-matrix debonding with constant $(\pi C/2E)$. The diagrams of Fig. 2 graphically detail the surface energy arguments which predict that water will substantially reduce the interfacial bond strength in composite SC1.

Fracture in interlaminar shear produces shear stresses which simultaneously fracture both the fiber-matrix interface and matrix continium between adjacent fibers. For fibers of uniform radius r_0 in regular hexagonal packing, the matrix distance, a, separating adjacent fibers is defined by the following expression [3]

$$a = r_0[1.074(\pi/V)^{1/2} - 2] \tag{13}$$

where $V =$ fiber volume fraction. Solving Eq 13 with $V = 0.40$ for Panel SC1 shows that $a = r_0$. The fractional areas for interfacial f_I and matrix f_M failure are given by the following relation

$$f_I = 1 - f_M = \frac{\pi r_0}{\pi r_0 + a} = 0.76 \tag{14}$$

The composite interlaminar shear strength λ_b, interfacial failure λ_I, and matrix failure λ_M are obtained from the rule of mixtures

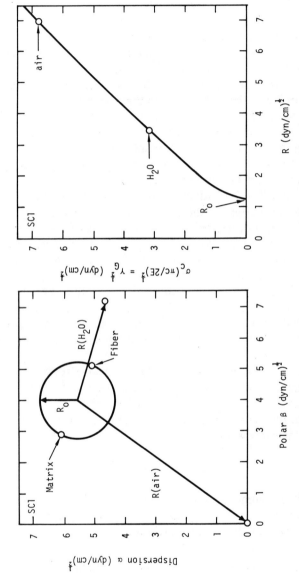

FIG. 2—*Surface energy analysis for fiber-matrix interactions for composite SC1 with air and water immersion phases; α versus β (left view). Griffith failure criterion $\sigma_c \propto \lambda_G^{1/2}$ for composite SC1 under air and water immersion (right view).*

$$\lambda_b = f_I \lambda_I + f_M \lambda_M \tag{15}$$

Consider that an unexposed laminate under air immersion displays interlaminar shear strengths

$$\lambda_{b0} = \lambda_{I0} = \lambda_{M0} \tag{16}$$

where the zero suffix represents the respective shear strengths at zero exposure time ($t = 0$) to water immersion. Under a condition of infinite ($t = \infty$) exposure time underwater immersion, let us further assume that

$$\lambda_{M\infty} = \lambda_{M0} \tag{17}$$

$$\lambda_{I\infty} = \lambda_{I0} \frac{\sigma_c(H_2O)}{\sigma_c(air)} \tag{18}$$

Substituting the statements of Eqs 16 through 18 into Eq 15 we obtain the following relation

$$\frac{\lambda_{b\infty}}{\lambda_{b0}} = (1 - f_I) + f_I \frac{\sigma_c(H_2O)}{\sigma_c(air)} \tag{19}$$

For panel SC1 with $\sigma_c(H_2O)/\sigma_c(air) = 0.463$ and $f_I = 0.76$ we obtain a prediction from Eq 19 that

$$\frac{\lambda_{b\infty}}{\lambda_{b0}} = 0.59 \tag{20}$$

These predictions are based upon surface energy arguments and a simplified model which translates interface degradation considerations into the composite shear failure of both interface and matrix.

Kinetic Aspects

Previous studies have shown that a finite time is required to establish equilibrium between a composite material response and the environment to which it is exposed [2,4-6]. A general procedure for expressing the cumulative damage effects of mechanical (M), thermal (T), or environmental (C = chemical or corrosive) stresses is by the relation proposed by Halpin and co-workers [11-13]

$$\phi = \exp(-Kt^b/a_T a_M a_C) \tag{21}$$

where ϕ is the cumulative degradation function; t the exposure time; K a system constant; a_T, a_M, a_C are time shift factors relating to respective thermal, mechanical, or chemical effects; and b is a time exponent. A specialized form of Eq 21 applicable to analysis of degradation of interlaminar shear would take the following form

$$\phi = \frac{\lambda_b(t) - \lambda_{b0}}{\lambda_{b0} - \lambda_{b\infty}} = \exp(-t/\tau) \qquad (22)$$

where it is assumed that $b = 1.0$ and the relaxation time $\tau = a_T a_M a_C / K$. Rearranging Eq 22 we obtain the following expression for the interlaminar shear strength $\lambda_b(t)$ at exposure time t by the following expression

$$\lambda_b(t) = \lambda_{b\infty} + (\lambda_{b0} - \lambda_{b\infty})\exp(-t/\tau) \qquad (23)$$

where the relaxation time τ is defined

$$\tau = -t/\ln\phi \qquad (24)$$

One objective of the present study was to evaluate both surface energy and kinetics aspects of interlaminar shear strength degradation as outlined by the foregoing discussion and detailed by Eqs 19 and 23.

Evaluation of Experimental Results

The experimental curves of Fig. 3 (upper portion) provide a graphical summary of the moisture content of composite Panel SCl, as a function of exposure time t to water vapor [95 percent relative humidity at 100 °C (212 °F)] and liquid water immersion at 100 °C (212 °F).

The effects of liquid water immersion on compressional interlaminar shear strength for composite SC1 are shown in Fig. 3 (lower portion). It may be recalled from Fig. 1 that the circled points represent shear parallel and diamond points transverse to the ply orientations. The experimental single test data of Fig. 3 show a monotonic decrease from initial maximum values of $\lambda_b = \lambda_0$ to final time invariant values $\lambda_b = \lambda_\infty$ which are approached at exposure times $t \geqslant 200$ h. A somewhat smaller decrease in the value of λ_b for water vapor immersion was found. The dashed curves of Fig. 3 are drawn to envelope the experimental λ_b data as suggested by Eq 23.

The average values of the relaxation time τ for environmental degradation appear to correlate with relatively long times required for moisture uptake as shown by the curve of Fig. 3. The liquid H_2O immersion condition for composite Panel SC1 produces an experimental value of $\lambda_{b\infty}/\lambda_{b0} =$

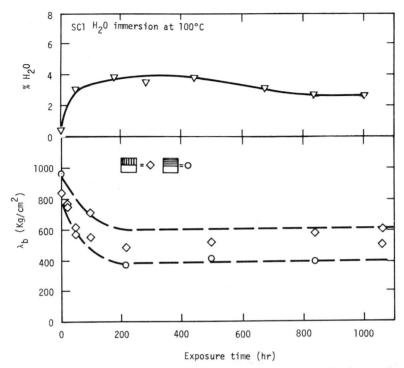

FIG. 3—*Moisture content (percent by weight H_2O) versus exposure time* (t) *of composites SC1 (upper view). Effects of moisture exposure time* t *on interlaminar shear strength λ_b of composite SC1 (lower view).*

0.56 which compares well with the calculated value $\lambda_{b\infty}/\lambda_{b0}$ = 0.59 from Eq 19.

Degradation Effects on Fracture Energy

Micromechanics Considerations

As shown by the data of the previous section, the effect of long-term exposure to either high humidity or water immersion in graphite fiber reinforced composites follows predictive relations which point out that the state of the interfacial bond depends upon the degree of equilibration to the adverse environment. Both the analysis and the experimental data point out that water exposure merely weakens rather than destroys the fiber-matrix shear bond strength. As noted in the introduction, previous experimental studies have shown that water exposure with lowered inter-laminar shear strength $\lambda_b(t)$ may produce both increasing or decreasing values of fracture energy W_b/A for crack propagation perpendicular to the fiber axis in uniaxially reinforced composites. This rather puzzling relationship between interlaminar shear and fracture energy behavior is clarified by a consideration of the micromechanical contributions to fracture energy in fiber-reinforced composites.

In a recently developed model to analyze the stress distributions and fracture energies associated with crack propagation and fiber pullout in reinforced composites, the work of fracture W_b/A per unit area of sample cross section A is defined as the sum of the matrix shear work W_{sb} for debonding and a frictional work W_{Fb} for fiber pullout by the following relations [3]

$$\frac{W_b}{A} = \frac{W_{Sb} + W_{Fb}}{A} \tag{25}$$

$$\frac{W_{SB}}{A} = f_1(V) f_2(V) r_0 \left(\frac{E}{2G}\right)^{1/2} \frac{\lambda_I}{\lambda_F} \left[\frac{\sigma_b}{2} - \lambda_I \left(\frac{E}{2G}\right)^{1/2} f_1(V)\right] \geqslant 0 \tag{26}$$

$$\frac{W_{fb}}{A} = \frac{f_2(V) r_0}{2\lambda_F} \left[\frac{\sigma_b}{2} - \lambda_I \left(\frac{E}{2G}\right)^{1/2} f(V)\right]^2 \geqslant 0 \tag{27}$$

where

$$
\begin{aligned}
\text{fiber radius} &= r_0 = 4.45 \cdot 10^{-6}\, \text{cm} \\
\text{matrix shear modulus} &= 1.19 \cdot 10^4\, \text{kg/cm}^2 \\
\text{fiber tensile strength} &= \sigma_b = 2.46 \cdot 10^4\, \text{kg/cm}^2 \\
\text{fiber volume fraction} &= V = 0.40 \\
\text{fiber Young's modulus} &= E = 2.53 \cdot 10^6\, \text{kg/cm}^2 \\
\text{volume fraction functions:}\ & f_1\,(V) = 0.832,\ f_2\,(V) = 0.268, \\
& f_3\,(V) = 0.236
\end{aligned}
$$

Since the locus of fiber tensile failure is statistically indeterminate, the range of expected fracture energy W_b/A lies within upper and lower bounds specified by the following relation [3]

$$\frac{W_{Sb} + W_{fb}}{A} \geqslant \frac{W_b}{A} \geqslant \frac{W_{Sb}}{A} \tag{28}$$

The two undetermined response properties in Eqs 26 through 28 are the critical interfacial shear stress λ_I which characterizes fiber-matrix debonding, and the frictional shear stress λ_F associated with fiber pullout from the matrix. Information concerning the magnitude λ_I is developed by interlaminar shear strength testing as identified in Eq 15 and subsequent relations which lead to the kinetic expression for shear strength degradation stated by Eq 23.

The magnitude of λ_F and its dependences upon moisture degradation effects can only be estimated by indirect methods such as thermoelastic calculations based on resin shrinkage about the fiber as demonstrated by Broutman [14]. By introducing the constants into Eqs 26 and 27 we obtain the following specific relations

$$\frac{W_{Sb}}{A} \frac{\text{kg}}{\text{cm}} = 1.025 \cdot 10^{-3} \frac{\lambda_I}{\lambda_F} (12300 - 8.58 \lambda_I) \tag{29}$$

$$\frac{W_{Fb}}{A} \frac{\text{kg}}{\text{cm}} = \frac{5.96 \cdot 10^{-5}}{\lambda_F} (12300 - 8.58 \lambda_I)^2 \tag{30}$$

where both λ_I and λ_F are expressed in kg/cm^2 units. The calculated functions of Fig. 4 present two examples of fracture energy predictions based upon Eqs 29 and 30. In upper Fig. 4 (Case I) the magnitude of $\lambda_F = 250$ kg/cm$^2 = 3450$ psi is held constant while λ_I is variable from $\lambda_I = 0$ to $\lambda_I = 1415$ kg/cm^2, which characterizes fiber fracture without debonding. In the lower curves of Fig. 4 (Case II) a proportionality condition $\lambda_F = \lambda_I/2.8$ is applied to represent a concurrent change in λ_F as λ_I is decreased by environmental degradation. These theoretical predictions of the dependence of W_b/A upon λ_I can be compared with measured values of W_b/A versus high moisture exposure time.

The shaded regions of Fig. 4 define the upper and lower bounds for W_b/A as defined by the constraints of Eq 28.

Evaluation of Experimental Results

A graphical summary of the effects of water immersion on the measured fracture energy W_b/A for crack propagation parallel (circles) and transverse (diamonds) to the fiber ply orientations for Panel SC1 are presented in the upper view of Fig. 5. The dashed curves of Fig. 5 represent the extreme values of the experimental data. In general the curves and single-test data points of Fig. 5 are seen to reflect the predictions presented by the shaded regions of Fig. 4. As shown in Fig. 5 the experimental values of W_b/A are low and display minimum scatter at $t = 0$ characteristic of high values of $\lambda_I \cong \lambda_M \cong 1000$ kg/cm^2. As exposure time increases from $t = 0$ to $t = 200$ h, characteristic of the initial rapid degradation of λ_I due to water absorption, the values of W_b/A increase and the scatter between maximum and minimum fracture energy increases as expected from the broadening of the shaded areas in Fig. 4. In general one finds a consistent increase in measured values of W_b/A with increasing time of moisture exposure which is consistent with degradation of λ_I and the fracture energy model summarized by Fig. 4.

This experimental study of moisture degradation effects on the work of fracture correlates closely with the results predicted by the micromechanics model summarized by Eqs 25 through 28. In effect, the micromechanics

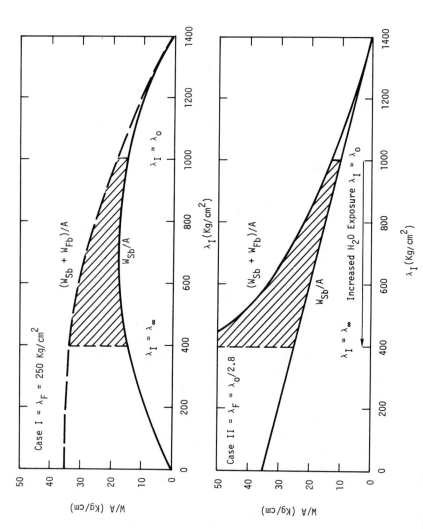

FIG. 4—Calculated fracture energy W/A versus fiber-matrix shear bond strength λ_I based on micromechanics analysis.

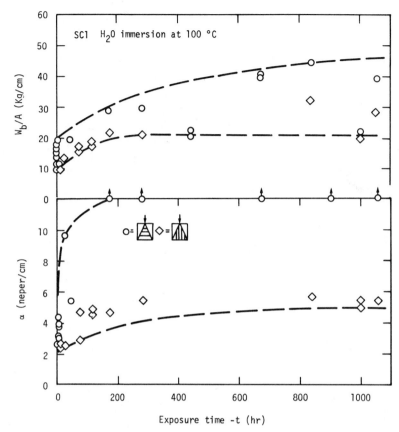

FIG. 5—*Effects of moisture exposure time* t *on fracture energy* W_b/A *of composite SC1 (upper view). Effects of moisture exposure time* t *on acoustic absorption coefficient* α *of composite SC1 (lower view).*

model predicts that fracture energy should increase by a factor of 2 to 5 when the interlaminar shear strength which influences λ_I decreases to approximately one-half its original value. These predictions, as graphically displayed in Fig. 4, apply to a strongly bonded composite where the initial value of $\lambda_0 \cong 1000$ kg/cm² and the final value $\lambda_\infty \cong 400$ kg/cm².

Degradation Effects on Acoustic Response

An important aspect in studies of environmental degradation is the investigation of nondestructive test (NDT) methods which indicate the state of degradation of composite response. The specific objective in our experiments was to determine whether sound velocity or attenuation measurements were directly sensitive to the state of the interfacial bond as evaluated by moisture absorption, interlaminar shear strength, or fracture energy.

Sound velocity measurements on desiccated specimens subject to prior history of moisture exposure, and fracture testing for interlaminar shear or fracture energy produced averaged values of sound velocity $C_L = 3.00 \pm 0.17$ Km/s at a frequency $f = 2.25$ MHz and temperature of $23 \pm 1\,°C$ (73 °F). No significant trends were observed in the data relating to fiber ply orientation or prior moisture exposure history.

Acoustic attenuation response of composite specimens under equivalent test conditions was sensibly influenced by prior moisture exposure history. Measured attenuation data for sound wave fronts parallel (circles) and transverse (diamonds) to the fiber ply orientation are plotted versus water immersion exposure time t in the lower portion of Fig. 5. Inspection of Fig. 5 shows that for transmission perpendicular to the fiber ply orientation, attenuation rises to $\alpha \geq 12$ nepers/cm. The attenuation parallel to the fiber plys levels at $\alpha = 5$ to 6 nepers/cm at exposure times $t > 200$ h.

Reversibility of Degradation Effects

The acoustic attenuation data of the previous section appear to show that prior moisture exposure effects induce permanent changes in the composite material which are not reversed by removal of the absorbed water by desiccation. This important question of reversibility of moisture degradation effects was examined in greater detail in a series of special experiments.

In the special tests for reversibility of composite response the measurement of fracture energy was chosen as a property which increases significantly during moisture degradation and which is predicted to remain at a higher value if the damage is fully irreversible. It was found that fracture energy increases caused by interface degradation under 1000 h water vapor exposure or water immersion are not reduced by ambient desiccation or 200 °C (392 °F) inert atmosphere exposure.

These results tend to support a conclusion of earlier studies [2] that moisture degradation of interfaces in graphite-epoxy composites is essentially irreversible. The explanation for this finding is related to the fact that fiber-matrix bonding occurs prior to crosslinking of the epoxy matrix where local stress relaxation processes permit rheological equilibrium to be achieved at the bonded interface. Subsequent to curing, the matrix remains in the crosslinked state and residual elastic stresses prevent rebonding of a damaged interface even when the resin is raised to above its glass transition temperature T_g to provide the response characteristic of a highly crosslinked elastomer [15].

Summary and Conclusions

The results of this study show a close correlation between analytical predictions and experimentally observed degradation of mechanical properties in graphite-epoxy composites under high moisture aging conditions. Unaged composite specimens exhibit high interlaminar shear strength $\lambda_b \geqslant 850$ kg/cm^2 (12 000 psi) and relatively low fracture energy $W_b/A \cong$ 10 to 20 kg cm/cm^2 (56 to 112 lb in./in.^{2}). Exposure to 95 percent relative humidity or water immersion at 100°C (212°F) for times $t \geqslant 200$ h produces a 30 to 50 percent reduction in interlaminar shear strength accompanied by a concurrent two to fivefold increase in fracture toughness and acoustic absorption properties. These property changes are shown to be irreversible and directly related to cumulative moisture degradation of the fiber-matrix interfacial bond. The magnitude of these property changes is consistent with surface energy analysis and micromechanics predictions which show that fracture energy response optimizes at intermediate values of shear bond strength.

The kinetic expression for cumulative moisture degradation of interlaminar shear strength (see Eq 24) defines an environmental relaxation time τ which appears to correlate with the time scales shown for water absorption into the composite test specimens. The additional parameters of this kinetic expression define relative shear strengths at exposure times $t = \infty$ and $t = 0$ by a dimensionless ratio $\lambda_{b\infty}/\lambda_{b0}$ which are calculated from equilibrium thermodynamic arguments summarized by Eq 19. Two technical approaches to reducing moisture sensitivity in graphite-epoxy composites are clearly identified by Eq 24. External protective coatings which lower the diffusion rate of water into the composite material would increase τ and thereby minimize degradation for exposure times where $t \ll \tau$. The success of this approach would depend entirely upon the resistance of the coating to damage due to environmental exposure or mechanical abrasion.

The second approach to high moisture resistance is fundamentally stated by making $\lambda_{b\infty}/\lambda_{b0} \cong 1.0$, and the solution involves the modification of the fiber-matrix interface such that the vectors R(air) and R(H$_2$O) shown by Fig. 2 display a ratio R(air)/R(H$_2$O) $\cong 1.0$. As discussed in previous reports, implementing this second approach requires new fiber surface treatments and selection of matrix polymers which are essentially nonpolar in both surface and bulk properties [1,2]. A recent report by Gauchel and co-workers [16], wherein halogenated epoxy resins are combined with surface treated S-glass fibers to form composites with remarkable moisture resistance, appears to involve this second approach.

Acknowledgment

The authors acknowledge helpful discussions with Dr. G. O. Garmong. This work was supported in part by the Rockwell International IR&D Interdivisional Technology Program under the sponsorship of the Composites Technical Panel.

References

[1] Kaelble, D. H., *Proceedings,* 23rd International Congress of Pure and Applied Chemistry, Vol. 8, Butterworths, London, pp. 265-302.

[2] Kaelble, D. H., Dynes, P. J., and Cirlin, E. H., *Journal of Adhesion,* Vol. 6, 1974, p. 23.

[3] Kaelble, D. H., *Journal of Adhesion,* Vol. 5, 1973, p. 245.

[4] Harris, B., Beaumont, P. W. R., and de Ferran, E. M., *Journal of Materials Science,* Vol. 6, 1971, p. 238.

[5] Beaumont, P. W. R. and Harris, B., "The Effect of Environment on Fatigue and Crack Propagation in Carbon Fiber Reinforced Epoxy Resin," Paper 49, *Proceedings,* International Conference on Carbon Fibers, The Plastics Institute, London, 1971.

[6] Beaumont, P. W. R. and Harris, B., *Journal of Composite Materials,* Vol. 7, 1972, p. 1265.

[7] Kaelble, D. H., *Physical Chemistry of Adhesion,* Chapter 5, Wiley, New York, 1971.

[8] Kaelble, D. H. and Cirlin, E. H., *Journal of Polymer Science,* Part C, Vol. 35, 1971, pp. 79, 101.

[9] Tattersall, H. G. and Tappin, G., *Journal of Materials Science,* Vol. 1, 1966, p. 296.

[10] Gahimer, F. H. and Nieske, F. W., *Insulation,* Aug. 1968, pp. 39-44.

[11] Halpin, J. C. and Polley, H. W., *Journal of Composite Materials,* Vol. 1, 1967, p. 64.

[12] Halpin, J. C., Kopf, J. R., and Goldberg, W., *Journal of Composite Materials,* Vol. 4, 1970, p. 462.

[13] Halpin, J. C., *Journal of Composite Materials,* Vol. 6, 1972, p. 208.

[14] Broutman, L. J., *Journal of Adhesion,* Vol. 2, 1970, p. 147.

[15] Kaelble, D. H., *Journal of Applied Polymer Science,* Vol. 9, 1965, p. 1213.

[16] Gauchel, J. V., Griffith, J. R., Steg, I., and Cowling, J. E., *Polymer Preprints,* American Chemical Society, Vol. 14, No. 2, Aug. 1973, p. 1148.

E. M. Wu[1] and D. C. Ruhmann[2]

Stress Rupture of Glass-Epoxy Composites: Environmental and Stress Effects

REFERENCE: Wu, E. M. and Rhumann, D. C., "**Stress Rupture of Glass-Epoxy Composites: Environmental and Stress Effects,**" *Composite Reliability, ASTM STP 580,* American Society for Testing and Materials, 1975, pp. 263–287.

ABSTRACT: This paper is concerned with the delayed fracture of composite materials under constant stress. The results of an investigation of the combined effect of an active environment (benzene) and stress on the survival life of an E-glass reinforced epoxy composite material are presented. Through the use of an appropriate failure criterion and representative median log-time to failure values, time-dependent failure surfaces were generated from data obtained when testing in (1) air and (2) benzene for the first quadrant of the stress space. These experimental results are used to extend the current kinetic theory of rate-dependent rupture to include both anisotropic and environmental effects.

KEY WORDS: composite materials, glass, epoxy resins, creep, stress-rupture, stresses, environments, tension tests, strength, variability, statistics, failure surfaces

The phenomenon of stress rupture in the presence of environmental influence is an important consideration in the engineering application of composite materials. For rational safe-life design, a failure criterion needs to be generalized for strength characterization in the time and environmental domains. Historically, such generalizations have been made for isotropic materials under simple loading conditions (notably the tensile stress condition) *[1,2].*[3] The effects of multiaxial complex loading and anisotropy, which are particularly pertinent to composites, have not received equal attention. On the other hand, the quasi-static strength criterion of anisotropic composites has been extensively studied, and it has been established that the tensor polynomial *[3]* is a general represen-

---

[1] Associate professor, Department of Mechanical Engineering, Washington University, St. Louis, Mo. 63130.

[2] Senior engineer, McDonnell Douglas Astronautics Company-East, St. Louis, Mo. 63166.

[3] The italic numbers in brackets refer to the list of references appended to this paper.

tation of the failure criterion presented to date and provides good correlation of experimentally observed composite strengths under multiaxial loadings. The formulation and operation of the tensor polynomial failure criterion together with experimental techniques and data analysis methods are summarized in Ref *4*. With the essentials of static anisotropic failure established, we can explore their generalization for characterization of the shape and magnitude change of the failure envelope in time and under the combined effect of stress and environment.

In addition, in order to assume safe-life design for conditions of complex stress as experienced by most structures, the observed variability of rupture strength and survival time must be incorporated into the design. The variability or degree of scatter of rupture strength can be a function of the state of multiaxial stress, environment, temperature, history of loading, and others. In this work, the multiparameter-dependent strength variability is incorporated into the failure criterion for the effects of stress and environment. Generalization into other parameters should be similar.

Research reported herein extends the static-failure criterion to characterize (1) the time-dependent failure surface (creep rupture), (2) the effect of the interaction of an active environment on the time-dependent failure surface, and (3) the stress and environment dependent strength variability of the failure surface. Experimental results are examined with respect to several current failure criteria, and the appropriate static-failure criterion is generalized for the description of transient strength through proper incorporation of rate equations for the multiaxially loaded condition.

Theoretical Foundation

The ever-increasing use of composite materials has resulted in the proposal of many failure criteria for the description of the response of the material system to external multiaxial excitations. Among the current criteria are the Mises-Hill, maximum strain, Hoffman, and the tensor polynomial formulation. These criteria have been reviewed *[4]* on a unified basis, where their similarities are emphasized, their mathematical limitation noted, and their capability of characterizing experimental results compared. In general, these criteria can be thought of as mathematical representations of a static-failure surface of the composite material system being investigated. A schematic static-failure surface labeled $f(\sigma_i, t_0)$ is illustrated in Fig. 1, where t_0 denotes quasi-static time.

If the functional form of $f(\sigma_i, t_0)$ has been established, the independent material strength parameters in $f(\sigma_i, t_0)$ can be evaluated through appropriate static tests *[5]*, and the failure criterion $f(\sigma_i, t_0)$ is then available for design of structures subjected to static multiaxial complex loadings. For long-term engineering applications of composites, static-failure surfaces cannot account for the well-known time-dependent loss of strength. Such

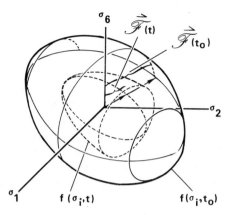

FIG. 1—*Time-dependent failure surfaces* f(σ_i, t_o) *and* f(σ_i, t) *with strength vectors* $\mathscr{F}(t_o)$ *and* $\mathscr{F}$(t) *at an arbitrary complex stress ratio.*

a strength loss in time under complex states of stress can again be represented by a new failure surface $f(\sigma_i, t)$ nested within the static-failure surface (under the assumption that strength does not increase in time). The time-dependent failure surface $f(\sigma_i t)$ is also schematically illustrated in Fig. 1, where the magnitude of the strength vector $\mathscr{F}(t_o)$ represents the static strength under a particular combined stress ratio and the magnitude of $\mathscr{F}(t)$ represents the residual strength after time t. Note that, in general, the time-dependent failure surface is not necessarily a proportional reduction of the static-failure surface due to such a physical phenomenon as the time-dependent loss of strength of the filaments being more gradual than that of the matrix. Hence the time-dependent strength characterization can be cast in the operational description of the parameters in the failure criterion $f(\sigma_i, t)$ which determine the magnitude *and* shape change of the time-dependent failure surface.

Likewise, when the service requirements for an engineering structure necessitate the use of composite material systems in hostile environments, the use of a failure criterion which does not include the effect of the environment on the time-dependent mechanical behavior of the material can lead to less than satisfactory results. The environmental effects are, in general, manifested by both a decrease in size of the failure surface and a change in shape of the surface due to different mechanistic effects of environment on the fiber and matrix strengths, respectively. Hence, the time-dependent strength characterization can be cast in the operational description of the parameters in the failure criterion $f(\sigma_i, t)$ which determine the magnitude and shape change of the time-dependent failure surface.

Finally, the design of composite structures is often performed using a failure criterion which provides information based only on the average strengths, that is, a mean failure surface. Additional considerations given to the observed variability in strengths are usually in the form of safety factors. At best, this approach can lead to a less than optimum design with unknown confidence levels of survival. Geometrically, in addition to the mean failure surface, the strength variability gives rise to several surfaces which are adjacent to the mean surface and which represent different probabilistic levels of failure. These surfaces are not necessarily concentric to the mean failure surface, since this depends on whether the strength variability is dependent on the state of stress (that is, for example, whether the distribution of shear strength is the same as the tensile strength). Obviously, these levels of probabilistic failure surfaces can be represented once the necessary statistical information has been incorporated into the strength parameters of the failure criterion.

We may now address some of the formalism of operating on the strength parameters to incorporate the characterization of time-dependent, environment-dependent, and probabilistic failure surfaces.

Time- and Environment-Dependent Failure Criterion

The composite material's strength under an arbitrary stress ratio loading can be represented by a strength vector, $\mathfrak{F}$, in the stress space (Fig. 1) whose magnitude is the radial distance from the origin to the failure surface, defined by

$$\mathfrak{F} = \vec{e}_i \, \sigma_i^* \qquad (1)$$

where $\vec{e}_i$ are unit vectors in the stress space and σ_i^* are the roots of the failure criterion. Similarly, the time-dependent strength under the same given stress ratio at a subsequent time t is given by (t), which can be expressed as

$$\mathfrak{F}(t) = \int_{t_0}^{t} \vec{\alpha}(\tau) \, d\tau + \mathfrak{F}(t_0) \qquad (2)$$

where

$$\alpha(\tau) = \frac{d\mathfrak{F}}{d\tau} \qquad (3)$$

and $\vec{\alpha}$ may be interpreted as the shift vector in the direction of $\mathfrak{F}$. In the limiting case of a uniaxial load, such as tension, $\vec{\alpha}$ becomes the well-known shift factor. The shift vector $\vec{\alpha}$ is a characteristic of each particular composite and may be determined from an experimentally observed time-dependent strength versus time relationship for any particular stress ratio. Assuming that the strength loss under a complex state of stress, following Zhurkov [1], is of the exponential decay form, we can express

$$|\mathfrak{F}(t)| = |\vec{\alpha}|\log(t/t_0) + \mathfrak{F}(t_0) \tag{4}$$

where the magnitude of the strength vector F, can be computed by

$$\mathfrak{F} = (\delta_{ij}\,\sigma_i^*\sigma_j^*)^{1/2}; \quad i, j = 1, 2, 6 \tag{5}$$

where δ_{ij} is the Kronecker delta function and σ_i^* and σ_j^* are failure stresses on the failure surface. Alternately, $\mathfrak{F}$ can be expressed in terms of a given stress, say σ_1, and the stress ratio $\sigma_i/\sigma_1 = m_{1i}$, in the form

$$\mathfrak{F} = \sigma_1^*\,(1 + \delta_{ij}\,m_{1i}m_{1j})^{1/2}; \quad i, j = 2, 6 \tag{6}$$

For the case of pure tension in the 1-direction, $\sigma_1 \neq 0$; $\sigma_2 = 0$, and therefore $m_{12} = m_{16} = 0$, and

$$\mathfrak{F} = \begin{cases} + \sigma_1^* = X_1 \text{ (longitudinal tensile strength)} \\ \\ - \sigma_1^* = X_1' \text{ (longitudinal compressive strength)} \end{cases} \tag{7}$$

It is important to note that Eq 4 is an assumed functional form subject to experimental verification. Other functional forms, when appropriate, should be used in place of Eq 4.

It follows that if a sufficient number of experiments are performed at different stress ratios covering distinct radial loading paths in the stress space (Fig. 1), then the shift vector $\vec{\alpha}$ can be determined for those loading paths and any time-dependent failure surface $f(\sigma_i, t)$ may be determined. Extemporaneous estimation would lead to the inevitable conclusion that this represents an impractically vast experimental program. From previous investigations [5,6], however, it has been demonstrated that a failure surface can be established from a limited number of key guiding experiments. Therefore, in order to minimize the experimental effort required, we need to incorporate the time-dependent strength (Eqs 2, 3, and 4) into the failure criterion.

As already noted, the strength dependency on time, environment, and probabilities of failure can result in failure surfaces which are different not only in size but also in shape. The size change can be readily characterized by scalar modification of the strength parameters. On the other hand, the shape change may require adopting different failure criteria for different condition of failure. Such analytical inconvenience, however, does not occur with the use of the tensor polynomial criterion, since the shape of any failure surface can be described by modifying the coefficients of the polynomial without modifying the functional form. Because of this simplicity, the formulation of the time, environmental, and probabilistic failure surface will be established for the tensor polynomial failure criterion. In contracted notation, such a failure criterion can be expressed as

$$f(\sigma_k, t, \Theta) = F_i(t, \Theta)\sigma_i + F_{ij}(t, \Theta)\,\sigma_i\sigma_j + \cdots = 1 \qquad (8)$$

where F_i, F_{ij}, ... etc. are functions of time t and environment Θ and are failure tensors of second, fourth, ..., rank. For the purpose of this discussion, we will limit the development to the second-order polynominal in stress σ_i; formulations presented herein combined with formulations given in Refs 4 and 5 can readily lead to establishment for third- and higher-order terms. The time- and environment-dependent failure tensors can be expressed in terms of the time- and environment-dependent strengths from the guiding key experiments $[4]$

$$F_i(t, \Theta) = \frac{1}{X_i(t, \Theta)} - \frac{1}{X_i'(t, \Theta)}$$

$$F_{ii}(t, \Theta) = \frac{1}{X_i(t, \Theta)\,X_i'(t, \Theta)} \qquad \text{no summation} \qquad (9)$$

$$F_{ij}(t, \Theta) = f_{ij}(\sigma_i\,(t, \Theta)\,\sigma_j(t, \Theta) \qquad i \neq j$$

where X_i, X_i' are, respectively, the positive and negative strengths under uniaxial stress σ_i. The interaction failure tensor F_{ij} (F_{12} and Fig. 9) is determined from optimal combined stress σ_i and σ_j experiments. The determination of optimal ratios for these experiments has been given in Refs 4, 5, and 6. For the time being, we will consider F_i, F_{ij} as average or medium-strength parameters. It is apparent that the formulation of Eq 8 can characterize the general case of time and environmental loss of strength, which depends on the sign of the load, such as tension or compression, under complex states of stress.

Obviously, the key experiments required by Eq 9 are special cases of Eq. 2. For example, the uniaxial strength along the fiber direction is the case where the strength vector $\mathfrak{F}$ is oriented along the σ_1 axis in Fig. 1. Under this uniaxial loading condition, the time-dependent strengths, that is, Eq 4, reduce to

$$X\,(t) = \alpha_i \log\!\left(\frac{t}{t_0}\right) + X_i(t_0)$$

and

$$X_i'\,(t) = \alpha_i' \log\!\left(\frac{t}{t_0}\right) + X_i'(t_0) \qquad (10)$$

where α_i and α_i' are the respective scalar components of the shift vector in the positive and negative ith directions (for example, tension and compression). Similar but algebrically more complex expressions can be written for the biaxial strengths.

Combining Eqs 9 and 10, the time/environmental-dependent failure tensors $F_i(t, \Theta)$, $F_{ij}(t, \Theta)$, etc. can be determined. The effects of the relative magnitudes of the shift factors α_i, α_i' on the failure tensors are schematically illustrated in Fig. 2. Substitution of the failure tensors at time t into Eq 8 and then solving for the roots of Eq 8 lead to development of time/environment-dependent failure surfaces.

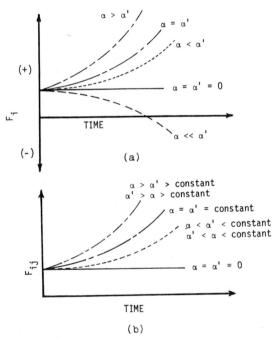

FIG. 2—*Effect of relative changes in shift parameters for tension and compression, α and α', respectively, on time-dependent strength tensor components* F_i *and* F_{ij}.

Thus the determination of the time/environment-dependent failure surface can be reduced to a tractable number of key experiments of the type indicated by Eq 10. A total of six such key experiments is required for two-dimensional orthotropic composites.

In the experimental program, we explore the viability of such a formulation.

Experimental Program

The experimental program is conducted on a two-dimensional orthotropic composite to explore the viability of the time/environment-dependent failure-surface formulation. To develop a complete failure surface for such a composite, the minimum number of six key experiments includes tension compression tests along and transverse to the fiber directions, respectively, a pure shear test, and a combined normal stress test at the optimal biaxial ratio. The total number of time-dependent experiments for these tests is quite large, while requiring relatively complex equipment for shear and biaxial tests. For exploratory purposes, we limited the experimental program reported herein to the establishment of the failure surface in the first quadrant, where all stress components are positive. For this stress quadrant, single tension and off-axis tension stress-rupture tests can be used to characterize the time-dependent failure surface. This experimental expediency results in the following constraints: (1) The off-axial tests do not provide optimal biaxial stress ratio for evaluating the interaction failure tensor F_{12}; (2) since no compressive tests are performed, the second-order failure tensor F_i cannot be evaluated. Thus, in the data correlation, we have to assume that time-dependent strength in tension and compression is the same. Taking into account the aforementioned constraints, the results presented herein should be considered as a first-order check of the characterization methodology proposed.

Specimen Preparation

The epoxy resin used in this study consisted of a mixture of 60 percent by weight Shell Epon 815 and 40 percent General Mills' Versamid 140. Chemical reaction between the amino groups of the Versamid resin and the epoxide groups of the Epon resin results in a cross-linked polymer. Mixing was conducted under vacuum to minimize the presence of voids. For the homogeneous resin specimens, the mixture was cast between parallel glass plates which had been treated with A-156 release agent and which were spaced 1/8 in. apart. The cure cycle consisted of a room temperature cure for 24 h, an intermediate cure at 100°C (212°F) for ½ h, and a final cure at 150°C (302°F) for 3½ h. This cure cycle results in a completely cross-linked resin.

The composite system studied had the foregoing epoxy resin as the matrix with the reinforcement being continuous unidirectional glass fibers. Composite material sheets were prepared by filament-winding five layers of Owens Corning Fiberglas 836AA-675 Type 30, continuous roving, which had a Type 836 silane sizing for adhesion with epoxy resins. Several preliminary sheets were prepared using PPG 1064 T6 glass, which had a proprietary glass surface treatment. The resulting unidirectionally reinforced sheets were approximately 0.05 in. thick. Fiber concentration of the sheets made from Owens Corning Fiberglas filament was determined by burn-off to be 51 percent by volume with a coefficient of variation of 4.4 percent. With the exception of a 4 h, rather than 24 h, room-temperature cure, the cure cycle was identical to that of the homogeneous material.

Tension and tension stress-rupture specimen blanks were cut from the homogeneous and composite sheets and then machined to the appropriate geometry. For the homogeneous and composite specimens with filament orientations of 15 through 90 deg, the familiar reduced cross section (dog-bone) geometry was used in accordance with the ASTM Test for Tensile Properties of Plastics (D 638), that is, a gage length of 2¼ in. with radii of 3 in. Straight-sided specimens with adhesively bonded tabs were used for the longitudinal (0 deg) tension and stress-rupture tests.

Experimental Procedure

Static Tension Tests—The ultimate tensile strength of the composite material was determined for fiber orientations of 0, 15, 30, 45, 60, 75 and 90 deg. Tension tests were conducted on an Instron Universal testing machine. The average time to failure for the series of specimens at each orientation was maintained at approximately five minutes by varying the crosshead speed.

Stress-Rupture Tests—The stress-rupture tests were also conducted on an Instron testing machine. A constant tensile creep load controlled by load feedback was applied to the test specimen. The ramp time to reach maximum creep load was approximately 30 s. The active environmental tests were performed by adapting a special grip and container assembly (shown schematically in Fig. 3) to the testing machine. This assembly allowed benzene, which was the active environment used in this study, to be in contact with the stressed specimen until fracture. The gripping areas were protected from benzene attack, and subsequent fracture, by the use of glycerine, as shown in Fig. 3.

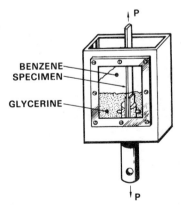

FIG. 3—*Schematic of active-environment container assembly.*

Experimental Results

Air Environment—Static tension tests were conducted with specimens having various filament orientations as discussed in the foregoing. The purpose of these tests was (i) to establish the static-failure surface and (ii) to provide baseline tensile strength data for the stress-rupture tests. The static shear strength was calculated from the off-axis tests as described earlier and was determined to be 4.6 ksi with a coefficient of variation of 12.2 percent, as given in Table 1. The static-failure surface, described by the tensor polynomial criterion in $\sigma_1 - \sigma_2 - \sigma_6$ stress space, is shown in Fig. 4. It should be noted that the failure surface shown in Fig. 4 was computed assuming first that $F_1 = F_2 = 0$ and second that $F_{12} = \frac{1}{2}$ (Stability limit value) $= -\frac{1}{2} (F_{11} F_{22})^{\frac{1}{2}}$. As discussed previously, the first assumption was required since compression tests were not conducted, and the second assumption was made since independent biaxial tests were not performed to independently characterize the F_{12} term.

Stress-rupture tests were conducted using groups of specimens (generally ten specimens in each group) having filament orientations varying from 0 to 90 deg at 15-deg intervals. Using the static strength results as a reference baseline, series of specimens were tested until rupture at decreasing values of constant stress, thereby allowing an assessment of (1) the time-dependent loss of strength at each orientation and (2) the distribution in time to failure for each orientation and test stress level. Analysis and discussion of the distributions in breaking time are presented later.

Representative cumulative distributions (or normalized survival population), $[n(t)]/N_T$, where $n(t)$ is the number of specimens surviving at time t, and N_T is the total number of specimens, are plotted in Fig. 5 versus the log time to failure for three representative filament orientations. From

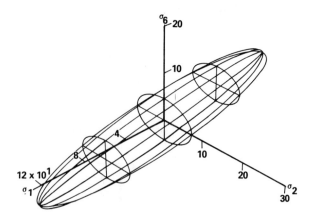

FIG. 4—*Quasi-static failure surface for glass-epoxy composite material* ($F_{12} = \frac{1}{2}$ *stability limit*).

TABLE 1—Computation of time-dependent shear strength.

| Time | Shear Strength, ksi | | | | | | Standard Deviation | Coefficient of Variation, % |
	15	30	45	60	75	Avg		
(Static Case)								
0.3 min[a]	5.24	4.43	5.14	4.35	3.91	4.61	0.563	12.2
100 min[a]	4.25	3.57	4.22	3.51	3.23	3.76	0.459	12.2
1000 min[a]	4.07	3.41	4.08	3.33	3.06	3.59	0.460	12.8

[a] F_{12} assumed equal to stability limit.

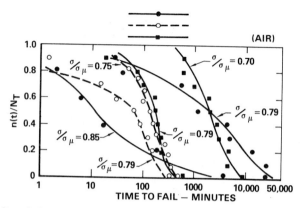

FIG. 5—*Cumulative distribution in breaking times for filament orientations of 0, 45, and 90 deg at varying stress levels.*

shifts in the median log time to failure with varying stress, the time-dependent loss of strength can be determined.

A three-dimensional plot of the loss in strength with increasing time as a function of filament orientation is shown in Fig. 6. The data points shown in this figure represent the median log time to break for each set of test parameters. It should be noted that the baseline strength values obtained from static tension tests have been shown at time = 0.3 min. The value of time has been computed using the relationship developed by Halpin for relating constant-loading-rate time to failure to creep time to failure [7]

$$\log t_b \text{ (under creep)} = t_b \text{ (constant loading rate)} + \log\beta \qquad (11)$$

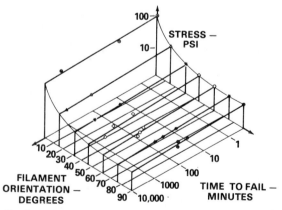

FIG. 6—*Results of stress rupture tests where median time to failure has been plotted as a function of stress level and filament orientation.*

where t_b is time to failure and β is the shape parameter of the Weibull distribution function describing the static tensile strength variability; β was determined to be approximately 14 for our static strength distributions.

Through the use of convolution techniques, the data presented in Fig. 6 can be compared in strength-orientation space. This is done in Fig. 7 where the stress-rupture data for all orientations have been convoluted to time = 100 min. The convolution was conducted using the observation of a linear decrease in strength with log time as described by Eq 4. For comparison, the static-strength curve versus filament orientation (time = 0.3 min) is also shown in Fig. 7.

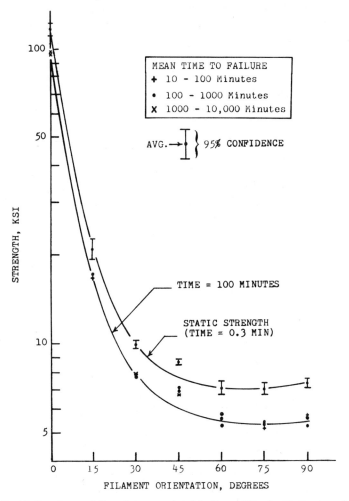

FIG. 7—*Median time-to-failure data convoluted to time=100 min. Static strength shown for reference.*

The linear decrease in strength with log time was observed for both simple and complex states of stress. This linear behavior was exhibited over a wide range of time. At very high creep stress (σ/σ ult > 0.88), however, where the breaking times are very short, a greater and nonlinear decrease in strength with time was observed. Due to this behavior, the selection of $F(t_0)$ must be made judiciously.

The strength tensors F_{11}, F_{22}, F_{12}, and F_{66} can be computed as a function of time through the use of the time-dependent loss-of-strength curves presented in Fig. 6. Note that the effect of time on F_{66} is not computed directly, but is determined by first calculating the loss in shear strength, S, using the known values of F_{11} and F_{22}, and the stability limit value for F_{12}. The calculated values for S at 100 and 1000 min are given in Table 1. The effect of increasing time on F_{11} and F_{12} is presented in Fig. 8 and on F_{22} and F_{66} in Fig. 9, respectively.

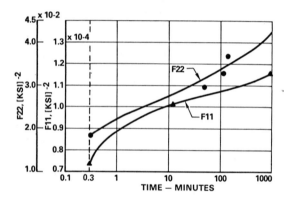

FIG. 8—*Time dependence of strength tensor components* F_{11} *and* F_{22}.

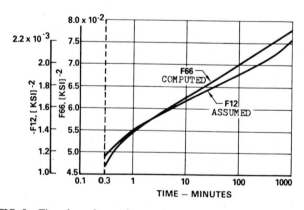

FIG. 9—*Time dependence of strength tensor components* F_{12} *and* F_{66}.

Based on the strength tensors' relationship with time, as shown in Figs. 8 and 9, the time/environment-dependent tensor polynomial criterion, Eq 8, can now be used to describe the failure surface at any arbitrary time. For example, Fig. 10 shows failure surfaces at time = 0.3 (static case) and 100 min. Only the first quadrant of the two failure surfaces has been shown in Fig. 10 since, as stated earlier, compression stress-rupture tests were not conducted. Note in Fig. 10 that the shape of the failure surface changes with increasing time, since the rate in loss of strength, that is, $\bar{a}$, varies as a result of material anisotropy.

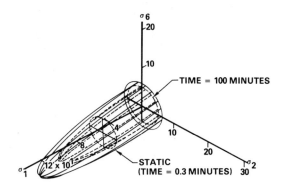

FIG. 10—*Effect of time on the first-quadrant failure surface.*

Benzene Environment—In addition to the tests conducted in air, stress-rupture tests were conducted also in a liquid benzene environment. The objectives of this series of tests were (1) to characterize the acceleration in time-dependent loss of strength resulting from the presence of benzene, and (2) to determine the effect of the benzene environment on the distribution in breaking times.

Tests were performed with groups of specimens having filament orientations at 0, 30, 45, 60, 75 and 90 deg, respectively. Figure 11 presents the experimentally observed cumulative distributions for the 0-deg orientation specimens at two stress levels. For comparison, the 0-deg specimen distributions obtained from air environment tests have also been presented and, as is observed, the benzene does not significantly change the variability in breaking times. Figure 12 presents the cumulative distributions for 45- and 90-deg specimen groups at three stress levels, respectively. As is illustrated in Fig. 12, the distributions in breaking time appear similar for these two orientations, and are significantly different from the 0-deg distributions. The variability in breaking times is discussed later.

The experimentally observed time-dependent loss of strength at each of the six orientations is shown in Fig. 13 where the median log time to

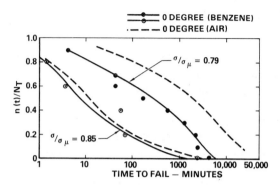

FIG. 11—*Cumulative distribution in time to failure for 0-deg specimens tested in benzene environment. Air environment tests shown for comparison.*

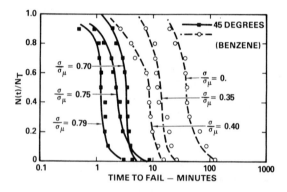

FIG. 12—*Cumulative distribution in time to failure for 45- and 90-deg specimens tested in benzene environment.*

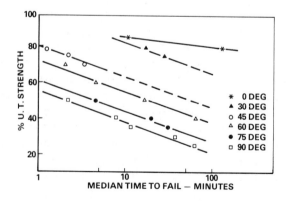

FIG. 13—*Time-dependent loss of strength of composite material at various filament orientations in the presence of benzene.*

failure $[n(t)/N_T = 0.5]$ versus ratio of applied creep stress to ultimate tensile strength is plotted. As is observed, there is a linear loss of strength with increasing log time, and the rate is similar for all orientations except 0 deg. Furthermore, the effect of increasing the orientation to the applied load from 30 to 90 deg at 15-deg intervals is simply to shift the strength-log time curve to a lower percent-ultimate-strength intercept. A comparison of the stress-rupture data from tests conducted in the benzene environment, convoluted to time = 100 min, with the data from the air environment tests is shown in Fig. 14. The effect of benzene is seen to significantly reduce the allowable stress level for a particular survival life-time, with the reduction in percent ultimate strength greatest at 90-deg orientations.

Values of the time/environment-dependent strength tensor components, that is, F_{ij}, were computed from the benzene environment stress-rupture data. Using the F_{ij} values at 100 min and the tensor polynomial criterion, Eq 8, a failure surface was generated for this time history and is shown in Fig. 15. For comparison, the failure surface at equal time, but with the air environment, is also shown. As is observed in this figure, the benzene has little effect on the longitudinal strength and significantly reduces both the transverse and shear strengths. This observation would indicate that the time-dependent loss of strength of E-glass filaments is not greatly increased in the presence of benzene, but that the time-dependent response of the matrix (Epon 815-Versamid 140) is dramatically changed—the latter possibly being due to a reduction in surface energy considerations for flaw growth.

It should be noted that the swelling stresses which are generated as a result of the sorption of benzene by the matrix do not significantly shorten the survival life since the magnitude of these stresses is negligible [8]. The time scale of the stress-rupture tests in benzene does not permit significant sorption of the benzene as is shown in Ref 9, where the sorption-kinetics of benzene by both the epoxy resin and composite material system are discussed in detail.

Statistical Variability in Rupture Times

In the preceding sections of this paper, failure surfaces in the first quadrant stress space have been developed from the time/environment-dependent tensor polynomial criterion and experimental observations of time-dependent loss of strength. The surfaces have been used to characterize the composite material's mechanical behavior in both air and benzene environments. The static and time/environment-dependent failure surfaces which have been generated, however, only represent the material's "average" strength characteristics and do not include the variability in strength and time to rupture. As is true with all materials, composites

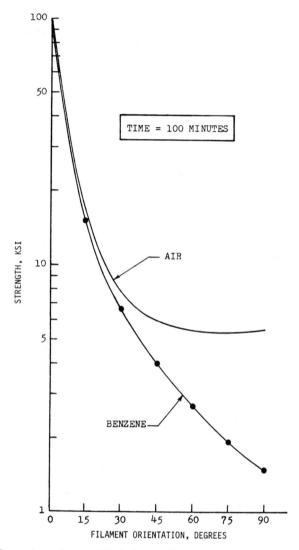

FIG. 14—*Comparison of strength in benzene with strength in air at time = 100 min. Data points indicate convoluted data.*

exhibit a large scatter in breaking strengths even when the specimens are prepared and tested under assumed identical conditions [10]. Likewise, composites show large scatter in stress-rupture times when tested under assumed identical conditions.

In order to employ shift parameters to predict a physical process (such as time-dependent fracture, in this case), it is necessary to establish that the physical process in question is the same within the time scale of the shift operation. A formulation such as Eq 8, which is used to define the failure surface, only operates on the median, characteristic, or average rupture time, and does not take into account the observed variability in rupture times.

As a result, a characterization of the distribution in time to failure (or strength) at increasing time must supplement the use of the time/environment-dependent strength tensors (Figs. 8 and 9) and Eq 4 in the complete description of the physical process of time-dependent loss of strength.

It has been postulated [7,10] that the effect of a chemical environment would be to change the characteristic lifetime without changing the dispersion of the data. Therefore, if this is the case, that is, if there is no change in the shape parameter when the tests are performed in an active environment, the operational techniques necessary to predict environmental effects would simply involve the generation of shift parameters. We show later that the effect of the active environment, in addition to significantly shifting the first-quadrant failure surface (Fig. 15), significantly alters the shape parameter.

The cumulative distribution of survival lifetime may be defined as

$$\frac{n(t)}{N_T} = \exp \left[- \left(\frac{t}{\hat{t}} \right)^{\beta} \right]$$ (12)

where

$n(t)$ = number of specimens surviving at time, t,
N_T = total number of specimens,
t = time,
$\hat{t}$ = characteristic time to failure, and
β = shape parameter.

The shape parameter can be determined from the experimentally ob-

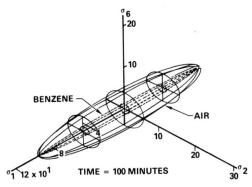

FIG. 15—*Effect of benzene on the failure surface at time = 100 min.*

served cumulative distribution by taking the ln ln of both sides of Eq 12, that is

$$\left[\ln - \ln\left[\frac{n(t)}{N_T}\right]\right] = \beta \ln t + K \qquad (13)$$

where $K = \beta \ln 1/\hat{t}$, and β is the slope of the line representing the distribution.

It has been observed earlier (Figs. 11 and 12) that the variability in breaking times for the 0-deg specimen sets was significantly greater than the 45- and 90-deg sets. In addition, the variability of the off-axis specimen time to failures decreased when testing in benzene, whereas the 0-deg specimen variability did not exhibit an appreciable change over that observed with the air environment. From these experimental observations, it may be concluded that the study of distributions in breaking times of composite specimens subjected to complex stress states, both with and without the presence of an active environment, is an extremely difficult task. This difficulty arises from the fact that a specimen group subjected to complex stress states (for example, off-axis tension) can result in a mixed distribution of breaking times. Under complex stress states, longitudinal and transverse stresses act simultaneously, with each having a distinct and separate distribution.

The failure surface which exists at any particular time and environmental condition has associated with it confidence surfaces which are analogous to confidence intervals in two-dimensional space. These surfaces may be computed with a knowledge of (1) the cumulative distributions of survival lifetime, Eq 12; (2) the time-dependent strength relationships, Eqs 2 and 4; and (3) the time/environment-dependent tensor polynomial criterion, Eq 8. For example, the lower-bound time to failure t can be computed, and is [10]

$$\check{t} = \frac{\hat{t}}{\left[\frac{1}{2n} \chi_Y^2 (2n)\right]^{1/\beta}} \qquad (14)$$

where n is the sample size, t is the estimated characteristic time to failure (one can use regression, least-square, or maximum-likelihood estimator methods), and $\chi_Y^2 (2n)$ is the chi-squared distribution with $2n$ degrees of freedom.

Having established $\check{t}$, the design-limit time to break can be computed from Eq 12, and is

$$t_R = \check{t} [\ln (1/R)]^{1/\beta} \qquad (15)$$

where R is the desired reliability. It should be noted that Eqs 14 and 15 require β to be known.

The limit vectors $\mathcal{F}$ of the strength vector $\mathcal{F}$ can now be determined as follows

$$\mathcal{F}^*(t_R) = \mathcal{F}(t) - \Delta\mathcal{F} \tag{16}$$

where

$$\Delta\mathcal{F} = \mathcal{F}(t_R) - \mathcal{F}(t) \tag{17}$$

and from Eqs 4 and 15

$$|\mathcal{F}^*(t_R)| = |\bar{\alpha}|\ln\{\check{i}\,[\ln(1/R)]^{1/\beta}/t_0\} + \mathcal{F}_0 \tag{18}$$

From Eqs 16 and 18, the confidence limits at any arbitrary stress ratio loading can be established.

The use of Eqs 14 through 18 requires the distributions in breaking times to remain constant during the time history experienced by the material. Furthermore, the distributions must remain constant at increasing time under simple or complex stress-state conditions.

In this study it was of interest to determine if, knowing the distributions in breaking times (or strengths) of the longitudinal and transverse specimen groups, the distributions of specimens under complex stress states could be predicted through the use of the confidence level failure surfaces as shown schematically in Fig. 16. A representative failure

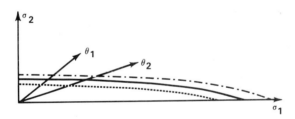

FIG. 16—*Schematic of failure surface and confidence interval surfaces in $\sigma_1 - \sigma_2$ space where Θ_1 and Θ_2 represent arbitrary stress ratios.*

surface has been illustrated in $\sigma_1 - \sigma_2$ space (for ease in visualization) with typical upper and lower confidence interval surfaces. At some arbitrary loading ratio, Θ_1 or Θ_2 for example, the variability in strength (or rupture time) is expected to be between the limits imposed by the longitudinal and transverse variability in strengths, respectively.

Typical distributions observed for several representative orientations (varying states of stress) are characterized in Fig. 17 (air environment) and Fig. 18 (benzene environment). The variability in failure times of the 0-deg specimen sets was identical for both air and benzene testing. Also,

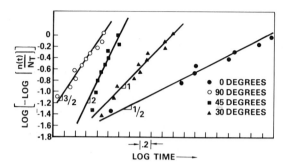

FIG. 17—*Plot of the log-log of the cumulative distribution versus log time to failure for computation of Weibull shape parameter (air environment).*

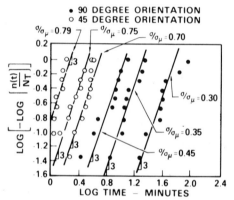

FIG. 18—*Plot of the log-log of the cumulative distribution versus log time to failure for computation of Weibull shape parameter (air environment).*

the statistical variability in data from tests at 45-deg orientations in air was approximately the same as the variability observed with homogeneous resin specimens tested in air. In addition, within experimental error, the distributions in time to failure for each orientation at various levels of constant creep stress, that is, different characteristic time to fail, did not change, and therefore satisfy the requirements of Eqs 14 through 18.

It should be noted that the effect of benzene on the behavior of the off-axis specimens, in addition to reducing the characteristic log time to fail, also significantly reduced the variability (larger β) in failure times. This experimental evidence appears to contradict the postulated environment effect discussed earlier.

The trend in the statistical variability of the stress-rupture data observed in Fig. 17 for the air environment and in Fig. 18 for the benzene environment—where the distribution of all orientations was very similar, as might be expected based on the shape of the failure surface (Fig. 15)—indicates that one may be able to use the tensor polynomial expression to characterize the statistical variability under any arbitrary complex loading condition. The distributions used to reach this *tentative* conclusion, however, were based on a relatively small number (generally 10) of specimens for each test condition; in addition, due to experimental limitations, tests were not conducted at all of the critical stress ratios necessary to fully characterize the surface. Accordingly, this conclusion should be considered as tentative, and contingent to future critical experimental verification.

Conclusion

The tensor polynomial strength criterion originally developed for the description of statis failure response surfaces of composite materials can be easily extended to permit a description of transient failure surfaces which result from the material's time-dependent loss of strength. The modified criterion, which retains all of the operational advantages of the original formulation, uses time/environment-dependent strength tensor components, $F_i(t,\Theta)$ and $F_{ij}(t,\Theta)$. In addition, it has been demonstrated that environmental effects on material response can be conveniently characterized and predicted through the use of the extended tensor polynomial strength criterion.

The strength vectors, $\mathfrak{F}$, having directions specified by the direction cosines and magnitudes defined as the radial distances to the failure surface, can be used with their associated vectorial shift parameters, α, to describe time-dependent changes in strength of composite materials subjected to complex stress states. Through the use of the strength vector concept, it is possible to extend the "classical" expressions for the material durability, which have been developed for characterizing material response under uniaxial loadings, to the case of complex loadings.

For the glass-epoxy material system used in this study, it may be concluded that the time-dependent loss of strength over a wide range of time in both environments, that is, air and benzene, and under both simple and complex stress states, is linear with increasing log time. This linear relationship, however, does not hold for short times (high creep stress, $\sigma/\sigma_{ult} > 0.88$), where a greater and nonlinear decrease in strength with time was observed. The rate of decrease in strength in the air environment was observed to be a function of filament orientation and hence the state of stress. The 0-deg specimens exhibited the smallest and the 90-deg specimens showed the largest relative decrease in strength with increasing time. The off-axis specimen groups ($0 < \Theta < 90$) showed rates of decrease in strength between the observed rates for 0 and 90-deg specimens, respectively; the rate increased with an increase in filament orientation to the applied load.

In contrast to results obtained from air environment tests, the rate of decrease in strength (that is, $\vec{a}$) of all orientation groups tested in benzene was approximately the same with the single exception of the 0-deg specimen group, which showed a significantly lower rate of loss in strength than the other orientations. In addition, all specimen groups tested in benzene had a greater decrease in strength with increasing time than comparable groups tested in air. Furthermore, the presence of benzene also shifted the median log time to failure at all filament orientations to significantly shorter times when compared with tests conducted in air at the same stress level.

For the transverse (90-deg orientation) specimens, a stress level of 50 percent of the ultimate tensile strength resulted in a median time to failure of only 2 min, and at stress levels greater than 50 percent the specimens failed on loading. For the longitudinal specimens, the effect of the benzene on survival life was considerably less drastic since the shift at a stress level of 79 percent ultimate tensile strength was less than one decade, whereas transverse specimens would not even sustain this stress level. The shift in median log time to failure for the off-axis specimen ($0 < \Theta < 90$) groups as a result of the benzene environment was between 0 and 90-deg limits.

Based on sorption kinetic studies conducted to characterize the environment/composite-material interaction, it may be concluded that the shift to lower characteristic times to failure when testing in benzene was not a direct result of the superposition of swelling stresses accompanying sorption. These stresses were computed to be less than 20 psi. It therefore can be concluded that the reduction in life in the presence of benzene is a result of the reduction in surface energy necessary for flaw growth or fiber-matrix debonding or both.

The statistical variability in strengths and rupture times can be incorporated into the time/environment-dependent tensor polynomial failure criterion for the design of fail-safe structures through the use of reliability limits on the strength vectors. Investigation of the statistical variability in rupture times observed during this research revealed (1) that the active environment, benzene, does not significantly change the distribution of 0-deg orientative specimen time to failure when compared with air testing, and (2) that benzene does change the distribution (that is, shape parameter) for all orientations other than 0 deg. As a result of item (2), the use of shift parameters alone cannot adequately describe the time-dependent response of composite materials in active environments.

Finally, the trend of the statistical variability of the stress-rupture data appears to indicate that one may be able to characterize variability under complex stress in a similar manner to that used to characterize strength in the complex stress domain. This conclusion, however, at best can be considered tentative and contingent to future critical experimental verification.

Acknowledgment

This work is part of the study of composites supported by the Monsanto/Washington University Association sponsored by the Advanced Research Project Agency, Department of Defense and the Office of Naval Research, under contract No. N00014-66-C-0218, formerly N00014-66-C-0045.

References

[1] Bartenev, G. M. and Zuyev, Vu S., *Strength and Failure of Visco-Elastic Materials,* Pergamon Press, Oxford, 1968.

[2] Kwei, T. K., *Journal of Applied Polymer Science,* Vol. 10, 1966, p. 1647.

[3] Tsai, S. W. and Wu, E. M., *Journal of Composite Materials,* Vol. 5, 1971, p. 58.

[4] Wu, E. M., "Phenomenological Anistropic Failure Criterion," *Treatise on Composite Materials,* Broutman, Krock and Sendeckyi, Eds., Academic Press, New York, 1973.

[5] Wu, E. M., *Journal of Composite Materials,* Vol. 6, 1972, p. 472.

[6] Wu, E. M. and Scheublein, J. K. in *Composite Materials: Testing and Design (Third Conference), ASTM STP 546,* American Society for Testing and Materials, 1974, pp. 188–206.

[7] Halpin, J. C., "Structural Reliability Characterization of Advanced Composites," *Proceedings of the Colloquium on Structural Reliability: The Impact of Advanced Materials on Engineering Design,* J. L. Swedlow, T. A. Kruse and J. C. Halpin, Eds., Carnegie Mellon University Press, Pittsburgh, Pa., 1973.

[8] Ruhmann, D. C. and Wu, E. M., "The Effect of Solvents and Stress on The Stress-Rupture Life of Glass Epoxy Composites," *American Chemical Society—Organic Coatings and Plastics Chemistry,* Vol. 31, No. 1, 1971, p. 501.

[9] Ruhmann, D. C. and Wu, E. M., "The Effect of Stress on Diffusion in Composites—Experimental Observations," *American Chemical Society—Polymer Preprints,* Vol. 14, No. 1, 1973, p. 475.

[10] Halpin, J. C., Kopf, J. R., and Goldberg, W., *Journal of Composite Materials,* Vol. 4, 1970, p. 462.

L. D. Berman[1]

Reliability of Composite Zero-Expansion Structures for Use in Orbital Environment

REFERENCE: Berman, L. D., "Reliability of Composite Zero-Expansion Structures for Use in Orbital Environment," *Composite Reliability, ASTM STP 580,* American Society for Testing and Materials, 1975, pp. 288–297.

ABSTRACT: Composite sandwich structures, composed of graphite-epoxy face sheets on aluminum honeycomb core, were found to successfully withstand 15 000 thermal cycles between −250 and 150°F (−157 and 66°C) in vacuum. Although thermal cycling induced microcracking in the face sheets, laminate flexural and tensile properties were unaffected, and the only noticeable effect was on the coefficient of thermal expansion and flatwise tensile strength of the sandwich. In addition, exposure of the structure to 95 percent relative humidity resulted in a finite change in dimensions, but no effect on the coefficient of thermal expansion.

These environmental effects were determined on composite sandwich structures selected for isotropy, uniformity of mechanical properties at temperature extremes, and balanced thermal expansion characteristics in two perpendicular directions.

KEY WORDS: composite materials, sandwich structures, thermal expansion, thermal cycling tests, vacuum, moisture, mechanical properties, microstructures

Spacecraft antenna reflectors for use at very high frequencies must be fabricated to extremely close tolerances and must maintain their precise shape throughout operational life in orbit. This requirement means that reflector structures must exhibit a coefficient of thermal expansion (α) close to zero over a temperature range of −250 to 150°F (−157 to 66°C).

Composite structures having near-zero coefficients have been fabricated and tested for the past several years and have been well characterized for structural, thermal, and physical properties. The remaining unknown delaying actual application in space flight centered on the reliability of the structure to maintain shape in high relative humidity storage conditions

[1] Assistant manager, Materials Engineering, TRW Systems, Redondo Beach, Calif. 90278.

and during deep thermal cycling in vacuum. Until 1972, the only known life testing done had determined the effect of limited thermal cycling on α, and proved that absorbed moisture affected the finite dimensions of graphite-epoxy laminates.[2] Only end point data, however, were available. There was no attempt to determine physical or mechanical changes as a function of cycling.

This paper deals with the reliability of composite sandwich structures during and after exposure to extensive thermal cycling in vacuum. The effect of cycling on mechanical, physical, and thermal properties is discussed. In addition, a high relative humidity storage environment has been evaluated for its effect on dimensional and contour measurement.

Materials

In order to meet structural and dynamic criteria applicable to reflectors, a sandwich construction was selected as the optimum design approach. The configuration consisted of graphite-epoxy multi-oriented face sheets bonded to an aluminum honeycomb core using a supported film adhesive. The use of aluminum core material gave rise to an immediate problem not only because of its high thermal expansion coefficient, but because it exerts a greater influence on thermal expansion of the sandwich in the core ribbon direction than in the transverse direction.

Extensive evaluation of fiber-resin combinations led to the conclusion that dimensional stability could best be obtained by using the very high-modulus fibers such as Celanese GY70, which also exhibit a highly negative α.[3] Further experimentation showed that six plies of preimpregnated tape per face sheet were necessary to provide sandwich balance, reasonable isotropy, and an α very close to zero. The bidirectional difference in α was substantially reduced by adjusting the relative locations of the 0 and 90-deg ply orientations with respect to distance from the core. In this manner, the final configuration, [90, -30, 30, 0, 60, -60/adhesive/core/adhesive/-60, 60, 0, 30, -30, 90], was utilized throughout the environmental test program.

Resin selections for tape preimpregnation were based on the cure procedure to be followed, resistance to microcracking at low temperature, and retention of room-temperature properties at high- and low-temperature extremes. Fiberite 934 was the primary choice, with Whittaker 5208 as a backup resin system. Celanese R-350A was selected for its ability to cure properly under vacuum conditions without augmented pressure. All

[2] Hertz, J., Christian, J. L., Varlas, M. et al, "Advanced Composite Applications for Spacecraft and Missiles," Technical Report ASML-TR-71-186, Vol. II, Air Force Materials Laboratory, Dayton, Ohio, Feb. 1972.

[3] Berman, L. D., "Advanced Composite Materials Studies," Technical Report 99994-6138-R0-00, TRW Systems, Redondo Beach, Calif., Dec., 1971.

three exhibited excellent retention of room-temperature properties at − 300 and 350 °F (− 184 and 177 °C).

Typical property data for GY70/934 laminates simulating face sheets obtained via a co-curing process are illustrated in Fig. 1. Mechanical property uniformity is demonstrated as a function of temperature for both unidirectional and multi-oriented laminates. In addition, isotropy of the oriented laminates has been achieved.

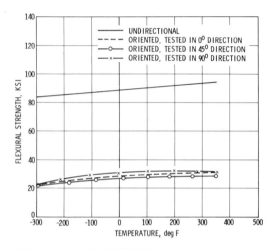

FIG. 1—*Flexural strength of GY70/934 laminates versus temperature.*

Three separate cure processes were used to fabricate specimens for the environmental test program so as to blanket the parameters of cost versus structural integrity. These cure processes are detailed in Table 1.

Each of the systems listed in the foregoing were fully evaluated in this environmental test program. In addition, to establish a trend, three other

TABLE 1—*Cure cycle for environmental test specimens.*

Fiber	Resin	Layup	Cure
GY70	Celanese R-350A	Single layup of core, adhesive and faces	Vacuum pressure only at 350 °F (177 °C)
GY70	Fiberite 934	(1) Six-ply-oriented faces	(1) 75-psi autoclave cure at 350 °F (177 °C)
		(2) Cured faces, adhesive and core	(2) Vacuum pressure only at 250 °F (121 °C)
GY70	Fiberite 934	(1) Single layup of core, adhesive and faces	(1) Vacuum pressure only to 250 °F (121 °C)
			(2) 50-psi autoclave pressure applied
			(3) 50-psi cure at 350 °F (177 °C)

co-cured systems were partially evaluated to determine the effect of thermal cycling in vacuum on α. These included GY70/5208 to provide a backup resin system, GY70/934 with 5000 Å of vacuum-deposited aluminum, and 0.005 in. of Z-93 thermal coating applied to one face, and a hybrid composed of interlayered GY70/934 and HM-S/934 in each face sheet. The latter was layed up with 0, 90, 60, -30, -60, 30-deg faces with the 0, 60, and -60-deg plies composed of GY70 fiber and the remaining plies of lower-modulus Hercules HM-S fibers.

Procedure

For each material system evaluated, sandwich panels, 6-ply unidirectional laminates, and 6-ply multi-oriented laminates were fabricated using the cure process designated for that system. The multi-oriented sandwich panel was used to provide tension, flatwise tension, weight loss, and microstructure specimens, and α specimens in two perpendicular directions. Multi-oriented laminates provided additional coupons for determination of tensile and flatwise tensile properties of laminates and to observe potential warpage due to thermal cycling.

The unidirectional laminate provided the necessary flexure test specimens. Unidirectional orientation was selected for flexure tests to eliminate any possible variance that might occur from application of load to opposite sides of the same configuration. The panels were machined to provide controls and specimens for environmental exposure.

Several bell-jar type vacuum systems were used in this program, each of which provided vacuum equivalent to 10^{-6} torr. Each contained copper mounting plates with brazed tubes through which liquid nitrogen and hot water flowed alternately to provide cooling and heating. Specimens were mounted using conductive silicones. Thermocouples were installed on the specimens, and preliminary test cycling was performed to establish cooling and heating times, with minimum dwell at the temperature extremes. Thereafter, the system was automatically controlled to operate between -250 and $150\,°F$ (-157 and $66\,°C$). A single heating and cooling cycle averaged 10 min.

Specimens were removed from the vacuum chambers at intervals of 10, 25, 50, 100, 250, 500, 1000, 3000, 8000, and 15 000 cycles. Flexure and weight loss specimens were tested immediately upon removal, while α coupons were sealed in nitrogen-filled bags until testing could be accomplished. All other specimens required further preparation before test results could be obtained. Flatwise tension specimens were prepared for test by bonding 2-in. cubes of aluminum to each face using a room-temperature setting adhesive. Tension specimens were prepared by reinforcing the ends with fiber glass. Clevis arrangements were attached to reinforced sandwich coupons for loading, while laminated coupons were simply held by self-aligning grips.

Flexure, tension, and flatwise tension specimens were tested in an Instron test machine. Thermal expansion characteristics were determined using a vertical quartz tube dilatometer designed and built at TRW.

Discussion of Results

Although several systems were evaluated, data are shown only for the GY70/934 co-cured system. All systems reacted similarly, with the exception that microstructure varied with cure process.

Typical photomicrographs of face sheets as a function of thermal cycling in vacuum are shown in Fig. 2. Whereas microcracks were not visible in any control specimens, they do appear after 50 cycles and continue to increase in quantity until about 3000 cycles have been reached. Thereafter, there is little change in quantity, but crack width generally is enlarged. In a few cases, particularly where cracks appear to emanate from voids, the beginnings of interlaminar separation can be seen. The importance of this is discussed in relation to flatwise tension test results.

Evidence of microcracking is directly proportional to void content, and hence varies with the cure process used. Void content resulting from the vacuum cure process is close to 10 percent and results in the largest number of microcracks due to cycling. Void content in faces autoclaved at 75 psi is on the order of 2 percent, while the co-curing process results in voids approximating 3 to 4 percent. The least number of microcracks occurs in fully autoclaved faces.

Despite the occurrence of cracking, flexural and tensile properties are essentially unchanged as a result of thermal cycling in vacuum, as can be seen in Figs. 3 and 4. This is strong evidence that microcracks, even though numerous after 15 000 cycles, have not resulted in enough broken fibers or debonding to significantly reduce mechanical properties.

The flatwise tensile strength of the sandwich structure is shown to decrease by about 50 percent (Fig. 5) as a result of environmental exposure. This value is still acceptable for structural integrity. All failures occurred in face sheets rather than face-to-core bond, however, indicating that failure was due to interlaminar separation resulting from propagation of microcracks. Laminate flatwise tensile strength, on the other hand, shows only about a 20 percent decrease, at average strengths far exceeding the failure strength of the sandwich. There are two reasons for this: (1) the laminate microstructure contains less voids than that of a co-cured face sheet, and (2) stresses induced during thermal cycling are higher in the sandwich structure due to additional positive expansion components present in the form of cured adhesive and aluminum core. This is further confirmed by the fact that all failures occurred between the first and second plies from the bond line.

Weight loss due to vacuum exposure was negligible. An initial loss of less than 1 percent was noted due to extraction of moisture. Further reductions in weight were approximately 0.1 percent for all material systems.

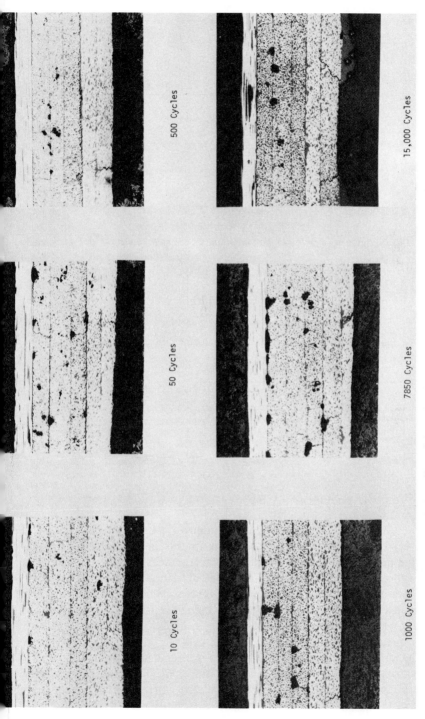

FIG. 2—*Effect of thermal cycling on GY70/934 microstructure (~ ×38).*

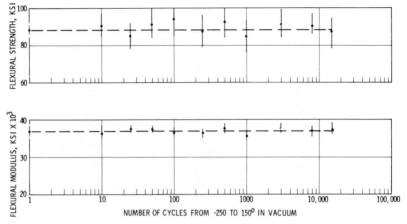

FIG. 3—*Effect of thermal cycling on flexural properties of unidirectional GY70/934 laminates.*

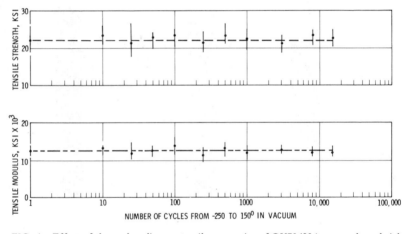

FIG. 4—*Effect of thermal cycling on tensile properties of GY70/934 co-cured sandwich.*

The effect of thermal cycling in vacuum on α is shown in Fig. 6. The real effect of microcracking is evident in this illustration. As thermal cycling progresses, and the quantity of microcracks increases, α decreases since the highly positive α resin matrix is deteriorating while the negative α fibers are still intact. At about 3000 cycles, α begins to level off and approach an asymptote. This behavior coincides with the microstructure study, which indicates very little change in quantity of microcracks with subsequent cycling.

The original difference in α, in two perpendicular orientations, disappears with thermal cycling, as shown in Fig. 6. This result can probably best be explained by considering the relative stiffness of the aluminum core in the two directions. In the 0-deg test configuration, both the core

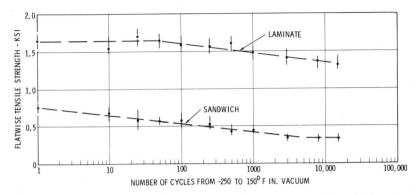

FIG. 5—*Effect of thermal cycling on flatwise tensile properties of GY70/934 laminates and co-cured sandwich.*

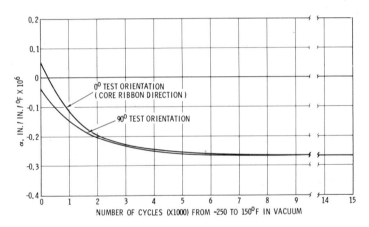

FIG. 6—*Effect of thermal cycling on thermal expansion of GY70/934 co-cured sandwich.*

ribbon and the third ply from the core are oriented in the test direction. In the 90-deg configuration, only the outer ply of graphite tape is oriented in the test direction. Since the 0-deg test coupons initially yield more positive α results, it is apparent that the direction of the core ribbon has an influence. During thermal cycling, this influence should result in higher induced stresses and, consequently, more microcracking. The α of 0-deg test coupons would therefore be lowered at a faster rate than that of 90-deg test coupons.

Hybrid Configuration

Because of the bidirectional difference in α, experimentation was initiated with the hybrid composite sandwich described earlier. The six-ply face constructed in this manner was arranged so that the core ribbon and one GY70/934 ply were oriented in the same direction. This placed a lower-modulus HM-S/934 ply at 90-deg to the core ribbon and resulted in a more positive α in that test direction, and virtual elimination of the bidirectional difference.

This construction was thermally cycled in vacuum in the same manner as previously exposed specimens to ascertain the effect on α. The bidirectional difference was eliminated not only at the outset, but never occurred during cycling, as shown in Fig. 7. Since a study of the microstructure was never performed, an experimental explanation cannot be offered.

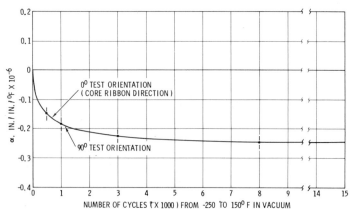

FIG. 7—*Effect of thermal cycling on thermal expansion of GY70/HM-S/934 co-cured sandwich.*

The hybrid construction, pending further studies, appears to offer advantages over single-fiber construction. Not only is the bidirectional differential α eliminated, but the partial use of HM-S material, which is 25 percent thinner than GY70 material, decreases the total weight of face sheets between 10 and 15 percent. A complete evaluation of this type of construction is warranted.

Moisture Effect

The effect of moisture was determined using α specimens which were initially dried in a vacuum oven. These specimens were placed in dilatometers in inert atmosphere, stabilized at room temperature, and dilatometer position recorded as shown in Fig. 8. Expansion was obtained between -300 and $212\,°F$ (-184 and $100\,°C$), represented by Curve A, followed by restabilization at room temperature. Specimens were then exposed to 95 percent relative humidity overnight, resulting in specimen growth as indicated. Helium was then substituted for moisture and a second expansion curve established from -300 to $212\,°F$ (-184 to $100\,°C$),

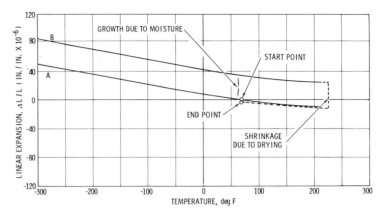

FIG. 8—*Effect of moisture on dimensions and expansion of GY70/934 co-cured sandwich.*

as represented by Curve B. There is no difference in slope between Curves A and B, signifying that moisture does not affect α. At the completion of this second heating cycle, the temperature was set at 225 °F (107 °C) and held overnight to extract moisture, resulting in shrinkage of the specimens to their approximate initial length. Specimens were then cooled at room temperature, stabilized, and the final position of the dilatometer recorded.

These data indicate that, although α is unaffected by moisture, finite dimensions are affected. Therefore, contour profiles of complex curvature structures must be measured in a controlled environment to ensure that the extremely tight tolerance on focal length can be met.

General Conclusions

The environmental testing performed has proven that thermally induced stresses in composite structures result in deterioration of the microstructure, but the resultant decay does not appreciably affect mechanical properties. Thermal expansion and flatwise tensile characteristics are affected, but only within a band believed acceptable for most applications. The test procedure which has been established is believed to be a relatively economical, short-duration method of predicting life of a structure in orbit and has been accepted for qualification as well as characterization of a materials system.

R. A. Heller,[1] A. B. Thakker,[1] and C. E. Arthur[1]

Temperature Dependence of the Complex Modulus for Fiber-Reinforced Materials

REFERENCE: Heller, R. A., Thakker, A. B., and Arthur, C. E., "**Temperature Dependence of the Complex Modulus for Fiber-Reinforced Materials,**" *Composite Reliability, ASTM STP 580,* American Society for Testing and Materials, 1975, pp. 298–308.

ABSTRACT: To examine the time-temperature dependence of fiber-reinforced composite materials, forced vibration experiments have been conducted. After suitable statistical smoothing techniques have been applied to the raw data, the complex moduli (storage and loss moduli) of boron-epoxy and graphite-epoxy have been determined for a wide range of temperatures and frequencies. The materials are shown to exhibit an Arrhenius type of behavior.

KEY WORDS: composite materials, fibers, reinforced plastics, epoxy resins, viscoelasticity, modulus of elasticity

The dynamic behavior of viscoelastic materials has in the past been successfully analyzed with the aid of the complex Young's modulus and the complex shear modulus which for viscoelastic materials are functions of time and environment (temperature, humidity, etc.).

The complex modulus is most conveniently determined from the measurement of antiresonant frequencies and the bandwidth of the impedence curve near antiresonance.

With suitable time-temperature shift parameters and "master" curves derived for specific reference conditions from the experiments, the complex modulus can usually be extrapolated to a wide range of frequencies and temperatures.

The most widely used method for the determination of the shift parameter and the master curve involves the graphical shifting of a family of log-time-modulus curves obtained at various temperatures until they over-

[1] Professor and graduate research assistants, respectively, Department of Engineering Science and Mechanics, Virginia Polytechnic Institute and State University, Blacksburg, Va. 24061.

lap each other [1].[2] This process is usually performed by eye and depends to a great extent on the experience of the observer, particularly when data obtained from a large group of specimens exhibit significant statistical dispersion.

In such cases the methodology of response surfaces may be utilized to obtain multidimensional "best fit" surfaces with the aid of a computer. Such a surface obviates the need for master curves and shift parameters and can be used for extrapolation and interpolation purposes. In addition, confidence and tolerance bands can be derived to aid in reliability calculations.

Fiber-reinforced epoxy matrix composite materials consist of a combination of elastic and viscoelastic components. Measurements of the complex modulus indicate time, temperature, and humidity sensitivity in those materials also. The large statistical dispersion of data characteristic of composites, however, has made the conventional methods of evaluation and extrapolation impractical.

Based on a large group of experiments, response surfaces have been generated from which the usual shift parameters can be evaluated directly, though the availability of the surface equations makes such computations unnecessary.

Measurement of the Complex Modulus

The definition of the complex modulus is based on a forced oscillation experiment in which the lag angle, δ, between the imposed sinusoidal strain

$$\varepsilon = \varepsilon_0 \exp j\omega t \tag{1}$$

and the resulting sinusoidal stress

$$\sigma = E^*\varepsilon = |E^*| \, \varepsilon_0 \exp j(\omega t - \delta) \tag{2}$$

is measured. In Eqs 1 and 2, ε_0 is the strain amplitude, ω is the circular frequency, j is the imaginary unit, t is time, and

$$E^* = E'(1 + j \tan\delta) \tag{3}$$

is the complex Young's modulus. The real part $E^*_{Re} = E'$ is the storage modulus and the imaginary part, for small values of the lag angle

$$E^*_{Im} = E'' = E' \tan\delta = E'\delta \tag{4}$$

is the loss modulus.

[2] The italic numbers in brackets refer to the list of references appended to this paper.

Forced-vibration experiments were performed [2] using transverse and axial excitation on two types of fiber-reinforced composite specimens [3]:

1. Boron-epoxy (Avco 55-05 tape, specific gravity = 2.012), and
2. Graphite-epoxy (Hercules X3501A-S tape, specific gravity = 1.476) in eight-ply layups with fiber directions arranged at 0, ±45, 0, ±45, 0-deg angles. The specimens were 0.045 in. thick, 3/4 in. wide, with lengths of 5, 10, 15 and 20 in.

For low frequencies (20 to 5000 Hz), specimens were vibrated in bending in a double-cantilever configuration by clamping them at midspan to an accelerometer mounted on the moving element of an electrodynamic shaker. For higher frequencies (4000 to 17 000 Hz), the same specimens were vibrated axially (vertically). In this configuration, one end of the specimen was clamped to the accelerometer.

The experiments were carried out in a temperature-controlled cabinet at six temperature levels ranging from −50 to +300°F (−46 to 149°C) while the excitation frequency was continuously varied. The frequency was monitored by an electronic counter and the shaker was programmed to produce a constant-amplitude acceleration.

A frequency-versus-force/acceleration diagram was automatically recorded on an X-Y plotter. Such curves (Fig. 1) reach a minimum value at a resonant frequency (when the amplitude of motion is the largest) and a maximum at the antiresonant frequency (when the amplitude of motion is a minimum). The antiresonant frequency is used to determine modulus and damping in a manner analogous to the use of the resonant frequency, but, in the case of the antiresonant peak the mass effects of the accelerometer and clamping device are not present. As a consequence, the cumbersome mass-elimination techniques required with resonant frequency testing are not needed here. The lowest three antiresonant peaks were generated for each specimen in bending as well as in axial excitation. Five specimens with identical geometries were used at each of six temperature levels.

The antiresonant frequencies were used along with isotropic beam analysis to calculate the lag angle (damping ratio) and storage modulus. Since the ratios of length to thickness were in a range of 445:1 to 110:1, effects of shear are negligible, and the Euler theory for bending should be sufficiently accurate.

For an isotropic bar in axial excitation, the normalized driving point impedence Z is given by [4]

$$\frac{Z}{j\omega M} = \frac{F_1/a_1}{j\omega M} = \frac{1}{n^*l} \tan n^*l + \gamma \tag{5}$$

where F_1 is the driving force; a_1 is the acceleration of the transducer whose

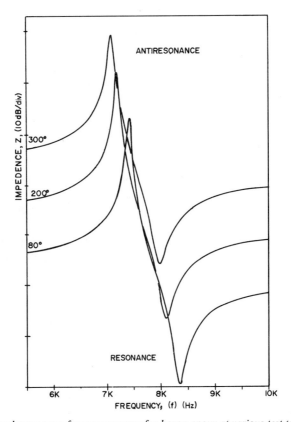

FIG. 1—*Impedence versus frequency curves for boron-epoxy at various test temperatures.*

mass is m_1; $M = \varrho_o Al$ is the mass of the bar, with ϱ_o the mass density, A the cross-sectional area, and l the length; $n^* = \omega\sqrt{\varrho_o/E^*}$ and $\gamma = m_1/M$. The relation between the elastic modulus and the frequency is given as

$$C^2 = \frac{E'}{\varrho_o} \tag{6}$$

where ϱ_o is the mass density; C, the wave speed, is

$$C = f_n\lambda_n \tag{7}$$

Here, f_n is the frequency (Hz) at an antiresonance and λ_n is the wavelength; for the antiresonance

$$\lambda_1 = 4l, \quad \lambda_2 = \frac{4l}{3}; \quad \lambda_3 = \frac{4l}{5} \tag{8}$$

Hence, from first antiresonance

$$E' = 16l^2 \, \varrho_o f_1{}^2 \qquad (9)$$

Near antiresonance $Z/j\omega M$ reaches a maximum.
It can be shown that at antiresonance, for small δ

$$\delta = \frac{\omega_2 - \omega_1}{\omega_n} = \frac{f_2{}' - f_1{}'}{f_n} \qquad (10)$$

Where f_n is the antiresonance frequency and $f_2{}'$, $f_1{}'$ are the half-power frequencies as shown in Fig. 1. At the half-power points the impedence is equal to $\sqrt{2}/2$ times its value at antiresonance. When plotted on a logarithmic scale the half-power points are 3 dB from the peak.

Similarly, it can be shown that the storage modulus for vibration of a double-cantilever beam driven by a sinusoidal force at midpoint is given by

$$E' = \frac{(2\pi f_n)^2 \varrho_o}{h^2/12} \left[\frac{l}{2(na)} \right]^4 \qquad (11)$$

where h is the thickness of the specimen. Values taken by the parameter na at antiresonance for the lowest-mode shapes are given in Ref 4: $(na)_1 = 1.8751$; $(na)_2 = 4.6941$; $(na)_3 = 7.8548$; δ is again obtained from Eq 9.

Figure 2 shows a typical set of δ values obtained for boron-epoxy at $-50\,°F$ ($-46\,°C$).

Generation of the Response Surface

An examination of Fig. 2 shows that the data are afflicted with a large amount of scatter. As a matter of fact, it would be quite difficult to fit a curve, by eye, to the observations. Furthermore, in order to satisfy the requirements of viscoelastic theory, curves obtained at various temperatures should, with appropriate shifting, overlap with each other.

A three-dimensional best-fit surface has therefore been generated with logarithmic time and temperature as the independent variables and $\ln E''$ or $\ln E'$ as dependent variables.

The generated surface is obtained by curvilinear least-square fitting. The computer program [5] determines not only the coefficients of the polynomial relation but chooses the highest required power for the various terms in order to produce the largest possible multiple correlation coefficient for the data. In all cases the highest-order terms chosen by the computer were quadratic, and the relations for the mean regression surfaces are of the form

$$\ln y = A + B \ln t + C/T + D (\ln t)^2 + E/T^2 + F/T \ln t \qquad (12)$$

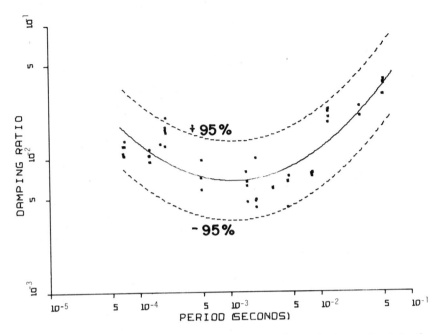

FIG. 2—*Test results and traces of the mean response surface and tolerance bands for the lag angle of boron-epoxy at* $-50°F(-46°C) = 227.44 K.$

where y stands for either E' or $E'' = E'\delta$. The coefficients are listed in Table 1.

Sample contour regions for values of the dependent variables have been plotted in Figs. 3 and 4 for the storage and loss moduli of boron-epoxy. Constant-temperature plots for the six test temperatures were also obtained. These cuts are parabolic lines as shown on Figs. 5 and 6, again for boron-epoxy.

Ninety-five percent tolerance bands, which indicate that the probability is 0.95 that an observation will fall between the bands, have also been generated. A set of these is shown for $-50°F(-46°C)$ in Fig. 2.

TABLE 1—*Coefficients of Eq 12 for degrees Kelvin and time* t *in sec;* (t = 1/f) f *in Hz.*

	Boron-Epoxy		Graphite-Epoxy	
	$\ln E'$	$\ln E''$	$\ln E'$	$\ln E''$
A	1.63×10	1.657×10	1.607×10	1.551×10
B	3.706×10^{-2}	1.370	4.301×10^{-2}	1.667
C	1.282×10^{2}	-4.400×10^{2}	8.538	2.446×10^{2}
D	2.313×10^{-3}	1.139×10^{-1}	1.742×10^{-3}	1.495×10^{-1}
E	-2.103×10^{3}	1.095×10^{5}	-5.909×10^{3}	6.765×10^{4}
F	-8.911	4.068×10	-7.595	9.202×10

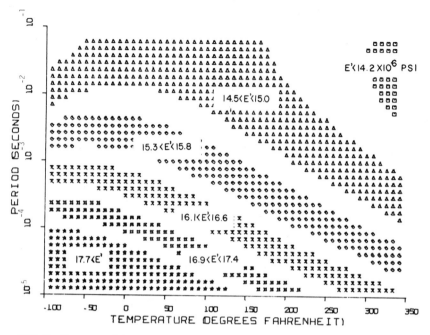

FIG. 3—*Contours of the mean response surface for the storage modulus of boron-epoxy (for E' in pascals, multiply by 6.8948 × 10³).*

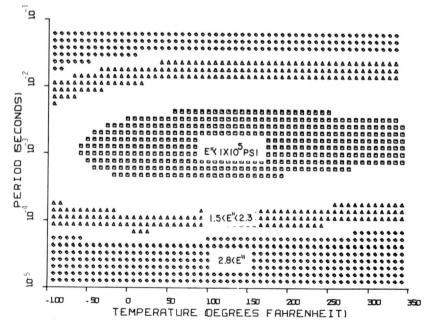

FIG. 4—*Contours of the mean response surface for the loss modulus of boron-epoxy (for E" in pascals, multiply by 6.8948 × 10³).*

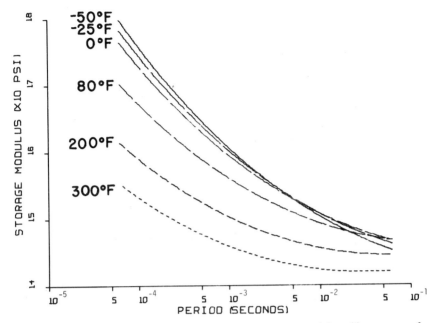

FIG. 5—*Traces of the mean response surface for the storage modulus of boron-epoxy for various constant temperatures (for E' in pascals, multiply by 6.8948 × 10³, K = [°F − 32]/ 1.8).*

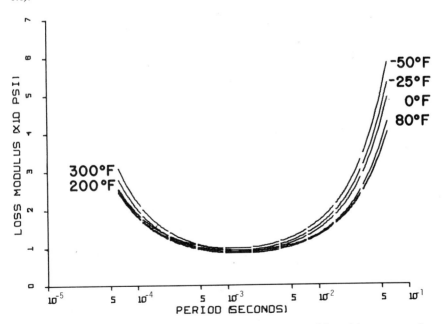

FIG. 6—*Traces of the mean response surface for the loss modulus of boron-epoxy for various constant temperatures (for E″ in pascals, multiply by 6.8948 × 10³, K = [°F − 32]/ 1.8).*

Response Surface and Shift Parameters

For a linear viscoelastic material, curves of storage-and-loss modulus versus time obtained at one constant temperature can be shifted horizontally along the LOG time axis for the purposes of extrapolation to shorter or longer periods [1]. The shift parameter

$$\ln \frac{t}{t_r} = Kf(T, t_r) = \ln a_T \tag{13}$$

is a function of the temperature, T, and an arbitrary reference temperature, T_r, for which the period is t_r. A vertical shift that depends on the change of density also exists for linear viscoelastic materials.

For a nonlinear viscoelastic material [1], there are additional vertical shifts along the $\ln E'$ or $\ln E''$ axis (Fig. 7). The vertical shift parameter

$$\ln \frac{E'}{E_r'} = Kg(T, T_r) \tag{14}$$

can also be determined, in this case from the response surface model.

The method is illustrated for the quadratic relation of Eq 12. Denoting $\ln t = x$, for simplification, the minimum (maximum) point on the curve, for $T = T_r$ = constant, will first be determined by differentiation and setting the derivative equal to zero. Equation 12 for $T = T_r$ can be written as

$$\ln y_r = A_r + B_r x + Dx^2 \tag{15}$$

where

$$A_r = A + C/T_r + E/T_r^2 \quad \text{and} \quad B_r = B + F/T_r$$

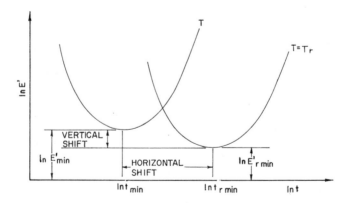

FIG. 7—*Horizontal and vertical shift parameters.*

$$\frac{d \ln y_r}{dx} = B_r + 2Dx = 0 \tag{16}$$

and hence the minimum point on the curve has coordinates of $x_{min} = B_r/2D$ and $\ln y_{r\,min} = A_r - (B_r^2/4D)$.

The minimum point can similarly be located for a curve at a second temperature. The difference

$$x - x_r = \ln \frac{t}{t_r} = -\frac{F}{2D}\left(\frac{1}{T} - \frac{1}{T_r}\right) \tag{17}$$

is the horizontal shift parameter, while

$$\ln y - \ln y_r = \ln \frac{y}{y_r} = C\left(\frac{1}{T} - \frac{1}{T_r}\right) + E\left(\frac{1}{T^2} - \frac{1}{T_r^2}\right) -$$

$$\frac{F}{2D}\left[B\left(\frac{1}{T} - \frac{1}{T_r}\right) + \frac{F}{2}\left(\frac{1}{T^2} - \frac{1}{T_r^2}\right)\right] \tag{18}$$

is equal to the vertical shift.

For viscoelastic response in the glassy region, an Arrhenius type of dependence is usually observed. The shift parameter, a_T, for this type of response is given by

$$\ln a_T = \frac{\Delta H}{R}\left(\frac{1}{T} - \frac{1}{T_r}\right) \tag{19}$$

where ΔH is the activation energy in K cal/mole, $R = 1.9869$ calories/K.

A comparison of Eqs 17 and 19 shows that the response surface predicts an Arrhenius type of behavior for both materials. The activation energy ΔH may be computed from the regression coefficients [6] as

$$\Delta H = -\frac{RF}{2D} \tag{20}$$

It should be noted that horizontal and vertical shift parameters are functions of the absolute temperature and the coefficients of the response surface. The horizontal shift exists only if a cross term $(\ln t/T)$ and a quadratic time term $(\ln^2 t)$ exist. Table 1 shows the coefficients necessary for the existance of the two shifts. Equations 16 and 17 have been found to be valid not only for the minimum points on the curves, but for all others. The shift parameters determined from Eqs 16 and 17 can be used to develop master curves for the two materials.

Conclusions

The complex moduli of two fiber-reinforced materials have been evaluated with the use of a statistical response surface. It has been found that horizontal and vertical shift parameters can be obtained from the surface equations. The model indicates an Arrhenius type of behavior.

Acknowledgments

This research has been sponsored by the U. S. Air Force Materials Laboratory under Contract No: F33615-72-C2111. The authors wish to express their appreciation to R. H. Mayers and A. S. Heller for their help in the development of the response surfaces.

References

[1] Halpin, J. C., "Introduction to Viscoelasticity," *Composite Materials Workshop*, Technomic, Stamford, Conn., 1968, p. 87.
[2] Arthur, C. E., Heller, A. S., and Thakker, A. B., "A Response Surface for the Complex Modulus of Composite Materials," AFML-TR-74-185, Air Force Materials Laboratory, Dayton, Ohio, Oct. 1974.
[3] Heller, R. A., Swift, G. W., Stinchcomb, W. W., Thakker, A. B., and Liu, J. C., "Time and Temperature Dependence of Boron/Epoxy and Graphite Epoxy Laminates," AFML-TR-73-261, Air Force Materials Laboratory, Dayton, Ohio, Nov. 1973.
[4] Snowden, J. C., *Vibration and Shock in Damped Mechanical Systems,* Wiley, New York, 1968, p. 271.
[5] Barr, A. J., and Goodnight, J. H., "SAS, A User's Guide to the Statistical Analysis System," North Carolina State University, Raleigh, N.C., 1972.
[6] Heller, R. A., Thakker, A. B., and Brinson, H. F., "Accelerated Characterization of Fiber/Epoxy Composites, Part I. Viscoelastic Methods," AFML-TR-74-256, Part I, Air Force Materials Laboratory, Dayton, Ohio, Feb. 1975.

Strength

L. B. Greszczuk[1]

Prediction of Transverse Strength and Scatter in Test Data for Unidirectional Composites

REFERENCE: Greszczuk, L. B., "Prediction of Transverse Strength and Scatter in Test Data for Unidirectional Composites," *Composite Reliability, ASTM STP 580*, American Society for Testing and Materials, 1975, pp. 311–326.

ABSTRACT: An approximate theory is presented for predicting the transverse tensile strength of composites from the properties of constituents and composite microstructure. The theory takes into account internal triaxial stress concentrations caused by fibers, triaxial stress concentrations caused by voids, and the interaction of stress concentrations from fibers and voids. The theoretically predicted transverse tensile strength is compared with test data for glass-epoxy and graphite-epoxy composites made with various resin systems. To establish the causes for test data scatter, systematic studies are conducted on the influence, on the predicted transverse strength, of fiber content, void content, specific gravity, and resin strength variations within the various groups of test specimens. The results of these studies are used to predict the scatter in transverse strength of composites. These scatter predictions are useful in identifying the major causes and variables which need closer control in order to minimize the scatter in test data and thereby improve the reliability of composites.

KEY WORDS: composite materials, fibers, transverse strength, failure, criteria, mechanical properties, voids, porosity, stress concentration, brittle fracturing, nonbrittle fracturing, graphite, glass, scatter predictions, reliability, epoxy resins

Nomenclature

σ_T	External transverse stress acting on a fiber-reinforced composite
$\sigma_1, \sigma_2, \sigma_3$	External stresses acting on a porous solid
$\sigma_x, \sigma_y, \sigma_z \ (K_x, K_y, K_z)$	Internal stresses (and triaxial stress concentrations) in the matrix of a fiber-reinforced composite
$X_n, Y_n, Z_n, \overline{X}_n, \overline{Y}_n$	Stress concentrations in a solid with voids ($n = x, y, z$)

[1] Advance Structures and Mechanical Department, McDonnell Douglas Astronautics Company, Huntington Beach, Calif. 92647.

K_x^*, K_y^*, K_z^* Stress concentrations due to fibers evaluated for $E_f/\bar{E}_r$, where $\bar{E}_r$ is the effective Young's modulus of resin with voids

σ_r Tensile strength of material or resin

$\sigma_T^*(\bar{\sigma}_T^*)$ Transverse tensile strength of ductile matrix (and brittle matrix) composites containing fibers, matrix, voids, and ineffective fibers

σ'_T Transverse tensile strength of void-free, fiber-reinforced composite

σ_T Strength of porous solid without any fibers

E Young's modulus

ν Poisson's ratio

k_v Void content

k_f Fiber volume fraction of composite

k_{if} Volume fraction of ineffective fibers in a composite

x, y, z
$1, 2, 3$ Cartesian coordinates

T Denotes transverse direction

L Denotes fiber direction

f Denotes fiber

r Denotes resin

The ability to efficiently design with advanced composites has been hampered by a lack of experimentally verified micromechanics failure criteria for predicting the strength of composites from the properties of the constituents and the composite's microstructure. Because such criteria are not available, extensive testing must now be performed to generate the mechanical properties data for composites. Lowest test values are generally selected for design allowables, which frequently leads to overdesign and weight penalties. Due to the high degree of scatter in test data, the generation of reliable design allowables requires an extensive amount of testing, which is both time-consuming and expensive. Although the "make it and break it" approach sufficed up to now, the present emphasis on cost effectiveness, increased reliability, and improved performance of composites points out the need for micromechanics failure criteria, which are the object of this paper.

Theoretical Considerations

The mathematical model used in formulating the failure criteria for composites subjected to transverse tensile loading is shown in Fig. 1. The fibers and the matrix are assumed to be elastic and isotropic. Portion of the fibers within a composite are assumed to have a perfect fiber-matrix bond whereby the load can be transmitted from the matrix to the fibers

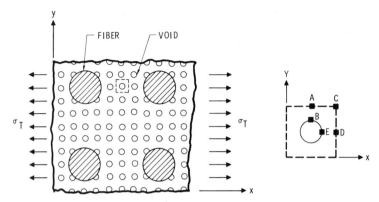

FIG. 1—*Idealized model composite containing fibers, voids, and matrix.*

without failure of the interface. The remaining fibers are assumed to be debonded from the matrix so that no load transfer can take place across the interface. As a first approximation, a composite with unbonded fibers is treated the same as a material with cylindrical voids in the amount equal to the volume fraction of unbonded fibers.

If the composite with microstructure shown in Fig. 1 is subjected to transverse loading, both the fibers and the voids will induce internal triaxial stress concentrations in the matrix. Moreover, if the voids are within the region of influence of stress concentrations caused by fibers, an interaction of stress concentration from fibers and from voids will take place, as shown in Fig. 2. The theoretical results were calculated from equations given in Refs *1* and *2* whereas the experimental results were obtained from tests on large-scale, two-dimensional photoelastic models *[1]*[2] similar to those shown in Figs. 3 and 4.

From Fig. 2, it is obvious that the prediction of the transverse tensile strength of composites must consider the interaction of stresses from fibers and voids since the resultant stresses arising from such interaction are higher than stresses caused by fibers or voids alone. Even though the results shown in Fig. 2 are for a two-dimensional model, similar stress interaction, in all three orthogonal directions, will occur in actual composites. The final triaxial stresses in the matrix as influenced by fiber-void stress interaction can be determined approximately by using appropriate superposition techniques *[1]*. If a solid containing a square array of cylindrical voids (Fig. 5a) is subjected only to remotely applied stress $\sigma_1 (\sigma_2 = \sigma_3 = 0)$, then at any given location such as point a

$$(\sigma_{na})_1 = X_{na}\sigma_1 \qquad (n = x, y, z) \qquad (1)$$

[2] The italic numbers in brackets refer to the list of references appended to this paper.

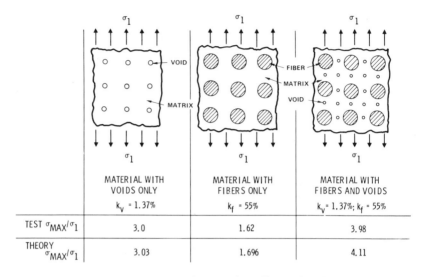

	MATERIAL WITH VOIDS ONLY $k_v = 1.37\%$	MATERIAL WITH FIBERS ONLY $k_f = 55\%$	MATERIAL WITH FIBERS AND VOIDS $k_v = 1.37\%; k_f = 55\%$
TEST σ_{MAX}/σ_1	3.0	1.62	3.98
THEORY σ_{MAX}/σ_1	3.03	1.696	4.11

FIG. 2—*Interaction of stresses from fibers and voids.*

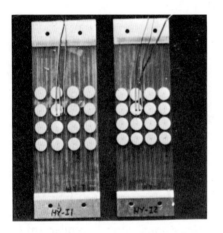

a. Circular Inclusions Simulating Fibers   b. Cylindrical Holes Simulating Voids

FIG. 3—*Photoelastic test specimens.*

where $X_{na}(n = x, y, z)$ are still unknown stress concentrations at the location of interest. Similarly, if a solid is subjected to remotely applied stresses σ_2 or σ_3, then

$$(\sigma_{na})_2 = Y_{na}\sigma_2, \quad (\sigma_{na})_3 = Z_{na}\sigma_3 \qquad (n = x, y, z) \qquad (2)$$

Thus, if the coefficients X, Y, and Z are known then for any given

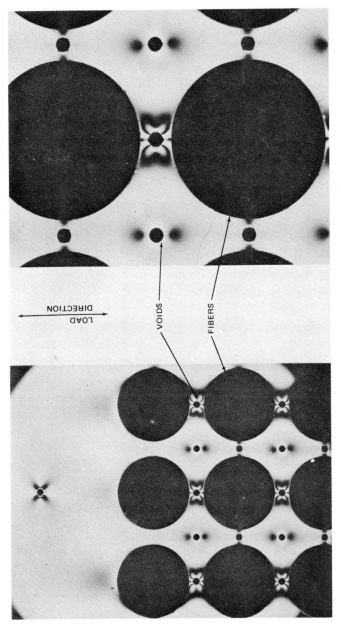

FIG. 4—*Photoelastic fringe pattern in a specimen containing fibers and voids ($k_v = 1.37$ percent; $k_f = 54.54$ percent).*

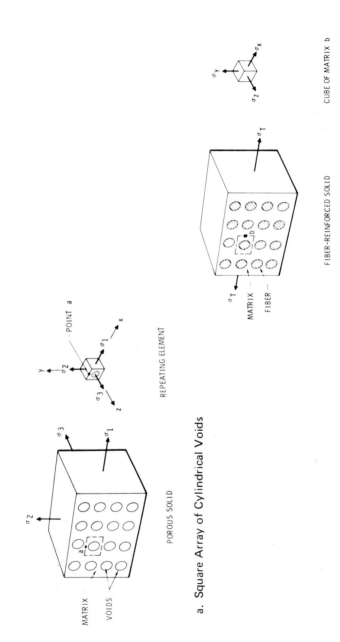

a. Square Array of Cylindrical Voids

b. Square Array of Fibers

FIG. 5—*Solids containing fibers or voids.*

combination of externally applied stresses (σ_1, σ_2, and σ_3), the total stresses ($\bar{\sigma}_{xa}$, $\bar{\sigma}_{ya}$, and $\bar{\sigma}_{za}$) at any given location in the matrix can be obtained by superposition

$$\bar{\sigma}_{xa} = X_{xa}\sigma_1 + Y_{xa}\sigma_2 + Z_{xa}\sigma_3$$

$$\bar{\sigma}_{ya} = X_{ya}\sigma_1 + Y_{ya}\sigma_2 + Z_{ya}\sigma_3 \qquad (3)$$

$$\bar{\sigma}_{za} = X_{za}\sigma_1 + Y_{za}\sigma_2 + Z_{za}\sigma_3$$

If one now considers a void-free, fiber-reinforced solid subjected to transverse loading (Fig. 5b), the stress state at any given location in the matrix, such as location b, will also be triaxial and will be of the form

$$\sigma_{nb} = K_n\sigma_T \qquad (n = x, y, z) \qquad (4)$$

where σ_T is the remotely applied transverse stress and $K_n(n = x, y, z)$ are the still unknown stress concentrations due to fibers. Finally, if a cube of matrix, b, contains a void, then the total stresses at point a can be obtained from Eq 3 if one sets $\sigma_1 = \sigma_{xb}$, $\sigma_2 = \sigma_{yb}$, $\sigma_3 = \sigma_{zb}$ and calculates K_x, K_y, and K_z using a reduced (because of voids) Young's modulus of the matrix $\bar{E}_r$ [1].

Strength of Composites Made With Nonbrittle Matrix

The failure stress for a composite can be predicted by applying the Hencky-von Mises distortion energy criterion to the triaxial stress state in the matrix. Although this criterion actually predicts yield stresses rather than the strength, it can be used to predict failure of many nonbrittle materials as discussed in Ref 3. The final equation for predicting the transverse strength of composites made with nonbrittle matrix is [1]

$$\sigma_T^* = \sigma_r\{(X_xK_x^* + Y_xK_y^*)^2 + (Y_yK_y^* + X_yK_x^*)^2$$
$$+ (Z_zK_z^*)^2 - [(X_xK_x^* + Y_xK_y^*)(Y_yK_y^* + X_yK_x^*) \qquad (5)$$
$$+ (Z_zK_z^*)(X_xK_x^* + Y_xK_y^*) + Z_zK_z^*(Y_yK_y^* + X_yK_x^*)]\}^{-1/2}$$

where for brevity the second subscripts of X, Y, and Z have been deleted, and to simplify the final equation small terms such as X_z, Y_z, Z_x, and Z_y have been neglected [1]. The asterisk used on K_x, K_y, and K_z denotes that the stress concentrations due to fibers have to be evaluated for $E_f/\bar{E}_r$.

For the model given in Fig. 1 it can be shown that a minimum value of σ_T^* will be obtained by considering the stress state in the vicinity of the void within the dashed square. The values of the various coefficients can be obtained from Ref *1*. The values of K_x, K_y, and K_z for various ratios of E_f/E_r are also given in Ref *2*. As to the values of the other coefficients appearing in Eq 5, approximate equations for these have been derived in Ref *1* and are summarized as follows

$$X_x \approx \frac{1}{1 - \lambda^*} \tag{6}$$

$$Y_x = \left(\frac{1 - \lambda^*}{2}\right)[(\lambda^*)^2 - \tfrac{3}{4}(\lambda^*)^4]\xi^* \tag{7}$$

$$X_y = \frac{3[(\lambda^*)^2 - (\lambda^*)^4]}{2 - (\lambda^*)^2 - (\lambda^*)^4} \tag{8}$$

$$Y_y = \frac{1 - \lambda^*}{2}[2 - 5(\lambda^*)^2 + 3(\lambda^*)^4]\xi^* \tag{9}$$

$$Z_z \approx \frac{1}{1 - \dfrac{\pi}{4}(\lambda^*)^2} \tag{10}$$

where

$$\lambda^* = \sqrt{\frac{4(k_v + k_{if})}{\pi[1 - (k_f - k_{if})]}} \tag{11}$$

$$\xi^* = \frac{2}{\sqrt{1 - (\lambda^*)^2}}\tan^{-1}\sqrt{\frac{1 + \lambda^*}{1 - \lambda^*}} - \frac{\pi}{2} + \frac{1 - \lambda^*}{1 - \dfrac{\pi}{4}(\lambda^*)^2} \tag{12}$$

Strength of Composites Made with Brittle Matrix

For this case, the transverse tensile strength can be predicted by using the maximum stress criterion and an approach similar to that described in the foregoing. The final equation is [1]

$$\bar{\sigma}_T{}^* = \sigma_r[\bar{X}_x K_x^* + \bar{Y}_x K_y^*]^{-1} \tag{13}$$

where $\bar{X}_x$ and $\bar{Y}_x$ denote the stress concentrations due to voids at the critical locations [1]

$$\overline{X}_x = \frac{6}{2 - (\lambda^*)^2 - (\lambda^*)^4} \tag{14}$$

$$\overline{Y}_x = -(1 - \lambda^*)\,\xi^* \tag{15}$$

In deriving Eq 13 it was assumed that the composite contained at least one critical void. In view of this assumption $\overline{\sigma}_T{}^*/\sigma_r \neq 1$ if $k_v = k_{if} = k_f = 0$.

Special Cases of Materials

Equations 5 and 13 can be used to predict strength of (i) porous, fiber-reinforced composites containing bonded and unbonded fibers if nonzero values are assigned to k_v, k_{if}, k_f; (ii) void-free, fiber-reinforced composites if k_v is set equal to zero; and (iii) porous, nonreinforced materials if $k_i = 0$. The matrix in any of these cases can be either brittle or nonbrittle. Moreover, the fibers can be completely unbonded to the matrix (if $k_{if} = k_f$), perfectly bonded to the matrix (if $k_{if} = 0$), or portion of the fibers can be bonded while the remainder are unbonded (if $k_{if} \neq 0$ and $k_{if} < k_f$).

If a composite contains no voids or ineffective fibers, it can be shown readily that Eq 5 reduces to

$$\sigma'_T = \sigma_r \{K_x{}^2 + K_y{}^2 + K_z{}^2 - (K_x K_y + K_z K_x + K_z K_y)\}^{-\frac{1}{2}} \tag{16}$$

whereas if a solid contains only voids but no fibers, Eq 5 reduces to

$$\sigma_T = \sigma_r X^{-1}\left\{1 + \frac{X_y}{X_x}\left(\frac{X_y}{X_x} - 1\right)\right\}^{-\frac{1}{2}} \cong X_x{}^{-1}\sigma_r = \left(1 - \sqrt{\frac{4k_v}{\pi}}\right)\sigma_r \tag{17}$$

which gives the strength of a porous, nonbrittle solid. For the case where the matrix material is brittle and contains only voids, the tensile strength can be obtained from Eq 13 by setting $k_f = k_{if} = 0$

$$\sigma_T = \sigma_r \overline{X}_x{}^{-1} = \left\{2 - \left(\frac{4k_v}{\pi}\right) - \left(\frac{4k_v}{\pi}\right)^2\right\}\frac{\sigma_r}{6} \tag{18}$$

In deriving Eqs 13 and 18, it was assumed that at least one critical void exists in the material.

Comparison of Predicted Tensile Strength with Test Data on Model and Actual Composites

To establish the validity of Eqs 5, 13, 17, and 18, tension tests were conducted on specimens containing only voids and on actual composites which contained fibers, matrix, and voids. Figure 6 shows the test-theory comparison of the tensile strength of brittle and ductile unreinforced materials containing only voids. The test data shown were obtained from carefully prepared models similar to those shown in Fig. 3b.

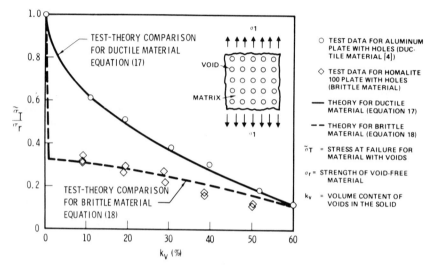

FIG. 6—*Influence of porosity on tensile strength of ductile and brittle materials.*

As the next step in failure theory verification, actual composites were fabricated and tested in transverse tension. The test variables were: fiber type (S-glass and Modmor II graphite fibers were used), fiber content, void content, and matrix materials. Several of the specimens were made with high void contents ($k_v > 5$ percent). Both straight-sided and dogbone-type specimens were used, with little difference found in transverse tensile strength data from the two types of specimens. Figures 7 and 8 show the comparison of theoretical predictions of the transverse tensile strength with the test data obtained on glass-epoxy and graphite-epoxy composites which are given in Table 1. The theoretical results shown in Fig. 8 were calculated taking into account, in an approximate manner, the anisotropy of graphite fibers. Finally, Fig. 9 shows the test-theory comparison of the normalized (with respect to resin strength) transverse tensile strength of glass-epoxy composites made with different resins. The ineffective fiber content, k_{if}, which appears in β was determined as described in Ref 6.

Prediction of Test Data Scatter for Transverse Tensile Strength

To establish the causes for the test data scatter shown in Figs. 7, 8, and 9, systematic studies were conducted on the influence, on the predicted

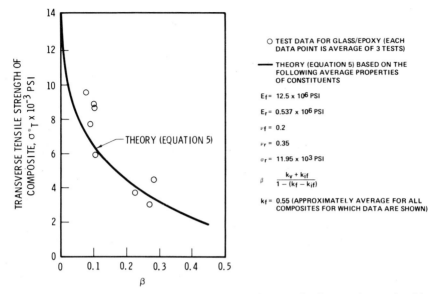

FIG. 7—*Test-theory comparison of transverse tensile strength of composites made with glass fibers.*

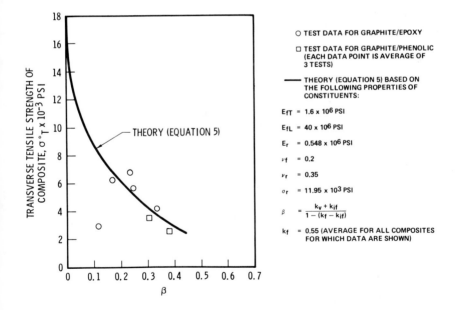

FIG. 8—*Test-theory comparison of transverse tensile strength of composites made with Modmor II graphite fibers.*

TABLE 1—Test data for glass-epoxy composites [1].

Specimen Number	Specific Gravity E^a	TTS^b	Avg	Resin Content, % E	TTS	Avg	k_v (%)	k_f (%)	$E_T \times 10^{-6}$ psi Actual	Avg	$\sigma_T \times 10^{-3}$ psi Actual	Avg
4-1	1.995	2.0099	2.0274	19.9	19.52	18.14	3.52	65.2	2.78	2.61	4.76	4.505
4-2		2.0303			17.89		3.84	67.4	2.45		4.25	
4-3		2.0420			17.01		4.01	68.2				
5-1	1.893	1.7993	1.7716	26.0	27.67	29.50	7.86	52.5	1.653	1.72	2.850	3.077
5-2		1.7706			29.15		8.28	50.5	1.877		2.720	
5-3		1.7448			31.68		7.89	48.1	1.614		3.660	
27-1	1.907	1.9043	1.9083	24.71	24.06	23.72	3.39	59.6	2.18	2.22	3.500	3.740
27-2		1.9216			23.45		4.77	59.4	2.21		4.400	
27-3		1.8990			23.64		5.75	58.5	2.26		3.320	
15-1	1.859	1.8507	1.8380	32.5	33.03	33.62	1.32	50.0	1.62	1.68	5.380	5.922
15-2		1.8401			32.85		2.00	49.9	1.76		6.060	
15-3		1.8231			34.97		1.41	47.9	1.73		5.150	
15-4									1.57		7.100	
2-1	1.820	1.8105	1.8356	36.0	36.05	34.64	1.29	46.8	1.61	1.65	7.88	7.78
2-2		1.8674			32.51		0.82	50.8	1.71		8.78	
2-3		1.8288			35.37		0.81	47.7	1.63		6.67	
28-1	2.072	1.9777	2.0145	18.8	22.11	21.64	0.86	63.6	2.41	2.66	8.17	9.56
28-2		2.0089			22.41		1.26	62.9	2.91		9.70	
28-3		2.0568			20.41		0.55	66.0			10.80	
10-1	1.963	1.9378	1.9091	25.6	28.25	29.64	0.32	56.1	2.01	1.89	9.30	8.69
10-2		1.8814			30.67		1.41	52.7	1.77		9.11	
10-3		1.9080			30.01		0.54	54.0	1.89		7.65	
3-1	1.988	1.9975	2.006	29.1	23.81	23.29	0.74	61.5	2.31	2.40	8.65	8.85
3-2		2.0294			21.27		1.17	64.2	2.54		10.06	
3-3		1.9749			24.79		1.10	59.2	2.34		7.84	

[a] E denotes that the results were obtained from the edge of the panel.
[b] TTS denotes that the results were obtianed from transverse tension coupons.

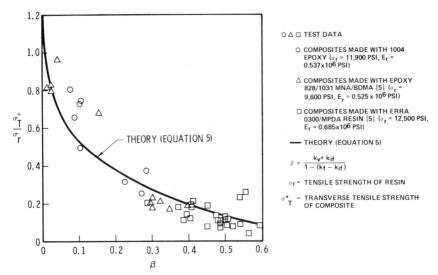

FIG. 9—*Test-theory comparison of transverse tensile strength of composites made with S-glass fibers and different resins.*

traverse strength, of such factors as experimentally determined fiber content, void content, specific gravity, and resin strength variations within the various groups of test specimens made from the same plate. In reference to Table 1, all the test specimens with the same first number, such as 4-1, 4-2, 4-3, were made from the same composite plate. For any group of specimens the variations in properties are quite apparent. Some of those variations are expected to be due to the experimental errors and some due to the variability of material from point to point. Whatever the cause of the property variations, it appears desirable to predict the influence of such variations on transverse strength and to predict the expected scatter in test data.

In making the test-theory comparison of the transverse tensile strength shown in Fig. 7, the theoretical curve was based on an average value of k_f. The values of k_f for various specimens (Table 1) ranged from 0.468 to 0.682. Although use of the β-parameter allows partial normalization of σ_T with respect to the influence of k_f, it does not do so completely. If one were to calculate σ_T's and plot them versus β for different values of k_f, a set of theoretical curves would be obtained as shown in Fig. 10a. As is readily seen, taking into account variations in k_f does not explain completely the scatter in test data. Further examination of results (Table 1) shows that there existed variations in the specific gravity, ϱ_m, within any one group of composite specimens machined from a given plate. Since resin burnout tests together with the measured values of specific gravity were used to determine k_v, this means that any errors or variations

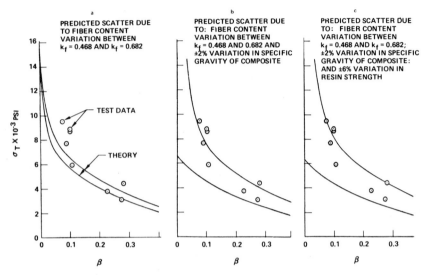

FIG. 10—*Predicted versus actual scatter in transverse tensile strength of S-glass composites.*

in the specific gravity of composites would cause errors or variations in k_v and also β. Of the various groups of specimens for which data are presented, the maximum variation of specific gravity in any one group was ± 2 percent (for specimens in Group 28). The influence of such error or variation in ϱ_m on the error or variation in k_v can readily be calculated from the following well-known equation[3]

$$k_v = 1 - \left\{ \frac{\varrho_m}{\dfrac{\varrho_f - \varrho_r}{1 + \dfrac{W_r \, \varrho_f}{W_f \, \varrho_r}} + \varrho_r} \right\} \tag{19}$$

where ϱ_m, ϱ_f, and ϱ_r denote the specific gravities of the composite, fiber, and resin respectively and W_r and W_f denote the resin and fiber contents by weight.

To determine how a variation of ± 2 percent in ϱ_m influences σ_T, calculations were made first of the possible variation in k_v due to ± 2 percent variation in ϱ_m. Next, using the new values of k_v and actual values of k_f, σ_T's were calculated from Eq 5. The final results showing the influence of variation in k_f and ± 2 percent variation or error in ϱ_m on σ_T are shown in Fig. 10b. From these results it is quite obvious that varia-

[3] The values of k_v's shown in Table 1 were determined using Eq 19 and measured values of ϱ_f, ϱ_r, W_r, W_f, and ϱ_m.

tions in ϱ_m contribute significantly to the scatter in transverse tensile strength of composites.

From the tension tests conducted on cast resin samples [1] it was found that the measured tensile strength of resin, σ_r, ranged from 11 400 to 12 770 psi, giving an approximate deviation from the average of ±6 percent. By taking into account the variation in σ_r on σ_T and the influence of those factors already discussed, the final results shown in Fig. 10c were obtained. Although not shown in Fig. 10, the influence of other factors which could contribute to scatter in σ_T was also considered including: fiber array, variations in Young's modulus of fibers and resin, and variations in specific gravity of fibers and resin. It was found that the latter parameters did not have a significant effect on σ_T.

Since the degree of scatter in properties data of a material is a measure of reliability, this means that the results such as presented in Fig. 10 can be used for establishing what causes the scatter in test data and what needs to be done to minimize the scatter and thereby improve the reliability of composites.

An approach similar to that described herein can and has been used [1] to predict the shear strength of composites as influenced by properties of constituents and composite microstructure. It has been shown [1] that in addition to the factors noted in the foregoing, the test method can also contribute significantly to the scatter in test data. Compression and shear test methods are two examples where the method of testing has been found to influence the strength properties. Thus when formulating failure criteria for types of loading other than considered herein, the influence of test method on experimental data used for verifying the failure theories has to be kept in mind.

Summary and Conclusions

Failure criteria have been formulated for predicting the transverse tensile strength of fiber-reinforced composites made with brittle and non-brittle matrix materials. Parameters accounted for in the failure theories include: fiber properties, matrix properties, fiber content, void content, volume fraction of ineffective or unbonded fibers, internal triaxial stresses due to fibers and voids, and stress interaction from fibers and voids. By setting the fiber volume fraction equal to zero, the resultant equations predict strength of brittle or nonbrittle solids containing cylindrical voids. Experimental results are presented which verify the validity of theoretical results. Test data on large-scale models are used to verify strength prediction of brittle or nonbrittle solids containing voids. Test data from actual composites are used to verify the failure criteria for fiber-reinforced resin containing voids and unbonded fibers. Types of composites used in failure theory verification include glass-epoxy, graphite-epoxy, and graphite-phenolic. Finally, theoretical predictions are made for scatter in transverse tensile strength data for composites, including the influence of errors and variation in fiber content, specific gravity, and material prop- erties on the scatter in test data. The predicted transverse strength of composites and the predicted scatter show good correlation with experimental results.

Acknowledgment

The work described herein was sponsored by the Naval Air Systems Command, Washington, D.C., under Contract No. N00019-72-0221.

References

[1] Greszczuk, L. B., "Micromechanics Failure Criteria for Composites," Final Report Prepared under U.S. Naval Systems Command Contract No. N00019-72-0221, May 1973.

[2] Greszczuk, L. B., Journal, American Institute of Aeronautics and Astronautics, Vol. 9, No. 7, 1971, pp. 1274–1284.

[3] Norris, C. B., "Strength of Orthotropic Materials Subjected to Combined Stresses," FPL 1816, Forest Products Laboratory Report, July 1950.

[4] Butcher, B. R., Journal of Material Science, No. 7, 1972.

[5] Noyes, J. V. and Jones, B. H., "Crazing and Yielding of Reinforced Plastics," AFML-TR-68-51, Air Force Materials Laboratory, Dayton, Ohio, March 1968.

[6] Greszczuk, L. B., "Micromechanics Failure Criteria for Composites," presented at American Institute of Aeronautics and Astronautics-American Society of Mechanical Engineers, 12th Structures, Structural Dynamics and Material Conference, Anaheim, Calif., April 1971.

C. C. Chamis[1] and T. L. Sullivan[1]

A Computational Procedure to Analyze Metal Matrix Laminates with Nonlinear Lamination Residual Strains

REFERENCE: Chamis, C. C. and Sullivan, T. L., "**A Computational Procedure to Analyze Metal Matrix Laminates with Nonlinear Lamination Residual Strains,**" *Composite Reliability, ASTM STP 580,* American Society for Testing and Materials, 1975, pp. 327–339.

ABSTRACT: An approximate computational procedure is described for the analysis of angleplied laminates with residual nonlinear strains. The procedure consists of a combination of linear composite mechanics and incremental linear laminate theory. The procedure accounts for initial nonlinear strains, unloading, and in-situ matrix orthotropic nonlinear behavior. The results obtained in applying the procedure to boron-aluminum angleplied laminates show that this is a convenient means to accurately predict the initial tangent properties of angleplied laminates in which the matrix has been strained nonlinearly by the lamination residual stresses. The procedure predicted initial tangent properties results which were in good agreement with measured data obtained from boron-aluminum angleplied laminates.

KEY WORDS: composite materials, fiber composites, boron-aluminum composites, nonlinear analysis, computational procedure, residual strains, initial properties, computer programs

Determining the reliability of structural components fabricated from fiber composites requires use of various deterministic mathematical models. These models, for example, may be for relating stresses to applied forces, stress intensities at the tips of cracks to nominal stresses in the component, buckling resistance to applied force, or vibration response to excitation sources. Deterministic models of the cases just mentioned require initial tangent and strain-dependent stress-strain relationships. Experimental data *[1]*[2] indicate that the presence of residual stress has significant influence on the initial tangent properties of boron-aluminum angleplied laminates. Analysis of experimental data shows that the

---

[1] Aerospace research engineer, NASA-Lewis Research Center, Cleveland, Ohio.
[2] The italic numbers in brackets refer to the list of references appended to this paper.

lamination residual stresses (the fabrication process induces thermal strains) may be of sufficiently high magnitude to strain the aluminum matrix nonlinearly in certain ply orientation configurations. When the matrix is strained nonlinearly, the stress-strain relationships of the laminate become load-path dependent. Although nonlinear response of composite behavior has received some attention [2–6], the lamination residual strain nonlinearity facet, including its effects on subsequent loading, has not been examined. It is the purpose of this investigation to describe a computational procedure for predicting initial tangent stress-strain relationships of angleplied laminates in which the matrix has been strained nonlinearly by the residual stress.

The computational procedure of interest herein was obtained by incorporating a few modifications in an existing, fully documented and experimentally verified computer code as will be noted later. Therefore, in this paper, only the modifications to this computer code are described, and results obtained therefrom are presented.

Background and Description of Procedure

The background leading to the procedure, its theoretical basis, and the computational procedure evolved are described in this section.

Background

The computational procedure described herein evolved from the analysis of test data from boron-aluminum angleplied laminates [1,7]. These laminates had various ply configurations and were loaded at various angles to their material axis of symmetry. Application of linear laminate analysis to these laminates predicted results for the initial tangent modulus (modulus of elasticity) which were considerably higher than the corresponding measured values. This observation suggested that the lamination residual stresses are present and of sufficient magnitude to strain the matrix nonlinearly in some plies. Further analysis of these data indicated that the residual stress may strain the matrix at considerably different nonlinear strain magnitudes along the fiber direction, transverse to it, and in intralaminar shear. It was concluded, therefore, that a computational procedure should allow for orthotropic nonlinear behavior of the in-situ matrix.

A computational procedure using the finite-element method [8–10] is a logical approach for such analyses. This method, however, consumes large computational times in nonlinear analyses. Therefore, an alternative approximate method was pursued. In addition, this alternative method could be readily implemented through the use of a presently available, fully documented, computer code [11] with the addition of three equations to be described subsequently.

Theoretical Basis

The computational procedure evolved is an approximate analysis. It consists of linear composite mechanics described in Ref *11* and modified to account for piece-wise linear laminate analysis to handle the nonlinear response of the in-situ matrix. Tangent properties at the current cumulative matrix strain level are used as inputs to compute the strains due to the next load increment. The equations of force equilibrium are satisfied at the micromechanics, macromechanics, and laminate levels. The equations describing composite micro and macromechanics, and laminate analysis, are given in Ref *11*, where they are programmed in module form to carry out the required computations. The equations are not repeated here because of space limitations. A brief description of the concept, however, and the additional equations needed, follows.

The macro- and micro-residual strains are obtained using linear composite mechanics and average matrix thermal and mechanical properties. These average properties are used as inputs in the micromechanics level to generate the ply properties. The ply properties and the temperature difference between processing and use-temperatures are used as inputs in the laminate analysis level to compute the residual strains and stresses in the plies. The maximum residual strains in the matrix are computed using the ply strains and the strain magnification factors *[11]*. The average residual strains in the matrix due to lamination residual stress (not micro-residual stress) are computed using the following equations

Along the fiber direction

$$\varepsilon_{m11R} = \varepsilon_{l11} - \Delta T \alpha_{l11} \qquad (1)$$

Transverse to the fiber direction

$$\varepsilon_{m22R} = 2\beta_{22}(\varepsilon_{l22} - \Delta T \alpha_{l22})/\pi \qquad (2)$$

Intralaminar shear

$$\varepsilon_{m12R} = 2\beta_{12}\varepsilon_{l12}/\pi \qquad (3)$$

where ε denotes strain, ΔT is the difference in temperature between processing and use-temperature, α is the thermal coefficient of expansion, and β is the matrix magnification factor. The subscript m denotes matrix, R residual, and l ply. The numerical subscript 1 denotes direction parallel to the ply fibers and subscript 2 normal to them. The biaxial stress effects on the strain magnification factors are accounted for via the micromechanics *[11]*.

Equations 2 and 3 were obtained by assuming that the transverse and intralaminar shear strains in the matrix decrease from their maximum values as a cosine function. Determining the integrated average of this cosine variation of strain yields the desired result.

The suitability of approximating the strain distribution in the matrix, assuming a cosine variation and integrating θ from $-\pi/2$ to $\pi/2$, was determined by comparing it with the corresponding distribution using a two-dimensional, second-order, finite-element analysis. The comparisons are shown in Fig. 1. As can be seen in this figure, the areas under the two curves are almost the same. Therefore, the integrated average of the cosine distribution for the average matrix strain is a reasonable approximation.

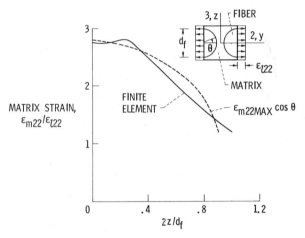

FIG. 1—*Strain distribution between fibers. Boron-aluminum composite with 0.05 fiber volume ratio (second-order element, 441 nodes).*

The average residual strains in the matrix in the various plies are used as inputs in the micromechanics level to compute the ply tangent properties with initial strains. The ply tangent properties and a small load increment are used as imputs in the laminate analysis level. The laminate analysis yields the initial tangent composite properties.

Computational Procedure

The computational procedure is in the form of a computer program. In the present investigation, the computer program was generated by modifying an available computer program [11,12]. Briefly, this program consists of a collection of functional modules to carry out composite micromechanics, macromechanics, and laminate analysis. The inputs to the program are constituent material properties and composite geometry. The program allows the *in-situ* matrix to be orthotropic.

In the modified version, the temperature-dependent thermal and mechanical properties of the matrix are read in the program in the form of tables. The fiber properties are read as in Ref *11*. A qualitative flow chart of the resulting computer program is shown in Fig. 2 where the four modification blocks are identified by a single asterisk. Note the temperature difference is read in. Note also the provision to check the positive definite condition of the array of the stress-strain relations of the aluminum matrix. Violation of this condition leads to predictions of negative moduli of elasticity for both the ply and the composite.

The last block in the flow chart, Fig. 2, is enclosed by an interrupted line. This is to note that the procedure can be readily extended to continue the nonlinear analysis due to mechanical or additional thermal loads or both.

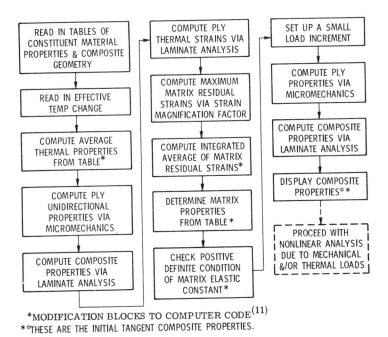

*MODIFICATION BLOCKS TO COMPUTER CODE[11]
**THESE ARE THE INITIAL TANGENT COMPOSITE PROPERTIES.

FIG. 2—*Flow chart of computational procedure for determining initial tangent properties in composites with nonliner residual strains.*

Application of Computational Procedure

The computational procedure described previously and shown in the qualitative flow chart, Fig. 2, was used to predict initial tangent properties of boron-aluminum composites. In this section, the computed properties are compared with the measured data reported in Refs *1* and *7*. The constituent materials for these composites were 4-mil-diameter boron fiber and 6061-0 aluminum alloy matrix. The fiber volume ratio was about 0.50. The laminates were made by hot pressing at 970 °F (521 °C).

Input Data and Test Specimens

The input data required for the computational procedure consisted of tabular data of matrix thermal properties and stress-strain data due to mechanical load. The thermal data of the matrix were obtained from Ref *13* and are shown in Table 1.

TABLE 1—*Matrix properties versus temperature, 6061-0 aluminum alloy.*

Temperature, °F	Modulus, 10^6 psi	Poisson's Ratio	Thermal Coefficient of Expansion, 10^{-6} in./in./°F	Yield Stress, psi
0	11.3	0.310	12.1	8500
100	11.0	0.330	12.8	8500
200	10.7	0.350	13.5	8500
300	10.4	0.345	14.1	8000
400	10.1	0.335	14.7	7000
500	9.9	0.330	15.2	4000
600	9.8	0.330	15.8	3000
700	9.3	0.330	16.5	2000
800	8.8	0.345	17.2	1000
900	8.0	0.350	17.9	0
1000	7.0	0.350	18.6	0

The initial temperature used in the residual strain computations in this investigation was 770 °F (410 °C). The reason for this is that the matrix starts supporting stress of greater than 1000 psi between 800 and 700 °F (427 and 371 °C). See Table 1. The final temperature was 70 °F (21 °C) (room temperature). This yielded a temperature difference of 700 °F (371 °C).

The mechanical load stress-strain data were obtained from axial tension and form torsion tests on thin tube made from 6061-0 aluminum at room temperature. The tube test section was 2 in. inside diameter, 10 in. long, and 0.060 in. in wall thickness. The tube was machined to the test section dimensions from commercial tube stock, allowing 1 in. at each end for gripping. The tubes were instrumented at their mid-length with strain-gage rosettes. The tubes were loaded in a multiaxial testing machine under tensile and torsional loads. Load and strain data were recorded at regular load intervals. These data were reduced to engineering stress-strain data using a strain-gage data-reduction program *[14]*. Tensile load data suitable for input into the computational procedure are given in Table 2. The corresponding shear data are given in Table 3.

TABLE 2—*Matrix stress-strain properties, 6061-0 aluminum alloy.*

Strain, %	Stress, psi	Modulus, psi	Poisson's Ratio
0	0	11.0×10^6	0.366
0.024	2 590	10.5	0.336
0.050	5 260	9.8	0.334
0.078	7 920	8.2	0.332
0.098	9 250	3.6	0.392
0.44	10 500	2.7×10^5	0.409
1.2	11 900	8.8×10^4	0.400
1.5	11 900	9.9×10^3	0.397
5.0	11 900	1.0×10^1	0.450

TABLE 3—*Matrix shear stress-strain properties, 6061-0 aluminum alloy.*

Strain, %	Stress, psi	Modulus, 10^6 psi
0	0	3.27
0.04	1150	3.44
0.07	2450	3.57
0.11	3760	3.56
0.15	5090	3.32
0.19	6430	2.03
0.33	7810	0.867
0.50	8300	0.100
1.00	8300	0.010

Additional input data were boron fiber material properties, composite geometry, and the correlation coefficients described in Ref *11*. The fiber properties used were: modulus = 57×10^6 psi, Poisson's ratio = 0.2, and thermal coefficient of expansion = 2.8×10^{-6} in./in./°F.

Results and Comparisons

As was mentioned previously, the computational procedure described herein was used to predict initial tangent properties for test specimens as described in Ref *1*.

A summary of the calculated lamination residual strains in the plies and the corresponding average residual strains in the matrix is given in Table 4. Compared with the corresponding strains in Tables 2 and 3, it is seen that the average residual strains in the matrix in some plies are of sufficient magnitude to strain the matrix well into the nonlinear range.

The matrix properties selected by the computational procedure ("Determined Matrix Properties" block—Fig. 2) to be used in subsequent cal-

TABLE 4—*Thermal strains in plies and in matrix, boron-aluminum composites; 4-mil fiber; 6061-0 aluminum alloy; 0.50 fiber volume ratio; $\Delta T = -700°F$.*

Composite Configuration	Ply	Thermal Ply Strains, %			Integrated Avg matrix Residual Strains, %		
		e_{l11}	e_{l22}	e_{l12}	e_{m11}	e_{m22}	e_{m12}
$[O_8]$	0	0	0	0	0	0	0
$[O_2 \pm 5]_s$	0	−0.248	−0.803	0	0	0.0020	0
	+5	−0.253	−0.799	−0.0963	−0.0043	0.0119	0.302
$[O_2 \pm 15]_s$	0	−0.250	−0.790	0	−0.0017	0.0339	0
	+15	−0.286	−0.757	−0.272	−0.0380	0.130	0.855
$[O_2 \pm 30]_s$	0	−0.267	−0.748	0	−0.0190	0.135	0
	+30	−0.388	−0.628	−0.416	−0.139	0.476	1.31
$[O_2 \pm 45]_s$	0	−0.322	−0.656	0	−0.0739	0.349	0
	+45	−0.489	−0.489	−0.334	−0.241	0.855	1.05
$[O_2 \pm 90]_s$	0	−0.473	−0.473	0	−0.225	0.912	0
	90	−0.473	−0.473	0	−0.225	0.912	0

culations are summarized in Table 5. The orthotropic nonlinear behavior of the *in situ* matrix is clearly illustrated by the results in this table, since $E_{m22} \neq E_{m11}$ for the majority of the cases shown.

Initial tangent modulus and Poisson's ratio values predicted by the computational procedure with and without residual strains are compared with measured data for several composites in Table 6. As can be seen in this table, the predicted moduli from the "With Residual Strain" case are in good agreement with the measured data. The predicted moduli

TABLE 5—*Summary of matrix properties selected by computational procedure in presence of nonlinear residual strains; 6061-0 aluminum alloy.*

Composite	Ply	Moduli in 10^6 psi			Poisson's Ratio, v_{m12}
		E_{m11}	E_{m22}	G_{m12}	
Matrix Only		11.0	11.0	3.6	0.34
$[O_2 \pm 5]_s$	0	11.0	10.6	3.3	0.35
	+5	10.1	8.3	0.07	0.33
$[O_2 \pm 15]_s$	0	11.0	10.2	3.3	0.35
	+15	10.1	3.3	0.04	0.36
$[O_2 \pm 30]_s$	0	10.6	4.1	3.3	0.36
	+30	3.2	1.3	0.01	0.40
$[O_2 \pm 45]_s$	0	8.4	0.6	3.3	0.37
	+45	2.2	0.2	0.01	0.40
$[O_2 \pm 90]_s$	0	2.4	0.2	3.3	0.40
	90	2.4	0.2	3.3	0.40

TABLE 6—*Comparisons of measured and predicted results, initial tangent elastic constants; boron-aluminum composites; 4-mil-diameter fiber; 6061-0 aluminum alloy; 0.50 fiber volume ratio; $\Delta T = -700°F$.*

Composite Ply Orientation	Loading Angle	Initial Tangent Modulus, 10^6 psi			Initial Tangent Poisson's Ratio		
		Predicted with			Predicted with		
		No Residual Strain	Residual Strain	Measured[a]	No Residual Strain	Residual Strain	Measured[a]
[O$_8$]	0	34	34	34	0.24	0.24	0.22
[O$_2$ ± 5]$_s$	0	34	34	33	0.26	0.26	0.26
[O$_2$ ± 15]$_s$	0	33	31	30	0.28	0.34	0.24
	−80	21	15	13	0.20	0.20	0.20
[O$_2$ ± 30]$_s$	0	30	23	23	0.33	0.72	0.33
	30	25	18	16	0.33	0.06	0.09
	−22.5	27	21	22	0.34	0.31	0.33
[O$_2$ ± 45]$_s$	0	27	17	18	0.34	0.69	0.30
	−37.5	25	14	16	0.30	0.20	0.24
[O$_2$ ± 90]$_s$	0	28	16	17	0.20	0.01	0.10
	−37.5	20	14	15	0.41	0.11	0.11

[a]Measured values were taken at about 10 percent of the composite fracture strain.

from the "No Residual Strain" case are considerably higher than the measured data. In some cases, the predicted values exceed the measured ones by as much as 35 percent.

The comparisons for the Poisson's ratio values, however, are not good for some composites for the "With Residual Strain" case. The difficulty in comparing Poisson's ratio value arises from the fact that in certain cases there is a transverse strain gradient through the thickness of the laminate (see Table 7). The predicted value is an average value while the measured value is a local one, that is, the value on the material surface.

To illustrate the aforementioned point, the following calculations were performed. For the $(0 ± 30)_s$ and the $(0 ± 45)_s$ laminates, the Poisson's ratios were computed for laminates consisting of all 0-plies, all ±30-plies, or all ±45-plies. In these computations, the presence of residual strains was incorporated by using aluminum matrix properties for each ply from corresponding plies in Table 5. The results from these calculations are compared in Table 7 with measured values. The measured value in Column A was obtained from a strain rosette on the surface (first ply) of the specimen; the measured value in Column B was obtained from a strain rosette on the second ply after the first ply was removed by grinding.

As can be seen from these comparisons, the measured Poisson's ratio

TABLE 7—*Comparison of predicted and measured values of Poisson's ratio.*

Laminate		Poisson's Ratio[a]	
		A	B
0	predicted	0.25	...
(0 ± 30)ₛ	measured	0.33	0.70
(±30)ₛ	predicted	1.68	...
0	predicted	0.25	...
(0 ± 45)ₛ	measured	0.30	0.40
(±45)ₛ	predicted	0.99	...

[a] Values in Column A were measured on specimen surface; values in Column B were measured on second ply after first ply was removed by grinding.

is between the two predicted values but closer to that for the all 0-plies as would be expected. To eliminate the transverse strain gradient, it is suggested that the following types of test specimens be used for measuring Poisson's ratio values in laminates with nonlinear residual stresses: (1) wide, flat test specimens to minimize or eliminate free-edge effects, (2) thin tube specimens, or (3) specimens subjected to biaxial stress fields.

Predicted initial tangent properties "with" and "without" residual strains are summarized in Table 8 for the composites investigated. As can be seen in this table, the differences are substantial, especially for the shear modulus.

Discussion and Implications

The computational procedure described previously was found to be a convenient tool to compute initial tangent properties in composites whose *in-situ* matrix had been strained nonlinearly by residual strains. In all the cases investigated, one load increment was sufficient to determine the initial tangent properties. The computer CPU time per case was less than five seconds in the UNIVAC 1106.

In the cases examined in the present investigation, no ply strain reversal occurred in any of the composites during the first load increment. Had the reversal occurred, then two or more load increments would have been required to establish the initial tangent properties. The actual computing time per load increment is about one to two seconds.

The procedure described herein has two important distinctions when compared with other available approaches. These are: (1) the approximate treatment of the interfiber matrix strain variation and (2) the accounting of orthotropic nonlinear behavior of the *in-situ* matrix. The main advantages of this approach are: (1) computer running time economy; (2) ease

TABLE 8—Predicted initial tangent elastic constants, boron-aluminum composites; 4-mil diameter fiber; 6061-0 aluminum alloy; 0.50 fiber volume ratio. (Subscript x denotes property along load direction; y is 90° to x; c denotes composite property; and sn denotes shear strain-normal strain coupling.

		No Residual Strain					With Residual Strain $T = -700°F$				
		Moduli in 10^6 psi			Poisson's Ratio,	Coupling Coefficient,	Moduli in 10^6 psi			Poisson's Ratio,	Coupling Coefficient,
Composite	Load Angle	E_{cxx}	E_{cyy}	G_{cxy}	v_{cxy}	v_{csn}	E_{cxx}	E_{cyy}	G_{cxy}	v_{cxy}	v_{csn}
$[0_8]$	0	33.9	21.3	7.0	0.25	0	33.9	21.3	7.0	0.25	0
$[0_2 \pm 5]_s$	0	33.7	21.2	7.0	0.26	0	34.0	22.5	4.5	0.27	0
$[0_2 \pm 15]_s$	0	32.5	20.9	7.5	0.28	0	31.3	18.6	4.5	0.34	0
	-80	20.7	30.9	7.8	0.20	0.06	14.7	27.6	4.5	0.20	0.13
$[0_2 \pm 30]_s$	0	29.5	20.4	8.9	0.33	0	23.0	6.0	6.1	0.72	0
	30	25.3	21.2	9.3	0.33	0.22	17.5	7.2	3.4	0.06	-0.40
	-22.5	26.8	20.8	9.1	0.34	0.21	20.6	5.7	4.8	0.31	-0.29
$[0_2 \pm 45]_s$	0	27.0	21.5	9.1	0.34	0	17.1	4.4	6.8	0.69	0
	-37.5	24.7	23.2	9.1	0.30	-0.12	14.3	8.1	2.4	0.20	-0.99
$[0_2 \pm 90]_s$	0	27.7	27.7	6.7	0.20	0	15.7	15.7	6.1	0.01	0
	-37.5	20.2	20.2	11.1	0.41	-0.14	13.7	13.7	7.4	0.11	0.05

of input data preparation; (3) measured nonlinear stress-strain data for the ply under combined load is not required because the nonlinearity is due to the matrix and is accounted for via the composite micromechanics; and (4) the three-dimensional tangent properties for both ply and composite are computed routinely as a part of the analysis.

In view of the differences in the predicted and measured data for Poisson's ratio and since the measured values appear to be sensitive to the ply stacking sequence, it might be necessary to measure these values in combined stress fields. This will assure constant transverse strain through the laminate thickness.

Additional experimental data are needed to assess the suitability of this computational procedure in predicting initial values for the elastic constants under combined loading. The computational procedure can handle combined loadings including bending and nonuniform temperature through the thickness.

Since the response of material with nonlinear initial strains becomes load-path dependent, care should be used in selecting measured properties for a particular design. If initial tangent properties are selected, the measured and predicted data should be consistent with the anticipated load path.

In view of the large residual strains in the matrix in some composite configurations, in order to avoid failure in a few cycles particular care should be taken when designing components from those composites which will be subjected to fatigue.

Summary of Results

A computational procedure has been described which can be used to accurately predict the initial tangent properties of metal matrix composites in which the in-situ matrix has been strained nonlinearly by the lamination residual strains. The computational procedure was readily obtained by incorporating a few modifications in an available and fully documented computer code.

Application of this procedure to various angleplied laminates made from 4-mil-diameter boron/6061-0 aluminum alloy composites predicted results which were in good agreement with measured data for the initial tangent modulus. This agreement was possible because the in-situ matrix was considered to respond nonlinearly in an orthotropic manner.

The results showed that predicted values for initial tangent modulus, not accounting for nonlinear residual strains, are higher than measured data by as much as 35 percent for some laminates.

References

[1] Chamis, C. C. and Sullivan, T. L., "Theoretical and Experimental Investigation of the Nonlinear Behavior of Boron Aluminum Composites," NASA TM X-68205, NASA-Lewis Research Center, Cleveland, Ohio, 1973.

[2] Lantz, R. B. and Foye, R. L. in *Analysis of the Test Methods for High Modulus Fibers and Composites, ASTM STP 521,* American Society for Testing and Materials, 1973, pp. 293–308.

[3] Foye, R. L., *Journal of Composite Materials,* Vol. 7, 1973, p. 310.

[4] Hashin, Z., Bebal, B., and Rosen, B. W., "Nonlinear Behavior of Fiber Composite Laminates," Report TFR/7309, Materials Sciences Corp., Blue Bell, Pa., 1973.

[5] Hahn, H. T., *Journal of Composite Materials,* Vol. 7, 1973, p. 257.

[6] Reed, R. L., "Point Stress Laminate Analysis," Report FZM 5494, General Dynamics/Fort Worth, 1970.

[7] Chamis, C. C. and Sullivan, T. L. "Nonlinear Response of Boron/Aluminum Angleplied Laminates Under Cyclic Tensile Loading, Contributing Mechanisms and Their Effects," TM X-71490, NASA-Lewis Research Center, Cleveland, Ohio, 1973 (also in *Fatigue of Composite Materials, ASTM STP 569,* American Society for Testing and Materials, 1975, pp. 95–114).

[8] Adams, D. F., *Journal of Composite Materials,* Vol. 4, 1970, p. 310.

[9] Foye, R. L., *Journal of Composite Materials,* Vol. 7, 1973, p. 178.

[10] Karlak, R. F., Crossman, F. W., and Grant, J., "Reinforcement Mechanisms in Metal-Matrix Composites," LMSC-D-31301, Lockheed, Palo Alto, Calif., 1972.

[11] Chamis, C. C., *Computer Code for the Analysis of Multilayered Fiber Composites—Users Manual.* NASA TN D-7013, NASA-Lewis Research Center, Cleveland, Ohio, 1971.

[12] Chamis, C. C., *Computers and Structures,* Vol. 3, 1973, p. 467.

[13] *Aerospace Structural Metals Handbook, Vol. II, Nonferrous Alloys,* AFML-TR-68-115, Air Force Materials Laboratory, Dayton, Ohio, 1974.

[14] Chamis, C. C., Kring, J., and Sullivan, T. L., "Automated Testing Data Reduction Computer Program," NASA TM X-68050, NASA-Lewis Research Center, Cleveland, Ohio, 1972.

I. M. Daniel,[1] T. Liber,[1] and C. C. Chamis[2]

Measurement of Residual Strains in Boron-Epoxy and Glass-Epoxy Laminates

REFERENCE: Daniel, I. M., Liber, T., and Chamis, C. C., "**Measurement of Residual Strains in Boron-Epoxy and Glass-Epoxy Laminates,**" *Composite Reliability, ASTM STP 580,* American Society for Testing and Materials, 1975, pp. 340–351.

ABSTRACT: Embedded-strain-gage techniques were developed and used for measuring strains in composite angle-ply laminates during curing and thermal cycling. The specimens were 2.54 by 22.9 cm (1 by 9 in.) eight-ply boron-epoxy and S-glass-epoxy $[0_2/\pm 45]_s$ laminates. Unidirectional $[0_8]$ specimens were also used for control purposes. Strain readings were corrected for the purely thermal output of the gages obtained from an instrumented quartz reference specimen. The strains measured during the cooling part of the curing cycle were in agreement with those recorded during subsequent thermal cycling, indicating that residual stresses induced during curing are primarily caused by differential thermal expansions of the various plies. Restraint strains, that is, the difference between unrestrained thermal strains of a given ply and the restrained strains in the laminate, were computed for the 0-deg and 45-deg plies of the angle-ply laminates tested. Residual stresses were obtained from these restraint strains using the anisotropic constitutive relations and taking into account the temperature dependence of stiffnesses and strains.

KEY WORDS: composite materials, residual stresses, curing, strain gages, constitutive relations, thermal strains, thermal expansion

The evaluation of a composite structural component from the point of view of stiffness and load-carrying capacity requires exact knowledge of the loading conditions, stress and strain distributions, material properties, and failure criteria. In the stress analysis of such components, the externally induced stresses must be superimposed on the preexisting residual stresses. Residual stresses of critical importance are those stresses

---

[1] Manager and senior research engineer, respectively, IIT Research Institute, Chicago, Ill. 60616.
[2] Aerospace engineer, NASA-Lewis Research Center, Cleveland, Ohio 44135.

produced during curing and caused by the different coefficients of thermal expansion of the various plies of a laminate. An extensive analysis of lamination residual stresses was given by Chamis [1].[3] Using a linear laminate theory, he presented results on residual stresses as a function of constituent properties, ply-stacking sequence and orientation, fiber content, cure temperature, and other variables. It was shown that residual stresses can reach values comparable to the transverse strength of the ply and thus induce cracking across the plies [1,2]. Residual stresses in each ply are equilibrated with interlaminar shear stresses transmitted from adjacent plies. The latter can cause interlaminar separation.

The present paper deals with the experimental determination of the magnitude of lamination residual stresses in boron-epoxy and S-glass-epoxy angle-ply laminates. Embedded-gage techniques, previously used in boron-epoxy composites at room temperature [3], were further developed by the authors for measuring strains in composite laminates during curing and thermal cycling [4].

Experimental Procedure

The specimens were 2.54 by 22.9 cm (1 by 9 in.) eight-ply boron-epoxy and S-glass-epoxy laminates of $[0_2/\pm45]_s$ construction. Unidirectional $[0_8]$ specimens were also used for control purposes to determine the basic thermal coefficients of expansion. The thickness of the boron-epoxy and S-glass-epoxy specimens was 1.04 mm (0.041 in.) and 1.32 mm (0.052 in.), respectively.

The boron-epoxy specimens were fabricated and instrumented with surface and embedded gages and thermocouples following previously established procedures [3]. The angle-ply laminate was instrumented with encapsulated three-gage rosettes (Micro-Measurements QA-05-125RD-350, Option B110) on the third, fifth and seventh plies, two-gage rosettes (EA-06-125TF-120) on the top and bottom surfaces, and an embedded thermocouple between the fourth and fifth ply. The unidirectional specimen was instrumented with a three-gage rosette and a thermocouple on the middle surface and two-gage rosettes on the top and bottom surfaces. The embedded gages were fully encapsulated and the attached ribbon leads were coated to prevent any current leakage through the conducting boron fibers.

To properly interpret the strain-gage output for the determination of residual strains, it was necessary to separate this output into the component due to deformation of the specimen (thermal strain) and the component due to change in resistivity of the gage with temperature (thermal output). For this purpose, a fused quartz specimen of known

---

[3] The italic numbers in brackets refer to the list of references appended to this paper.

thermal expansion (0.7×10^{-6} K^{-1}, 0.4×10^{-6} in./in./°F) was instrumented with a strain gage and a thermocouple.

The instrumented boron-epoxy and quartz specimens with all wiring connected to a digital data acquisition system were placed in the autoclave. Vacuum was drawn in the bagged composite specimens and a 5.7-atm (85 psi) external pressure was applied. The temperature was raised from ambient to 450 K (350°F) at approximately 3 K/min (5°F/min), held at 450 K for 2 h and then reduced gradually to room temperature in approximately four hours. Strain-gage and thermocouple readings were recorded at 5.5 K (10°F) intervals during the heating and cooling cycles.

To compare strains during curing with those due to purely thermal expansion, the same specimens mentioned were subjected to a thermal cycle from room temperature to 450 K (350°F) and down to room temperature. Strain gages and thermocouples were recorded at 5.5 K (10°F) intervals.

The $[0_2/\pm45]_s$ S-glass-epoxy specimen was instrumented with three-gage rosettes (EA-06-125RD-350) on the fourth, fifth and seventh plies, two-gage rosettes (EA-06-125TM-120) on the top and bottom surfaces, and a thermocouple between the fourth and fifth ply. The unidirectional control specimen was instrumented with a two-gage rosette (EA-06-125-TQ-350) and a thermocouple on the middle surface, and two-gage rosettes on the top and bottom surfaces.

The instrumented S-glass-epoxy specimens along with a reference quartz specimen were bagged and placed in the autoclave. Vacuum was drawn and the temperature raised to 420 K (300°F); then a 1.7-atm (25 psi) external pressure was applied. The specimens were allowed to cure under these conditions for 30 min; then the temperature was raised to 435 K (325°F) and the specimens were allowed to postcure at that temperature for 4 h; and finally the temperature was reduced to ambient over a period of 5 h. Strain-gage and thermocouple output was recorded throughout the curing cycle. Subsequently, the same specimens were subjected to a thermal cycle from room temperature to 435 K (325°F) and down to room temperature. Strain gages and thermocouples were recorded at frequent intervals.

Results and Discussion

The apparent strains recorded during the first part of the curing cycle (increasing temperature) exhibited appreciable scatter, but in general they indicated isotropic thermal expansion of the order of 20×10^{-6} K^{-1} (11 $\mu\varepsilon$/°F). This corresponds to thermal expansion of the gage alloy and its polymeric backing and it indicates that the gage is probably "suspended" in the uncured matrix with no external strains transmitted to it.

Strain buildup occurs only upon solidification of the resin at the peak curing temperature and during subsequent cooldown.

The true thermal strains ε_t during cooldown were obtained by subtracting algebraically from the recorded apparent strains ε_a the output of the gage on the quartz specimen ε_q and adding the known thermal expansion of quartz ε_{t_q}

$$\varepsilon_t = \varepsilon_a - \varepsilon_q + \varepsilon_{t_q}$$

In the boron-epoxy laminates, curing was achieved at the peak temperature of 450 K (350°F). Thermal strains recorded during cooldown and corrected for the purely thermal output of the gage as in the foregoing were plotted in Figs. 1 and 2 for the $[0_8]$ and $[0_2/\pm 45]_s$ specimens. The strains plotted are the averages from all embedded and surface gages as there was no significant variation through the thickness. Also plotted in these figures are the thermal strains obtained during the subsequent thermal cycling of the specimens averaged for the ascending and descending parts of the cycle. The agreement between the two sets of strains is satisfactory, and it indicates that the curing strains in the second half of the curing cycle are caused by thermal expansion of the material. Therefore, the residual strains induced during curing are caused by differential

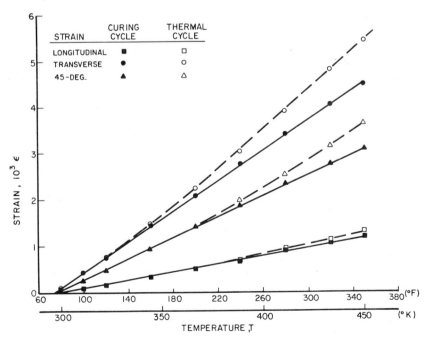

FIG. 1—*Strains in [0₈] boron-epoxy specimen during curing and thermal cycle.*

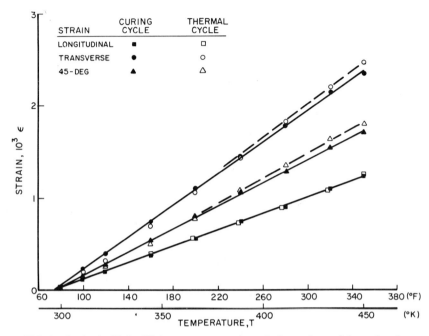

FIG. 2—*Strains in [O₂/ ±45]ₛ boron-epoxy specimen during curing and thermal cycle.*

thermal expansion of the various plies. The small discrepancies between curing and thermal strains observed at the higher temperatures may be related to different rates of temperature variation and also to the fact that some degree of curing is still taking place during thermal cycling. It is worth noting that the strain variation during curing is perfectly linear with temperature.

The residual stresses induced in each ply correspond to the so-called restraint strains, that is, the difference between the unrestrained thermal expansion of that ply and the restrained expansion of the laminate. The restraint or residual strains for the 0-deg ply of the $[0_2/ \pm 45]_s$ boron-epoxy laminate were obtained by subtracting from the longitudinal, transverse, and 45-deg thermal strains of Fig. 2 the corresponding strain components measured in the unidirectional laminate. These strains are plotted as a function of temperature by setting the 450 K (350°F) temperature as the stress-free level (Fig. 3). The residual strains in the 45-deg ply were obtained in a similar fashion by subtracting the free-expansion normal strain components of the ply from the corresponding measured strain components in the angle-ply laminate (Fig. 4). Any three components of strain are sufficient to define the state of deformation of the ply, including the thermally induced shear deformation.

As in the case of the boron-epoxy specimens, the strain readings for the S-glass-epoxy specimens obtained in the first half of the curing cycle are

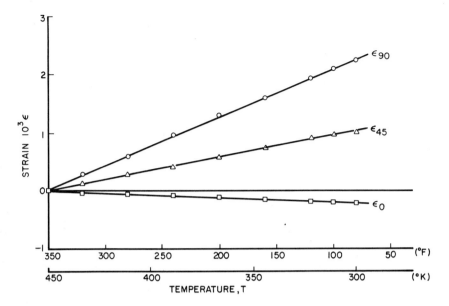

FIG. 3—*Residual strains in 0-deg plies of $[0_2/\pm 45]_s$ boron-epoxy specimen.*

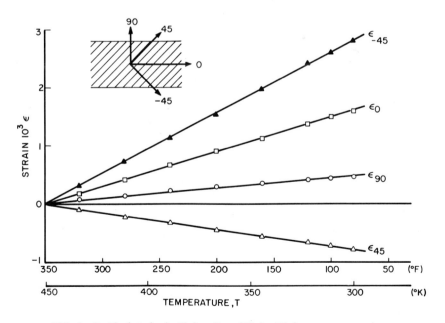

FIG. 4—*Residual strains in 45-deg plies of $[0_2/\pm 45]_s$ boron-epoxy specimen.*

not significant. However, a strain change, which must be attributed partly to the curing process, was observed during the dwell periods at 420 K (300 °F) and 435 K (325 °F). Thermal strains obtained for the second part of the curing cycle (decreasing temperature) for the $[0_8]$ and $[0_2/\pm45]_s$ S-glass-epoxy specimens are plotted in Figs. 5 and 6. Also plotted in these figures are the thermal strains obtained during thermal cycling of the specimens subsequent to curing. Again, the agreement between the two sets of strains is satisfactory, indicating that residual strains due to curing are primarily induced by the differential thermal expansion of the various

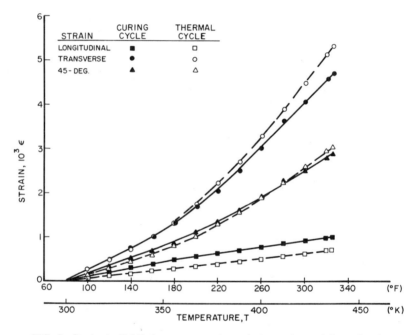

FIG. 5—*Strains in $[0_8]$ S-glass-epoxy specimen during curing and thermal cycle.*

plies. The strains in the unidirectional laminate are characteristically non-linear, unlike those in the boron-epoxy specimen. The thermal strains in the $[0_2/\pm45]_s$ laminate, however, are essentially linear with temperature.

Residual strains in the 0-deg and 45-deg plies of the $[0_2/\pm45]_s$ S-glass-epoxy laminate were obtained as before by subtracting the unrestrained thermal expansion of each ply from the corresponding restrained expansion of the laminate. These residual strains were plotted as a function of temperature with 435 K (325 °F) as the stress-free level (Figs. 7 and 8).

Residual stresses are computed from the residual or restraint strains in the foregoing using the orthotropic constitutive relations, taking into

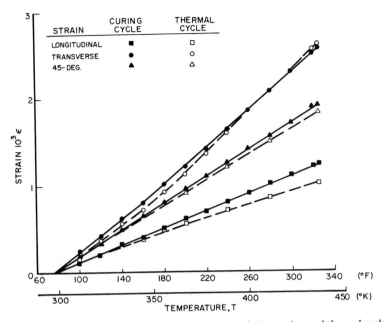

FIG. 6—*Strains in $[0_2/\pm45]_s$ S-glass-epoxy specimen during curing and thermal cycle.*

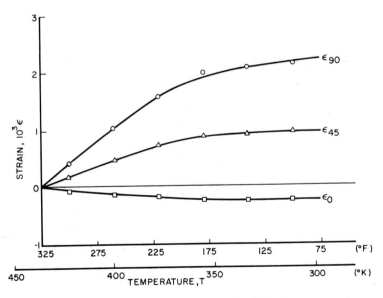

FIG. 7—*Residual strains in 0-deg plies of $[0_2/\pm45]_s$ S-glass-epoxy specimen.*

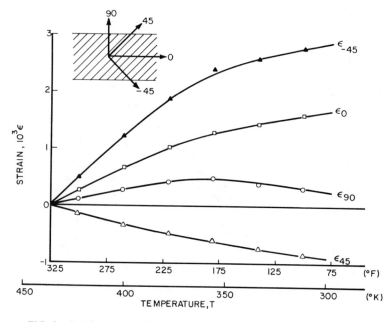

FIG. 8—*Residual strains in 45-deg plies of [0₂/ ± 45]ₛ S-glass-epoxy specimen.*

consideration the temperature dependence of the stiffnesses and strains. The stress difference between two temperature levels T_i and T_0 is given by

$$[\sigma_{ij}]_{T_0}{}^{T_i} = \int_{T_0}^{T_i} [Q] \frac{\partial}{\partial \tau}[\varepsilon_{ij}]d\tau$$

where $[Q]$, $[\sigma_{ij}]$, and $[\varepsilon_{ij}]$ are the temperature-dependent stiffness, stress, and strain matrices, respectively.

For the 0-deg plies of the $[0_2/ \pm 45]_s$ laminate, where the material axes of the ply coincide with the material axes of the laminate and the principal stress and strain directions, the stresses are

$$\sigma_{11}(T) = \int_{T_0}^{T} \left[Q_{11}(\tau) \frac{\partial \varepsilon_{11}}{\partial \tau} + Q_{12}(\tau) \frac{\partial \varepsilon_{22}}{\partial \tau} \right] d\tau$$

$$\sigma_{22}(T) = \int_{T_0}^{T} \left[Q_{12}(\tau) \frac{\partial \varepsilon_{11}}{\partial \tau} + Q_{22}(\tau) \frac{\partial \varepsilon_{22}}{\partial \tau} \right] d\tau$$

$$\sigma_{12}(T) = 0$$

where subscripts 1 and 2 correspond to directions parallel and transverse to the fibers. The stiffness matrix components are related to measured quantities as follows

$$Q_{11} = \frac{E_{11}}{1 - \nu_{12}\nu_{21}}$$

$$Q_{12} = \frac{\nu_{21}E_{11}}{1 - \nu_{12}\nu_{21}} = \frac{\nu_{12}E_{22}}{1 - \nu_{12}\nu_{21}}$$

$$Q_{22} = \frac{E_{22}}{1 - \nu_{12}\nu_{21}}$$

$$Q_{66} = G_{12}$$

The residual stresses in the 0-deg plies of the $[0_2/\pm45]_s$ boron-epoxy laminate are obtained as a function of temperature by using the residual strains of Fig. 3 and the temperature variation of the elastic constants [5]. The values of the elastic constants used in the numerical integration of the constitutive relations are given in Table 1.

The reference temperature T_0 was the stress-free temperature 450 K (350°F). The results in Fig. 9 show that the 0-deg plies are under compressive residual stress in the direction of the fibers and under tensile stress in the transverse direction. The former varies nearly linearly with temperature as it depends primarily on the longitudinal modulus E_{11}, which varies little with temperature. The transverse residual stress varies nonlinearly as

TABLE 1—*Elastic constants of unidirectional boron-epoxy as a function of temperature.*

Temperature, K (°F)	Longitudinal Modulus, E_{11} GPa (psi × 10⁶)	Transverse Modulus, E_{22} GPa (psi × 10⁶)	Shear Modulus, G_{12} GPa (psi × 10⁶)
297 (75)	207 (30.0)	20.7 (3.00)	7.6 (1.10)
311 (100)	207 (30.0)	19.9 (2.88)	7.5 (1.09)
325 (125)	207 (30.0)	19.0 (2.76)	7.4 (1.08)
339 (150)	207 (30.0)	18.0 (2.61)	7.3 (1.07)
353 (175)	207 (30.0)	16.1 (2.34)	7.2 (1.05)
366 (200)	207 (30.0)	15.1 (2.19)	7.1 (1.02)
380 (225)	206 (29.9)	13.9 (2.01)	6.8 (0.99)
394 (250)	205 (29.7)	12.4 (1.80)	6.5 (0.94)
408 (275)	204 (29.6)	11.6 (1.68)	5.9 (0.86)
422 (300)	203 (29.4)	10.4 (1.50)	5.3 (0.77)
436 (325)	201 (29.1)	9.3 (1.35)	4.6 (0.66)
450 (350)	199 (28.8)	8.3 (1.20)	3.0 (0.44)

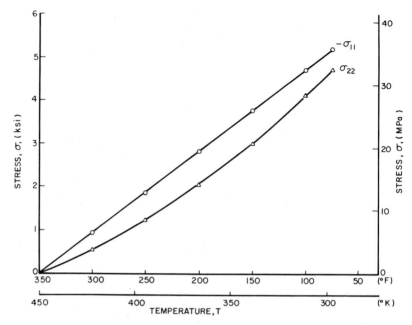

FIG. 9—*Residual stresses in 0-deg plies of [0₂/ ± 45]ₛ boron-epoxy specimen.*

shown in Fig. 9, because it is related to the highly temperature-dependent transverse modulus E_{22}. This transverse stress is the more significant of the two because it is tensile and reaches a value of 32 400 kPa (4700 psi), or approximately 50 percent of the transverse strength of the unidirectional material.

Residual stresses in the 45-deg plies are obtained in a similar fashion from the residual strains of Fig. 4.

Summary and Conclusions

Embedded-strain-gage techniques were extended to the measurement of strains in composite laminates during curing. Strains during curing and thermal cycling were measured in $[0_2/ \pm 45]_s$ and $[0_8]$ boron-epoxy and S-glass-epoxy specimens. Strain readings were corrected for the purely thermal output of the gage, which was determined from a reference quartz specimen instrumented with similar strain gages.

Strains recorded in the first part (heating) of the curing cycle are not significant as they correspond to the fluid state of the matrix resin.

Strains measured in the second part (cooling) of the curing cycle were in satisfactory agreement with strains measured during subsequent thermal cycling. This indicates that, for composites experiencing unrestrained expansion during curing until resin solidification, residual stresses are set up during cooldown as a result of differential thermal expansion of the various plies.

The strains in the boron-epoxy specimens and the angle-ply S-glass-epoxy specimen vary linearly with temperature. However, thermal strains in the unidirectional S-glass-epoxy were characteristically nonlinear.

Restraint or residual strains were computed for the 0 and 45-deg plies of the $[0_2/\pm45]_s$ laminates by taking the differences of the measured laminate strains and the corresponding unrestrained strains of that ply. These strains vary with temperature linearly for the boron-epoxy and non-linearly for the S-glass-epoxy specimens.

Residual stresses as a function of temperature were computed from the residual strains by using the anisotropic constitutive relations and taking into account the temperature dependence of the stiffnesses and strains. In the case of the 0-deg plies in the boron-epoxy laminate, a maximum transverse residual stress of 32 400 kPa (4700 psi) was determined. This means that approximately 50 percent of the transverse strength of these plies has been exhausted in the curing process.

Acknowledgments

The work described here was sponsored by the NASA-Lewis Research Center, Cleveland, Ohio. We wish to thank K. E. Hofer and T. Niiro of IIT Research Institute for their assistance.

References

[1] Chamis, C. C., "Lamination Residual Stresses in Cross-Plied Fiber Composites," *Proceedings* of the 26th Annual Conference of the Society of the Plastics Industry, Reinforced Plastics/Composites Division, Paper No. 17-D, Feb. 1971.

[2] Chamis, C. C., "Design and Analysis of Fiber Composite Structural Components," NASA Report SP227, National Aeronautics and Space Administration, Washington, D.C., 1970, pp. 217-228.

[3] Daniel, I. M., Mullineaux, J. L., Ahimaz, F. J., and Liber, T. in *Composite Materials: Testing and Design (Second Conference), ASTM STP 497,* American Society for Testing and Materials, 1972, pp. 257-272.

[4] Daniel, I. M. and Liber, T., "Lamination Residual Stresses in Fiber Composites," NASA Contract No. NAS3-16766, IIT Research Institute Quarterly Reports Nos. 1, 2 and 3, Nov. 1972, Feb. 1973, and May 1973.

[5] *Advanced Composites Design Guide,* 3rd ed., Vol. IV, Materials, Jan. 1973 (prepared by Rockwell International Corporation for the Air Force Materials Laboratory).

G. J. Mills,[1] *G. G. Brown,*[1] *and D. R. Waterman*[1]

Reducing Variability in Composite Tensile-Strength Properties

REFERENCE: Mills, G. J., Brown, G. G., and Waterman, D. R., "**Reducing Variability in Composite Tensile-Strength Properties,**" *Composite Reliability, ASTM STP 580,* American Society for Testing and Materials, 1975, pp. 352–363.

ABSTRACT: Variability in composite tension-test values limits the application of advanced composite materials to structural design loads far below the capabilities inherent to the reinforcing fibers. Failure probabilities of boron and graphite filaments on the low-strength side of the skewed distribution contribute to composite fracture initiation early in the loading cycle. Dispersion in composite test values at these low levels imposes restrictions on allowable design values to conform to the minimum in the test data population. Prestressing the prepreg materials affects a fiber strength property improvement by prebreaking the filaments at the defect sources of low load failure. Increases in "B" design allowable levels for boron and graphite-epoxy material systems are shown to relate to reductions in fiber strength dispersions accompanied by increases in the average values. Projections of composite "B" allowables to 297 ksi are made for defect-free filaments.

KEY WORDS: composite materials, mechanical properties, prestressing, failure, boron, graphite, epoxy resins, variability

The high strength levels achieved by advanced composite materials promote them as favored candidates in primary and secondary load-bearing applications. The greater our assurance that a given load level can be sustained without property degradation or ultimate material failure, the more confident we can be in designing our structures to these allowable levels. Qualification of a composite material system to a prescribed design allowable is first established through statistical analyses of coupon test data prior to the final, full-scale structural performance verification. The "B" design allowable basis *[1]*[2] is used to compute the value above which at least 90 percent of the test data population are expected to fall, with a confidence of 95 percent. For a more critical structural design, the "A" basis might

---

[1] Assistant for technical planning, senior engineer, and research associate respectively, Northrop Research & Technology Center, Northrop Corp., Hawthorne, Calif. 90250.
[2] The italic numbers in brackets refer to the list of references appended to this paper.

be used, wherein 99 percent of the population of values must fall. The allowable strength levels are computed from the test data as follows:

$$\text{``B''} = \overline{F}_{tu} - K_B \cdot S,$$

where $\overline{F}_{tu}$ is the average of the individual tensile values, K_B is a one-sided tolerance level factor obtained from tables for various sample sizes, and S is the standard deviation of the test data. Although the absolute values for "B" or "A" design allowable levels are only valid for a normal distribution of test data, the relationship between average strength and standard deviation provides a convenient method for calculating differences or changes between populations. Our main objective in this paper is to emphasize the importance of considering test statistics when evaluating composite performance and to demonstrate how processing can change the statistics to a more useful performance level. The application of advanced composites to critical structures is, therefore, not only dependent upon the average strengths achievable, but also the dispersion or variability in the strength values and the sample size upon which the test data are based.

This paper discusses the importance of strength property variability, for current production boron- and graphite-epoxy systems, in limiting design values. The effects of reducing the dispersions by the prestressing process [2], and thereby raising the allowable strengths to levels where design benefits can derive, are presented.

Background [3-5]

The importance of unidirectional strength test data dispersion on "B" allowable levels is shown in Fig. 1. A 30-coupon test, averaging 230 ksi in strength at a dispersion of 5.5 percent, would produce a "B" allowable of 208 ksi. This same material, typical of current production boron-epoxy prepreg, when reduced in data spread to 3 percent, could be used in structural design to a "B" value of 218 ksi. Likewise, a 200-ksi average test strength composite, with a 7 percent coefficient of variation, produces a 174-ksi "B" allowable. Reducing the dispersion by 50 percent to a 3.5 percent value would permit design to 188 ksi. Such "B" increases could assure design to 180 ksi for the marginal 200-ksi material and permit increasing load levels to above 210 ksi for the better-quality production prepreg. Similar increases are possible with current graphite-epoxy materials where comparable dispersions in test values are experienced.

Rule of Mixtures: Fiber-Composite Strength Relations

Figure 2 shows a schematic for a typical distribution in boron filament strength on the right ordinate and the respective unidirectional tension test data distribution at a 50 percent fiber volume composite. The three levels of

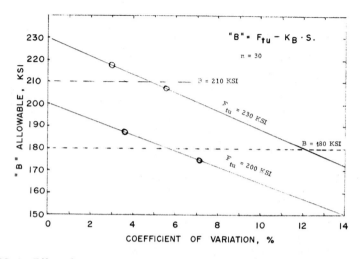

FIG. 1—*Effect of composite strength data dispersion on "B" design allowable levels.*

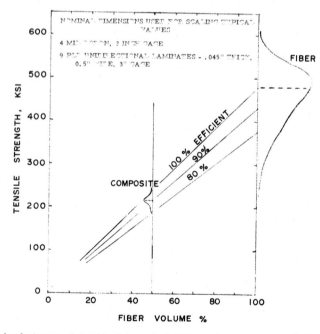

FIG. 2—*Rule-of-mixtures relationships between typical fiber and composite strength distributions.*

efficiency are calculated as a percent of the average fiber strength to reflect the respective fiber performance at the various volume loadings. For this 480-ksi average strength fiber, containing appreciable filament failures down to 200 ksi, one would predict at 100 percent fiber efficiency a 240-ksi strength composite. Boron-epoxy composites normally produce strengths at an 80 to 90 percent efficiency level, or 192 to 216 ksi for this fiber. The importance of the weak filament failures in controlling the composite fracture process, however, is becoming more clear. Improvement in filament strengths to 500 ksi have not yielded proportionate composite strength increases. Correlations of fiber strength distributions with composite test data dispersions have shown that fiber efficiency is a misleading factor when referring to filament/composite failure processes. The filament fracture sequence, as the composite is being loaded, is dependent upon the strengths of the individual fibers which make up the composite. The average filament strength is a statistic, describing only one feature of the population which the total distribution more completely represents. The limits within which the composite strengths can range are, thus, more directly related to the filament failure sequence at the low-strength end of the fiber distribution. Any changes affecting this portion of the filament strength population will be reflected in the composite data dispersion and consequent allowable design level.

Results and Discussion

Fiber Strength Distribution Improvements

Boron fiber strengths are characterized by extracting filaments from a six-inch length of prepreg and testing a random sampling of 100 from this group at a three-inch gage length. Within a one-pound roll of three-inch-wide prepreg, we have found little variation from one end of the roll to the other. Also, the composites fabricated from the prepreg normally are obtained from a 16-ft length subsequent to the fiber test sampling. The fiber tests are, therefore, considered to represent the filament tensile characteristics which go into the composite.

Fibers, such as boron *[3,4]* and graphite *[5]*, exhibit distributions in tension test data indicative of defect-controlling failure statistics. Changes in these distributions as a function of test gage length further emphasize the significant contribution defects make to filament fracture probabilities. At long lengths, the preponderant failure mode occurs at strength levels as low as 300 ksi. As the length is decreased, a high, inherent fiber strength mode becomes more dominant until, at very short lengths, such as ½ in., the fiber exhibits a single, high strength mode as high as 600 ksi. The average filament strength is affected correspondingly, being 500 ksi at ½ in. and decreasing to 350 ksi at 12 in. It is in the 3-in. range that the fiber and 50 percent fiber volume composite coupons are normally tested and where defect-controlling processes would be experimentally observed.

A typical boron filament strength distribution is shown in Fig. 3, where the 3-in. gage test values range between about 120 ksi and 500 ksi (a 27.3 percent coefficient of variation) with an average of 427 ksi. The low-strength "tail" indicates a defect-controlling failure process, a source for premature composite fracture. The prestressing process was developed to prebreak the low-strength filaments at the weaker defect sites, thus precluding their initiating low-strength fractures in the composite. The process applies a bend stress to the prepreg fibers, and the resulting change in strength statistics of fibers removed from the prepreg is seen in Figure 4. The minimum fiber strength is now 200 ksi with a consequent increased average to 478 ksi and a reduced, 16.7 percent, dispersion in values.

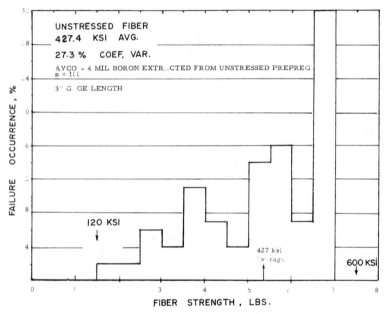

FIG. 3—*Boron filament tensile strength histogram.*

Fiber Strength Potential

The prestressing process, when employed as a simple bending method, is limited in its capability to prebreak at all potentially weak defect sites. Although the "upper" limit has not been experimentally established, analysis suggests it to be considerably less than the inherent strength levels of the filaments. Fiber test strength distributions show maxima of 600 ksi, with

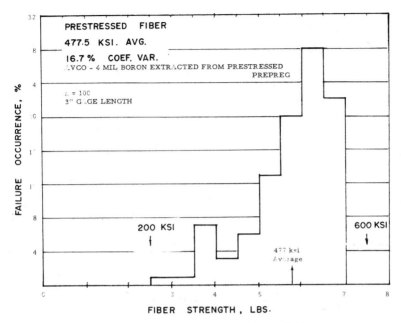

FIG. 4—*Prestressed boron filament tensile strength histogram.*

averages in the 450 to 500-ksi range. Complete removal of the "tail" would shift the statistics to still higher levels, accompanied by a narrow dispersion. Current production boron fibers, therefore, have a prestressed potential for perhaps a 550-ksi average at a 10 percent coefficient of variation. At this fiber performance level, substantially improved "B" design allowables could be realized.

Further improvements in fiber strength have recently been achieved through a new treatment process which "heals" the defects. This process is accomplished at modest temperatures, with short exposure times to a specific gas environment. Figure 5 shows the changes in fiber test strength statistics observed for one set of processing conditions. Five tension specimens from unidirectional epoxy composites fabricated from these filaments produced average strengths of 218 ksi untreated and 274 ksi treated. With optimum treatment, to eliminate all defects, it is reasonable to expect a 600-ksi fiber with a 6 percent coefficient of variation. Composites strengths of 280 ksi, or higher, with 1.5 percent dispersion, are then feasible.

Composite Strength Behavior

The translation of fiber strength statistics into composite test value dispersion is shown in Fig. 6, in the form of a rule-of-mixtures plot. The fiber strength dispersion of Fig. 3 is reproduced on the right ordinate scale. The

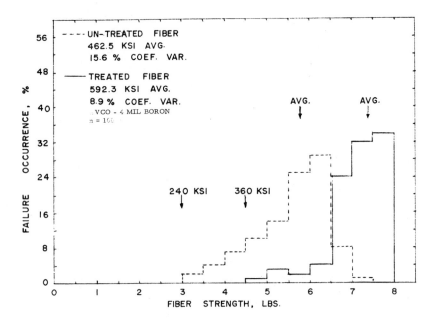

FIG. 5—*Comparison of strength distributions for boron filaments before and after defect-curing treatment.*

50 percent fiber volume composite tension data, for a 30-coupon test specimen size, are shown to range, by 54 ksi, between 172 and 226 ksi, with a 199-ksi average. The composite behavior appears to relate to fiber strengths between the 427-ksi average and the one standard deviation strength value of 310 ksi. The calculated "B" allowable for this material is 175 ksi, almost equivalent to the 172-ksi minimum test strength value.

Prestressing of this same prepreg material produced the results in Fig. 7, where the composite data spread is decreased to 29 ksi and ranges between 195 and 224, with a 209-ksi average. Here again, the composite behavior appears to relate to fiber strength fracture initiation in the region between the 477-ksi average and the one standard deviation 400-ksi value. Reduced fiber dispersion has thus produced corresponding decreases in composite variability. This prestressed composite developed a 197-ksi "B" allowable, a 13 percent increase over the conventionally processed material. Similar relationships between fiber and composite strength properties have been observed on high-quality boron prepreg. A reduction in fiber strength dispersion, through prestressing, has translated into comparable reductions in composite data spread, from 48 ksi down to 30 ksi, contributing to a "B" value increase from 202 ksi to 219 ksi.

Studies on prestressed, 5.6-mil boron-epoxy prepreg have produced similar levels of composite property improvements, with the fiber changes at the

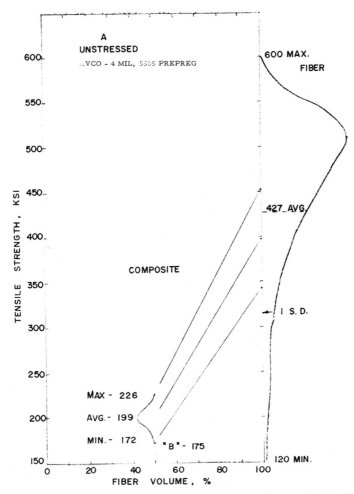

FIG. 6—*Rule-of-mixtures comparison of boron-epoxy composite strength data dispersion with constituent fiber distribution.*

low defect strength levels producing the reductions in data spread. "B" allowables of 221 ksi and 239 ksi for unstressed and prestressed composites, respectively, are attributable to a 5 percent average composite strength increase with a 25 percent standard deviation reduction.

Equivalent effects were obtained for graphite-epoxy composites, as shown in Fig. 8. Tow prepreg was prestressed and cured for comparison with cured unstressed, 3-in. gage length tow test specimens. The cured tows had nominal dimensions of 0.118 in. width and 0.01 in. thickness with a 60 percent fiber volume. Note that prestressing has decreased the dispersion from 21.3 percent to 13.7 percent, with the average strength increasing from 168 to 198

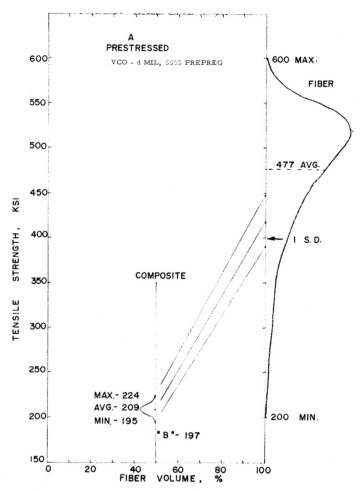

FIG. 7—*Rule-of-mixtures comparison of prestressed boron-epoxy composite strength data dispersion with constituent fiber distribution.*

ksi. Composites of 59 percent fiber volume, fabricated from these tow materials, produced average strengths for the 0.5-in.-wide, 0.08-in.-thick, 3-in.-gage specimens of 168 ksi unstressed and 178 ksi prestressed, with coefficients of variation 10.1 and 5.5 percent, respectively. These property improvements result in a prestressed 161-ksi "B" value, in contrast with an original 138-ksi value, a 17 percent increase.

Summary and Conclusion

The tensile-strength data for boron- and graphite-epoxy unidirectional composites are summarized in Table 1, with corresponding "B" design allow-

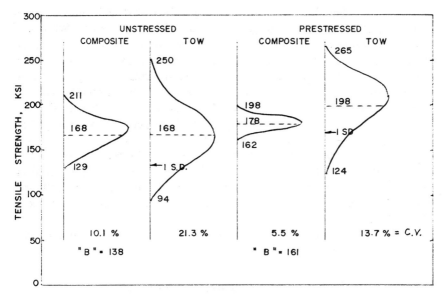

FIG. 8—*Effect of prestressing graphite-epoxy tow prepreg on tow and composite strength distributions.*

TABLE 1—*"B" design allowable unidirectional laminate increases from prestressing prepreg.*

	Unstressed			Prestressed		
Material Systems	Avg Tensile Strength, ksi (n)	Coefficient of Variation, %	"B," ksi	Avg Tensile Strength, ksi (n)	Coefficient of Variation, %	"B," ksi
Graphite-epoxy[a]						
HTS 3002	168 (30)	10.1	138	178 (34)	5.5	161
SP 286	191.1 (20)	6.1	166.4	209.8 (20)	3.6	195.7
UC 2544	181.6 (20)	6.6	158.5	205.6 (20)	5.5	182.2
Boron-epoxy (4.0 mil)[b]						
3M SP272	198.5 (38)	6.8	175.4	209.4 (35)	3.4	197.1
AVCO 5505	223 (30)	5.3	202	232 (30)	3.2	219
Boron-epoxy (5.6 mil)[c]						
AVCO 5505	225.3 (15)	5.7	198.8	235.2 (18)	4.8	212.9
AVCO 5505	240.4 (25)	4.5	220.5	251.4 (20)	2.6	239.1

[a] Eight-ply test specimen, ½ in. wide, nominal 0.043 in. thick, 3 in. gage.
[b] Nine-ply test specimen, ½ in. wide, nominal 0.045 in. thick, 3 in. gage.
[c] Nine-ply test specimen, ½ in. wide, nominal 0.059 in. thick, 3 in. gage.

able levels tabulated. Collectively, the largest factor in "B" value increases is the reduction in property dispersion produced by prestressing. With optimum processing conditions and conventional production controls, a 50 percent decrease in property dispersion is within the capability of the present prestressing method. Composite average strength increases are more difficult to estimate. The extensive experience relative to fiber strength changes, however, suggests that a 10 percent improvement is achievable with refinements, such as tension, tape alignment, and temperature control, to the current prestressing machine. Figure 9 plots the predicted "B" values for these changes in composite failure statistics, at strength levels up to a "theoretical" of 325 ksi. For a 180-ksi "B" allowable acceptance level, prepreg material producing an average composite strength of 200 ksi would be required. Prestressing of this prepreg would rise its "B" to 208 ksi, far above the 180-ksi basis.

Conventional processing of a 175-ksi material would result in a 150-ksi

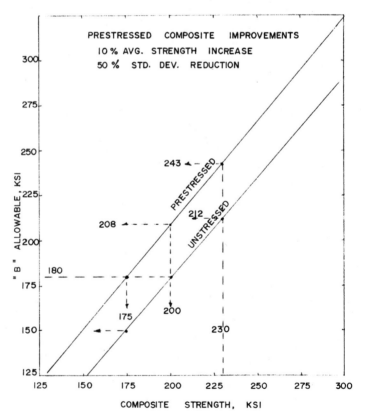

FIG. 9—*Potential improvements in "B" design allowable levels for filamentary reinforced composites.*

"B" composite, whereas prestressing would produce a composite at 180-ksi acceptance level. For a better-quality prepreg, at 230-ksi composite strength, the projected "B" value for conventional processing is 212 ksi; however, prestressing raises this to 243 ksi, a level to which minimum design values could be increased with significant impacts on weight, performance, and cost. The prestressing process thus provides a capability for raising those low-strength test values upon which structural designs are based.

References

[1] Military Standardization Handbook: Metallic Materials and Elements for Aerospace Vehicle Structures," Vol. 2 of two volumes, MIL-HDBK-5B, Sept. 1971.

[2] Patent Pending #390,595, Aug. 22, 1973.

[3] Mills, G. and Dauksys, R., "Effects of Prestressing Boron/Epoxy Prepreg on Composite Strength Properties," Journal, American Institute of Aeronautics and Astronautics, Vol. 2, No. 11, Nov. 1973, pp. 1459–1460.

[4] "Effects of Prestressing Boron/Epoxy Prepreg on Composite Strength Properties," AIAA Paper No. 73-382, American Institute of Aeronautics and Astronautics-American Society of Mechanical Engineers-Society of Aeronautical Engineers, 14th Structures, Structural Dynamics, and Materials Conference, Williamsburg, Va., 20–22 March 1973.

[5] Mills, G., Brown, G., and Waterman, D., "Prestressing of Boron and Graphite Epoxy Prepreg for Composite Strength Improvement," Technical Report AFML-TR-73-118, Air Force Materials Laboratory, Dayton, Ohio, June 1973.

J. G. Davis, Jr. [1]

Compressive Strength of Fiber-Reinforced Composite Materials

REFERENCE: Davis, J. G., Jr., "**Compressive Strength of Fiber-Reinforced Composite Materials,**" *Composite Reliability, ASTM STP 580,* American Society for Testing and Materials, 1975, pp. 364–377.

ABSTRACT: Results of an experimental and analytical investigation of the compressive strength of unidirectional boron-epoxy composite material are presented. Observation of fiber coordinates in a boron-epoxy composite indicates that the fibers contain initial curvature. Combined axial compression and torsion tests were conducted on boron-epoxy tubes and it was shown that the shear modulus is a function of axial compressive stress. An analytical model which includes initial curvature in the fibers and permits an estimate of the effect of curvature on compressive strength is proposed. Two modes of failure which may result from the application of axial compressive stress are analyzed—delamination and shear instability. Based on tests and analysis, failure of boron-epoxy under axial compressive load is due to shear instability.

KEY WORDS: composite materials, boron, epoxy resins, compressive strength, shear strength, shear modulus

Nomenclature

A_m Cross-sectional area of mth layer
a_o Amplitude of initial displacement; see Fig. 2
b Width of beam
E_m Young's modulus of mth layer
F_i First moment of area of ith layer about midplane
G Shear modulus of composite
G_i Shear modulus of ith layer
G^* Apparent shear modulus of composite
h_i Thickness of ith layer
I_m Moment of inertia of mth layer about midplane
L Length of laminate

[1] Structural materials engineer, NASA-Langley Research Center, Hampton, Va. 23665.

n Total number of layers above midplane

P_f Applied compressive load on the fiber layer

P_m Applied compressive load on matrix or mth layer

P_x External shear load

P_z External transverse load

P Applied compressive load on a beam

$\mathbf{P}_p$ Load vector at pth node

R_p, S_p, T_p Submatrices that form part of finite difference equations

U Change in strain energy in going from initial position to buckled position

V_i Volume fraction of ith layer

W Work done by applied load in going from initial position to buckled position

w_0 Initial transverse displacement of laminate

w_1 Transverse displacement of laminate due to bending and shear loads

w Total transverse displacement of laminate

x, y, z Coordinates

$\mathbf{Y}_p$ Solution vector for pth node point along beam

γ_i Shear strain in ith layer of a multilayered media

δ Displacement of applied axial force in going from initial position to buckled position

θ_i Angle between z-axis and initial position of cross section of ith layer

σ_c Compressive stress

σ_{cr} Applied compressive stress at which shear instability occurs

τ_i Shear stress in ith layer

$\tau_{m,m}$ Interlaminar shear stress above mth layer and acting on mth layer

Φ_i defined by $(\psi_i - \theta_i)$

ψ_i angle between z-axis and final position of deformed cross section of ith layer

The behavior of unidirectionally fiber-reinforced composite materials when subjected to an axial compressive loading parallel to the fibers has been investigated both analytically and experimentally during the past decade. At the beginning of the study reported herein, an in-depth review of the literature was conducted [1]² and the following was evident: (1) A unified theory for predicting compressive strength did not exist. (2) Data tended to support three possible modes of failure—delamination, microbuckling of the fiber, and fiber-matrix separation followed by microbuckling of the fiber. (3) A direct relationship between compressive strength and interlaminar shear strength had been noted for some mate-

---

² The italic numbers in brackets refer to the list of references appended to this paper.

rials. Study of these points led to postulation of an analytical model which allows microbuckling or delamination as potential failure modes and provided an explanation for the relationship between interlaminar shear and compressive strength. The model, analyses, and experiments performed to correlate the model with the behavior of boron-epoxy are discussed in this paper.

Analytical Model

The model postulated herein is compared with the one used by Rosen [2] in Fig. 1. Each model is built up from a series of hard and soft

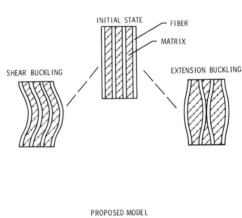

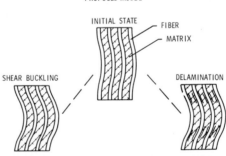

FIG. 1—*Analytical model of fiber-reinforced composite material.*

laminas. Rosen assumed that the laminas were initially straight and predicted two buckling modes: extension and shear. The advantages of the Rosen model are that strength is related to the matrix properties and the resulting equations are easy to use. As for disadvantages, predicted values are usually much larger than experimental measurements, fiber geometry is not taken into account, and the effect of nonlinear behavior of the matrix is not explicit.

The present model permits the laminas to contain initial curvature. As a consequence, under an increasing axial load the laminas undergo lateral deflection, which induces interlaminar shear stress and may result in failure by delamination, for example, some of the early graphite-epoxy laminates. The second mode of failure considered is shear instability of the laminas. If the matrix material behaves in a nonlinear manner, the induced interlaminar shear stresses will cause the shear modulus of the composite to decrease and, correspondingly, the axial compressive stress at which shear instability occurs will decrease. Important features of the present model include: (1) Strength is related to constituent properties and geometry. (Both the fiber and matrix properties are taken into account; filament size, initial curvature and collimation are reflected in the value of a_0 and L.) (2) An explanation for the relation between compressive and interlaminar shear strengths is offered. (3) A decrease in shear modulus with increasing applied axial load is explained. The major disadvantage is that the model contains only two dimensions whereas the filamentary composite is a three-dimensional material. As a result, the full significance of local stress concentrations due to filament misalignment may not be analyzed.

Analysis

A brief description of the analysis utilized to predict interlaminar shear stress and shear instability in the analytical model follows. Complete derivations are presented in Ref *1*.

Interlaminar Shear Stress

A repeating element which consists of one fiber layer and two half layers of matrix material was analyzed as a multilayered Timoshenko beam loaded in axial compression (see Fig. 2). Each layer in the beam contains an initial transverse deflection, w_0, which can be represented by a sine wave. Both bending and shearing deformations are permitted in each layer. Since the beam represents a repeating element, the horizontal displacement, u, due to bending and shearing must vanish along the upper and lower surfaces in order to satisfy continuity of displacements. Subdividing the beam into $2n$ layers, taking into account symmetry about the midplane and applying the equations of equilibrium to each layer, leads to the set of governing differential equations for the problem. Summation of moments yields

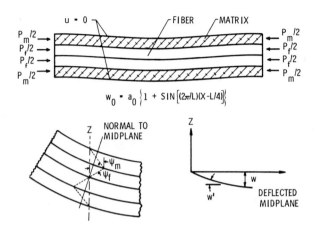

FIG. 2—*Multilayered beam used in shear stress analysis of the composite material.*

$$\sum_{i=1}^{m} [E_i(I_i - F_ih_i)(\psi_i'' - \theta_i'') + E_iF_i \sum_{k=1}^{i-1} (h_{k+1} - h_k)(\psi_k'' - \theta_k'')]$$

$$- \sum_{i=1}^{m} G_iA_i(\psi_i - \theta_i + w_1') + h_{m+1}P_x/2$$

$$+ h_{m+1} \sum_{i=m+1}^{n} [E_i(F_i - A_ih_i)(\psi_i'' - \theta_i'')$$

$$+ E_iA_i \sum_{k=1}^{i-1} (h_{k+1} - h_k)(\psi_k'' - \theta_k'')] = 0 \qquad (1)$$

Summation of vertical forces yields

$$\sum_{i=1}^{n} G_iA_iw_1'' + \sum_{i=1}^{n} G_iA_i(\psi_i' - \theta_i') + P_z/2 - Pw'' = 0 \qquad (2)$$

Continuity of displacements provides the remaining governing equation

$$\phi_1h_2 + \phi_2(h_3 - h_2) + \cdots + \phi_n(h_{n+1} - h_n) = 0 \qquad (3)$$

Expressing the derivatives of ψ_i, θ_i, ϕ_i, and w in terms of finite differences, dividing the beam into J intervals, and applying fixed-end boundary conditions permits one to transform Eqs 1 through 3 into the following set of matrix equations

$$
\begin{bmatrix}
S_2 & T_2 & 0 & 0 & 0 & . & . & . \\
R_3 & S_3 & T_3 & 0 & 0 & . & . & . \\
0 & R_4 & S_4 & T_4 & 0 & . & . & . \\
. & . & . & 0 & 0 & R_{J-1} & S_{J-1} & T_{J-1} \\
. & . & . & 0 & 0 & 0 & R_J & S_J
\end{bmatrix}
\begin{bmatrix}
Y_2 \\ Y_3 \\ . \\ . \\ . \\ Y_{J-1} \\ Y_J
\end{bmatrix}
=
\begin{bmatrix}
P_2 \\ P_3 \\ . \\ . \\ . \\ P_{J-1} \\ P_J
\end{bmatrix}
\quad (4)
$$

Considering the kth node along the beam, the solution vector Y_k includes the rotation ϕ_i of each layer, the transverse deflection w_1, and the interlaminar shear stress which acts on the outer layers.

A computer program which utilizes the tridiagonal method of solution and had been written earlier by Swift [3] was modifed to solve Eqs 4. The computer program adjusts the coefficient matrices to account for nonlinear shear stress-strain behavior in the layers as the axial compressive loading is monotonically increased in uniform increments.

After the solution vectors are computed, interlaminar shear stresses may be computed by the following equation

$$
\tau_{m,m} = \frac{1}{bh_{m+1}} \left\{ \sum_{i=1}^{m} [E_i(I_i - F_i h_i)(\psi_i'' - \theta_i'') \right.
$$

$$
+ E_i F_i \sum_{k=1}^{i-1} (h_{k+1} - h_k)(\psi_k'' - \theta_k'')]
$$

$$
\left. - \sum_{i=1}^{m} [G_i A_i(\psi_i - \theta_i + w_1')] \right\} \quad (5)
$$

Equation 5 can be used to compute interlaminar shear stresses as a function of applied axial compressive stress. If the value of $\tau_{m,m}$ computed with Eq 5 equals or exceeds the interlaminar shear strength of the composite material, failure will occur by delamination.

It will be shown herein that the axial compressive stress at which shear instability occurs is dependent on the shear modulus of each layer in the beam. Using the following equation, the average shear stress in each layer can be computed as a function of axial compressive stress

$$
\tau_{avg} = \tau_{m,m} + \frac{E_m}{3}(h_{m+1} - h_m)^2(\psi_m'' - \theta_m'')
$$

$$
+ \frac{E_m}{2}(h_{m+1} - h_m)\sum_{i=1}^{m-1}(h_{i+1} - h_i)(\psi_i'' - \theta_i'') \quad (6)
$$

Using values of shear stress computed by Eq 6 and the shear stress strain curves for each material in the composite, the shear modulus of each layer can be computed as a function of axial compressive stress for subsequent use in the stability analysis.

Shear Stability

Figure 3 shows a segment of the multilayered beam used to represent the composite material. The length-to-width ratio of each layer is assumed to be small and thus bending is precluded. The magnitude of the applied end loads is such that a uniform axial strain is imposed. The repeating element is assumed to be symmetric about its midplane, and compatability of displacements along the boundaries is imposed. As a result, the average vertical displacement at the upper ends of the $+n$th and $-n$th layers will equal the displacement at the midplane of the repeating element. For convenience, the applied axial loads are replaced by a single load acting at the midplane of the repeating element.

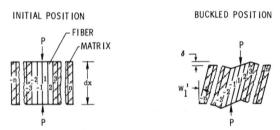

FIG. 3—*Shear buckling of a multilayered beam.*

The axial load, which initiates shear buckling, may be calculated using an energy analysis, as indicated by Foye [4]. Referring to Fig. 3, it is noted that the work done by the external forces in going from the initial position to the buckled position is

$$W = P\delta \tag{7}$$

Noting

$$\delta = (1 - \cos w_1')\, dx \quad \text{and} \quad \cos w_1' \approx 1 - w_1'^2/2$$

Eq 7 becomes

$$W = P\, w_1'^2\, dx/2 \tag{8}$$

Since bending is precluded, the change in strain energy in going from the initial position to the buckled position is due only to shearing stresses and is given by

$$U = \sum_{i=1}^{n} \tau_i \gamma_i A_i \, dx \qquad (9)$$

Expressing shear stress and strain in terms of displacement and rotations, Eq 9 becomes

$$U = \sum_{i=1}^{n} G_i A_i (\phi_i + w_1')^2 \, dx \qquad (10)$$

Equating W and U leads to

$$P w_1'^2 = 2 \sum_{i=1}^{n} G_i A_i (\phi_i + w_1')^2 \qquad (11)$$

Equation 11, plus the following equation, which imposes continuity of displacements along the vertical edges of the repeating element, are the governing equations for predicting shear instability

$$\sum_{i=1}^{n} A_i \phi_i = 0 \qquad (12)$$

The minimum value of axial compressive load, P, which satisfies the governing equations can be determined using the method of Lagrange multipliers. Further, noting the relationship between axial load and stress and the definition of volume fractions, V_i, leads to the following equation for predicting the axial compression stress at which shear buckling occurs

$$\sigma_{cr} = \frac{G_1 G_2 \cdots G_n}{V_1 G_2 \cdots G_n + V_2 G_1 G_3 \cdots G_n + \cdots + V_n G_1 \cdots G_{n-1}} \qquad (13)$$

Shear moduli values substituted into Eq 13 should be those corresponding to the average shear stresses induced by axial compression and calculated with Eq 6. Neglecting to take into account the induced shear stresses and the corresponding reduction in shear modulus, Eq 13 would predict the same value of axial stress for shear instability as given by Rosen [1] and Foye [4].

Experiment and Results

Fiber Curvature

The analytical model postulated herein is based on the assumption that the reinforcing fibers contain initial curvature. In order to verify that assumption, the coordinates of five arbitrarily selected fibers in a boron-epoxy laminate were measured (see Fig. 4). A 1.27-cm-wide (0.50 in.) strip was machined from the central portion of a 15.24-cm-wide (6.00 in.) by 10.16-cm-long (4.00 in.) 12-ply laminate. The fibers were aligned in the length direction of the strip. The strip was sliced into nominally 2.50-mm-long (0.10 in.) coupons. Each slice across the strip removed approximately 1.78 mm (0.070 in.) of material. Thus the front faces of successive coupons were spaced at approximately 4.28-mm (0.170 in.) intervals. The length of each coupon was measured with a micrometer and the coordinates of the five fibers labeled in Fig. 4 were measured with a toolmaker's microscope.

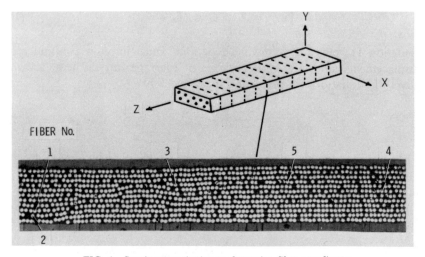

FIG. 4—*Specimen sectioning to determine fiber coordinates.*

Figure 5 shows typical results obtained from 22 cross sections along the length of the strip. Examination of the results for all fibers indicates that (1) variation in the x-coordinate was larger than in the y coordinate; (2) the fiber is skewed with respect to the z-axis; (3) the fiber is essentially parallel to the x-z plane; and (4) the fiber exhibits waviness along its length. Item (4) is perhaps the most important since it leads to the development of shear stresses when the fiber is compressed in the axial direction. As discussed earlier, the induced shear stresses can cause the composite to delaminate or reduce the shear modulus of the composite sufficiently to cause failure by shear instability.

Displacements ranging from 15.24 to 30.48 μm (0.0006 to 0.0012 in.) over a span of 0.864 cm (0.34 in.) were measured in the five fibers. Due to the irregular wave shape along each fiber, no attempt was made to express the displacement by a mathematical function. If segments of

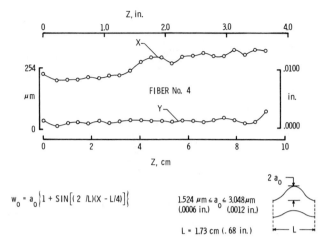

$$w_o = a_o \left\{ 1 + SIN \left[(2 \ /L)(X - L/4) \right] \right\}$$

1.524 μm $\leq a_o \leq$ 3.048μm
(.0006 in.)   (.0012 in.)

L = 1.73 cm (.68 in.)

FIG. 5—*Fiber coordinates.*

fibers are examined, however, and the displacement equation shown in Fig. 2 is used, values of a_o/L required to fit the deflection will range approximately from 0.0009 to 0.001875. As will be shown later, these deflections are sufficient to considerably influence the axial compressive strength.

Combined Compression and Torsion Test

In order to determine the influence of compressive stress on shear modulus, boron fiber uniaxially reinforced epoxy tubes were subjected to combined axial compression and torsion tests using the apparatus shown in Fig. 6. The specimen was mounted in series with a load cell and supported by a thrust bearing assembly. Compressive loading was applied by raising the lower platen, whereas torque was applied by attaching weights on two strings which connected to the moment arms. Magnitude of the applied torque was determined by measuring rotation of the lower end of the load cell with respect to the upper end. This rotation was measured with two direct current differential transformers (DCDT's). Diametrically opposite strain-gage rosettes and a single strain gage located midway between the two rosettes were attached to the middle of the specimen.

Figure 7 shows shear stress-strain curves that were developed. During each test the axial stress was held constant at a predetermined value. The curves indicate that the initial slope which is equal to the apparent shear modulus $(G - \sigma)$ decreases as the axial compressive stress increases. The initial slope of each curve shown in Fig. 7 is plotted as a function of applied compressive stress in Fig. 8. If the shear modulus of the composite, G, is assumed to be independent of axial compressive stress, the dashed curve represents the predicted behavior for the apparent shear modulus.

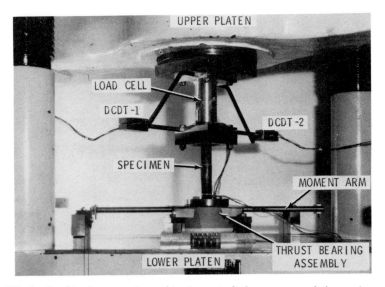

FIG. 6—*Combined compression and torsion test of a boron-epoxy tubular specimen.*

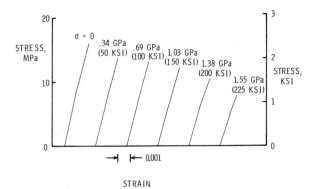

FIG. 7—*Shear stress-strain plots for boron-epoxy.*

Except for low values of compressive stress, the experimentally determined values of apparent shear modulus are less than those predicted by the dashed line. The difference increases with increasing values of compressive stress and thus indicates that shear modulus of the composite decreases with increasing applied compressive stress. A curve intersecting the abscissa at the highest compressive strength for boron-epoxy known to the author has been drawn through the data. Based on the data shown, it appears that the maximum compressive strength of boron-epoxy is limited by shear instability, which occurs when the apparent shear modulus equals zero.

σ, PSI
0
.5
1.0 x 10^6
1.5 x 10^6
EXP. DATA
COMP. STRENGTH
(REF. 5)
G*,
GPa
G*,
PSI
σ, GPa
τ = (G-σ)γ
G* = G-σ
σcr = G

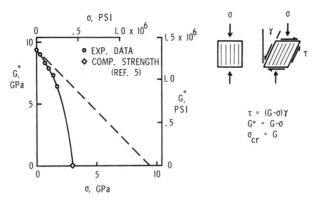

FIG. 8—*Effect of compressive stress on the shear modulus of boron-epoxy.*

Comparison of Experiment and Theory

Results from the combined compression and torsion tests were compared with computed results based on the interlaminar shear stress analysis. The boron-epoxy composite was modeled as shown in Fig. 9. The nonlinear shear stress-strain response of the epoxy matrix was calculated using the experimentally determined shear stress-strain curve for a boron-epoxy tube and assuming a stiffness in series model. Four values of initial deflection amplitude, a_0, were selected for use in the computations. The resulting values of a_0/L extended over the range of experimentally determined values reported herein.

A comparison of the experimental data and computed results is shown in Fig. 10. Examination of the figure and computations indicates the following: (1) Computed curves of apparent shear modulus as a function of

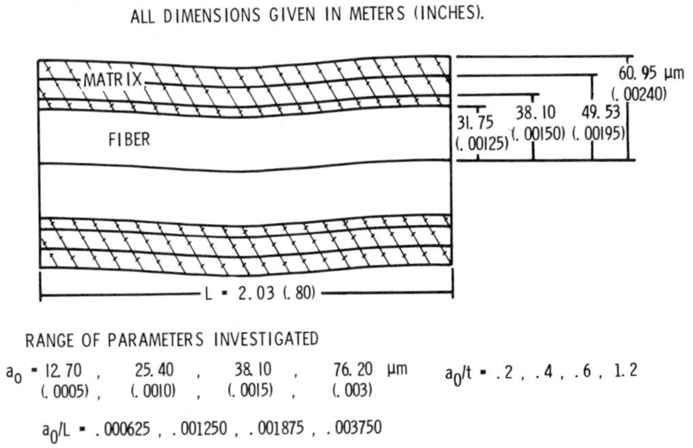

ALL DIMENSIONS GIVEN IN METERS (INCHES).
MATRIX
FIBER
60.95 μm
(.00240)
31.75
(.00125)
38.10
(.00150)
49.53
(.00195)
L = 2.03 (.80)
RANGE OF PARAMETERS INVESTIGATED
a0 = 12.70 , 25.40 , 38.10 , 76.20 μm
(.0005) , (.0010) , (.0015) , (.003)
a0/t = .2 , .4 , .6 , 1.2
a0/L = .000625 , .001250 , .001875 , .003750

FIG. 9—*Model used to simulate boron-epoxy in the stress analysis.*

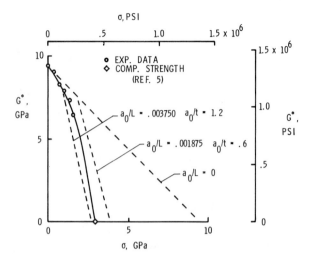

FIG. 10—*Comparison of measured and predicted values of apparent shear modulus.*

axial compressive stress, based on assumed initial deflections corresponding to a_0/L equal to 0.001875 and 0.003750, bound the data reasonably well. (2) These values of a_0/L are of the same order of magnitude as the measured deflections reported herein. (3) Small initial deflections, $0.001875 \leqslant a_0/L \leqslant 0.003750$, reduce the axial compressive stress at which shear instability is predicted to occur from approximately 9.308 GPa (1350 ksi) to the range of 2.758 to 3.792 GPa (400 to 550 ksi). (4) Within the region bounded by $0.001875 \leqslant a_0/L \leqslant 0.00375$, the maximum computed interlaminar shear stress was approximately 75.842 MPa (11 000 psi), which is less than the interlaminar shear strength of the boron-epoxy composite and indicates that failure was due to shear instability and not due to delamination. (5) Neglecting initial curvature in the fibers (assuming $a_0/L = 0$), as assumed in Refs *1* and *4*, leads to a predicted value of compressive strength which is significantly higher than the experimentally determined value.

Conclusions

Experimental evidence that the fibers in a boron-epoxy composite contain initial curvature and that the shear modulus is a function of axial compressive stress was obtained. An analytical model which includes initial curvature in the fibers and which can be used to explain the observed behavior has been proposed. Two modes of failure, delamination and shear instability, were analyzed. Based on the test results and analysis, failure of the boron-epoxy under axial compressive loading is due to shear instability.

References

[1] Davis, John G., Jr., "Compressive Strength of Lamina Reinforced and Fiber Reinforced Composite Materials," Ph.D. thesis, Virginia Polytechnic Institute and State University, Blacksburg, Va., May 1973.

[2] Rosen, B. W., "Mechanics of Composite Strengthening," *Fiber Composite Materials,* American Society of Metals, Metals Park, Ohio, Oct. 1964.

[3] Swift, G. W., "The Solution of N Simultaneous Second Order Coupled Differential Equations by the Finite Difference Method," Department of Engineering Mechanics, Virginia Polytechnic Institute Report No. VPI-E-71-3, Contract No. DAA-F07-70-C-0444, Feb. 1971.

[4] Foye, R. L., "Compressive Strength of Unidirectional Composites," AIAA Paper No. 66-143, American Institute of Aeronautics and Astronautics, Jan. 1966.

[5] Suarez, J. A., Whiteside, J. B., and Hadcock, R. N. in *Composite Materials: Testing and Design (Second Conference), ASTM STP 497,* American Society for Testing and Materials, 1972, pp. 237–256.

Creep, Fatigue, and Impact

R. L. Foye[1]

Creep Analysis of Laminates

REFERENCE: Foye, R. L., "**Creep Analysis of Laminates**," *Composite Reliability, ASTM STP 580,* American Society for Testing and Materials, 1975, pp. 381–395.

ABSTRACT: Results are presented for an analytical investigation of the creep response of laminated composites. This analysis relates the creep response of the composite to the fiber-matrix creep properties. First, the method of predicting the biaxial creep response of a unidirectional composite is described and some qualitative results given. Some interesting effects are the time dependence of the coefficients of thermal expansion of the composite and the pseudo-primary creep stage in a composite whose constituents only exhibit secondary creep. The analysis is then extended to symmetric laminates and the creep response of boron-epoxy and boron-aluminum composites are investigated.

KEY WORDS: composite materials, creep tests, finite elements, laminates, mechanical properties, thermal expansion, stress analysis, boron fibers

A sizable effort has been expended in the development of analysis programs for predicting the elastic and inelastic response of composite materials and laminates. However, to date, only a few of these programs[2,3] have considered time-dependent strains. Conceptually, such an addition or modification is no more complex than an elastic-plastic laminate analysis. This paper gives the results of an analytical investigation that relates the fiber-matrix creep properties to the time-dependent behavior of the unidirectional material and laminates made from the unidirectional material. The related computer program consists of a combination of classical lamination theory for predicting the general response of a laminate and a finite-element analysis of an idealized, rectangular, reinforcing array for establishing the instantaneous micromechanical stress fields in each ply of the laminate, as required. The computations proceed as follows.

[1] Foye, R. L., Aerospace technologist, U.S. Army Air Mobility Research & Development Laboratory, Langley Research Center, Hampton, Va. 23665.

[2] Branca, T. R., "Creep of a Uniaxial Metal Matrix Composite Subjected to Axial and Normal Lateral Loads," Department of Theoretical and Applied Mechanics, University of Illinois at Urbanna-Champaign, T&AM Report 341, June 1971.

[3] McQuillan, E. J., "Viscoelastic Creep and Relaxation in Laminated Composites," Report No. NADC-AM-7115, Naval Air Development Center, June 1971.

First, the entire time interval of interest is divided into a large number of small time increments. At the onset of each time increment the complete internal stress state in each ply is presumed known. The unconstrained creep strain increments of each finite element of the regular arrays which represent each ply are then calculated from the flow rules and uniaxial creep laws of the constituent materials (assuming constant stress conditions throughout the time increment). The conditions of creep strain compatibility within each ply are then enforced, by finite-element analysis, in order to obtain the unconstrained creep strain increments of each ply. The conditions of strain compatibility of the total laminate are then enforced, by classical laminate analysis, in order to obtain the actual creep strain increments of the assembled laminate. The prevailing stresses and total creep strains in each ply and in each finite element of each ply are then revised in preparation for the next time increment. Unlike the analysis of Branca[2] no iterations are performed within a time increment. Despite this simplification, the analysis has been stable and accurate for reasonably large time increments.

The data requirements are: (1) a description of the laminate configuration (orientation and stacking sequence); (2) the average microgeometric dimensions (fiber diameter, ply thickness, etc.); (3) the fiber and matrix thermoelastic properties; (4) the constant-stress creep data for the fiber and for the matrix materials at the temperatures of interest; and (5) the load ratios, load level, and temperature as a function of time.

The analytical methods are applied first to unidirectional composites. The analysis is then extended to symmetric laminates made from unidirectional plies. Some general related phenomena are noted and the analytical results are compared with existing boron laminate creep data.

In addition to conventional laminate creep-strain analysis, these methods have various practical applications such as the study of residual curing stresses in laminates, the estimation of thermal expansion coefficients, the investigation of residual stress effects on yield and post-yielding response of composites, and creep buckling analysis.

Unidirectional Creep Analysis

To analyze a unidirectional composite, a number of assumptions must be introduced. The first of these is the use of a regularly spaced rectangular array of parallel cylindrical fibers, perfectly bonded to a homogeneous matrix material, in place of the actual layer of unidirectional composite. The regular array is then reduced (by symmetry conditions) to the smallest, fully informative, repeating segment (see Fig. 1). This segment is subsequently modeled as an assemblage of orthotropic, constant-strain, triangular, prismatic elements. The resolution of the internal loads and deformations within this network, corresponding to a sequence of applied

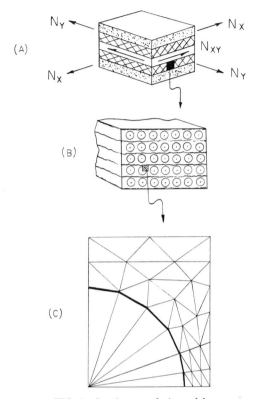

FIG. 1—*Laminate analysis model.*

stress or strain states, yields sufficient information to obtain both the overall elastic properties of the single ply and the details of the stress and strain distributions within the fiber and matrix materials corresponding to any applied stress state.[4] The manner in which this analysis can be extended to calculate creep strains will now be considered.

The total time span of interest is first divided into a large number of small subintervals. The creep-strain and stress increments are calculated for each subinterval of time and summed up at the end of each subinterval to obtain a discrete approximation to the continuous time history of the stress and creep strain in each element. The average creep strain history of the rectangular array of elements is calculated simultaneously.

For the duration of the first time increment the stresses in every element are presumed to be fixed by the stress values at the onset of the first time increment, namely, the elastic stresses at $t = 0$. The equivalent stress ($\bar{\sigma}$),

[4]Foye, R. L., "An Evaluation of Various Engineering Estimates of Transverse Properties of Unidirectional Composites," *Proceedings of the 10th National Society of Aerospace Materials and Process Engineering Symposium,* San Diego, Calif., Nov. 1966.

the equivalent creep-strain increment ($\Delta\bar{\varepsilon}$), and the actual creep strain increments ($\Delta\varepsilon_x^c$, $\Delta\varepsilon_y^c$, $\Delta\varepsilon_z^c$, $\Delta\gamma_{xy}^c$, $\Delta\gamma_{xz}^c$, $\Delta\gamma_{yz}^c$) are then calculated for each finite element of the rectangular array using the four subsequent formulas

$$\sqrt{2}\,\bar{\sigma} = \sqrt{(\sigma_x - \sigma_y)^2 + (\sigma_y - \sigma_z)^2 + (\sigma_z - \sigma_x)^2 + 6\,(\tau_{xy}^2 + \tau_{xz}^2 + \tau_{yz}^2)} \quad (1)$$

where (σ_i, τ_{ij}) designate stress components

$$\Delta\bar{\varepsilon} = \Delta\bar{\varepsilon}_I + \Delta\bar{\varepsilon}_{II} = (A - B\bar{\varepsilon}_I)\,\Delta t + (C)\,\Delta t \quad (2)$$

where Δt is the length of the time interval, $\bar{\varepsilon}_I$ ($\Delta\bar{\varepsilon}_I$) the equivalent primary creep strain (increment), $\Delta\bar{\varepsilon}_{II}$ the equivalent secondary creep-strain increment, and

$$A, B, C = \beta_i\left(\frac{\bar{\sigma}}{\delta_i}\right)^{\eta_i} \quad (i = 1, 2, 3) \quad (3)$$

where β_i, δ_i, and η_i are empirical material parameters that are selected so as to achieve a best fit between the constant-stress creep data for the constituent material and the analytical expressions for the primary and secondary creep rates contained in the bracketed terms of Eq 2. The creep-strain increments ($\Delta\varepsilon_i^c$, $\Delta\gamma_{ij}^c$) for the first subinterval of time are then computed from the Prandtl-Reuss flow rules

$$\begin{array}{ll}
\Delta\varepsilon_x^c = \xi_{xyz}\,(\Delta\bar{\varepsilon}/\bar{\sigma}), & \Delta\gamma_{xy}^c = 3\,\tau_{xy}\,(\Delta\bar{\varepsilon}/\bar{\sigma}) \\
\Delta\varepsilon_y^c = \xi_{yxz}\,(\Delta\bar{\varepsilon}/\bar{\sigma}), & \Delta\gamma_{xz}^c = 3\,\tau_{xz}\,(\Delta\bar{\varepsilon}/\bar{\sigma}) \\
\Delta\varepsilon_z^c = \xi_{zxy}\,(\Delta\bar{\varepsilon}/\bar{\sigma}), & \Delta\gamma_{yz}^c = 3\,\tau_{yz}\,(\Delta\bar{\varepsilon}/\bar{\sigma})
\end{array} \quad (4)$$

where $\xi_{ijk} = \sigma_j - 0.5(\sigma_i + \sigma_k)$.

It remains to calculate the average (or composite) creep-strain increments that take place during the first subinterval of time. This is done by calculating the system of elastic nodal forces necessary to duplicate the creep-strain increments in each triangular finite element. This calculation involves only the stress-strain laws of the constituent materials and the nodal force-stress equations of each element. The application of this system of nodal forces to the finite-element array (with suitable constraints from the symmetry conditions enforced), followed by an elastic analysis of that array, leads directly to the average (composite) creep-strain increments and the stress increments for the first subinterval of time. The stress and strain increments are added to the prevailing state of stress and strain at $t = 0$ to obtain the values of stress and strain at $t = \Delta t$. These calculations can be repeated N times to obtain the detailed state of stress and strain in each finite element and the average (composite) state of strain in the rectangular fiber-matrix array at time $t = N\Delta t$. If there is any change in the temperature or applied loads, then an additional elastic analysis must be performed and the new set of prevailing stresses and strains resolved before continuing the investigation of the time history of the composite response.

As an example of the application of this analysis, consider a square-packed unidirectional material with no residual stresses at room temperature. For simplicity, the fiber will be assumed not to creep at any stress or temperature, and the matrix will be assumed to exhibit only secondary creep. Then, let the temperature suddenly be raised 55.5 °C (100 °F), at which point the constituent properties are as given in Table 1.

TABLE 1—*Constituent properties.*

	Fiber	Matrix
E = Young's modulus	393 GN/m^2 (57 × 10^6 psi)	3.44 GN/m^2 (0.5 × 10^6 psi)
v = Poisson's ratio	0.2	0.3
G = shear modulus	165 GN/m^2 (24 × 10^6 psi)	1.38 GN/m^2 (0.2 × 10^6 psi)
α = thermal expansion coefficient	4.8 × 10^{-6}°C^{-1} (2.7 × 10^{-6}°F^{-1})	54.0 × 10^{-6}°C^{-1} (30 × 10^{-6}°F^{-1})
β_3	0	1.0 min^{-1}
δ_3	6.89 × 10^3 N/m^2 (1.0 psi)	6.89 × 10^3 N/m^2 (1.0 psi)
η_3	1.0	3.0
v = volume fraction	0.5	0.5

The initial coefficients of thermal expansion of the unidirectional material, as determined by the initial finite-element thermoelastic analysis, are $\alpha_L = 5.42 \times 10^{-6}$°$C^{-1}$ (3.01 × 10^{-6}°F^{-1}) and $\alpha_T = 30.7 \times 10^{-6}$°$C^{-1}$ (16.75 × 10^{-6}°F^{-1}). However, due to creep in the matrix material, which is now under stress (on account of the different coefficients of thermal expansion of the fiber and matrix), the coefficients of free thermal expansion of the unidirectional composite become time dependent. The two principal coefficients of thermal expansion are plotted as functions of time in Figure 2. There is virtually no change in the longitudinal coefficient of expansion, α_L, but a significant increase in the transverse coefficient of expansion, α_T, is evidenced. Figure 2 shows an initial portion of the α_T curve that exhibits something which closely resembles curvilinear primary creep response, despite the fact that the bulk constituents contain only secondary creep response. This effect, which has been observed by others[4], is in evidence to some degree for any applied loading, mechanical

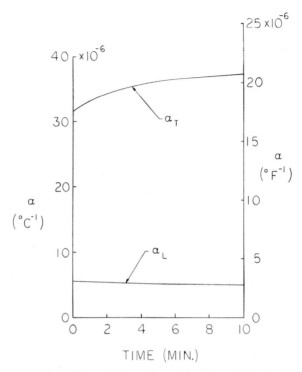

FIG. 2—*Calculated coefficients of thermal expansion for a unidirectional composite.*

or thermal. It is attributable to inhomogenieties in both the material properties and the matrix stress field. The different secondary creep rates of the fiber and matrix lead to a time-dependent redistribution of the internal loads. These changing loads cause small transient deformations that resemble primary creep in the composite. The same effect is produced by inhomogenieties in the matrix stress field. The highly stressed regions relax more rapidly than the low-stressed ones, leading to a general internal load redistribution with a tendency to greater stress uniformity with increasing time. Figure 3 shows some of the changes in the internal stress distribution for the previous example. There is a noticable reduction in the peak stress level.

The foregoing example shows that the thermal strains in a composite structure are generally time dependent, even for composites which have a zero or negative coefficient of thermal expansion. This fact may be of practical importance in the design of antenna support structure where the thermal distortions are critical. In such a design the selection of materials for a zero thermal expansion coefficient may not suffice to eliminate small distortions over longer periods of time.

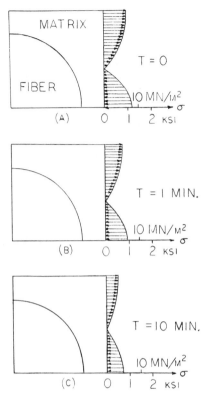

FIG. 3—*Calculated thermal stresses in a unidirectional composite.*

Creep of Laminates

The analysis for the creep response of a laminate is more complex than the corresponding analysis at the single-ply level. The laminate creep analysis, which is reported here, models each ply of the laminate with a 45-element, constant-strain, finite-element idealization based on rectangular fiber-matrix arrays, and proceeds as follows. First, as in the unidirectional case, the time interval of interest is divided into smaller subintervals. Ideally, these subintervals are so short that nowhere does the creep strain ever progress to the point where the element stresses at the end of any interval are significantly different from the values that existed at the beginning of that interval. At the onset of each time interval, the components of stress and creep strain are assumed to be known at every point (that is, within each constant-strain finite element of each ply). Equations 1, 2, 3, and 4 are applied to each element of each ply to obtain the unconstrained creep-strain increments. Then, as was done in the previous section, the strain compatibility of the elements within each ply are enforced in order to obtain the average creep-strain increments of each ply acting independently of every other ply. The average in-plane loads necessary to restore each ply to its undeformed state are then calculated from the single-ply stress-strain laws. These single-ply loads are summed over the total laminate and equal—but oppositely directed—resultant forces are applied to the assembled laminate. Classical lamination theory then gives the average creep-strain increments of the assembled laminate. These strains are also the average creep-strain increments for each ply assuming no bending or twisting deformations. Thus, with a knowledge of both the unconstrained creep-strain increment of each ply and the final constrained creep-strain increments, the ply load increments are calculated from the average stress-strain laws of each ply. Another finite-element analysis of each ply then obtains the compatible creep-strain increments and the stress increments in each element of each ply. The prevailing stress in each element and the total laminate strains are then updated in preparation for the next time increment.

The only exception to this step-by-step computational process occurs when there is an applied load and (or) temperature change. When this happens, a new set of loads, stresses, and stiffness matrices must be computed.

As an example of the application of this analysis, consider the state of stress in the matrix of one ply of a (0/90) boron-epoxy laminate when the temperature is increased 55.5 °C (100 °F) from its stress-free state. The constituent properties from the example in the previous section are used. Figure 4a shows the normal stress distribution along one side of a repeating element immediately following the temperature change. Figure 4b and c shows the results for 1 and 10 min later, after matrix creep relaxation has been allowed to take place. There is some variation of stress with time but the variation is not as large as in the case of the unidirectional material. There is no noticeable decrease in the maximum normal stress in the matrix because the matrix is in a virtual state of hydrostatic stress at the point of maximum stress concentration, and not much relaxation can occur under these conditions. Figure 5 shows the principal coefficient of thermal expansion for the (0/90) laminate. The coefficient of expansion increases to about 110 percent of its original value in the first ten minutes.

Data Correlation

This section presents a comparison between the predicted creep response of two different boron composites and the measured creep data for the same laminates.

The first composite consists of a 55 percent fiber volume fraction boron-epoxy. The fiber and matrix materials are assigned the initial static

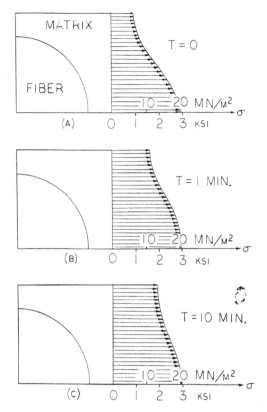

FIG. 4—*Calculated thermal stresses in a (0/90) composite.*

properties given in Table 2. The experimental creep curves for the matrix are shown in Figure 6. This figure also shows the corresponding matrix creep curves obtained by the judicious selection of the matrix creep parameters β_i, δ_i, and η_i and the application of creep Eqs 1 through 4. Although the epoxy creep strains are approximately proportional to the applied stress at room temperature, this was not generally the case for other temperatures within the useful range of this material. The room temperature creep rates for boron fibers were assumed to be the same as for the Borsic filaments reported by Erickson.[5] These experimental curves and the analytical counterparts that were used in the subsequent laminate analyses are compared in Figure 7. There are some obvious discrepancies in the initial strain measurements of the borsic filaments, which should behave almost linearly to fracture.

McQuillan (footnote 3) presents some boron-epoxy creep data on $(0/\pm45/0/90)$ and $(0/\pm45/90)$ laminates under constant tensile stress in

[5] Erickson, R. H., *Metallurgical Transactions,* Vol. 4, July 1973.

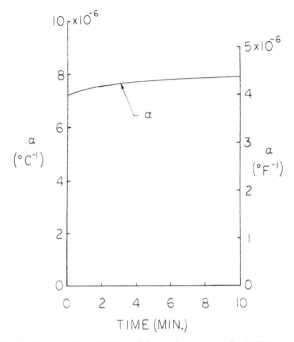

FIG. 5—*Calculated coefficient of thermal expansion for (0/90) composite.*

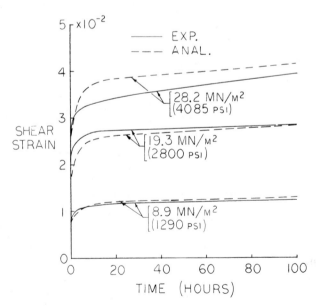

FIG. 6—*Creep curves for epoxy matrix material in shear.*

TABLE 2—*Initial static properties.*

	Boron Fiber	Epoxy Matrix
E = Young's modulus	393 GN/m^2	3.44 GN/m^2
	(57 × 10⁶ psi)	(0.5 × 10⁶ psi)
ν = Poisson's ratio	0.2	0.3
G = Shear modulus	165 GN/m^2	1.38 GN/m^2
	(24 × 10⁶ psi)	(0.2 × 10⁶ psi)

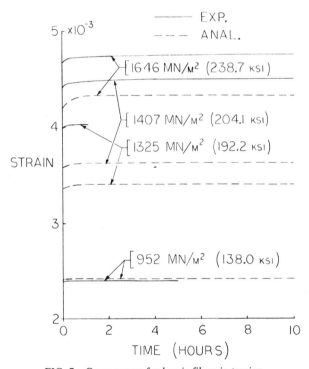

FIG. 7—*Creep curves for borsic fibers in tension.*

the 0 deg direction. These tests were conducted at room temperature. Figures 8 and 9 show the creep curves predicted by the analysis program and the measured data. The correlation is reasonably good. Most of the discrepancies are in the initial moduli.

Erickson (footnote 5) gives several constant-stress tensile creep curves for borsic-aluminum laminates in (0), (90), (±45) and (0/±60) orientations. This reference also includes the corresponding creep data for the constituent materials. Figure 10 contains the aluminum matrix creep

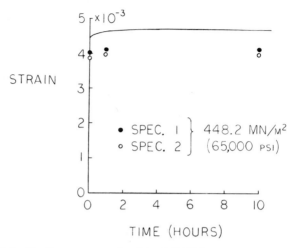

FIG. 8—*Tensile creep curves for (0/±45/0/90) boron-epoxy composite.*

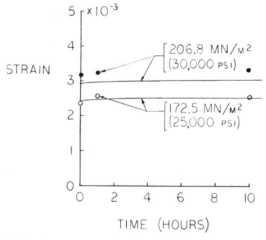

FIG. 9—*Tensile creep curves for (0/±45/90) boron-epoxy composite.*

curves and the analytical approximations to them. Using these fiber and matrix properties and a fiber volume fraction of 35 percent, the unidirectional and laminate creep predictions are shown in Figures 11 through 14 along with the experimental data. In the case of the (±45), (90), and (0, ±60) laminates, which involved substantial levels of initial nonlinear strains, the theoretical curves were given the same initial strain values as the experiment indicated. The absence of nonlinear corrections to the initial stress state did not seem to invalidate the creep strain predictions. Again the correlation is reasonably good considering the level of data scatter that is commonly encountered in this type of testing. The

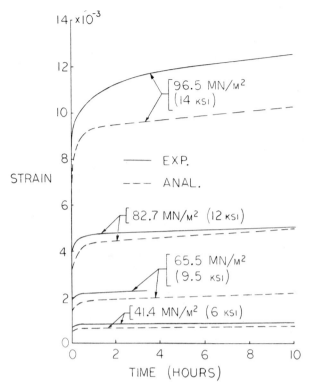

FIG. 10—*Creep curves for aluminum matrix in tension.*

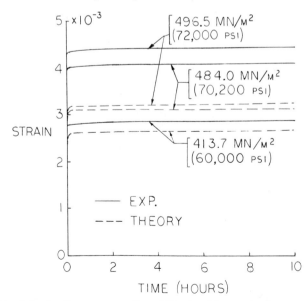

FIG. 11—*0 deg tensile creep curves for unidirectional boron-aluminum composite.*

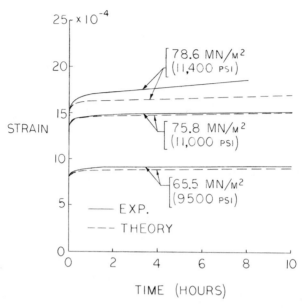

FIG. 12—*90 deg tensile creep curves for unidirectional boron-aluminum composite.*

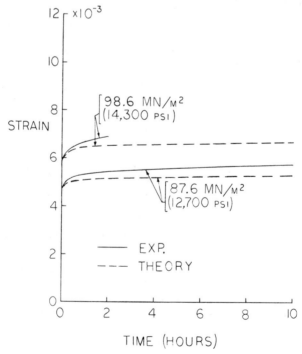

FIG. 13—*Tensile creep curves for (±45) boron-aluminum composite.*

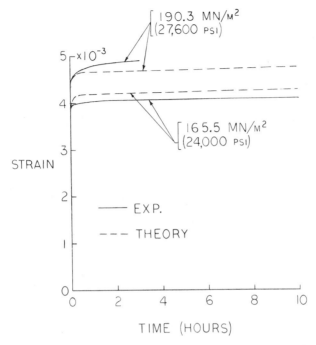

FIG. 14—*Tensile creep curves for (0/ ± 60) boron-aluminum composite.*

analysis appears to inherently underestimate the laminate creep strain levels. This could be accountable to matrix or interfacial crazing and cracking as well as to the discrepancies between the experimental creep data for the constituent materials and the analytical approximations to the same. Another source of error is associated with the use of the model shown in Figure 1 in place of the actual composite geometry, which is statistical in nature.

Conclusions

1. The correlation between the analytical creep predictions and a limited amount of test data indicates that the program is capable of making reasonable creep-strain predictions for simple laminates made from unidirectional materials.

2. The time-dependent nature of the thermal expansion coefficients for composites is demonstrated for both unidirectional material and laminates.

3. The analysis program can predict the complex changes in the internal fiber/matrix stress fields resulting from creep of the constituents.

J. E. Schwabe[1]

Composite Matrix Fatigue Crazing— Detection and Measurement

REFERENCE: Schwabe, J. E., "Composite Matrix Fatigue Crazing—Detection and Measurement," *Composite Reliability, ASTM STP 580,* American Society for Testing and Materials, 1975, pp. 396–404.

ABSTRACT: Crazing has recently become of interest in composite materials having organic matrices, and the development of crazes has been suggested as a failure criterion in the fatigue testing of susceptible composites.

This paper reports the results of an experiment to find a practical means of detecting and monitoring the development of crazing during fatigue testing of fiber-reinforced epoxy matrix composite materials. A specimen of such material was strain-gaged with one 2-in.-long (0.051 m) foil gage, and with thirty 2/100-in.-long (0.508 mm) gages. The apparent strain of each gage was monitored during displacement control tension-tension fatigue testing.

The experimental results demonstrated that the maximum difference between apparent strains as measured by the small strain gages provided a sensitive means of detecting crazing. It was concluded that thirty small strain gages with appropriate instrumentation could provide a practical means of automatically detecting crazing during such fatigue tests of composite materials.

KEY WORDS: composite materials, epoxy laminates, fiberglass reinforced plastics, reinforced plastics, fiber composites, tests, mechanical tests, tension tests, fatigue (materials), fatigue tests, failure, crazing, detection, strain gages

This paper reports the results of an experiment to determine the feasibility of using foil strain gages for the detection and measurement of matrix crazing in a fiberglass-reinforced plastic during fatigue testing. Crazing, for the purposes of this investigation, was considered to include the development of matrix microfissuring during fatigue testing. Some investigators have implied a more restrictive definition of crazing, describing it as the development of regions of high light reflectivity relative to that of the surrounding material, resulting in what appear to be planar cracks but with no actual discontinuity [1].[2] These regions have been shown to be highly localized areas of yielding, and are typically perpen-

[1] Senior research engineer, Babcock & Wilcox Co., Alliance Research Center, Alliance, Ohio 44601.
[2] The italic numbers in brackets refer to the list of references appended to this paper.

dicular to the principal direction of the applied stress. Some consider crazing to be a mode of plastic deformation in glassy polymers occurring in the presence of lateral restraint [2]. It has been reported that for some polymer systems the structure of a craze consists of fibrils 100 to 300 Å (10 to 30 nm) in diameter interspaced by voids of the same dimensions, the crazes being thin planes passing through the bulk polymer [3-18].

The majority of crazing studies have been conducted using unreinforced plastics, but crazing has been observed in fiber-reinforced composites. The development of matrix crazing due to fatigue has been reported to accompany a reduction in off-axis composite mechanical properties during longitudinal tension fatigue testing with little corresponding change in the longitudinal properties. This can cause difficulty in defining failure in specimens with continuous reinforcement when off-axis properties are of interest, since in extreme cases the in-plane shear stiffness of a specimen may drop drastically due to crazing even though it is still capable of supporting the longitudinal tensile loads imposed by the test with little loss in longitudinal stiffness. This has led to the experimentally inconvenient procedure of having to interrupt longitudinal fatigue tests in order to assess off-axis specimen damage. Besides the direct effect on mechanical properties, crazing can be significant in other ways. Examples are that crazing may expose the reinforcement to attack by the environment or that crazing may constitute failure in applications requiring uniform surface appearance.

Basis of Experimental Approach

The most common method used to detect crazing has been visual inspection. Other methods have used conductive coatings; absorption of solvents; absorption of radioactive material; and photometric methods utilizing the change in light transmitivity of crazed specimens, the increase in light reflectivity of crazed surfaces, or the change in the index of refraction at the craze-parent material boundary [5,19,20]. For one reason or another these techniques were felt to be unsatisfactory for our purposes, and the use of foil strain gages was investigated in an attempt to obtain an electrical output indicative of the state of crazing.

The literature indicated that crazes nucleate and grow in at least two manners. The first, which might be considered nucleation-controlled, results in a relatively low density of crazes which develop into microfissures with the continuous appearance of new crazes during testing. The second type of development, growth-controlled, involves a more nearly simultaneous appearance of crazes over a relatively large area, the crazes growing more in individual severity than in total number as testing continues. The actual density of the crazes to be expected, the manner of their growth, and their extent were not known for the material and test conditions to be used in this investigation. It was expected that the response of a strain gage to an underlying craze would markedly depend on the craze width relative to the gage length; that very small strain gages could indicate subnominal strains if a craze were just outside the gage length, relaxing the material under the gage; or that very small strain gages could indicate strains much larger than the nominal strain if an underlying craze were a larger fraction of the strain gage's length than the fraction of total craze width to specimen length. Strain-gage response to crazing for gages of different length was investigated by instrumenting a specimen with many small strain gages and with one large strain gage having a gage length two orders of magnitude greater than that of the small gages and then examining their relative outputs during tension-tension axial fatigue testing.

Specimen Description

A straight-sided tension specimen, shown in Fig. 1, with 31 strain gages, detailed in Fig. 2, was used. The specimen was of S-glass reinforced Fiberite 904 epoxy. The strain-gaging consisted of three M&M EA-06-020MT-120 coupons, each coupon being ten 0.020-in. (0.508 mm)

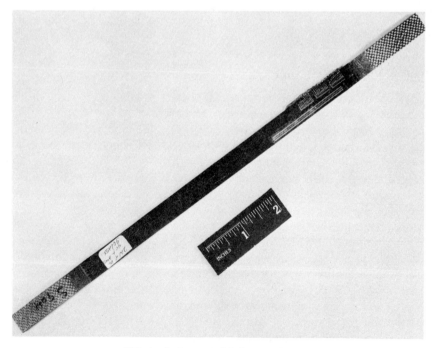

FIG. 1—*Instrumented fatigue specimen.*

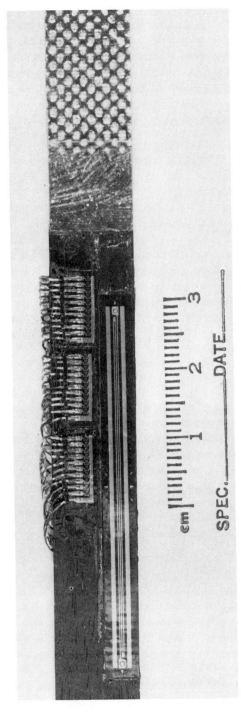

FIG. 2—Closeup of strain gaging.

gage-length gages. One M&M EA-06-19CDK-120 gage of 2-in. (0.0508 m) gage length was also used. This gage is referred to as the master gage later in this paper. The gage length ratio between the master gage and the smaller gages was therefore 100:1. The gages were positioned in an area on the specimen where failure, should it occur, was anticipated because of damage to one edge.

Experimental Technique

The specimen was mounted and tested in tension-tension fatigue in a 50-kip (222 kN) MTS testing machine at room temperature. The specimen was cycled between near-zero and 50 000-psi (345 MPa) tensile stress using sinusoidal displacement control. At intervals of approximately 200 cycles, the test was interrupted and the apparent strain at each gage recorded by a multichannel data-acquisition system which pulsed the strain gages instead of supplying continuous gage excitation. Use of this piece of equipment minimized gage drift due to strain-gage heating. During each interruption the specimen was visually inspected for crazing. Underpeak detection set for a 2 percent drop in load was used, but the specimen never lost enough stiffness during a test segment to trigger the equipment. A gradual drop in stiffness did occur during testing, and the nominal stress level was adhered to by increasing the stroke at the start of each test segment if required.

Experimental Results

Table 1 summarizes the strain-gage readings at each test interruption. The stress on the specimen during these readings was 25 000 psi (172 MPa). The specimen displayed crazing at the 1570-cycle interruption. The photograph illustrating crazing (Fig. 3) was taken after 2000 cycles. As the test progressed, the visible crazing became more uniform and more finely distributed over the specimen, and the small strain gages began to fail until all had failed by 5570 cycles.

Discussion of Results

As shown in Table 1 and in Fig. 4, the range of apparent strain as measured by the small strain gages increased during the test. An increase in the compliance during the test as measured by the master gage is also indicated in the table. At the point where crazing became visible, the readings of the small strain gage had a spread (range/average) of 30 percent. Prior to visible crazing the average of the small-gage apparent strains was always less than the master-gage strain but never by an amount considered significant. This difference decreased from the beginning of the experiment, became zero at about the time that crazing was

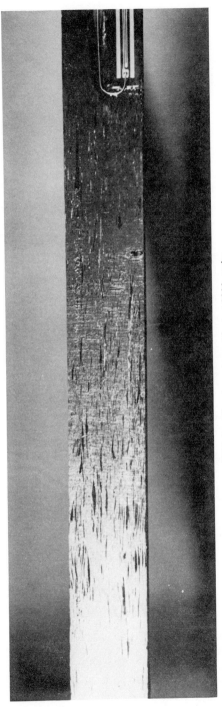

FIG. 3—*Visual crazing evident at 2000 cycles.*

TABLE 1—*Apparent strains at intervals during the tension-tension fatigue stress test.*

Apparent Strain (μin./in. or μm/m) at 25 000-psi (172 MPa) Sustained Stress

Test Interruption Point, cycles	Master Gage Reading	0.020 in. (0.508 mm) Gage Readings				No. failed
		min	max	avg	range, spread	
0	3 257	3 172	3 300	3 242	178 (4%)	0
280	3 435	3 270	3 482	3 380	212 (6%)	0
360	3 485	3 318	3 536	3 453	218 (6.1%)	0
950	3 811	3 545	4 181	3 799	636 (16.2%)	0
1 570	4 177	3 791	5 090	4 209	1 299 (30.2%)	0
1 700	4 257	3 844	5 249	4 288	1 405 (32.1%)	0
2 000	4 414	3 945	5 847	4 531	1 902 (41.9%)	0
2 200	4 537	4 038	6 577	4 758	2 539 (54.4%)	0
2 400	4 651	4 117	7 544	5 020	3 427 (71.7%)	0
2 680	4 831	4 280	8 482	5 454	4 202 (84.5%)	2
2 800	4 880	4 312	7 640	5 544	3 328 (66.2%)	3
3 000	5 018	4 421	9 848	6 003	5 427 (105.1%)	4
3 230	5 164	4 548	14 412	6 354	9 864 (185.6%)	5
3 410	5 288	4 685	22 388	6 958	17 703 (325.2%)	6
3 600	5 422	4 873	17 284	7 667	12 411 (222.4%)	10
3 820	5 599	5 106	25 104	8 450	19 998 (347.1%)	14
4 010	5 763	5 351	18 130	8 828	12 779 (215.5%)	26
4 610	6 372	8 838	10 324	8 217	1 486 (22.65%)	16
5 000	6 909	7 433	11 837	10 277	4 404 (61.9%)	27
5 570	7 892	9 403	...	...	...	29

MATRIX CRAZING DETECTION

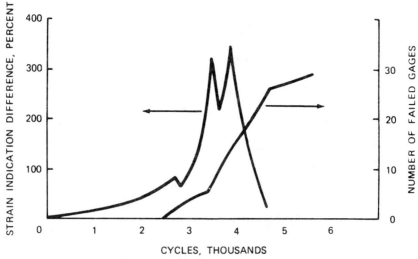

FIG. 4—*Small strain gage apparent strain spread (range/average) and number of failed small gages versus number of cycles.*

visually detected, changed sign and increased significantly in magnitude as the experiment continued. This behavior was hypothesized as being due to crazes under some of the small strain gages, and due to their smaller ability relative to that of the master gage to integrate the crazing strain over a larger gage length because of their much smaller size. The high failure rate among the small gages later in the experiment was attributed to the same cause.

The lowest value of apparent strain indicated by any of the 30 small strain gages was always smaller than the master strain-gage reading until very late in the experiment when the remaining small gages were nearing failure, which always consisted of the gage indicating a very large strain and then becoming an open circuit. The fact that a subnominal value of apparent strain was always seen by one of the small strain gages, with the aforementioned exception, indicated that there was some irregularity in either growth rate or in distribution of the crazes or that a nearby craze was relaxing the strain to a subnominal value under the small gage. The nominal strain was taken as that indicated by the master gage.

The most important observation during this experiment was that visible crazing corresponded to a 30 percent spread in the small-gage readings for this particular material. For the purpose of crazing detection, the master gage was not necessary. The experiment demonstrated that the use of three coupons of ten very small strain gages would produce an usable apparent strain spread which, with appropriate instrumentation, could be used to provide an electrical signal indicative of the presence and extent of crazing.

Conclusions

1. Matrix crazing in composite materials can be detected by an array of strain gages having short gage lengths.

2. A differential scanner which selects each gage in turn and compares the selected gage's strain with that of its companion gages taken in turn could be used to automatically monitor crazing during fatigue testing.

Acknowledgment

This work was funded in part by the Advanced Composites Department of the Babcock & Wilcox Company.

References

[1] Smith, J. T., Hamilton-Miller, J. M. T., and Knox, R., *Nature,* Sept. 29, 1962, p. 1299.
[2] Brady, T. E. and Yeh, G. S. Y., *Journal of Materials Science,* Vol. 8, 1973, p. 1083.
[3] Rabinowitz, S. and Beardmore, P., *CRC Critical Reviews in Macromolecular Science,* Jan. 1972, p. 13.
[4] Kambour, R. P. and Robertson, R. E., "The Mechanical Properties of Plastics," *Materials Science of Polymers,* North Holland, Amsterdam, 1971.

[5] Kambour, R. P., *Applied Polymer Symposia,* No. 7, Interscience, New York, 1968, p. 215.

[6] Beahan, P., Bevis, M., and Hull, D., *Philosophy Magazine,* Vol. 24, 1971, p. 192.

[7] Kambour, R. P. and Russell, R. R., *Polymer,* Vol. 12, 1971, p. 237.

[8] Harris, J. S. and Ward, I. M., *Journal of Materials Science,* Vol. 5, 1970, p. 573.

[9] Murray, J. and Hull, D., *Polymer Letters,* Vol. 8, 1970, p. 159.

[10] Kambour, R. P. and Holick, A. S., *Journal of Polymer Science,* Part A-2, Vol. 7, 1969, p. 1393.

[11] Kambour, R. P. and Holick, A. S., *Polymer Preprints,* American Chemical Society, Vol. 10, 1969, p. 1182.

[12] Kambour, R. P., *Polymer,* Vol. 5, 1964, p. 143.

[13] Spurr, O. K. and Niegisch, W. D., *Journal of Applied Polymer Science,* Vol. 6, 1962, p. 585.

[14] Klemperer, W. B., *Theodore von Karman Anniversary Volume,* Applied Mechanics, California Institute of Technology, 1941, p. 328.

[15] Sternstein, S. S., Ongchin, L., and Silverman, A., *Applied Polymer Symposia,* No. 7, Interscience, New York, 1968, p. 175.

[16] Bevis, M. B. and Hull, D., *Journal of Materials Science,* Vol. 5, 1970, p. 938.

[17] Wang, T. T., Matsuo, M., and Kwei, T. K., *Journal of Applied Physics,* Vol. 42, 1971, p. 4188.

[18] Kambour, R. P., *Industrial and Engineering Chemistry, Product Research and Development,* Vol. 11, No. 2, p. 140.

[19] Leghissa, S. and Salvatore, O., *Polymer Engineering and Science,* April 1966, pp. 127–130.

[20] Kinna, M. A. and Choi, S. S., *Modern Plastics,* Sept. 1966, p. 169.

D. W. Petrasek[1] and R. A. Signorelli[1]

Stress-Rupture Strength and Microstructural Stability of W-Hf-C Wire-Reinforced Superalloy Composites

REFERENCE: Petrasek, D. W., and Signorelli, R. A., "**Stress-Rupture Strength and Microstructural Stability of W-Hf-C Wire-Reinforced Superalloy Composites,**" *Composite Reliability, ASTM STP 580,* American Society for Testing and Materials, 1975, pp. 405–424.

ABSTRACT: W-Hf-C/superalloy composites were found to be potentially useful for turbine blade applications on the basis of stress-rupture strength. The 100- and 1000-h rupture strengths obtained for 70 volume percent fiber composites tested at 1090 °C (2000 °F) were 420 and 280 MN/m^2 (61 000 and 41 000 psi). The investigation indicated that with better quality fibers, composites having 100- and 1000-h rupture strengths of 570 and 370 MN/m^2 (82 000 and 54 000 psi) may be obtained. Metallographic studies indicated sufficient fiber-matrix compatibility for long-time applications at 1090 °C (2000 °F) for 1000 h or more.

KEYS WORDS: composite materials, fiber composites, heat resistant alloys, creep rupture strength

The developers of gas turbines have recognized for years the many benefits to be realized by going to higher engine operating temperatures. The use of superalloys for turbine blade materials for reasonable lifetimes is currently limited to a material temperature of approximately 980 to 1010 °C (1800 to 1850 °F) because of the stresses imposed on the blade. It seems unlikely that further substantial high-temperature strength improvements will be made with superalloys by conventional metallurgical techniques. To some extent the deficiences of high-temperature materials can be overcome by design. Superalloys have been used as turbine blades with operating temperatures of 1260 °C (2300 °F) and above by cooling the blades with bleed air from the compressor. However, further increases in performance for turbines will require materials with increased operating temperature capability because further gains possible from cooling of presently available

---

[1] Lewis Research Center, Cleveland, Ohio 44135.

materials are limited. Therefore, an important objective of materials research for turbine engines is to develop materials that will permit higher operating temperatures. One of the materials under study for use in higher-temperature turbine blades is a composite consisting of a superalloy matrix reinforced by refractory metal fibers.

Tungsten alloy/superalloy composites which have been investigated at a number of laboratories [1–5][2] have the potential of combining the high-temperature strength of a refractory metal with the oxidation resistance, toughness, and ductility of a superalloy. Previous work at the Lewis Research Center demonstrated that 70 volume percent fiber composites could be produced to have 100- and 1000-h rupture strengths at 1090°C (2000°F) of 338 and 255 MN/m² (49 000 and 37 000 psi) [5].

A potential further improvement in composite strength for turbine blade application can be achieved through the use of stronger tungsten alloy fibers than were used in the past. Improved high-strength tungsten alloy fibers have been made available as part of a continuing contract effort by the Lewis Research Center to obtain higher-strength fiber materials.

The object of the present investigation was to determine the potential for turbine blade application of superalloy composites in terms of the 1090°C (2000°F) stress-rupture strength using improved high-strength fibers of W-Hf-C. Composites consisting of a nickel-base alloy reinforced with up to 60 volume percent W-Hf-C fibers were fabricated. The composite specimens and W-Hf-C fiber were evaluated in stress-rupture at 1090°C (2000°F). A metallographic and electron beam probe analysis was conducted to determine the extent of reaction between the W-Hf-C fiber and nickel-base alloy for exposure times up to 300 h at 1090°C (2000°F).

Materials, Apparatus, and Procedure

Fiber and Matrix Material

The fabrication history of the W-Hf-C fibers used in this investigation is reported in Ref 6. The fiber was developed as part of a continuing program support by NASA Lewis Research Center to provide improved property fibers for fiber composite use. The fiber was experimentally developed and not optimized. Its diameter was 0.038 cm (0.015 in.), and it was received in the as-drawn, cleaned, and straightened condition. The nominal chemical composition in weight percent of the fiber was 0.03 carbon, 0.37 hafnium, with the balance made up of tungsten. The fiber was split longitudinally throughout most of its length and was not fully straightened. The radius of curvature for the W-Hf-C fiber was calculated to be 7 cm (3 in.) compared with fully straightened tungsten (218 CS) fibers which have a radius of curvature of 100 cm (40 in.).

---

[2] The italic numbers in brackets refer to the list of references appended to this paper.

The composition of the nickel-base alloy matrix material was selected based upon its compatibility with the fiber as determined in a prior investigation [1]. The nominal composition of the nickel alloy was 56 percent nickel, 25 percent tungsten, 15 percent chromium, 2 percent aluminum, and 2 percent titanium. The nickel alloy powder was vacuum cast and atomized into fine powder ranging in size from −325 to +500 mesh.

Composite Specimen Fabrication

Composites containing the tungsten alloy wire and the nickel alloy were made by a slip casting process described in detail in Ref. 1. Hot isostatically pressed rods of over 99 percent theoretical density were produced and machined into specimens to be tested in stress-rupture.

Testing Procedure

Stress-rupture tests on the wire material were conducted at 1090 and 1200 °C (2000 and 2200 °F) in a measured vacuum of 7 × 10⁻³ N/m² (5 × 10⁻³ torr) using a stress-rupture apparatus specifically designed for the testing of small-diameter fibers. A detailed description of this apparatus may be found in Ref 7.

Stress-rupture tests at 1090 °C (2000 °F) were conducted on composite test specimens using conventional creep machines and a helium atmosphere.

Metallographic Study

Stress-rupture specimens were examined metallographically to determine the depth of the reaction zone between the nickel alloy matrix and the W-Hf-C wire and to determine the fiber content of the specimens. The depth of reaction was measured optically on transverse sections of composite specimens at a magnification of ×150. The depth of the reaction zone was defined as the distance from the fiber-matrix interface to the interface in the fiber where a microstructural change was observed. The fiber content of each composite specimen was determined by sectioning the specimen transversely in an area immediately adjacent to the fracture. The sections were mounted, polished, and photographed at a magnification factor of 25. A wire count was obtained from the photographs, and the volume percent fiber contents were calculated.

Replica electron micrographs were taken of transverse sections of wire and composite specimens in an area adjacent to the fracture edge. A two-step technique was used to replicate the specimens. The specimens were first viewed in an electron microscope and photographs were taken at magnification factors of 8000 and 28 000.

Electron Microprobe Studies

Electron microprobe studies were conducted on transverse sections of composite specimens. These studies were made to determine if there was elemental diffusion between the W-Hf-C wire and the matrix and to try to identify these elements and the extent to which they diffused. The probe was also operated to scan for secondary electron backscatter images and X-ray fluorescense images for the elements aluminum, chromium, hafnium, nickel, titanium, and tungsten.

Results

Fiber Material

Stress-Rupture Properties—The stress-rupture properties of the W-Hf-C fibers used in this investigation are listed in Table 1. The fibers tested were taken from several ingots and spools. The T and N designations for the ingots refer to the tail and nose sections of extruded ingots from which the fibers were drawn. Variations in time to rupture at a specific stress exists from ingot to ingot and from spool to spool. Figure 1 is a plot of the time to rupture as a function of the stress on the W-Hf-C fibers tested at 1090 and 1200 °C (2000 and 2200 °F). The curves are fitted to the data by least squares. The stress to cause rupture in 100 and 1000 h at 1090 °C (2000 °F) was 1060 and 890 MN/m² (154 000 and 129 000 psi). The 1200 °C (2200 °F) test results indicated 100- and 1000-h rupture strengths for the fiber of 715 and 590 MN/m² (103 000 and 85 000 psi). Figure 2 is a plot of the reduction in area at fracture as a function of the time to rupture for fibers tested at 1090 °C (2000 °F). The plot shows a steady decrease in ductility at fracture with increasing time to rupture. At 1200 °C (2200 °F) the reduction in area at fracture is relatively constant at about 10 to 20 percent as shown in Table 1, and no trend as a function of rupture time is observed.

Microstructure—Figure 3 shows electron micrographs of a W-Hf-C fiber

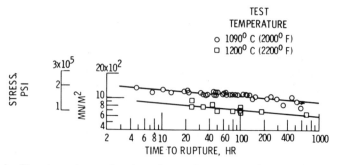

FIG. 1—*Time to rupture as function of stress for W-Hf-C wire at 1090 °C (2000 °F) and 1200 °C (2000 °F).*

TABLE 1—*Stress-rupture properties of W-Hf-C fiber.*

Ingot Number	Spool Number	Test Temperature °C	°F	Stress MN/m²	psi	Life, h	% Reduction in Area
4027	1	1090	2000	1300[a]	189 000	4.4	44.2
				1290[a]	187 000	10.3	58.4
				1230[a]	178 000	21.1	23.2
				1210[a]	175 000	19.1	35.0
				1150[a]	167 000	61.5	44.5
				1110[a]	161 000	108.3	18.0
				1040	150 000	247.9	11.9
				1000	145 000	449.7	20.6
				986	143 000	286.1	18.1
				896	130 000	520.6	Test stopped before fracture
		1200	2200	918[a]	133 000	28.3	15.3
				841[a]	122 000	42.9	21.9
				765[a]	111 000	104.3	11.5
				689[a]	100 000	188.4	28.5
				620	90 000	705.6	14.4
4034T	1	1090	2000	1170	170 000	64.0	27.2
				1100	160 000	92.3	31.7
	3			1100	160 000	65.4	46.7
				758	110 000	586.7	10.7
	4			1100	160 000	113.8	24.2
				965	140 000	140.5	24.3
	5			1100	160 000	129.9	14.4
				965	140 000	211.6	10.3
4034T"B"	2	1090	2000	1170	170 000	22.5	27.2
				1100	160 000	85.2	31.7
				827	120 000	345.6	11.6
4034N	1	1090	2000	1100	160 000	78.6	15.4
				1170	170 000	44.6	20.2
	2			1170	170 000	46.7	32.6
				1100	160 000	114.7	23.7
				1030	150 000	152.8	12.9
	3			1170	170 000	49.2	26.4
				1100	160 000	78.0	17.8
4035T	3	1090	2000	1170	170 000	31.2	38.7
				1100	160 000	33.6	38.6
	4			1100	160 000	47.1	27.2
	5			1170	170 000	7.5	70.1
				1100	160 000	34.8	27.2
		1200	2200	758	110 000	33.1	16.6
				689	100 000	49.7	16.6
	10	1090	2000	1170	170 000	12.9	78.8
				1100	160 000	72.2	26.0
	6	1200	2200	689	100 000	79.0	22.5
				655	95 000	99.1	12.9
4035N	10	1090	2000	1100	160 000	78.6	...
	12			1100	160 000	65.0	23.7
	13			1100	160 000	57.7	19.0
	14			1100	160 000	48.5	23.7
		1200	2200	758	110 000	23.6	25.0
				689	100 000	97.7	17.9
4037N	1	1090	2000	1170	170 000	7.5	30.0
				1100	160 000	37.2	28.9

[a]Data from Ref *12*.

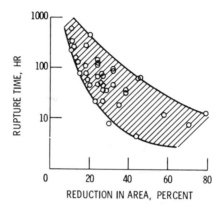

FIG. 2—*Reduction in area as function of rupture time for W-Hf-C wire at 1090°C (2000°F).*

tested at 1090°C (2000°F). The fiber failed in stress-rupture after 12.9 h. Figure 3*a* is a transverse section at the edge of the fiber and Fig. 3*b* is a transverse section near the center of the fiber. Similar structures, particle distribution, and particle size are seen for both sections.

Figures 4*a* and *b* are electron micrographs of a fiber which failed in stress-rupture in 586.7 h. A transverse edge section is shown in Fig. 4*a* and sections near the center of the wire are shown in Figs. 4*b* and *c*. The edge and center sections in Figs. 4*a* and *b* appear to have larger particles than those observed in the preceding fiber specimen, which was exposed for only 12.9 h. There were areas in the center portion of the fiber, however, such as in Fig. 4*c*, which had an equivalent structure to that observed for the short-time exposure.

The fiber specimen of Fig. 3 (short-time exposure) failed in stress-rupture with a very ductile fracture while the fiber specimen shown in Fig. 4 (long-time exposure) failed in a much less ductile manner. The electron micrograph study indicated that some particle coarsening occurred in the fiber exposed for the long time period and that this particle coarsening may have resulted in a less ductile material. Particle coarsening rates calculated for HfC particles contained in a tungsten alloy in Ref *8* indicated that the HfC particles should be very stable at 1090°C (2000°F). Results obtained in this investigation indicate that HfC particles contained in the tungsten alloy fiber are not stable for long-time exposure at 1090°C (2000°F). The difference in stability of the HfC particles observed in this investigation as compared with that calculated from Ref *8* may be related to stored energy in the fiber due to the large amount of cold working employed in the wire drawing process. The recrystallization temperature of this material could be lowered due to the large amount of cold work given the fiber. In a previous investigation (Ref *9*), grain broadening was observed for W-Hf-C fibers exposed at 1090°C (2000°F) for long time periods. Particle growth could be accelerated as grain boundaries sweep over the particles.

FIG. 3—*Replica electron micrographs of W-Hf-C wire tested at 1093°C (200°F). Stress, 1170 MN/m² (170 000 psi); time to rupture, 12.9 h (×28 000).*

Matrix Material

Stress-Rupture Properties—Vacuum-cast stress-rupture specimens of the nickel-base alloy matrix were obtained from the master melt used to make the powder, were tested in a past program, and are reported in Ref *1*. The 100-h rupture strength for the nickel alloy was found to be 23 MN/m² (3200 psi) at 1090°C (2000°F).

Composite Material

Stress-Rupture Properties—The stress-rupture properties obtained for the composites are given in Table 2. The composite specimens had fiber contents ranging from about 15 to 60 volume percent and were tested at stress levels from 138 to 379 MN/m² (20 000 to 55 000 psi). Calculation of com-

(a) EDGE SECTION.   1 μm

(b) CENTER SECTION, AREA 1.   1 μm

(c) CENTER SECTION, AREA 2.   1 μm

FIG. 4—*Replica electron micrographs of W-Hf-C wire tested at 1093°C (2000°F). Stress, 758 MN/m² (110 000 psi); time to rupture, 586.7 h (×28 000).*

TABLE 2—*Stress-rupture properties for W-Hf-C wire-nickel alloy composites; test temperature = 1090°C (2000°F).*

Specimen No.	Specimen Diameter		Composite Stress		Fiber Stress		Rupture life, h	Volume % fiber	Reaction Zone Depth	
	cm	in.	MN/m²	psi	MN/m²	psi			cm	in.
570	0.3203	0.1261	220	32 000	1180	172 000	0.7	18.8	0.0003	0.0003
569	0.3155	0.1242	138	20 000	885	128 000	9.3	15.6	0.0013	0.0005
619	0.3139	0.1236	310	45 000	875	127 000	15.7	35.5	0.0018	0.0007
587	0.3137	0.1235	345	50 000	825	120 000	20.8	41.7	0.0020	0.0008
584	0.3254	0.1281	345	50 000	825	120 000	24.6	41.8	0.0053	0.0021
590	0.3124	0.1230	172	25 000	615	89 000	32.8	28.1	0.0020	0.0008
597	0.3139	0.1236	379	55 000	820	119 000	59.0	46.4	0.0033	0.0013
617	0.3150	0.1240	276	40 000	605	88 000	68.0	45.6	0.0053	0.0021
592	0.3152	0.1241	207	30 000	620	90 000	73.7	33.3	0.0041	0.0016
616	0.3150	0.1240	276	40 000	655	95 000	78.7	42.3	0.0041	0.0016
591	0.3152	0.1241	207	30 000	715	104 000	84.2	28.8	0.0041	0.0016
582	0.3162	0.1245	310	45 000	725	105 000	95.7	42.7	0.0046	0.0018
625	0.3162	0.1245	207	30 000	495	72 000	128.2	41.9	0.0066	0.0026
631	0.3132	0.1233	310	45 000	560	81 000	137.7	55.5	0.0058	0.0023
578	0.3254	0.1281	345	50 000	660	96 000	148.3	52.1	0.0053	0.0021
589	0.3099	0.1220	310	45 000	525	76 000	159.2	59.1	0.0053	0.0021
581	0.3127	0.1231	241	35 000	525	76 000	165.2	46.2	0.0061	0.0024
580	0.3142	0.1237	310	45 000	570	83 000	170.1	54.5	0.0066	0.0023
620	0.3152	0.1241	207	30 000	455	66 000	230.6	45.1	0.0066	0.0026
613	0.3157	0.1243	207	30 000	515	75 000	268.7	39.9	0.0056	0.0022
557	0.3282	0.1292	207	30 000	410	59 000	324.8[a]	51.2	0.0079	0.0031
598	0.3117	0.1227	172	25 000	345	50 000	413.6	50.2	0.0084	0.0033

[a]Test stopped before fracture.

posite stress-rupture strength for a specific life at a specific fiber content other than those actually tested necessitates a determination of the fiber stress carrying capability in the composite. The stress on the fiber was calculated by neglecting the stress on the matrix and by dividing the composite specimen load by the area of fiber contained in the composite. The fiber was assumed to carry the entire load during the stress-rupture test and the matrix contribution was assumed to be negligible, which is in accordance with the analysis of the stress-rupture properties of composites reported in Ref 10. The stress-carrying capability of the fiber in the nickel alloy matrix material was thus calculated and is given in Table 2. Figure 5 is a plot of the stress on the W-Hf-C fiber contained in the nickel alloy matrix

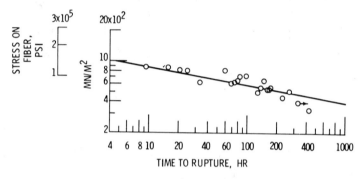

FIG. 5—Stress on fiber as function of rupture time for W-Hf-C composites at 1090°C (2000°F).

as a function of time to rupture at 1090°C (2000°F). The least-square fit of the data indicates that the fiber stress for rupture in 100 h is approximately 600 MN/m² (87 000 psi) while that for 1000 h is 400 MN/m² (59 000 psi). Approximately 57 percent of the stress-rupture strength of the W-Hf-C fiber was retained in the composite for rupture in 100 and 45 percent for rupture in 1000 h compared with as-received fibers tested in vacuum. The strength retension of the W-Hf-C fiber was expected to be low because of the manner in which the specimens were fabricated and the presence of fiber splits. Because of wire bend and the method of fabricating specimens, fiber ends were exposed on the surface of the specimen test section. The fibers exposed on the surface of the test section debonded and pulled out during the test and did not contribute their full strength to the composite. Pullout of the fibers occurred because of misalignment of these fibers to the tensile axis of the specimen. The magnitude of these strength losses resulting from fiber pullout and fabrication defects is treated in more detail in the discussion section of this paper.

Fiber-Matrix Reaction—The depth of reaction between the matrix and fiber is listed in Table 2 and plotted as a function of rupture time in Fig. 6.

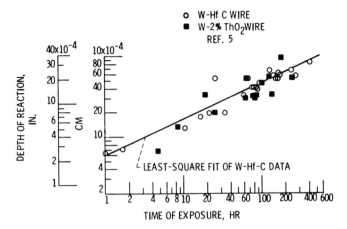

FIG. 6—*Depth of reaction as function of time of exposure for W-Hf-C composites at 1090°C (2000°F).*

A least-square fit of the W-Hf-C fiber data and also data from Ref 5 for W2-ThO₂ fibers in the same matrix material are shown. The depth of reaction after 100 h exposure was 0.0046 cm (0.0018 in.). The depth of reaction between the matrix and the W-Hf-C fiber was similar to that observed for composites containing W2-ThO₂ fibers and having the same matrix composition. Replica electron micrographs of composite specimens indicated that large HfC particles and large grains are formed in the fiber-matrix reaction zone.

Electron Microprobe Study—Backscatter electron and X-ray images of composite specimens indicated a chromium concentration in the tungsten alloy fiber reaction zone; however, no nickel concentration was indicated. X-ray raster micrographs for aluminum and titanium did not indicate any concentrations of these elements in the reaction zone of the fiber. X-ray raster micrographs for hafnium indicated that the concentration of hafnium in the matrix increases with time at temperature.

The results of the electron probe study indicated some penetration of titanium, aluminum, nickel, and chromium from the matrix into the tungsten fibers, but the depth of penetration into the fibers was relatively small. The depth of reaction zones measured optically was generally much greater than the penetration indicated by the electron probe study for the foregoing elements.

The most significant findings of the electron probe study were the results obtained for the hafnium and carbon traces. Figures 7 and 8 are plots of concentration versus distance from the fiber-matrix interface for carbon and hafnium. The profiles show the variation in relative concentration of either carbon or hafnium rather than the actual concentration

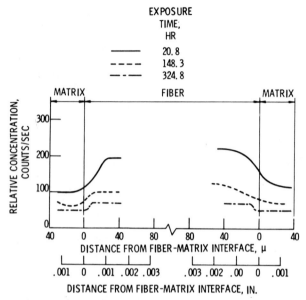

FIG. 7—*Variation in concentration of carbon in fiber and matrix for various exposure times at 1090°C (2000°F).*

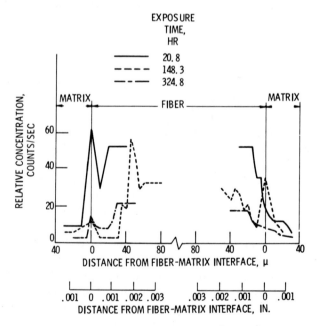

FIG. 8—*Variation in concentration of hafnium in fiber and matrix for various exposure times at 1090°C (2000°F).*

of each element. Specimens which were exposed to 1090 °C (2000 °F) for three different time periods are plotted in the figures. Figure 7 shows that the concentration gradient for carbon between the fiber and matrix decreases with time of exposure, indicating diffusion of carbon from the fiber into the matrix. Figure 8 shows a similar trend, that is, hafnium diffusing into the matrix. The hafnium and carbon composition of the fiber implies that some excess carbon is available as an interstitial in the tungsten, whereas all of the hafnium was available for the formation of HfC particles in the tungsten. The X-ray raster micrographs and electron probe traces thus indicate that HfC decomposes and free carbon and hafnium diffuse into the matrix. The nickel alloy matrix contained 0.0032 weight percent carbon while the fiber had a carbon content of almost 10 times that amount, 0.03 weight percent. The results imply that it may be beneficial to add hafnium to the matrix or to increase the carbon content in an attempt to inhibit the decomposition of HfC particles in the fiber.

Discussion

Current Composite Stress-Rupture Properties

The stress-rupture properties of W-Hf-C/superalloy composites containing varying volume fiber contents can be calculated through the use of the plot shown in Fig. 5. The stress on the fiber to cause rupture in a specific time to rupture (determined from the curve presented in Fig. 5) is multiplied by the volume fraction fiber content of the specimen. From the data shown in Fig. 5, for example, a composite containing 70 volume percent W-Hf-C fibers would be expected to have a 100-h stress-rupture strength at 1090 °C (2000 °F) of 420 MN/m² (61 000 psi), that is, 0.70 × 600 MN/m² (0.70 × 87 000 psi). The foregoing method was used to calculate the 1000-h rupture strength of a composite containing 70 volume percent W-Hf-C fibers. The 1000-h rupture strength for the composite was calculated to be 285 MN/m² (41 000 psi). Prior to this investigation the strongest refractory metal fiber reinforced superalloy composite was a W2-ThO₂ fiber composite having a 100-h specific strength of 2100 m (83 000 in.) and a 1000-h specific strength of 1600 m (63 000 in.). The results of this investigation indicate that W-Hf-C/superalloy composites show an improvement in specific strength over W2-ThO₂ fiber composites. The 100-h specific rupture strength for the W-Hf-C composite is 2650 m (104 000 in.) and the 1000-h specific rupture strength is 1800 m (70 000 in.). The 100-h specific rupture strength for the composite is over twice that for conventional cast superalloys. The 1000-h specific rupture strength for the composite is over three and one half times that for conventional cast superalloys.

Potential Composite Stress-Rupture Properties

The stress-rupture strengths obtained for the W-Hf-C fiber composites studied in this investigation are lower than those which can be achieved with this system. Higher stress-rupture strengths than those obtained were expected based on the compatibility of the W-Hf-C fiber with the matrix. The results obtained in this investigation showed that the degree of fiber-matrix reaction for the W-Hf-C composites was similar to that observed for composites containing W2-ThO$_2$ fibers. The rupture strengths for W2-ThO$_2$ fibers contained in the composite were 75 percent for rupture in 100-h and 59 percent for rupture in 1000-h compared with as-received fibers tested in vacuum (Ref 5).

Further, composite rupture strength for 218 CS tungsten and W2-ThO$_2$ reinforced superalloy composites had been related to depth of reaction (Ref 1). Since the depth of reaction with the matrix was similar for W-Hf-C and W2-ThO$_2$ fibers, their strength retentions should be similar. Based on depth of reaction, the W-Hf-C fibers contained in the composite should have a 100-h and 1000-h rupture strength of 800 and 520 MN/m^2 (116 000 and 76 000 psi) rather than the values of 600 and 400 MN/m^2 (87 000 and 59 000 psi) obtained in this investigation. As was noted in the "Results" section of this paper, the W-Hf-C fibers were bent and misaligned to the tensile axis of the test specimens, and fiber ends were exposed on the surface of the test section due to the machining process employed as well as the fabrication method used to obtain specimens. The fibers exposed on the surface of the test section pulled out of the matrix during the test and did not contribute their full strength to the composite. Another factor lowering the strength contribution of the W-Hf-C fibers was the presence of fiber splits. The majority of fibers contained in the composite exhibit fiber splits which resulted from the fiber drawing process prior to composite fabrication. The number of fibers containing fiber splits and the width and depth of the fiber split varied for the composite specimens tested. The area of fiber reacted as a function of time at temperature is increased because of the increase in fiber surface area exposed to the matrix due to the splits.

Since increased fiber reaction lowers composite strength, elimination of fiber splits would increase fiber and composite strength. Sepcimens containing split-free fibers or moderately split-free fibers would be expected to be stronger than specimens containing severely split fibers. The majority of specimens tested contained only split fibers. Some specimens did, however, contain some split-free fibers and these specimens were found to be stronger than the specimens containing only split fibers. A more realistic appraisal of the potential of W-Hf-C fiber composites can be gained by considering only those specimens containing some split-free fibers and by taking into account that the fibers exposed on the surface of the test specimen do not contribute to composite strength.

The specimens selected for the foregoing appraisal are listed in Table 3. It was assumed that the exposed surface fibers did not contribute to composite strength. The stress carried by the remaining fibers was found by

TABLE 3—Stress rupture properties for W-Hf-C nickel alloy composites containing more than 15 percent split-free fibers and neglecting surface fibers; test temperature = 1090°C (2000°F).

Specimen No.	Composite Stress		Effective Volume % Fiber Content	Calculated Fiber Stress		Rupture Life, h	Percent Split-Free Fibers
	MN/m²	psi		MN/m²	psi		
587	345	50 000	33.9	1110	147 000	20.8	39
584	345	50 000	32.9	1050	152 000	24.6	25
597	379	55 000	35.3	1080	156 000	59.0	92
592	207	30 000	27.7	745	108 000	73.7	26
591	207	30 000	24.9	830	120 000	84.2	24
582	310	45 000	37.7	820	119 000	95.7	54
578	345	50 000	46.6	740	107 000	148.3	15
580	310	45 000	42.6	730	106 000	170.1	24

dividing the load placed on the specimen by the area of the remaining fibers, since it was assumed that those fibers carried all of the load. The effective volume percent fiber content shown in the table is that volume fiber content which carries the load and thus does not include the surface fibers. The number of split-free fibers was determined for each specimen by visual observations of the transverse section of each specimen, and this value was divided by the number of load-carrying fibers to arrive at the percent split-free fibers present in each specimen. Only composite specimens containing 15 or more percent split-free fibers were considered so that the effect of split fibers on the stress-rupture strength of the fibers would be reduced. The majority of composite specimens listed in Table 3 contained approximately 25 percent split-free fibers. One specimen contained 92 percent split-free fibers. This specimen had the largest positive deviation from the least-squares fit of the rupture data as shown in Fig. 5. Figure 9 is a plot of the stress carried by the fibers versus time to rupture at 1090 °C (2000 °F) for the specimens listed in Table 3. A least-square fit of the data indicates a 100-h rupture strength of 810 MN/m² (117 000 psi) and a 1000-h rupture strength

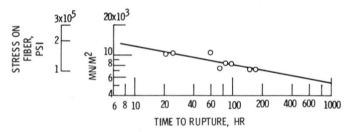

FIG. 9—*Stress on fiber as function of time to rupture for W-Hf-C composite (neglecting surface fibers at 1090°C (2000°F). Specimens contain more than 15 percent split-free fibers.*

of 530 MN/m² (77 000 psi). The retained rupture strength of W-Hf-C fibers contained in the composite based on these results and assumptions was 76 percent for rupture in 100 h and 60 percent for rupture in 1000 h compared with as-received fibers tested in vacuum; this is in agreement with the retention values obtained for W2-ThO₂ fibers contained in the same matrix (Ref 5). The foregoing strengths obtained for W-Hf-C fibers are assumed to be more truly representative of the potential of this fiber and are the strength values which will be used for the following comparisons.

Figure 10 compares the calculated 100-h rupture strengths of various refractory fiber/nickel-base alloy composites containing 70 volume percent fiber with those of conventional superalloys at 1090 °C (2000 °F). The 100-hour rupture strength for the W-Hf-C composite containing 70 volume percent fiber was calculated to be 570 MN/m² (82 000 psi), that is, 0.7 times 810 MN/m² (0.7 times 117 000 psi). The W-Hf-C composite is seen to be the

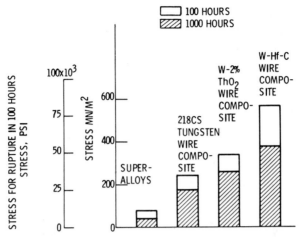

FIG. 10—*A 100-h and 1000-h rupture strength for refractory wire/nickel-base alloy composites at 1090°C (2000°F). Fiber content = 70 volume percent.*

strongest fiber composite system and represents a significant improvement over W2-ThO$_2$ fiber composites. A 65 percent improvement in the 100-h rupture strength is obtained when W-Hf-C fibers are used compared with W2-ThO$_2$ fibers [570 versus 340 MN/m^2 (82 000 versus 49 000 psi)]. The W-Hf-C composite is almost seven times as strong as conventional superalloys for this temperature and time and is stronger than most refractory metal alloys.

A similar type of comparison was made for the 1000-h rupture strength of these materials and is also shown in Fig. 10. A 45 percent improvement in the 1000-h rupture strength is obtained for W-Hf-C composites compared with W2-ThO$_2$ fiber composites [370 versus 255 MN/m^2 (54 000 versus 37 000 psi)]. The W-Hf-C composite is about nine times as strong as conventional superalloys at this temperature and time to rupture.

Prior to this investigation the strongest refractory fiber/superalloy composite was the W2-ThO$_2$ fiber composite having a 100-h specific strength of 2100 m (83 000 in.) and a 1000-h specific strength of 1600 m (63 000 in) at 1090°C (2000°F). The results of this investigation indicate that W-Hf-C/superalloy composites show an improvement in specific strength over W2-ThO$_2$ fiber composites. The 100-h specific rupture strength for the W-Hf-C composite is 3500 (140 000 in.) and the 1000-h specific rupture strength is 2300 m (92 000 in.). The W-Hf-C composite is over three times as strong on a specific strength basis as superalloys for rupture in 100 h and over four times as strong for rupture in 1000 h.

A comparison of the specific strength properties of superalloys and composite materials indicates the potential of composite materials for turbine blade use. The 70 volume percent W-Hf-C fiber composite has a calculated specific 1000-h rupture strength of 2350 m (92 000 in.) at 1090°C (2000°F). The strongest conventional superalloys have a specific 1000-h rupture strength of 2350 m (92 000 in.) at 930°C (1700°F). The W-Hf-C composite based on this comparison has a 160°C (300°F) use temperature advantage over the strongest conventional superalloys.

Potential Application

Fiber-reinforced composite materials have been the subject of intensive research because they offer the potential for substantially improved properties compared with currently used materials. Their use could permit increased performance in many engineering systems. One of the systems that is limited by the capability of current materials is the turbojet engine. Designers would prefer to increase operating temperatures of such engines to increase efficiency and reduce pollution. Increased strength at elevated temperatures may be achieved with W-Hf-C fiber/superalloy composites compared with superalloys. This in turn would permit an increase in turbine operating temperature.

A persistent concern about tungsten-wire-superalloy composites has been the large weight penalty associated with their use despite their superior strength/density values compared with superalloys. However, the turbine blade weight for a solid blade of tungsten fiber/superalloy composite need not greatly exceed that for a similar blade made from a conventional superalloy if reasonable measures are taken in design and fabrication of the composite. Two variables can be used to overcome the high density of the refractory alloy fiber. The fiber content can be varied along the blade span so as to tailor strength to that needed, and the blade airfoil thickness near the base can be slightly reduced compared with a superalloy blade because of the improved strength/density properties of the composite. Blades with varying fiber content can be fabricated using conventional diffusion bonding techniques. Fiber-free superalloy foil and monolayer superalloy matrix composite tape, each cut to the appropriate contours, can be stacked and bonded in closed dies.

Fiber content variation or selective reinforcement can reduce the average fiber content significantly. Sample blade density calculations made to illustrate the effectiveness of selective reinforcement are presented in Ref *11*. The average fiber content of the blade was found to be less than one half of the maximum fiber content at any one cross section of the blade.

It was assumed in Ref *11* that a blade material must have a stress/density value of 1525 m (60 000 in.) for rupture in 1000 h. The fiber content necessary for a 1000-h rupture strength/density value of 1525 m (60 000 in.) for the W-Hf-C/superalloy composite described in this investigation would be 36 percent, the maximum fiber content necessary at any one cross section of the blade. The average fiber content of the blade would be less than 18 percent. A W-Hf-C fiber/superalloy composite having a fiber content of 18 percent and a matrix similar to that used in this study would have a density of 10.9 g/c³ (0.396 lb/in.³). High-strength superalloys which have about a 980°C (1800°F) use temperature limit as turbine blades have densities as high as 8.97 g/c³ (0.325 lb/in.³). Superalloys are currently limited to 980°C (1800°F) while the composite can be used at the same strength-to-density level at 1090°C (2000°F), 110°C (200°F) higher than superalloys.

Summary of Results

The potential for turbine blades of superalloy composites using improved high-strength fibers of W-Hf-C was determined in terms of the 1090°C (2000°F) stress-rupture strength. The following results were obtained:

1. Composites were fabricated having high stress-rupture properties at 1090°C (2000°F) compared with superalloys. The 100-h stress-rupture strength obtained for 70 volume percent fiber composites at 1090°C (2000°F) was 420 MN/m² (61 000 psi) as compared with 80 MN/m² (11 500 psi) for the strongest cast nickel alloys. The 1000-h stress-rupture strength obtainable (by extrapolation from data obtained up to 400 h) for the composite was 285 MN/m² (41 000 psi).

2. The high density of the tungsten alloy fiber reduced the strength advantage of the composite in comparison with that of lower density materials. However, the 70 volume percent W-Hf-C fiber reinforced composite had a 100-h specific rupture strength of 2650 m (104 000 in.) and an extrapolated 1000-h specific rupture strength at 1090°C (2000°F) of 1780 m (70 000 in.). The 100-h specific rupture strength for the composite is over twice that for conventional cast superalloys. The 1000-h specific rupture strength for the composite is over three and one half times that for conventional cast superalloys.

3. The W-Hf-C/superalloy composite stress rupture data at 1090°C (2000°F) reported in this investigation are higher than data reported in the literature for any other composite.

4. The HfC dispersion-strengthened fiber exhibited particle coarsening after long-time exposure at 1090°C (2000°F).

5. The depth of reaction between the W-Hf-C fiber and nickel-base alloy matrix was 0.0046 cm (0.0018 in.) after 100-h exposure at 1090°C (2000°F).

6. Decomposition of HfC particles in fibers contained in the composite and diffusion of carbon and hafnium into the matrix were found to occur for composites exposed at 1090°C (2000°F).

7. When composite data were corrected to account for fiber imperfec-

tions, the resulting composite properties approached those calculated based on defect-free fiber data. For example, the 100-h stress-rupture strength calculated for a 70 volume percent fiber composite at 1090 °C (2000 °F) was 570 MN/m² (82 000 psi). The 1000-h rupture strength of the composite at the same temperature was 370 MN/m² (54 000 psi). The 70 volume percent fiber composite had a calculated 100-h specific rupture strength of 3500 m (140 000 in.) and a 1000-h specific rupture strength of 2350 m (92 000 in.) at 1090 °C (2000 °F).

8. The W-Hf-C 70 volume percent fiber composite has a 160 deg C (300 deg F) use temperature advantage over the strongest conventional superalloys based on the 1000-h specific rupture strength.

9. Turbine blades of W-Hf-C/superalloy composites would offer a 110 deg C (200 deg F) increase in engine operating temperature without a severe weight penalty if the fiber content is varied along the blade span so as to tailor strength to that needed.

References

[1] Petrasek, D. W., Signorelli, R. A., and Weeton, J. W., "Refractory Metal Fiber Nickel Base Alloy Composites for Use at High Temperatures," NASA Report TN D-4787, National Aeronautics and Space Administration, Washington, D.C., Sept. 1968.

[2] Glenny, R. J. E., *Proceedings of the Royal Society of London,* Series A, Vol. 319, No. 1536, Oct. 6, 1970, pp. 33–44.

[3] Kovtov, V. F., Fonshtein, N. M., and Shvarts, V. I., *Metallovendenie i Termicheskaia Obrabotka Metallov,* No. 8, 1971, pp. 20–22.

[4] Morris, A. W. H. and Burwood-Smith, A., *Fibre Science Technology,* Vol. 3, No. 1, 1970, pp. 53–78.

[5] Petrasek, D. W. and Signorelli, R. A., "Preliminary Evaluation of Tungsten Alloy Fiber/Nickel-Base Alloy Composites for Turbojet Engine Applications," NASA Report TN D-5575, National Aeronautics and Space Administration, Washington, D.C., Feb. 1970.

[6] King, G. W., "Development of Wire Drawing Processes for Refractory Metal Fibers," NASA Report CR-120925, Westinghouse Electric Corporation, Bloomfield, N.J., Jan. 1972.

[7] McDanels, D. L. and Signorelli, R. A., "Stress-Rupture Properties of Tungsten Wire from 1200° to 2500°F," NASA Report TN D-3467, National Aeronautics and Space Administration, Washington, D.C., July 1966.

[8] Klopp, W. D. and Witzke, W. R., "Mechanical Properties of Arc-Melted Tungsten-Rhenium-Hafnium-Carbon Alloys," NASA Report TN D-5348, National Aeronautics and Space Administration, Washington, D.C., July 1969.

[9] Petrasek, D. W., "High-Temperature Strength of Refractory-Metal Wires and Consideration for Composite Applications," NASA Report TN D-6881, National Aeronautics and Space Administration, Washington, D.C., Aug. 1972.

[10] McDanels, D. L., Singorelli, R. A., and Weeton, J. W., "Analysis of Stress-Ruature and Creep Properties of Tungsten-Fiber-Reinforced Copper Composites," NASA Report TN D-4173, National Aeronautics and Space Administration, Washington, D.C., Sept. 1967.

[11] Signorelli, R. A., "Review of Status and Potential of Tungsten-Wire-Superalloy Composites for Advanced Gas Turbine Engine Blades," NASA Report TM X-2599, National Aeronautics and Space Administration, Washington, D.C., Sept. 1972.

K. L. Reifsnider,[1] *W. W. Stinchcomb,*[1] *R. S. Williams,*[1] *and*
H. M. Turgay[1]

Frequency Effects on Flawed-Composite Fatigue Reliability

REFERENCE: Reifsnider, K. L., Stinchcomb, W. W., Williams, R. S., and
Turgay, H. M., **"Frequency Effects on Flawed-Composite Fatigue Reliability,**
Composite Reliability, ASTM STP 580, American Society for Testing and Materials, 1975, pp. 425–442.

ABSTRACT: Variations in the degradation and subsequent fatigue reliability of laminated composite plate specimens with a center hole due to changes in cycle frequency have been identified and investigated. Boron-epoxy and boron-aluminum specimens were examined, principally for stiffness and strength variations. Various combinations of stiffness and strength changes were observed as a function of cycle frequency and specimen material, including a mode wherein stiffness decreased significantly while residual strength increased. A kinetic damage model was developed and combined with a Weibull extreme value expression to attempt to represent the stochastic aspects of the fatigue process. The model shows some promise, especially from the standpoint of representing widely varying fatigue behavior, including the unusual situation of stiffness drop with strength increase. Frequency dependence is included in the model.

KEY WORDS: reliability, composite materials, fatigue (materials), stiffness, damage, fracture strength, boron epoxy, boron aluminum, laminates, models

From the standpoint of mechanics, fatigue damage in composites is rather poorly defined. In general, no single simple characterization of the phenomenon can be made such as the familiar crack propagation process in uniform materials with the attendent linear elastic fracture mechanics interpretation of the singular field at the defect. Instead, fatigue in composite materials apparently consists of many contributing phenomena, including fiber breakage, debonding, delamination, and matrix cracking. The number of permutations and combinations of those phe-

---

[1] Associate professor, assistant professor, and graduate students, respectively, Engineering Science and Mechanics Department, Virginia Polytechnic Institute and State University, Blacksburg, Va. 24061.

nomena which can cause degradation or failure, or both, is large. Selection of the contributing failure-mode components for a given situation is apparently made on the basis of constituent materials and their interfaces, geometry, loading, and environment. Recently, the authors have found that frequency of cycling in fatigue loading can also significantly affect this complex damage process and cause widely different collective results under otherwise identical fatigue conditions.

Earlier work has provided considerable evidence that cycle frequency can significantly influence the fatigue behavior of boron-epoxy and boron-aluminum crossply laminated specimens [1,2].[2] The present report identifies several additional effects, and reports data from additional material types. Interpretation of the results is attempted within the context of a kinetic damage model based on a fracture mechanics approach similar to that used by Waddoups et al [3], combined with an analysis of statistical characteristics using an approach similar in its structure to that of Halpin et al [4]. Distinct differences in the basic nature and magnitude of the fatigue response of the present specimens caused by variations in cycle frequency are identified and described.

Experimental Data

The data presented and analyzed in this paper were obtained from strain-controlled fatigue tests, with positive strain ratios, performed on boron-epoxy specimens (Types I and II) and boron-aluminum specimens. The Type I boron-epoxy specimens had ply orientations of [0, ±45, 0, 0, ±45, 0], while the Type II boron-epoxy and boron-aluminum specimens each had a [0, ±45, 0]$_s$ stacking sequence. All specimens were 1 in. by 7 in. by 8 plys with a 0.25-in.-diameter center hole. The tests were conducted in an MTS servohydraulic testing system using a clip gage to control deformations over a 1-in. gage length. The hole was in the gage length so that damage-related stiffness changes could be measured. The specimens were cycled at frequencies of 15, 30, and 45 Hz for 1.2 to 1.5 million cycles during which time the changes in load amplitude and dynamic stress-strain data (as measured by the clip gage and load cell) were recorded. Stress and strain outputs were monitored by an oscilloscope to insure fidelity to desired test conditions. A more complete description of the experimental procedure may be found in Ref 1.

The response of the materials to repeated loading was characterized by performing cyclic stress-strain tests [1] at the selected frequencies. The family of curves for 15-Hz loading shown in Fig. 1 reveals the importance of this characterization. Both the boron-aluminum and Type I boron-epoxy reach an "ultimate" stress followed by a lower fracture stress. The ultimate cyclic strengths are greater than the static fracture strengths

---

[2] The italic numbers in brackets refer to the list of references appended to this paper.

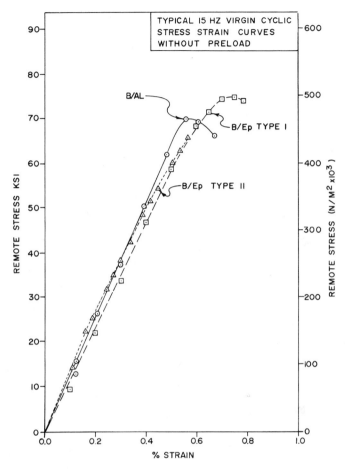

FIG. 1—*Virgin cyclic stress-strain curves for three composite materials tested at 15 Hz.*

(Table 1) by 7 percent for boron-aluminum and by 10 percent for Type I boron-epoxy. On the other hand, Type II boron-epoxy exhibited cyclic stress-strain properties nearly identical to static properties at all test frequencies. Furthermore, the peak in the boron-aluminum and Type I boron-epoxy curves implies a strain level beyond which the specimen is damaged so as to reduce the stiffness and, therefore, the load required to achieve the desired strain. This behavior was not observed in Type II boron-epoxy. In general, these observations were substantiated by the extent of visual damage to the specimens; that is, the two materials which suffered the most fatigue damage were the same two materials which showed a maximum in the cyclic stress-strain curve, whereas the cyclic and static fractures of Type II material were quite similar.

During the course of a fatigue test at constant strain amplitude, the

TABLE 1—*Some average properties of the composite materials for two test frequencies.*

	Boron-Aluminum		Boron-Epoxy (Type I)		Boron-Epoxy (Type II)	
	15 Hz	45 Hz	15 Hz	45 Hz	15 Hz	45 Hz
Virgin cyclic strength, ksi	65.9	54.6	72.7	45.5	63.6	68.2
Residual cyclic strength, ksi	48.1	53.7	60.2	48.3	68.8	70.9
Percent decrease in dynamic stiffness	50	14	...	...	10	10
Percent decrease in static stiffness	8	0	...	...	21.5	16
Static remote strength, ksi	61.4		64.8		64.4	

development of fatigue damage is associated with changes in stiffness or compliance (dynamic stiffness or compliance values were determined from σ-ε data recorded during the test). Figures 2 and 3 show the changes in compliance as a function of strain cycles for several boron-aluminum fatigue tests at 15 and 45 Hz with a maximum cyclic strain of 0.39 percent and a strain ratio of 0.36. (The symbols in Figs. 2–5 indicate data points for the individual tests.) All specimens were subjected to a quasi-static prestrain of 0.39 percent before the cyclic loading. The change in compliance for those specimens cycled at 15 Hz was greater than that for the 45-Hz tests. In most cases, the compliance increased (maximum load and stiffness decreased) during the test; however, two specimens cycled at 45 Hz did not develop fatigue cracks and showed a decrease in compliance. The residual cyclic strengths of these two specimens, determined by cyclic stress-strain tests, were greater than the 45-Hz virgin cyclic strength for boron-aluminum. In all other cases, the compliance increased during the fatigue tests and the residual cyclic strength of the boron-aluminum specimens was less than the virgin cyclic strength for corresponding frequencies.

Similar observations of compliance changes were also made for the Type II boron-epoxy specimens (Figs. 4 and 5). The compliance changes for the 15-Hz cases were slightly greater than those for the 45-Hz tests but continued to increase throughout the entire test, whereas the compliance stabilized for long periods during the 45-Hz tests. In contrast to the decreased residual cyclic strengths discussed previously for boron-aluminum, the Type II boron-epoxy possessed residual cyclic strengths greater than either the static or virgin cyclic strengths for corresponding frequencies.

Figure 6 demonstrates the effect of strain amplitude on the fatigue response of the Type II boron-epoxy. For the 30-Hz data shown, the com-

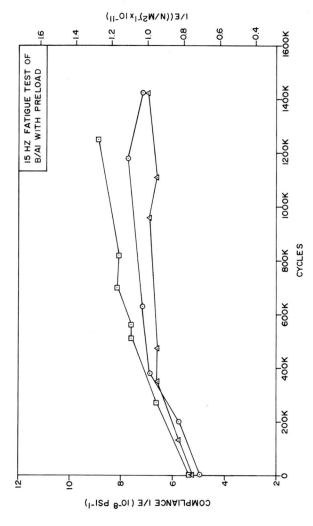

FIG. 2—Increase in compliance during 15-Hz fatigue tests of boron-aluminum at the same cyclic strain amplitude.

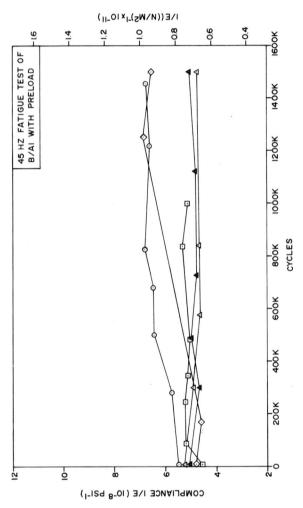

FIG. 3—*Changes in compliance during 45-Hz fatigue tests of boron-aluminum at the same cyclic strain amplitude.*

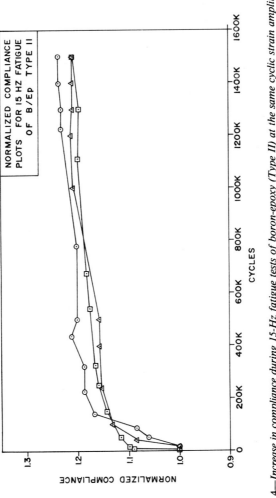

FIG. 4—*Increase in compliance during 15-Hz fatigue tests of boron-epoxy (Type II) at the same cyclic strain amplitude.*

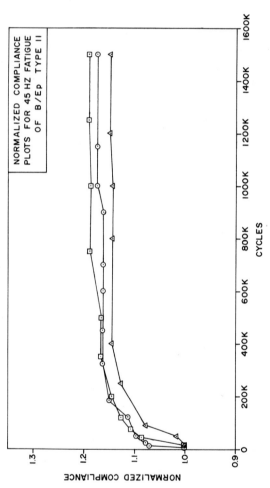

FIG. 5—*Increase in compliance during 45-Hz fatigue tests of boron-epoxy (Type II) at the same cyclic strain amplitude.*

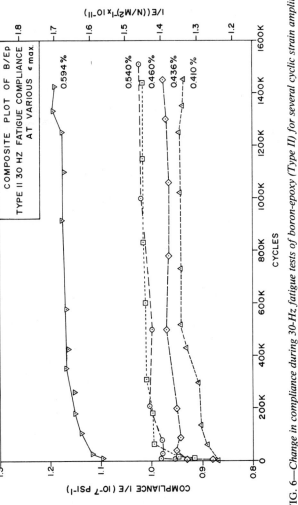

FIG. 6—*Change in compliance during 30-Hz fatigue tests of boron-epoxy (Type II) for several cyclic strain amplitudes.*

pliance is clearly dependent on the strain amplitude and increases with increasing cyclic strain. It is interesting to note that the cyclic strain amplitude of 0.594 percent is about 5 percent greater than both the static and 30-Hz cyclic fracture strains for this material. All of the specimens represented in this figure were statically prestrained to 0.4 percent strain and then loaded with gradually increasing cyclic strains until the desired amplitudes were achieved, usually before 40 000 cycles. Such "conditioning" of the specimen may bring about improvements in the local geometry of the flaw by creating subcritical damage which serves as a blunting mechanism to prevent the spread of fatigue damage developed at the higher strain levels.

In strain-controlled testing, increases in compliance, such as those discussed in the foregoing, are conjunctively associated with decreases in applied stress such as is shown in Fig. 7 for Type I boron-epoxy tested at several frequencies. The changes in properties which occur during the course of a fatigue test, however, are not limited to changes in dynamic response alone. For example, the static moduli of the Type II boron-epoxy specimens, for which compliance data are shown in Figs. 4 and 5, decreased an average of 21.5 percent (15 Hz) and 16 percent (45 Hz) after the cyclic loading (Table 1). Yet, notwithstanding a reduction in both static and dynamic stiffness due to fatigue damage, the cyclic strength of the material actually increased by as much as 14 percent. An interpretation of the data is presented in the following section.

Some Related Analysis

In order to enhance our understanding and application of the present data concerning the reliability of composites, it is useful to attempt to model some aspects of the observed behavior.

Fatigue damage in composites rarely consists of a single through-crack which nucleates and propagates until the component fails, especially in crossply laminates. In the present case, although the center hole is the cause of local damage events which occur preferentially in the concentrated stress region, the damage occurs in a dispersed, complex manner, by means of debonding, delamination, matrix cracking, and fiber breakage.

For the purpose of the present model, however, the spread of damage away from the hole will be characterized by some length, L, which represents, in some sense, the damaged region. Since longer cracks grow faster under constant applied conditions in uniform materials, it would appear to be reasonable to assume that the rate of increase in the size of our characteristic damage zone size, L, is proportional to L itself, whereupon we postulate

$$\frac{dL}{dn} = AL^m \qquad m > 1 \qquad (1)$$

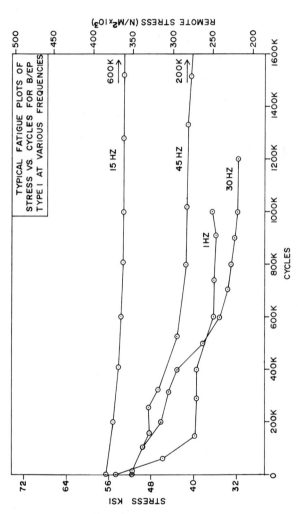

FIG. 7—*Reduction in remote stress during fatigue tests of boron-epoxy (Type I) at several frequencies.*

where the power, m, depends on the material and the failure mode. The applied conditions determine the proportionality constant A. Fatigue cycles are represented by n.

The fatigue loading in the present case was strain-controlled. Hence, on the basis of a closed-form formulation and asymptotic solution of the problem of a propagating crack in a nonuniform material developed by Reifsnider and Kahl [5], it would appear reasonable to postulate

$$A = B\varepsilon_0{}^{2m}E^m \tag{2}$$

where B is a constant, ε_0 is the (constant) strain amplitude, and E is the instantaneous stiffness of the specimen.

Again, by analogy to linear elastic fracture mechanics in isotropic uniform materials, we can talk about a toughness (or crack growth resistance [6]) which characterizes the local resistance to damage development for our material. The existence of that quantity implies a unique relationship between the applied stress at failure and the characteristic length, L, for a given geometry. For our plate specimen with a center hole, a relationship of the form given by Bowie [7] is appropriate. The critical toughness is then given by

$$K_{\mathrm{Ic}} = \alpha F\sqrt{L}f(L/r) \tag{3}$$

where α is a constant with the dimensions of inverse squared length, F is the applied load, r is the radius of the center hole, and $f(L/r)$ is a function of the type defined by Bowie [7]. For an isotropic, uniform, infinite plate

$$1.0 \leqslant f(L/r) \leqslant 3.39 \tag{4}$$

These plates, however, are not isotropic or uniform. The local influence of the hole is quite different from the Bowie situation. More will be said of this later. At this point, we will be more concerned with damage controlled by stiffness reduction and dispersed damage as described in the following. Therefore, we postpone discussion of the $f(L/r)$ influence and drop it from Eq 3 for now.

Although K_{Ic} is written in the notation of fracture mechanics and is taken to be the material characteristic toughness for Mode I loading of our plates, it is not implied that it is the stress amplitude of a local singular stress field.

One additional observation should be made at this point. The instantaneous dynamic stiffness, E, in Eq 2, varied during each test as fatigue damage developed. In many cases, the variation could be represented by the relationship

$$E = E_0 (1 + an) \tag{5}$$

where E_0 is the initial stiffness value and a is a stiffening or weakening parameter. Then Eqs 5, 3, 2, and 1 can be integrated to obtain

$$\left(\frac{F(t_1)}{K_{1c}}\right)^{2(m-1)} = \left(\frac{F(t_0)}{K_{1c}}\right)^{2(m-1)}$$

$$- \left(\frac{m-1}{m+1}\right)\frac{B}{a} \varepsilon_0{}^{2m}E_0{}^m \left[(1 + an)^{m+1} - 1\right] \qquad (6)$$

where t_0 and t_1 denote initial and final points in time. For convenience, and with some supporting evidence [3], we take K_{1c} to be constant and rewrite Eq 6 as

$$\underbrace{[F(t_1)]^{2(m-1)}}_{I} = \underbrace{[F(t_0)]^{2(m-1)}}_{II}$$

$$\underbrace{- \left(\frac{m-1}{m+1}\right)\frac{\overline{C}}{a}\left[(1 + an)^{m+1} - 1\right]}_{III} \qquad (7)$$

where $\overline{C}$ has been used to represent the constants collectively. The damage model, Eq 7, suggests two types of fatigue behavior. A large reduction in stiffness will drive the value of III up and the final strength, in I, will be reduced from the initial strength, in II, accordingly. Likewise, if the stiffness increases, it would appear that a reduction of final strength is still possible.

Because of the stochastic nature of the fatigue process in composite materials, it is also instructive to incorporate our damage model into an elementary statistical model. It is common to assume that the initial strength, $F(t_0)$, has a Weibull (extreme value) distribution, although the interpretation of this quantity is a somewhat unsettled question. In any case, if the initial strength, F_s, has the distribution

$$P\left(F_s > F_0\right) = \exp - \left(\frac{F_s - F_0}{F_c(t_0)}\right)^{b_0} \qquad (8)$$

where b_0 and $F_c(t_0)$ are the shape and scale parameters, it can be seen that the set of values for which the instantaneous residual strength, $F(t)$, is greater than the applied load on the specimen is coincident with the set of values for which

$$F_s = F(t_0) > \left\{[F(t)]^{2(m-1)} + \left(\frac{m-1}{m+1}\right)\frac{C}{a}\left[(1 + an)^{m+1} - 1\right]\right\}^{1/2(m-1)} \qquad (9)$$

Then Eq 8 yields

$$P[F(t) > F]$$

$$= \exp - \left\{ \frac{\left\{ [F(t)]^{2(m-1)} + \left(\dfrac{m-1}{m+1} \right) \dfrac{\overline{C}}{a} [(1 + an)^{m+1} - 1] \right\}^{1/2(m-1)} - F_0}{F_c(t_0)} \right\}^{b_0}$$

(10)

which we approximate as

$$P[F(t) > F]$$

$$= \exp - \left\{ \frac{[F(t)]^{2(m-1)} + \left(\dfrac{m-1}{m+1} \right) \dfrac{\overline{C}}{a} [(1 + an)^{m+1} - 1] - F_0^{2(m-1)}}{F_c(t_0)^{2(m-1)}} \right\}^{b}$$

(11)

where $b = [b_0/2(m - 1)]$, F is the applied load, and b_0 and m are constants for a given material and geometry. Equation 11 implies that the distribution of residual strength to the power $2(m - 1)$ should have a shape parameter, b, and a scale parameter, $F_c(t_0)^{2(m-1)}$ which are determined by the initial characteristics of the material and its subsequent resistance to damage as specified by m and a. The minimum strength of the residual distribution is given by:

$$\frac{\overline{C}}{a} \left(\frac{m-1}{m+1} \right) [(1 + an)^{m+1} - 1] - F_0^{2(m-1)}$$

(12)

while F_0 is the initial minimum strength value. We notice that Eq 12 can be either positive (indicating a finite probability of the residual strength being zero) or negative (predicting a probability of one that the specimens will have a residual strength greater than some minimum value).

To illustrate the usefulness of this model, some of the present data will be analyzed. We consider, first, the boron-aluminum tests presented earlier. Maximum static strength values were plotted, using median-rank estimates of population behavior, on Weibull probability paper. The characteristic strength was found to be 3360 lb and b_0 was about 12. (See Table 2.) Specimens were then fatigued, at constant strain amplitude, for 1.2 to 1.5 million cycles. Residual strengths were then determined from cyclic stress-strain tests. The results of the present statistical analysis appear in Table 2.

Stress reduction during the 45-Hz tests was statistically negligible. The large data spread was due, in part, to a fracture-mode transition which just begins to occur at 45-Hz for the strain amplitude used. Greater load reduction occurred for those specimens which did develop a cracklike transverse plane of damage, as observed in the 15 Hz-tests. The residual strengths were plotted to the $2(m - 1)$ power for several m values for each frequency. A value of $m = 3$ was the best fit to all of the data. For that case, the predicted shape factor for the distribution of final strengths was $b = 3$. The observed values were reasonably close to the predicted one as shown in Table 2.

Values for C were determined from observed minimum strength values taken from the power plots of residual strength. If C is independent of frequency, it should have the same value for all of our data. For 15 Hz, however, the minimum strength was found to be zero, while for 45 Hz it was 1778 lb. That yielded the values in Table 2, seen to be somewhat different from one another. The scale factors from the plots were compared to the predicted value of $F_c(t_0)^{2(m-1)}$. No reasonable correlation was found; however, it was found that an excellent determination of characteristic strength could be obtained by reducing the initial value by exactly the percentage of load reduction during the (constant strain amplitude) test. As shown in Table 2, those values match the raw data plot characteristic strengths to within 1 percent for 45 Hz and 3 percent for 15 Hz.

The model was also applied to the six-test series (three at 15 Hz and three at 45 Hz) conducted on boron-epoxy Type II specimens described earlier. The results contrast sharply with the boron-aluminum data. The m value for a proper fit of a Weibull distribution was found to be about 1.5. Hence, our analysis predicts $b_0 = b$; that is, the shape factor is unchanged. Plots of final residual strengths confirmed that $b_0 = b = 10$.

The a and c values were negligibly small for these boron-epoxy data. There was relatively little damage in these specimens as evidenced by examination and by the small changes in specimen stiffness. In particular, the damage appeared to be concentrated near the hole. For that case, Eq 6 predicts that the initial and final strengths will be coincident. The correction for the stress concentration caused by the hole, however, must be included for a local arguement. We return to Eq 3, then, and write

$$[F_c\sqrt{\pi L}\, \alpha' f(L/r)]_{\text{initial}} = [F_c \sqrt{\pi L}\, \alpha' f(L/r)]_{\text{final}} \qquad (13)$$

if the toughness of the material is unchanged, and stiffness changes are negligible. F_c is the critical load or strength of the specimens. For the purpose of discussion, we replace $\alpha' f(L/r)$ with a function, $f'(L/r)$, which varies in proportion to the $\sigma_{\theta\theta}$ stress along an axis transverse to the load direction in compliance with the behavior and interpretation of $f(L/r)$ described by Bowie for uniform, isotropic plates [7]. Using a three-

TABLE 2—*Results of the statistical analysis using the kinetic damage model.*

	45 Hz	15 Hz
Boron Aluminum		
Remote stress after 1.2 million cycles	64.06 ksi	49.25 ksi
Unbiased standard deviation	11.9 ksi	1.77 ksi
Percent standard deviation	18.6%	3.5%
Stress reduction during test	9%	31%
Number of tests	4	4
Compliance after 1.2 million cycles	$5.73 \times 10^{-8}\text{psi}^{-1}$	$7.5 \times 10^{-8}\text{psi}^{-1}$
Unbiased standard deviation	$1.18 \times 10^{-8}\text{psi}^{-1}$	$1.01 \times 10^{-8}\text{psi}^{-1}$
Percent standard deviation	20%	13.5%
Compliance increase during test	14%	50%
Characteristic strengths from power plots	3267 lb.	2483 lb.
Characteristic strengths from raw data plots	3250 lb.	2470 lb.
Characteristic strength prediction from percent stiffness reduction during strain-controlled test	3215 lb.	2386 lb.
Initial characteristic static strength	3360 lb	
Initial shape factor *(b₀)*	12	
Final predicted shape factor *(b)*	3	
Measured shape factors *(b)*	1.45	2.68
Stiffness reduction parameters *(a)*	-6.7×10^{-8}	-3.68×10^{-7}
Damage constant *(C)*	$33 \times 10^{6}(\text{lb})^{4}$	$61.8 \times 10^{6}(\text{lb})^{4}$
Boron Epoxy		
Shape factor $b_0 = b$	10	10
Characteristic strengths from final data	3125 lb	2950 lb
Estimated characteristic strengths from model	2900 lb	2900 lb
Predicted characteristic damage length	0.08 in.	0.074 in.
Effective toughness, K_{Ic}	$52 \text{ ksi}\sqrt{\text{in.}}$	

dimensional finite-element analysis of the present specimens, including anisotropy and laminar inhomogeneity, a variation of the type

$$1 \leqslant f'(L/r) \leqslant 6.2 \qquad (14)$$

is obtained. The $\sigma_{\theta\theta}$ values used in Expression 14 were those which occur in the outer 0-deg layer where damage appears to initiate [8]. The function $f'(L/r)$ is more rapidly decreasing than the classical $f(L/r)$. In fact, while $f(L/r)\sqrt{L/r}$ is monotonic increasing, $f'(L/r)\sqrt{L/r}$ is monotonic decreasing. Equation 13 then implies that the lateral spread of damage should arrest itself (for our constant-amplitude tests) after some growth. For all but the highest strain levels in boron-aluminum (where the static-elastic Eq 13 cannot hope to describe the fatigue situation), that behavior is observed. In any case, for the boron-epoxy specimens under discussion here, Eq 13 predicts a K_{Ic} value of about 52 ksi$\sqrt{\text{in.}}$ and a critical damage length of about 0.065 in. If the damage length after fatigue cycling is 15 percent greater than the critical static value, a final strength of about 2900 lb is predicted, which is very close to the observed values given in Table 2. In general, Eq 13 suggests that for these laminates, for load or strain levels for which damage is localized near the hole and the nature of the damage is brittle—essentially identical to the quasi-static situation—the residual strength can be increased by growth of fatigue damage zones. In addition to the present data which show that effect, other investigators have observed this behavior [3].

It would appear that the present kinetic model is reasonable and valuable, but imperfect and insufficient, based on the limited application of it which has been carried out here. In some cases at least, important predictions of characteristic strengths and distribution shapes after fatigue damage can be made for quite different modes of fatigue damage. These facts suggest that the model warrants further study as a possible method of representing composite material reliability under fatigue loading.

Discussion

The experimental data presented show that the stiffness and residual strength of the composite materials tested are dependent on the frequency of the cyclic strain. Although both static and dynamic moduli are reduced by the development of fatigue damage (the amount of the reduction being frequency-dependent), the residual strength was observed to increase for certain particular cases, but to decrease for others. The fatigue process and the effects of frequency are modified by improvements in local geometry of the flaw as influenced by the early stress-strain history of the fatigue test. It is important to note that while the residual strength of these materials increased under some circimstances, the overall reliability may be degraded by significant reductions in static or dynamic stiffness, or both.

The analytical model which we have postulated shows some encouraging results. With known static information (shape and scale factors) and fracture mode characterization to specify m in Eq 1 and C in Eq 11, predictions of the shape factor of the final distribution and characteristic strength values can be made for any number of cycles in some cases, defining the statistical aspects of the material reliability. Much additional understanding is needed, especially in the formulation of improved versions of Eq 1 and 5, but the basic approach appears to be useful. The degree to which the representations fit observed facts can, in fact, be used as a discriminatory guide to the proper modeling of the damage process. It does appear that widely different behavior, including frequency effects, can be represented by the model. Especially interesting are the general predictions of the model that any large decrease in stiffness, such as occurred in boron-aluminum, will always cause reduction in strength, and that small (or negligible) changes in stiffness, such as occurred in boron-epoxy, can be accompanied by an increase in strength. It also predicts that widely dispersed damage will be associated with strength reductions, while increases in strength are possible for small amounts of localized damage near the hole, a behavior observed here. Finally, it suggests an arrest in the lateral spread of damage for boron-epoxy during constant-amplitude fatigue; this arrest and subsequent vertical spread occurs in virtually all of our data.

Acknowledgments

The authors gratefully acknowledge the support of this research by the Air Force Office of Scientific Research, under Contract No. AFOSR-72-2358, monitored by Dr. Jacob Pomerantz.

They also wish to express their appreciation to the shop personnel in the Engineering Science and Mechanics Department for their valuable assistance, to John Kennedy and Dan Huffman for help with the drafting, and to Mrs. Nell Stallard for typing the manuscript.

References

[1] Stinchcomb, W. W., Reifsnider, K. L., Marcus, L., and Williams, R. W., "Effects of Cyclic Frequency on the Mechanical Properties of Composite Materials," VPI-E-73-25, Virginia Polytechnic Institute, June 1973, AFOSR TR-73-1907, Air Force Office of Scientific Research.

[2] Reifsnider, K. L., Stinchcomb, W. W., Williams, R. S., and Marcus, L., "Heat Generation in Composite Materials During Fatigue Loading," VPI-E-73-21, Virginia Polytechnic Institute, May 1973, AFOSR TR-73-1961, Air Force Office of Scientific Research.

[3] Waddoups, M. E., Eisenmann, J. R., and Kaminski, B. E., *Journal of Composite Materials,* Vol. 5, 1971, p. 446.

[4] Halpin, J. C., Jerina, K. L., and Johnson, T. A. in *Analysis of the Test Methods for High Modulus Fibers and Composites, ASTM STP 521,* American Society for Testing and Materials, 1973, pp. 5–64.

[5] Reifsnider, K. L. and Kahl, M., *International Journal of Mechanical Sciences,* Vol. 16, 1974, pp. 1–15.

[6] Kendall, D. P., "Crack Growth Resistance in Laminated, Glass-Epoxy Sheet," WVT-7158, Benet R. & E. Laboratories, Watervliet, N.Y. Oct. 1971.

[7] Bowie, O. L., *Journal of Mathematics and Physics,* Vol. 35, 1965, p. 60.

[8] Marcus, L. A., Stinchcomb, W. W., and Turgay, H. M., "Fatigue Crack Initiation in a Boron Epoxy Plate with a Circular Hole," AFOSR TR-74-0833, Air Force Office of Scientific Research, Feb. 1974.

P. W. R. Beaumont[1] *and W. L. Server*[2]

Some Observations on the Dynamic Fracture Behavior of Carbon Fiber-Strengthened Epoxy Resin

REFERENCE: Beaumont, P. W. R. and Server, W. L., "**Some Observations on the Dynamic Fracture Behavior of Carbon Fiber-Strengthened Epoxy Resin,**" *Composite Reliability, ASTM STP 580,* American Society for Testing and Materials, 1975, pp. 443–457.

ABSTRACT: The dynamic fracture behavior of 0/90 carbon fiber-strengthened epoxy resin composites is described in terms of the dynamic fracture toughness parameters K_{Id} and G_{Id} as a function of temperature and strain rate. It is shown that the fracture toughness is dependent on the elastic characteristics of the fibers and is insensitive to strain rate and temperature. The crack propagation energy is controlled by the properties of the epoxy resin and fiber-matrix interface and is sensitive to changes in strain rate at elevated temperatures.

KEY WORDS: composite materials, epoxy resins, carbon fibers, crack propagation, mechanical properties, fracture strength

In many fibrous composites of structural importance, microcracking precedes fast (unstable) fracture. It may take the form of cracking in the matrix or breakage of fibers at weak points. The propensity for brittle fracture to occur at the onset of cracking can be reduced by dissipating the stored energy necessary for crack propagation in the form of "plastic" work at the crack tip. This expended energy can be considered equivalent to the reversible surface energy term (γ) in the Griffith-Irwin fracture criteria, and depends on the conditions that exist at the crack tip. For example, during crack propagation in brittle fiber-strengthened polymers, a variety of energy absorbing microfailure mechanisms can occur, including matrix crazing and cracking, interfacial breakdown, fiber fracture, and pullout *[1]*.[3] In fiber-reinforced viscoelastic materials, for example,

---

[1] Lecturer in the Department of Engineering, University of Cambridge, Cambridge, England.

[2] Research Manager, Effects Technology Inc., Santa Barbara, Calif.

[3] The italic numbers in brackets refer to the list of references appended to this paper.

carbon fiber-epoxy resins or glasses, the time-dependent characteristics of the matrix and interface can affect the fracture behavior of the composite. Whether this would reflect in a time-dependence of crack initiation energy or crack propagation energy would depend on the sequential stages of crack growth. The successful exploitation of the polymer-based (or glass-based) composite therefore requires a thorough understanding of the time-dependent failure processes that may occur during crack growth.

Variable strain-rate (loading-rate) experiments are currently used for fracture strength and toughness evaluations in an attempt to understand how these properties are affected by microstructure and environment. The conventional Charpy impact test, for example, has been widely used to measure total fracture energies and allow simple comparisons to be made between different composite systems at high rates of loading [2-6]. However, it does not provide any useful information which can be directly applied to fracture-safe design of fibrous materials. A more significant and useful parameter would be the stress intensity factor, K, used in classical linear elastic fracture mechanics (LEFM) analysis, where

$$K = \sigma_a \, (\alpha \pi a)^{\frac{1}{2}} \tag{1}$$

where σ_a is the applied stress, a the crack length, and α a geometrical parameter; this is a function of crack size and component geometry.

Unstable fracture occurs when the local stress (or strain) at the crack tip reaches a critical value that depends on the material and environmental conditions. This implies that a critical amount of work, G, has to be done for fracture to occur $(G = G_c)$,[4] and implies also a critical stress intensity factor $(K = K_c)$. The relationship between K and G for isotropic materials is

$$K_{Ic} = (EG_{Ic})^{\frac{1}{2}} \text{ (plane strain conditions)} \tag{2}$$

(where E is Young's modulus and the subscript I refers to the opening mode of macroscopic crack propagation. At present, considerable controversy surrounds the validity of this approach to composites in view of their anisotropic, heterogeneous nature [7].

Since fiber-strengthened polymer systems are likely to be used at moderate temperatures (150 °C +) (302 °F +), when the matrix is likely to become significantly strain-rate sensitive, static fracture toughness (K_{Ic}) tests would not be representative of the conditions close to the advancing crack tip, and a dynamic fracture toughness parameter, K_{Id}, would be more useful for fracture-safe design purposes. Ideally, a description of dynamic failure is required that relates the effect of temperature and

---

[4] In LEFM terminology $G_c = 2\gamma$

strain rate on K_{Id}. Accurate predictions could then be made of the effects of microstructure on the macrofracture toughness, K_{Id}, as a function of temperature.

Failure models *[8–11]* have already been developed which can relate G to microscopic parameters (for example, fiber strength, fiber volume fraction, interfacial shear strength), and therefore offer some encouragement for achieving these predictions. The present work was undertaken on three 0/90 crossply carbon fiber-reinforced epoxy resin composites to investigate the effect of temperature and strain rate (displacement rate) on the dynamic fracture toughness, K_{Id} (and G_{Id}). An instrumented Charpy impact machine[5] is used to determine K_{Id} and an attempt is made to separate the total work of fracture, G_F, into the energies of crack initiation, G_{Id}, and crack propagation, G_p, taking into account any change in hammer velocity as it loses kinetic energy. First, the effect of specimen geometry on K_{Ic} and K_{Id} is evaluated. This is followed by a study of displacement-rate (δ) effects on K_{Ic} and K_{Id}. Finally, the effect of temperature on fracture stress and toughness is determined. Estimations of G_{Id} and G_p as a function of temperature and displacement rate (δ) are made by relating K_{Id} and G_{Id} using a modified Eq 2 that takes into account changes in the elastic constants, E_{11} (E_{22}), G_{12}, etc., of the composite with temperature. Values of G_p are obtained by subtracting G_{Id} from total work of fracture measurements, G_F, in "quasi-controlled" fracture tests.

Materials and Specimen Design

The materials investigated are 0/90 balanced crossply carbon fiber-epoxy resin composites ($V_f = 0.60$) containing 20 plies stacked alternately. Three types of carbon fibers are evaluated, namely, Courtaulds HTS (high strength), HMS (high modulus), and AS (intermediate strength) fibers. All fibers are surface-treated to provide a strong mechanical bond between fiber and matrix. A brittle (proprietary) epoxy resin is used as the matrix material. Charpy impact specimens were machined from 4-mm-thick laminated plates such that the crack would propagate perpendicular to the 0 deg fibers. The test specimen configuration used is similar to that employed in an earlier study *[12]*. Single edge-notches were machined to various depths in 10-mm-deep beam samples using a 0.25-mm slitting wheel, resulting in a range of crack size to specimen depth ratios (a/d) from 0.1 to 0.8. The specimen depth, d, is also controlled between 6 and 10 mm but maintaining a constant a/d ratio of one third. A square-sectioned (4 mm by 4 mm) bar containing a triangular cross section at the midpoint (a "decreasing-K" specimen) is also used to evaluate the total work of fracture, G_F, of the composite.

---

[5] A "Dynatup" model supplied by Effects Technology Inc.

Quasi-Static and Dynamic Failure Criteria

Quasi-Static Failure

In a slow-bend test using a decreasing-K specimen, the load increases to a maximum value, at which point a crack nucleates at the apex of the triangle and propagates under decreasing loads in a quasi-controlled manner *[13]*. The total work of fracture per unit fracture area, G_F, is simply the integral of the load/deflection curve divided by the area of the triangle

$$G_F = \frac{2E_T}{bd} \tag{3}$$

where the energy term, E_T, includes the energy dissipated during the crack initiation and growth stages of fracture.

Dynamic Failure

In the fracture of brittle materials, the difference between the initial, v_0, and final, v_f, hammer velocities in a conventional Charpy impact test is small, and therefore the effective velocity of the tup, v^*, during dynamic fracture is simply

$$v^* = (v_f + v_0)/2 \tag{4}$$

where $v_0 = \sqrt{2gh}$, where g is the acceleration due to gravity and h is the drop height of the tup.

The actual transient loads on the specimen are recorded by a storage oscilloscope, and the total energy, E_T, expended in the fracture process is

$$E_T = v^* \left(\frac{C_x C_y P_d}{Ca} \right) A \tag{5}$$

where P_d is the force per volt output, C_a the area of one square division on the oscilloscope record, C_x the time sweep rate per division, C_y the vertical sensitivity per division, and A the area under the voltage-time curve. Equation 5 is therefore equivalent to the integral of the load/time curve

$$E_T = v^* \int P \, dt \tag{6}$$

The maximum load at fracture is P_{ld}, and the dynamic fracture stress, σ_F, can be calculated using simple beam theory

$$\sigma_F = \left(\frac{3}{2} \frac{P_{Id}L}{bd^2} \right) \tag{7}$$

where L is the distance between the supports (4 cm), and b and d are the specimen width and depth, respectively. It is assumed that all the composites evaluated behave essentially in an elastic manner up to the point of failure. In terms of the dynamic fracture toughness, K_{Id}

$$K_{Id} = Y\sigma_F\sqrt{a} \tag{8}$$

where Y is $f(a/d)$ [14].

If the fibrous composite is considered at the macroscopic level as an homogeneous, orthotropic solid, then Eq 2 can be modified to describe crack growth in anisotropic materials [15]

$$K = \sqrt{ \left\{ \left(\frac{a_{22}a_{11}}{2} \right)^{1/2} \left[\left(\frac{a_{22}}{a_{11}} \right)^{1/2} + \left(\frac{a_{66} + 2a_{12}}{2a_{11}} \right)^{1/2} \right] \right\}^{-1} } G \tag{9}$$

where E has been replaced with an "effective" modulus parameter, E^*, which is a function of the orthotropic compliance values, a_{11}, a_{22}, etc. (Table 1).

Combining Eqs 8 and 9 and solving for crack initiation energy

$$G_{Id} = \frac{9Y^2L^2P_{Id}^2a}{4E^*b^2d^4} \tag{10}$$

$$= C \left(\frac{P_{Id}^2a}{E^*} \right) \tag{11}$$

where C is a geometrical constant and has the value 8×10^{10} m^{-4} for the specimen design and loading configuration.

The values of the orthotropic compliances, a_{11}, a_{22}, etc., are temperature-sensitive and therefore E^* is a function of temperature. Evaluation of crack initiation energy, G_{Id}, therefore requires experimental determination of K_{Id} and a_{11}, a_{22}, etc. f (temperature).

Results and Discussion

Dynamic Fracture Toughness, K_{Id}

The fracture of carbon fiber composites can be extremely complex and may involve a number of different stages, often occurring in both a sequential and parallel manner as the crack tip opens. Previous work [16–23]

TABLE 1—*Elastic properties of carbon fibers and 0/90 CFRP (V_f = 0.60) composites.*

	Fiber Properties		Elastic Constants of 0°/90° CFRP							
			E_{11} (E_{22}) (GNm^{-2})		G_{12} (GNm^{-2})		ν_{12}	(ν_{21})	E^* (Plane stress) (GNm^{-2})	
Type	Strength (GNm^{-2})	Modulus (GNm^{-2})	-20°C (-4°F)	175°C (347°F)	-20°C (-4°F)	175°C (347°F)	-20°C (-4°F)	175°C (347°F)	-20°C (-4°F)	175°C (347°F)
HMS	2.06–2.2 (2.07)[a]	365–405 (379)	89.5	89.5	4.47	3.44	0.05	0.02	38	34
HTS	2.68–3.16 (2.76)	248–290 (262)	79	67.5	4.46	1.25	0.05	0.02	35	18
AS	2.42–2.54 (2.48)	183–234 (186)	63.2	58.5	4.12	2.06	0.05	0.02	30	21

(HMS = high-modulus fibers; HTS = high-strength fibers; AS = intermediate-strength fibers.
[a]Figures in parentheses are mean values.

$$E^* = \text{``Effective modulus''} \left\{ \left(\frac{\dot{a}_{11} a_{22}}{2} \right)^{1/2} \left[\left(\frac{a_{22}}{a_{11}} \right)^{1/2} + \frac{a_{66} + 2a_{12}}{2a_{11}} \right]^{1/2} \right\}^{-1}$$

has shown the fracture stress and toughness of carbon fiber-reinforced polymers (CFRP) to depend on the elastic behavior of the carbon fibers and the strength of the fiber-resin interface. The contribution of the matrix to the fracture toughness of the composite was considered to be small, at least at room temperature. In these composites crack propagation occurred by the simultaneous breakage of fibers lying perpendicular to the notch in the beam, and cracking between the fibers lying parallel to the notch, and through the resin matrix. No splitting or delamination between the plies or perpendicular to the notch was observed at the tip of the propagating crack. Figures 1 and 2 show the apparent independence of fracture toughness (K_{Ic} and K_{Id}) on specimen geometry and crack size at room temperature, although it should be emphasized that at small initial values of notch size, the notch length to notch width ratio is about 4, which may lead to erroneous results using classical fracture mechanics. To be more definite about the independence of $K f(a, d)$ would require a large number of specimens tested and a statistical approach to the fracture stress of the composite. The dynamic fracture toughness (K_{Id}) values were calculated from the load/time traces, and the shape of these curves is clearly dependent on the elastic properties of the carbon fiber and test temperature (Figs. 3, 4). First, the higher tensile strength composite has a greater failure load, P_{Id}, and a larger area under the load/time curve than the high stiffness material; second, increasing the temperature results in a larger area under the nonlinear portion of the curve. This area represents

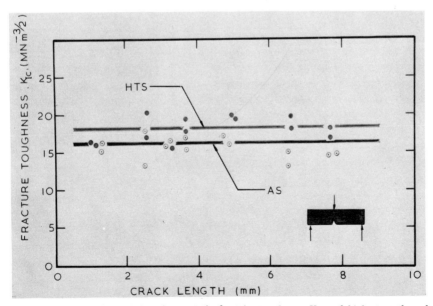

FIG. 1—*Effect of crack length on static fracture toughness, K_{Ic}, of high-strength and intermediate-strength 0/90 crossply carbon fiber-epoxy resin ($\bar{V}_f = 0.60$) at room temperature.*

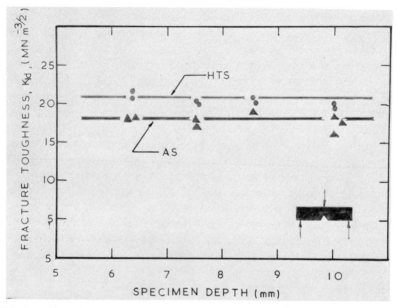

FIG. 2—*Effect of specimen depth on dynamic fracture toughness,* K_{Id}, *of high-strength and intermediate-strength 0/90 crossply carbon fiber-epoxy resin* ($V_f = 0.60$) *at room temperature.*

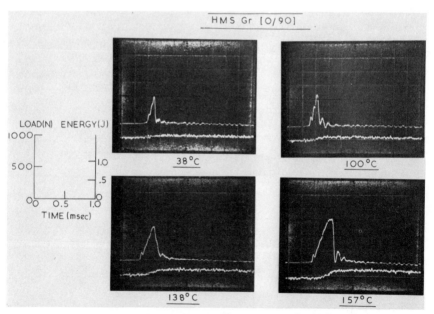

FIG. 3—*Some typical load/energy/time oscilloscope traces for high-modulus 0/90 crossply carbon fiber-epoxy resin* ($V_f = 0.60$) *at various temperatures* ($V^* = 1.5$ ms^{-1}).

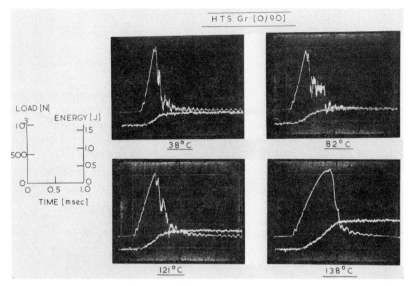

FIG. 4—*Some typical load/energy/time oscilloscope traces for high-strength 0/90 cross-ply carbon fiber-epoxy resin (V$_f$ = 0.60) at various temperatures (V* = 1.5 ms^{-1}).*

an increase in the nonrecoverable energy term in the total fracture energy. No variation was found in K_{Id} over six decades of displacement rate, $\dot{\delta}$ (Fig. 5); neither was there any significant effect of temperature on K_{Id} (Fig. 6.). The differences between the three composites in terms of fracture stress and toughness reflect the dependence of K_{Id} on the strength and stiffness characteristics of the carbon fibers. This accounts for the $\dot{\delta}$ and temperature insensitivity of the composites. The inflections in the increasing portion of the load/time traces at low loads are caused by vibrations in the impact hammer.

Dynamic Crack Growth

Tests were carried out in the temperature range −20 to 175°C (−4 to 347°F), at displacement rates between 2 × 10^{-5} ms^{-1} and 2 ms^{-1} in an attempt to evaluate the time/temperature-dependent failure processes in CFRP. The total work of fracture, G_F, as a function of temperature is shown in Fig. 7 for high and low rates of loading. At low temperatures [−20°C (−4°F) → room temperature], the difference between the slow bend and impact values is small and only becomes significant when the temperature approaches the glass transition (softening) temperature, T_g, of the matrix. Above 60°C (140°F) the time-dependent nature of the epoxy resin is apparent, shown by the strain rate and temperature sensitivity of the work of fracture, G_F; that is, at $T > 60$°C (140°F), the position of the $G_F(T)$ curve depends on the response time of the matrix.

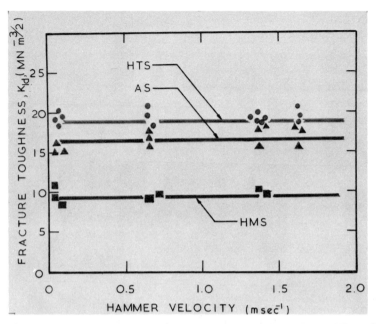

FIG. 5—*Effect of displacement rate (ȯ) on the fracture toughness, K_{Ic} and K_{Id}, of high-strength, high-modulus, and intermediate-strength 0/90 crossply carbon fiber-epoxy resin ($V_f = 0.60$) at room temperature.*

The crack initiation energies of the three composites exhibit only a small dependence on temperature and increase only by about a factor of 2 over the entire temperature range investigated (Fig. 8). Also in this figure is shown the total work of fracture, G_F, measured in impact. In the low-temperature region, the difference between G_F and G_{Id} is negligible but increases as the temperature approaches T_g of the matrix ($\sim$ 150°C (302°F) at $\dot{o} = 1$ ms^{-1}). This difference, represented by the shaded area between the two solid curves for each composite, can be considered equivalent to the energy of crack propagation, G_p.

Crack Initiation Energy, G_{Id}

For elastic fracture, the stored elastic strain energy can be considered as the average energy density in the deformed specimen multiplied by a geometrical parameter that depends on specimen design and loading configuration. If the composite response is assumed to be elastic up to the maximum applied load, then the critical strain energy release rate per unit fracture area can be described by simple beam theory. In three-point bending

$$\text{critical strain energy} = \frac{L}{9} \frac{\sigma_c^2}{E_c} \tag{12}$$

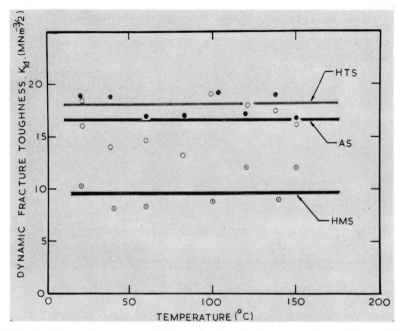

FIG. 6—*Effect of temperature (°C) on the dynamic fracture toughness,* K_{Id}, *of high-strength, high-modulus, and intermediate-strength 0/90 crossply carbon fiber-epoxy resin (*V_f = 0.60).

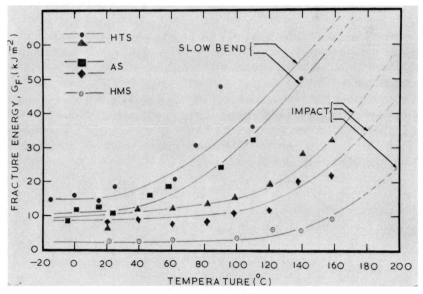

FIG. 7—*Effect of temperature (°C) on the total fracture energy,* G_F, *of high-strength, high-modulus, and intermediate-strength 0/90 crossply carbon fiber-epoxy resin (*V_f = 0.60) *measured in slow bending (*V^* = 2 × 10^{-5} ms^{-1}), *and impact loading (*V^* = 1.5 ms^{-1}).

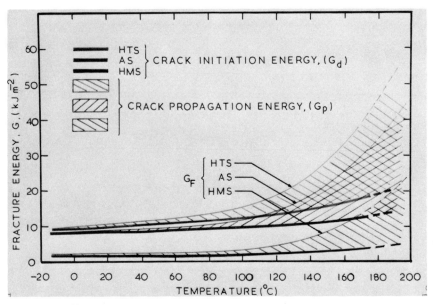

FIG. 8—*Effect of temperature (°C) on the crack initiation energy, G_{Id}, and total work of fracture, G_F, of high-strength, high-modulus, and intermediate-strength 0/90 carbon fiber-epoxy resin (V_f = 0.60) measured under impact loading (V^* = 1.5 ms^{-1}). (The shaded areas represent the crack propagation energies of the three materials as a function of temperature.)*

where L is the span distance (4 cm) and σ_c and E_c are the maximum stress and modulus of the composite in the 0 deg fiber direction, both of which are functions of the elastic properties of the fiber and fiber orientation.

Substituting the appropriate values for the HTS and HMS carbon fiber composites (see Table 1) into Eq 12 produces 9.2 and 3.4 kJm^{-2} at room temperature, and 10.7 and 3.4 kJm^{-2} at 175°C (347°F), respectively. These values are similar to the fracture surface energies, G_{Id}, obtained using the LEFM approach.

The apparent increase in stored elastic strain energy at fracture with increasing temperature for the HTS composite can be accounted for by the corresponding decrease in modulus (Table 1). It does not, however, explain the discrepancy between G_{Id} and the estimated stored elastic strain energy in the specimen at high temperatures [~ 175°C (347°F)]. At this end of the temperature range, the composites do not remain totally elastic up to the maximum load, particularly the low stiffness (HTS) composite. Some volume of material "yields" at the crack tip before fracture commences, and the possible microfailure modes mentioned earlier may occur and result in subcritical microcrack growth. Contributions from matrix flow and fiber pullout to the fracture energy are likely to be significant at elevated temperatures and may account for this discrepancy.

Crack Propagation Energy, G_p

The total work of fracture, G_F, can be considered as the sum of the crack initiation and crack propagation energies. At low temperatures, values of G_F measured in slow bending are similar to the observed dynamic toughness, G_{Id}, measurements (Fig. 8). It can be argued that in this temperature region (-20 to $50\,°C$) (-4 to $122\,°F$), failure occurs by brittle fracture, and the work of fracture simply evaluates the material's resistance to crack initiation in terms of the stored elastic strain energy in the specimen. But this will include a kinetic energy term and may therefore be an overestimate of the actual fracture surface energy of the composite. As the temperature increases, increasing amounts of fibrous fracture and matrix flow occur. These modes of failure are energy-absorbing processes and, therefore, the crack propagation energy, G_p, becomes a function of temperature. In Fig. 8, G_p is represented by the shaded area between the solid $G_F(T)$ and $G_{Id}(T)$ curves. A transition from brittle to "ductile" fracture for CFRP is not as rapid as for low-strength steels, but increases steadily as the temperature is raised. The *rate of increase* in G_p becomes greater as the temperature approaches T_g (matrix) and is strain-rate dependent. The contributions of the matrix fracture energy, G_m, and the fiber pullout energy, G_{IIp}*, to G_p are clearly a complex function of strain-rate and temperature as shown by the shift of the fracture energy, G_F, curves along the temperature scale with a change of $\dot{d}$ (Fig. 7).

It is difficult to separate the relative influences of these two cases on the crack propagation energy since both are clearly sensitive to strain rate and temperature. A crude estimation of fiber pullout energy, G_{IIp}, can be arrived at using Cottrell's analysis [9]

$$G_{IIp} = \frac{V_f \tau_i' l_c^2}{12d} \tag{13}$$

It is reasonable to assume that only the $0°$ fibers contribute to G_{IIp}, and therefore $V_f = 0.30$. The critical fiber transfer length, l_c, can be estimated using the relationship

$$l_c = \frac{\sigma_f \cdot d}{2\,\tau_i} \tag{14}$$

The fiber diameter, d, is 8×10^{-6} m and the interfacial shear strength,

---

τ_i, is close to 80 MN m^{-2} at room temperature. Values of σ_f for HTS and HMS fibers are listed in Table 1. We can only assume at this stage that $\tau_i \cong \tau_i'$, the frictional shear stress acting at the interface during fiber extraction, although these properties are likely to be $\dot{\varepsilon}$, T-dependent. Inserting the appropriate values into Eq 13 gives G_{IIp} values of 9.5 and 5.4 kJ m^{-2} for the HTS and HMS carbon fiber composites, respectively, which are not unlike the G_{Id} values obtained.

It is interesting to note that changes in fiber pullout lengths with variations in crack velocity (strain-rate) have been observed in carbon fiber-reinforced epoxy resin [16,24] and carbon fiber-reinforced glass [25], which serves to illustrate the rate dependence of G_{IIp}. Scanning electron microscopy studies need to be carried out in order to assist in analyzing quantitatively the time and temperature dependence of G_{IIp} and G_m.

Summary and Conclusions

Dynamic crack growth has been investigated for three 0/90 carbon fiber-strengthened epoxy resin composites, specifically in terms of the influence of temperature on the LEFM parameters K_{Id} and G_{Id}. An attempt has been made to separate the total fracture energy, G_F, into its two constituent components, crack initiation energy, G_{Id}, and crack propagation energy, G_p, during impact fracture. A comparison of G_{Id} and G_p suggests that the overall toughness of the composite is the sum of these two terms

$$G_F = G_{Id} + G_p$$

where the first term is essentially independent of temperature and strain rate and depends on the elastic characteristics of the carbon fibers, similar to K_{Id}. The second term, G_p, is controlled by the time-temperature behavior of the matrix and interface and as a first approximation can be considered as the sum of the two microfailure processes, matrix shear and fiber pullout

$$G_p(t, T) = G_m(t, T) + G_{IIp}(t, T)$$

In engineering terms, an increase in temperature reduces the likelihood for brittle fracture to occur without any loss of composite fracture strength. However, if the loading rate (strain rate) increases at the elevated temperature, the tendency toward brittle fracture returns.

Acknowledgments

This work was supported on a United States Army Contract,

R. G. 2206. We wish to thank Mr. D. Cox for collecting the "quasi-static" fracture data and Effects Technology Inc. of Santa Barbara for use of their facilities.

References

[1] Beaumont, P. W. R., *Journal of Adhesion,* Vol. 4, 1973, pp. 1–31.

[2] Novak, R. C. and DeCrescente, M. A. in *Composite Materials: Testing and Design (Second Conference) ASTM STP 497,* American Society for Testing and Materials, 1972, pp. 311–323.

[3] Chamis, C. C., Hanson, M. P., and Serafini, T. T. in *Composite Materials: Testing and Design (Second Conference), ASTM STP 497,* 1972, pp. 324–349.

[4] Toland, R. H. in *Instrumented Impact Testing, ASTM STP 563,* American Society for Testing and Materials, 1974, pp. 133–145.

[5] Toland, R. H., "Failure Modes in Impact-Loaded Composite Materials," *Failure Modes in Composites,* AIME Spring meeting, Boston, May 1972.

[6] Broutman, L. J. and Rotem, A., "Impact Strength and Toughness of Fiber Composite Materials," AFOSR Grant AFOSR-72-2214, Department of Metallurgical and Materials Engineering, Illinois Institute of Technology, Nov. 1972.

[7] Zweben, Carl, *Engineering Fracture Mechanics,* Vol. 6, 1974, pp. 1–10.

[8] Outwater, J. O. and Murphy, M. C., 24th Annual Technical Conference, RPI/Composites Division, 1969.

[9] Cottrell, A. H., *Proceedings of the Royal Society,* Series A, Vol. 282, 1964, p. 2.

[10] Kelly, A., *Proceedings of the Royal Society,* Vol. 319, 1970, p. 95.

[11] Fitz-Randolph, J. et al, *Journal of Materials Science,* Vol. 7, 1972, pp. 289–294.

[12] Beaumont, P. W. R., Riewald, P. G. and Zweben, C. in *Foreign Object Impact Behavior of Composites, ASTM STP 568,* American Society for Testing and Materials, 1974, pp. 134–158.

[13] Harris, B., Beaumont, P. W. R. and Moncunill de Ferran, E., *Journal of Materials Science,* Vol. 6, 1971, pp. 238–251.

[14] Brown, W. F. and Srawley, J. E. in *Plane Strain Crack Toughness Testing of High-Strength Metallic Materials, ASTM STP 410,* American Society for Testing and Materials, 1966.

[15] Sih, G. C., Paris, P. C., and Irwin, G. R., *International Journal of Fracture Mechanics,* Vol. 1, 1965, p. 189.

[16] Beaumont, P. W. R. and Harris, B., *Journal of Materials Science,* Vol. 7, 1972, pp. 1265–1279.

[17] Beaumont, P. W. R. and Tetelman, A. S., "Fracture Stress and Toughness of Fibrous Composites," *Failure Modes in Composites,* American Institute of Mining, Metalliagical, and Petroleum Engineers, AIME Spring meeting, Boston, May 1972.

[18] Bader, M., Bailey, J. and Bell, I., paper presented at Institute of Physics meeting on "Failure Modes in Fiber Composites," University of Surrey, Guildford, July 1972.

[19] Harris, B., and Ellis, C., paper presented at Institute of Physics meeting on "Failure Modes in Fiber Composites," University of Surrey, Guildford, July 1972.

[20] Barker, A., paper presented at Institute of Physics meeting on "Carbon Fibers," London, England, Feb. 1971.

[21] Hancox, N. L., "Izod Impact testing of Carbon Fiber Reinforced Plastic," AERE Report R-6669, Atomic Energy Research Establishment (Harwell), England, Jan. 1971.

[22] Phillips, D. C., "Fracture Mechanics of Carbon Fiber Laminates," AERE Report R-7443, Nov. 1973.

[23] Fila, M., Bredin, C., and Piggott, M. R., *Journal of Materials Science,* Vol. 7, 1972, pp. 983–988.

[24] Arridge, R. G. C., "Fracture of Fiber Reinforced Materials," *Nature,* Vol. 223, Aug. 30, 1969.

[25] Phillips, D. C., "Interfacial Bonding and the Toughness of Fiber Reinforced Ceramics," AERE Report R-7594, Jan. 1974.

J. C. Carlisle,[1] *R. L. Crane,*[1] *W. J. Jaques,*[1] *and*
L. T. Montulli[1]

Impact Damage Effects on Boron-Aluminum Composites

REFERENCE: Carlisle, J. C., Crane, R. L., Jaques, W. J., and Montulli, L. T.,
"Impact Damage Effects on Boron-Aluminum Composites," *Composite Reliability,*
ASTM STP 580, American Society for Testing and Materials, 1975, pp. 458–470.

ABSTRACT: The foreign-object damage problem associated with jet engines was
investigated by impacting both titanium (6Al-4V) and boron-aluminum specimens
with either steel or room-temperature vulcanizing rubber spheres to simulate the
two principal types of ingested foreign objects. To simulate engine operating conditions, some specimens were impacted while under a tensile load. Results indicate
that a prestressed composite suffers much greater damage than simple cantilevered
specimens. Ti-6Al-4V exhibits excellent impact resistance, loosing only 10 percent
of its ultimate tensile strength up to the highest prestresses and impact velocities.
Composite specimens react much differently depending on the type of impactor.
Steel spheres cause severe damage at very low impact velocities. Room-temperature
vulcanizing rubber, on the other hand, causes little damage up to a velocity thresh-
old. Above this point, specimen failure was observed at some prestresses upon
impact. The residual tensile and low-cycle fatigue strength of both boron-aluminum
and titanium was documented for various impacting velocities and prestresses. A
fracture-mechanics analysis is presented which successfully predicts the effects of
room-temperature vulcanizing rubber impact on boron-aluminum composites.

KEY WORDS: composite materials, damage, boron, aluminum, fracture properties,
impact, strength

Recent interest in the use of boron-aluminum composites in jet engine
components has been stimulated by the high specific strength and stiffness
of this material. The U. S. Air Force has supported many programs to
demonstrate the feasibility of producing and using composite compressor
blades. One of the major obstacles to the use of boron-aluminum in this
application, however, is its low impact resistance. Recently it was demonstrated that composite blades may experience catastrophic failures from
small-bird ingestion *[1]*.[2] Even if blades can be designed to withstand the

---

[1] Graduate student, materials engineer, graduate student, and assistant professor, respectively, U. S. Air Force Institute of Technology, Dayton, Ohio 45433.
[2] The italic numbers in brackets refer to the list of references appended to this paper.

initial strikes, there still remains the problem of the effect of hard- and soft-particle impact on residual mechanical properties. Therefore, it is mandatory that the effects of foreign-object damage (FOD) on the mechanical properties of boron-aluminum composite be documented before viable blade designs can be developed.

Two important areas for consideration are the residual, or postimpact, tensile and fatigue strengths of boron-aluminum composite. Such information would be useful in constructing models of the life expectance of composite blades in the service environment. Unfortunately, very little data exist for boron-aluminum subjected to impact loading. Herman [2] has shown that the application of a load or prestress to a composite specimen increases significantly the severity of damage suffered as a result of impact with small steel spheres. The residual tensile strength of impact-damaged resin matrix composites has been treated in an eloquent manner recently by Husman et al [3]. Their results, however, are not directly applicable to metal matrix composites without the inclusion of matrix plasticity effects. The fracture toughness and Charpy impact energy of boron-aluminum composites have been determined [4,5], but attempts to relate these data to the ability of a blade to withstand bird strikes have not been entirely successful [6].

Since composite compressor blades are subjected to a spectrum of fatigue loading, the effect of FOD in the form of through-the-thickness cracks on the residual high- and low-cycle fatigue strength of boron-aluminum must be documented. It is well known that composites exhibit excellent fatigue resistance when compared with monolithic materials. This is particularly true for axially loaded specimens which contain cracks or machined notches perpendicular to the applied load. These cracks are very quickly blunted by matrix-fiber delamination at low cyclic stress levels [7,8]. The fatigue strength of impact-damaged boron-aluminum in the low-bending-stress, high-cycle regime has been investigated by Gray [9]. He postulated that in unidirectional composites, fatigue crack propagation is inhibited by the aforementioned mechanism. It was only in the area of the effect of impact-produced damage on low-cycle, high-stress fatigue strength that questions remained. Whether shock damage existed beyond the visible matrix cracking around the impact site and how it might affect the fatigue strength were two important unknowns.

The analysis of the strength of composites which contain flaws or machined notches has relied heavily on the principles of linear-elastic fracture mechanics developed for isotropic materials [4,10,11]. In the region around the crack tip, very high stresses exist which may result in material damage prior to crack propagation. In the monolithic metals, this zone is accounted for with the plasticity correction factor. Since composites have a limited strain capability before fracture, however, the concept of "damage zone" c_y has been proposed [12,13].

Experimental Procedure

It was the intent of this study to provide a matrix of data for the residual tensile and low-cycle axial fatigue strengths of unidirectional boron-aluminum composites impacted at various velocities and prestresses. The velocities, which ranged from 0 ft/s to about 4000 ft/s, were chosen as representative of those that could be expected for foreign-object/jet-engine-blade impacts. The prestresses, which were 0, 22, 44, 66, and 90 ksi, represented the range of stress levels calculated for boron-aluminum compressor blades [1,14].

The materials used in this study were sheet Ti-6Al-4V and eight-ply boron-aluminum (6061) composite. The titanium used was 0.067-in.-thick sheet stock which had been annealed. Specimens, 6 in. long by 1 in. wide, were cut such that the long dimension of the specimen was parallel to the rolling direction of the alloy sheet. The specimen dimensions and microstructure simulated the standard forged titanium fan and compressor blades. The composite specimens were cut from eight-ply sheet stock to the following dimensions; 4.5 in. long by 1 in. wide by 0.052 to 0.056 in. thick. All composite material was fabricated using the standard diffusion bonding scheme from 5.6-mil-diameter boron fiber and 6061 aluminum alloy sheet. Specimens were zero degree or unidirectional boron-aluminum and cut so that the fiber direction was parallel to the long dimension of the specimen. End tabs of 2024-To aluminum were attached to specimens with an aluminum matrix epoxy to facilitate gripping.

A description of the ballistics facility in which specimens were impacted is covered in detail elsewhere [15]. Briefly, the specimens were gripped with wedge-action grips and impacted with either 0.177-in.-diameter steel or room temperature vulcanizing rubber (RTV) spheres. The steel and RTV spheres were used to simulate the two principal types of foreign objects that jet engines encounter in service. The steel spheres simulate such items as nails, rocks, and rivets while the RTV simulates such things as birds, tire tread, and rags [16]. These spheres were launched in a sabot with either a powder charge or nitrogen gas pressure. The velocity of the projectile in each shot was measured with an electronic timer as the sphere interrupted two laser beams. All specimens were impacted normal to their surface. Both the impacted side and reverse surface of each specimen were photographed after each shot. The dimensions of any crack or hole were measured for each specimen. Two specimens were used to check the validity of the fracture mechanics analysis of the ballistic impact. Slots approximately 0.005 in. wide by either 0.05 or 0.60 in. long were electro-discharge machined in the specimens.

Specimens were tension tested in a standard Instron tension testing machine at a crosshead speed of approximately 0.05 in./min using wedge-action grips. Fatigue testing was performed on a Schenck Fatigue machine at a cyclic frequency of about 40 Hz. An *R* ratio of 0.1 was maintained during tests to ensure the alignment of the specimens in the machine's wedge-action grips. It should also be noted that jet engine compressor blades experience only tension-tension low-cycle fatigue, necessitating an *R* ratio greater than zero.

Results and Discussion

The results produced from this study are best understood when classified into three major groups. The first concerns the data taken to quantify the loss of tensile load-carrying ability of boron-aluminum from simulated FOD. The second is the effects on residual fatigue strength from FOD, and third is the application of fracture mechanics principles for the prediction of these damage results.

Residual Tensile Strength

Figure 1 presents the results of normalized residual tensile strength of Ti-6-4 as a function of the velocity of an impacting steel ball. These data indicate a loss in strength of approximately 10 percent at the highest impact velocities. Similar tests (now shown) were conducted with RTV impactors. The RTV results showed no effect on the residual tensile strength of Ti-6-4 for velocities approaching 4700 ft/s. The test variables

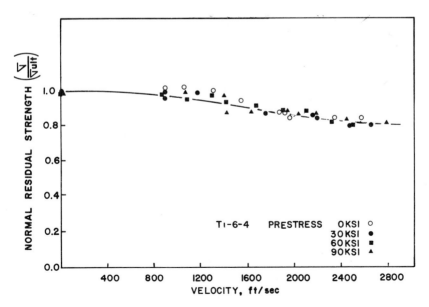

FIG. 1—*Residual tensile strength of Ti-6Al-4V (σ_{ULT} = 147 ksi) impacted by a 0.177-in. steel ball.*

included the four prestress levels: 0, 30, 60, and 90 ksi. For Ti-6-4, the effect of prestress on the residual tensile strength is very small.

Figure 2 illustrates the effects on the residual strength of unidirectional boron-aluminum when impacted with an 0.177-in. steel ball at three prestress levels; 0, 44, and 90 ksi. For no prestress, the residual strength was found to decrease by 50 percent of the virgin strength for an impact velocity as low as 400 ft/s. At 44-ksi prestress, the specimen broke upon impact at 600 ft/s. At higher impact velocities, the specimen remained intact but had a clean hole punched through it. At 90-ksi prestress, a phenomenon similar to that at 44-ksi prestress was observed. These data illustrate that a foreign-object impact on an operating blade can cause substantial or even catastrophic damage. Blades of boron-aluminum, as they are presently fabricated, will require elaborate protection devices to allow them to survive in the harsh environment of the jet engine.

Figure 3 depicts the effects on the residual strength of unidirectional boron-aluminum when it was impacted by RTV. At the three prestresses shown, no loss in strength was detected until an impact velocity of approximately 1700 ft/s was reached. At this velocity, cracks on the reverse side of the impact face of the specimen were first observed. Residual strength tests clearly show the effect of this damage. For no prestress, a 50 percent loss in load-carrying ability was measured for an increase in impacting velocity of 400 ft/s. At higher prestress levels the residual strength decreases even more rapidly until velocities of impact are reached which

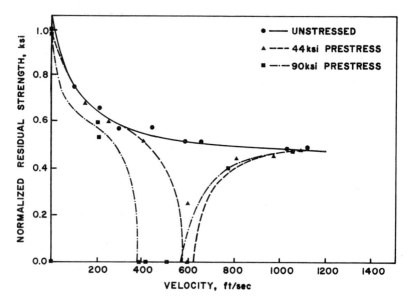

FIG. 2—*Residual tensile strength of boron-aluminum [o(avg)$_{ULT}$ = 207 ksi] impacted by a 0.177-in. steel ball.*

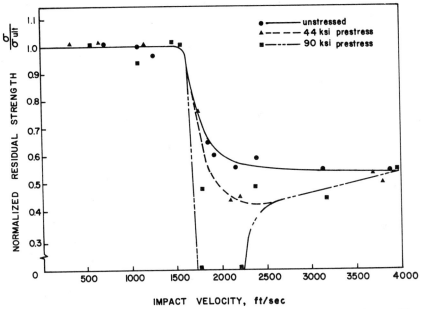

FIG. 3—*Residual tensile strength of boron-aluminum [o(avg)$_{ULT}$ = 207 ksi] impacted by a 0.177-in. RTV ball.*

produce clean holes. Above this point, the residual strength returns to about 50 percent of the average. These data when compared with those of Fig. 2 point out the dramatic difference in damage caused by the two different types of foreign objects. Recent tests in which a full stage of boron-aluminum compressor blades were subjected to foreign-object ingestion also showed that small hard debris caused clearly visible damage to the blades at the lowest velocities tested [1]. These same engine tests, however, found no visible damage for bird impacts until a critical velocity was reached which caused catastrophic failure. The data collected in this study by tension coupon tests appear to parallel the results of the full engine tests.

Residual Fatigue Strength

A significant part of this investigation was the study of the fatigue characteristics in boron-aluminum after either RTV or steel sphere impacts. First, a baseline was established, utilizing Ti-6-4. A sample of results is shown in Fig. 4, which illustrates test results for four impact velocities at a 90-ksi prestress level. The fatigue test results indicate a significant loss of load-carrying ability compared with undamaged specimens. These effects can be observed by comparing the results for 1031-ft/s

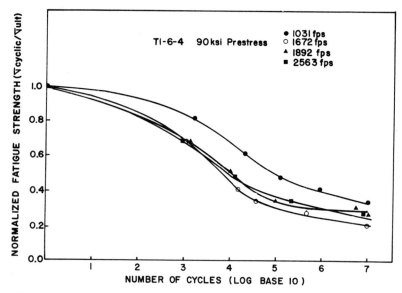

FIG. 4—*Fatigue strength of Ti-6Al-4V (σ_ULT = 147 ksi) impacted by a 0.177-in. steel ball.*

impact, which caused little visible damage to the specimen, with 2563-ft/s, where a clean hole was produced.

Figures 5, 6, and 7 present samples of boron-aluminum fatigue data. The test procedure required that tension-tension fatigue be applied until longitudinal shear cracks appeared which blunted the transverse cracks and made further fatigue testing pointless. Then the specimens were removed from the fatigue machine and tension tested. The results of these tests are plotted for various prestress levels with previous strength results. Figure 5 shows the results for steel ball impacts. The blunted crack fatigue tension tests show higher residual load-carrying results than the pure tension tests. Similar results may be observed in Figs. 6 and 7 for soft-body impact tests.

Application of Fracture Mechanics

The data in Figs. 1 through 7 illustrate the significance of FOD upon the static and fatigue load-carrying ability of boron-aluminum as well as Ti-6-4. The data as presented are dependent on impactor and specimen size, both of which influence the extent of damage. To alleviate this dependence, as well as to uncouple the impact damage problem from the subsequent problem of predicting those damage effects on the load-carrying ability of the materials, an analytical fracture analysis was desirable. Many investigators [4,10,13] have shown that the Griffith-Irwin fracture criterion is applicable to elastic orthotropic materials if the crack

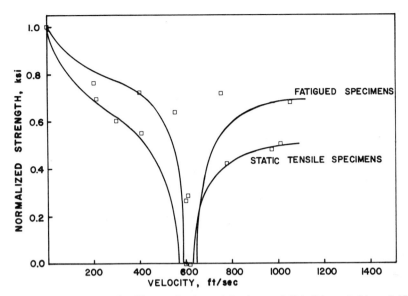

FIG. 5—*Fatigue strength of boron-aluminum [o(avg)$_{ULT}$ = 240 ksi] impacted by a 0.177-in. steel ball at a zero prestress.*

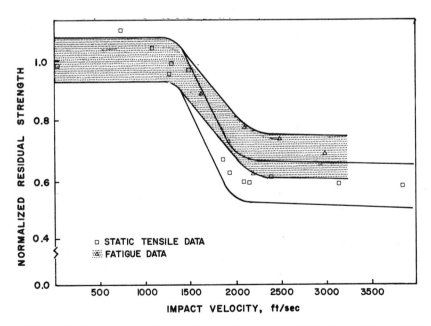

FIG. 6—*Residual strength of boron-aluminum [o(avg)$_{ULT}$ = 207 ksi] impacted by a 0.177-in. RTV ball at a zero prestress.*

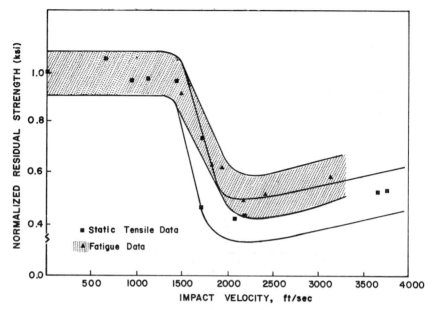

FIG. 7—Residual strength of boron-aluminum [σ(avg)$_{ULT}$ = 207 ksi] impacted with a 0.177-in. RTV ball at a 44-ksi prestress.

is propagated along one of the principal directions of elastic symmetry. Since these conditions existed in this study, a fracture mechanics analysis could procede directly. The crack extension force, G, may be written in terms of the stress intensity factor, K, for which there exists a family of theoretical expressions for various geometries and loadings. In the case of an orthotropic material, this expression according to Sih et al [11] is

$$G = K_I^2 \left\{ \left(\frac{S_{22}S_{11}}{2} \right)^{1/2} \left[\left(\frac{S_{11}}{S_{22}} \right)^{1/2} + \frac{S_{66} + 2S_{12}}{2S_{22}} \right]^{1/2} \right\} \qquad (1)$$

where S_{ij} are the compliance constants for boron-aluminum indexed in accordance with the conventions of lamination theory. The compliance term, in the braces, corresponds to an effective modulus of the material. The damage zone or apparent virgin flaw half-length, c_y, was calculated using the procedure outlined by Waddoups et al [12]. This value was used in the finite width-center cracked model

$$K_I = \sigma \left\{ \pi(a_c + c_y) \sec \left[\frac{\pi(a_c + c_y)}{\omega} \right] \right\}^{1/2} \qquad (2)$$

where σ is the far field stress, a_c is the observed half-crack length, and ω is the plate width.

To apply this analysis, a measure of the energy required to form the new crack surface was needed as an approximation of the critical strain energy release rate, G_c. Although Charpy impact energy is not an exact measure of this quantity, it does give a "ball park" figure. Dardi and Kreider [5] found that the Charpy impact energy of Borsic-aluminum composites can be given by the following expression

$$E = 26 + 8.5 \times 10^{-3} \frac{\sigma_f^2 d_f v_f}{\tau_m} \qquad (3)$$

where E is the Charpy impact energy in in·lb/in.², τ_m is the matrix shear yield strength, and σ_f, d_f, and v_f are the fiber strength, diameter, and volume fraction respectively. A value of $K_{1c} = 106$ ksi $\sqrt{in}$. is calculated by equating E with G; and this value of K_{1c}, when used in Eq 2, allows calculation of reasonably accurate values of the fracture stress. These results are plotted in Fig. 8 and are seen to form an upper bound to the experimental data obtained in this study. A lower bound of $K_{1c} = 75$ ksi $\sqrt{in}$. is also plotted to indicate the extent of the strength scatter. As the hard- and soft-impact data fall within the theoretical fracture prediction, the applicability of this analysis seems confirmed. Two specimens with machined slots were also tested and their strengths fall in the middle of the scatter band as seen in Fig. 8.

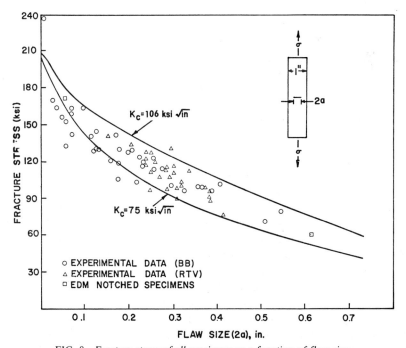

FIG. 8—*Fracture stress of all specimens as a function of flow size.*

To illustrate the applicability of the fracture-mechanics analysis to the FOD problem, the crack length and hole diameters from boron-aluminum specimens impacted with RTV at a prestress of 44-ksi were plotted versus velocity. There was a great deal of scatter in these measurements, particularly in measuring the hole diameters. An average curve was drawn through the data which is shown in Fig. 9. Residual strength calculations utilizing Fig. 9 data and specimen geometry, and assuming a K_{Ic} of 91.6 ksi $\sqrt{in.}$, were made. For cracked specimens, Eq 2 was used. The Bowie solution for a symmetrical crack emanating from a hole was used for specimens with penetration holes. In this analysis, the virgin flaw half-length, c_y, was used in place of an actual crack. The results of this analysis are plotted along with the experimental data in Fig. 10.

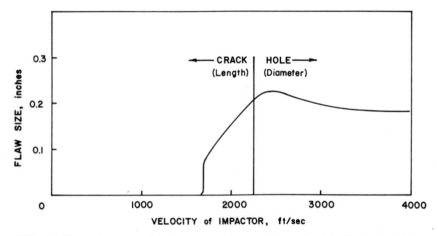

FIG. 9—*Observed average flow size versus impact velocity of a 0.177-in. RTV ball on boron-aluminum at a 44-ksi prestress.*

Conclusions

1. The postimpact strength of Ti-6-4 is reduced to approximately 90 percent of the virgin strength for a wide range of impact conditions (Figs. 1,4).

2. Both soft and hard impacts cause significant static and fatigue strength losses in boron-aluminum. For hard objects, very low impact velocities cause rapid loss of postimpact strength. Soft impacts appear to cause little damage until a critical velocity is reached, at which point complete failure may be expected (Figs. 2,3,5–7).

3. The Griffith-Irwin fracture criterion has been successfully applied to the problem of predicting the effects of FOD on boron-aluminum. This criterion allows for the successful decoupling of the impact problem from the subsequent prediction of post-damage strength (Figs. 8–10).

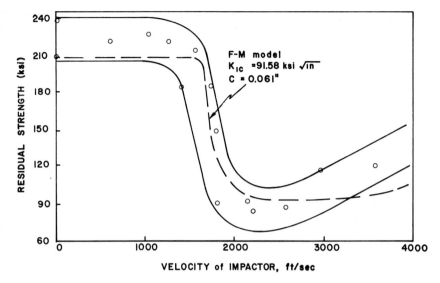

FIG. 10—*Predicted residual strength versus impact velocity of a 0.177-in. RTV ball on boron-aluminum at a 44-ksi prestress.*

References

[1] Steinhagen, C. A. and Stanley, M. W. "Boron/Aluminum Compressor Blades," AFML-TR-73-285, Air Force Materials Laboratory, Dayton, Ohio, Oct. 1973.

[2] Herman, M., Second Air Force Materials Laboratory-Industry Workshop on Foreign-Object Damage, Dayton, Ohio, May 30, 1973.

[3] Husman, G. E., Whitney, J. M., and Halpin, J. C., "Residual Strength Characterization of Laminated Composites Subjected to Impact Loading," to be published as AFML-TR-73-309, Air Force Materials Laboratory, Dayton, Ohio.

[4] Kreider, K. G. and Dardi, L. E., *Failure Modes in Composites,* The Metallurgical Society, New York, 1973, p. 193.

[5] Dardi, L. E. and Kreider, K. G., *Failure Modes in Composites,* The Metallurgical Society, New York, 1973, p. 231.

[6] Stanley, M. W., Second Air Force Materials Laboratory-Industry Workshop on Foreign-Object Damage, Dayton, Ohio, May 30, 1973.

[7] Shimmin, K. D. and Toth, I. J., *Failure Modes in Composites,* The Metallurgical Society, New York, 1973, p. 357.

[8] Prewo, K. M. and Kreider, K. B., *Failure Modes in Composites,* The Metallurgical Society, New York, 1973, p. 395.

[9] Gray, T. L., "Damage Interactions in Composites," M.S. thesis, U. S. Air Force Institute of Technology, Dayton, Ohio, June 1973.

[10] Beaumont, P. W. R. and Tetelman, A. S., *Failure Modes in Composites,* The Metallurgical Society, New York, 1973, p. 49.

[11] Sih, G. C., Paris, P. C., and Irwin, G. R., *International Journal of Fracture Mechanics,* Vol. 1, 1965, pp. 189–203.

[12] Waddoups, M. E., Eisenmann, J. R., and Kaminski, B. E., *Journal of Composite Materials,* Vol. 5, 1971, pp. 446–455.

[13] Halpin, J. C., Jerina, K. L., and Johnson, T. A. in *Analysis of the Test Methods for High Modulus Fibers and Composites, ASTM STP 521,* American Society for Testing and Materials, 1973, pp. 5–64.

[14] Randall, D., Private communication, Pratt & Whitney Aircraft, East Hartford, Conn.
[15] Carlisle, J. G., "Hard-Body Impact Damage Effects on Boron-Aluminum Composites," M.S. Thesis, U. S. Air Force Institute of Technology, Dayton, Ohio, March 1974.
[16] Hopkins, A. K., Second Air Force Materials Laboratory-Industry Workshop on Foreign-Object Damage, Dayton, Ohio, May 30, 1973.

Fracture

K. L. DeVries,[1] B. A. Lloyd,[1] and T. B. Wilde[1]

Molecular Correlations with Fracture in Fibers and Granular-Filled Composites

REFERENCE: DeVries, K. L., Lloyd, B. A., and Wilde, T. B., "**Molecular Correlations with Fracture in Fibers and Granular-Filled Composites,**" *Composite Reliability, ASTM STP 580,* American Society for Testing and Materials, 1975, pp. 473–489.

ABSTRACT: Failure in polymeric materials might be envisioned as occurring by any of several molecular mechanisms. Where homolytic bond rupture occurs, free radicals (unpaired electrons) result. This paper presents results of electron spin resonance studies of chain-scission kinetics in (1) oriented nylon fibers and (2) in granular-filled elastomer composites.

The most extensive work to date has been done on high-strength oriented fibers. It has been concluded that many of the desirable properties of fibers can be attributed to their own microscopic physical composite nature. A reaction-rate molecular model is proposed and is successfully used as a failure criterion to predict failure under various loadings.

The model assumes a statistical distribution in stress on the polymeric chain structure. Failure first occurs in the more highly stressed regions with a subsequent redistribution of the load among the unfractured elements in the fiber. Once the physical parameters are determined for a given material, behavior for other loading is predicted by numerical techniques. Electron spin resonance was used also to investigate interfacial failure in filled composites. Depending on the magnitude of the interactive forces, failure at the interface between the filler and the matrix may be largely adhesive (dewetting) or cohesive in nature. In the former case little or no detectable bond rupture occurs while in the latter case significant free radical concentrations may be produced. Electron spin resonance and scanning electron microscopy are used to systematically investigate the role of the surface interaction, dewetting, etc. on the strength and toughness of composites.

KEY WORDS: composite materials, fibers, elastomers, polymers, failure, nylon fibers, bonding strength, toughness

An important role of materials for the mechanical engineer is the prediction or prevention of fracture. Most engineering design criteria treat structural materials as a continuum. Composites and "single component" systems on a sufficiently small scale are not continua. A thorough understanding of fracture must therefore involve knowledge of what is

[1] Professor of mechanical engineering, post-doctoral fellow, and research assistant, respectively, Mechanical Engineering Department, University of Utah, Salt Lake City, Utah.

happening on macroscopic, microscopic, and molecular (or atomic) scales. Such an understanding would not only be useful for design but also would give insight into means by which the structure of the material might be modified to improve ultimate properties. Newly developed materials are often used in applications where the intended life far exceeds the total experience with the particular material. Certainly in such cases a meaningful extrapolation from test conditions to service conditions (often differing in time scale, environment, etc. from the test conditions) requires an understanding of the fundamental mechanisms involved in failure. Recently, methods such as electron microscopy techniques, electron spin resonance, (ESR), and infrared spectroscopy (IR) [1,2][2] have allowed investigators to observe fracture on ever increasingly small scales. The last two in fact allow the observation of occurrences directly related to atomic phenomena. ESR measurements were the primary tool in the study to be reported here.

Experimental Equipment and Procedures

A thorough development of ESR principles would be rather complex and involve sophisticated quantum mechanics and mathematics. Fortunately, for our purposes here, only a brief, superficial explanation is required. Basically, an ESR spectrometer detects the presence of unpaired electrons. This is accomplished by observation of the resonant absorption of microwaves by the electrons in a carefully controlled magnetic field; hence the name electron spin resonance (ESR), or electron paramagnetic resonance (EPR).

In order to exhibit paramagnetic resonance absorption, a solid must contain electrons that are unpaired, that is, which are not interacting with neighboring electrons to such an extent as to be governed by the Pauli exclusion principle and hence have their spins "paired." When degradation (chain scission) of a polymer takes place, the two electrons making up the unbroken covalent bond are uncoupled, forming two free radicals which can, in principle, be detected and identified by ESR. In practice, ESR detection has two stringent requirements: the free radicals must be produced in sufficient number and be sufficiently stable as to accumulate concentrations of at least 10^{13} in the approximately two cubic centimeters of volume available in the microwave cavity. These requirements are discussed in detail elsewhere [4].

The equipment used in this study consisted of a Varian E-3 Spectrometer equipped with a modified Varian E 4557 temperature accessory (-179 to $+300\,°C$) (-290 to $572\,°F$). A servocontrolled hydraulic loading system was designed and built to be used in conjunction with the spectrometer. Using appropriate command circuitry, load, and displacement, stress or

---

[2] The italic numbers in brackets refer to the list of references appended to this paper.

strain can be controlled according to any desired time-dependent program. The system simultaneously recorded sample load, sample elongation, and free radical (chain scission[3]) concentration.

Materials

Fibers

Highly oriented nylon 6 fibers (tire yarn supplied by Allied Chemical Corporation) were wound in tension specimen bundles containing approximately three thousand 0.001-in.-diameter (0.0025 cm) fibrils and tested using the Varian E-3 spectrometer with modified variable-temperature accessory and specially built servocontrolled hydraulic system.

Filled Rubbers

Five types of filled rubbers were tested: (1) ethylene-propylene terpolymer (EPDM) filled with 29 μm untreated glass beads, (2) HiSil 233 (quartz)-filled polyisoprene, (3) sodium-chloride-filled polyisoprene, (4) glass-bead-filled polyisoprene, and (5) silane-treated glass-bead-filled polyisoprene. The first three provided very weak, intermediate, and strong adhesive interaction between filler and matrix respectively, while the latter two provided a comparison between untreated and coupling agent-treated filling materials. All samples were filled between 50 and 60 percent by weight. The treated beads were prepared by soaking in a 2 percent solution of silane in methanol supplied by Dow Corning and then in a 5 percent solution of Shell Kryton (polyisoprene) dissolved in toluene. The beads were then milled into the polyisoprene material and cured as with other fillers.

Fracture Phenomena

Fracture in polymers is at best a complex phenomenon. Based on current experimental evidence, the semicrystalline-oriented fibers, for example, are commonly "pictured" as being composed of microfibrils which in turn have a sandwich structure of crystalline and amorphous regions [5-7]. These microfibrils are in turn assumed to be approximately axially aligned and rather loosely transversely connected to form the macrofiber. We note, therefore, that these chemically single-component systems are in actuality physical composites. In fact, as we shall discuss later, the ultimate properties of this type of material are closely related to this composite nature. It is little wonder that fracture in polymers is

---

[3] Zhurkov et al [1] reported recently studies of end-group analysis after fracture with IR, suggesting that each free radical detected by ESR may represent a number of ruptured bonds. For our purposes here, it matters little if ESR gives the number of chain scissions or a number proportional to it as suggested by Zhurkov (see Lloyd et al [5]).

difficult to explain since the mechanical disintegration of such a structure might occur through any or a combination of such processes as chain scission, secondary bond rupture, and slip or chain pullout.

In multicomponent systems such as filled composites, fracture behavior may be even more complex. To date, our study has been confined to granular-filled composites. Fillers in polymers are used for various purposes, including modification of mechanical properties, as extenders (that is, to reduce the amount of polymer per unit volume, and hence cost), and to add another chemical agent (for example, an oxidizer in a rubber-based solid rocket propellant). In any case, the presence of such fillers increases the complexity of the micromechanics of deformation and might modify the fracture modes. The presence of the filler results in local strain redistributions, a very nonhomogeneous localized stress field, and introduces the possibility of separation between matrix and filler (that is, dewetting), etc. Filler particles might also act as crack arresters or initiators, or both, and hence modify the energy absorbed in the fracture process.

Model of Fracture in Fibers

Many aspects of fracture in oriented fibers can be explained by the assumed 'sandwich type' structure. In these models the highly ordered and aligned crystalline regions of the polymer are alternately tied together by disordered or amorphous phases of the polymer. This aspect of sections acting like 'crystalline blocks' interspaced with 'amorphous-flaw' regions is in basic agreement with several observations of this laboratory [8].

In essence the oriented fibers *act* under load much like a two-phase material, where the weakest regions, that is, the critical flaw regions, undergo homolytic bond failure and the strong regions, that is, the more closely packed oriented regions, act as crack arresters. This type of structural arrangement contributes to a uniformly distributed failure process occurring throughout the fiber in the flaw regions, with microscopic cracks following a path of "least resistance" around the stronger regions.

The failure characteristics and strength of the oriented nylon 6 fiber materials, here observed from ESR spectra and stress-strain data, indicate a strong dependence on the distribution of stress or load on polymer chains within flaw regions.

The distribution of these critical flaws in the test material can be viewed as originating from at least three possible factors: (1) a macroscopic distribution of flaws in the test material, such as differences in fiber lengths created during manufacturing filament windings or during sample preparation; (2) microscopic structure arrangement of flaw regions of varying strength and number distributed throughout each individual fibril; and (3) a distribution of the number and length of individual polymer chains in the individual critical flaw regions.

The model developed by the authors for oriented fibers, although concentrating on the latter of these three types of distributions, is certainly potentially applicable to the other types of distribution patterns.

Incorporating the foregoing concepts, the mathematical model proposed uses a basic alternating-sandwich structure of highly oriented crystalline block regions interspaced by critical flaw regions. The flaw regions are assumed to comprise polymer tie chains distributed in number and effective length according to experimentally observed EPR data.

The model assumes that failure occurs largely in the amorphous regions and that there is a distribution of stresses on the chains in these regions or between regions. Bond scission is governed by Tobolsky-Eyring [9] kinetic rate process theory, that is

$$\frac{dC_{Bi}}{dt} = C_{ui} w_0 \exp \frac{-(U_o - \gamma\sigma_i)}{kT} \tag{1}$$

where dC_{Bi}/dt is the rate of bond rupture of the ith group of chains (that is, those chains with stress σ_i); C_{ui} is the instantaneous member of unbroken chains of the ith group; w_0, U_o, and γ are kinetic constants commonly called the collision parameter, the activation energy, and activation volume respectively; k is Boltzmann's constant and T is the temperature. Macroscopic failure is assumed to occur as a result of the accumulated failure of the groups of polymer tie chains.

Various aspects of the model and its agreement with experiments are discussed elsewhere [5,7]. In the allocated space, these can only be very briefly discussed. This model differs from most previous reaction-rate models of fracture in the interpretation of Eq 1. Earlier models would have omitted the subscript i. The stress was taken as proportional to macroscopic stress σ. In the current model there is assumed to be a distribution in the σ's. The macroscopic load must, of course, equal the sum of the loads (stresses) on the individual chains, but as the more highly stressed chains rupture the stress is redistributed among the remaining unbroken chains. Making use of observations from ESR and other analytical measurements, a preliminary model was developed. With the aid of a computer to evaluate the model's behavior under various loading conditions, it was possible to compare bond rupture kinetics and mechanical loading behavior with experimental observations.

Results and Discussion

Fibers

Using the ESR spectrometer in conjunction with the specially built servocontrolled hydraulic loading system, experimental stress, strain, and free radical concentration data were obtained for various loadings. These data were then compared with the theoretical predictions for the same applied loadings using the reaction-rate failure model. Many of the experimentally observed properties of these highly oriented fibers seem to be related to a knowledge of the distribution of stresses in the polymer microstructure. Theoretical calculations of the strength of a single polymer chain result in tensile strength values of approximately 70×10^9 N/m^2. Tensile strengths, however, of most of the highly oriented polymer fibers rarely exceed 1×10^9 N/m^2 [1,3]. This large difference has been explained as a consequence of the inhomogeneity of the micromorphology in the fiber structure. Chain ends, dislocations, disorder, disorientation, chain folds, and number and length of tie molecules have all been suggested as elements that prevent a uniform stress distribution in the fiber and result in regions of high stress concentration which in turn lowers the maximum attainable tensile strength. Characterizing this distribution from ESR step strain tests and relating it to the tie chains in the critical flaw regions turned out to be the key result in the success of this study [5,7]. In these tests by the authors, the specimen was loaded to the point just before bond breakage was detected. The strain was then stepped in equal increments and the number of bonds broken during each increment of extension recorded (see Fig. 1a). The apparent or effective distribution evident from such experimental data was found to be a function of the polymer fiber material and the test temperature. The effect of the width of the distribution on the ultimate stress obtained from constant strain rate tests for various nylon fibers and temperatures is shown in Fig. 1b. The interesting result from this plot is that a direct correlation appears to exist between the width of the distribution and the ultimate strength independent of the type of nylon fiber; that is, as the width of the distribution increases, the maximum strength of the fiber decreases.

One can gain some insight into this effect by considering the extremes. If the chains were all equally stressed, corresponding to a standard deviation of zero, the strength of the fiber would be the 'strength' of each chain multiplied by the number of chains across the critical cross section of the sample. Alternately, one might envision such a wide distribution in chains that one chain is stressed and ruptured at a time. In this case the strength of the fiber reduces to the 'strength' of the individual chains although the energy dissipated during fracture and the strain at fracture are both greatly increased. Real fibers behave more nearly like the former than the latter of these extremes, but it is rather amazing the very large differences that small changes in the standard deviation of chain length can have on fiber strength.

The distribution values obtained experimentally from ESR data were characterized in terms of their standard deviation value and used as a

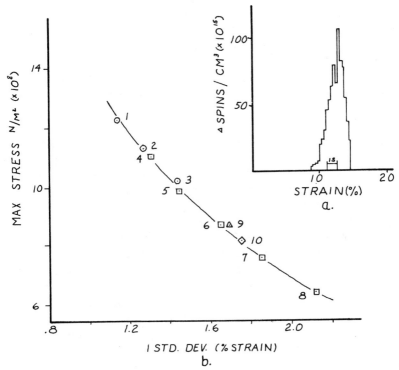

FIG. 1—(a) *Histogram from step strain-ESR data for nylon 6 No. 2 at room temperature.*
(b) *Effect of "apparent or effective" distribution on ultimate strength of nylon fibers:
Points 1, 2, 3—nylon 6 No. 1 at −25°C (−13°F), room temperature, and 50°C (122°F)
respectively; Points 4, 5, 6, 7, 8—nylon 6 No. 2 at −25°C (−13°F), room temperature,
50, 75, and 100°C (122, 167, and 212°F) respectively; Point 9—nylon 6 No. 2 annealed
at 200°C (392°F) and tested at room temperature; Point 10—nylon 66 at room temperature.*

parameter in the theoretical model solution. Several other parameters,
however, were also necessary to obtain a theoretical solution. It was
decided that those parameters that were best known, either from experiment or theory, would be selected as base values. This included the distribution standard deviation value (S) obtained from ESR data, the modulus
of elasticity (E_b) for a single nylon 6 chain from Treloar [10], and the
rate-theory collision parameter (w_0) from Zhurkov and Tomashevskii
[2]. The remaining four parameters—R_c, the ratio of the number of polymer chains in the crystalline block region to the number of the chains in
the flaw region; R_L, the ratio of the original length of the crystalline block
region to the original length of the flaw region; U_o, the activation energy
and γ, the activation volume—were selected by comparison of the
theoretical solution (by using various combinations of the parameters)
with the experimentally observed data from constant strain rate and
constant stress (creep) tests of nylon 6 at room temperature. Four average

experimental curves (two strain rate and two creep) were selected as the comparison standards. With these guidelines, parameter values at room temperatures were then obtained and the theoretical results plotted and compared with the experimental standards. After considerable analysis, a group of parameters was selected as the 'best fit' with the knowledge that moderate variations would not substantially degrade and possibly would improve the comparison with the experimental standards of nylon 6 at room temperature. Once these room temperature parameters were determined for nylon 6, they were used to predict behavior at other strain rates, creep, constant stress rate, stress relaxation, several frequencies of cyclic stress fatigue, and various temperatures. A very satisfactory correlation between experimental results and theoretical predictions from the model was found. Examples of the excellent agreement between experimental observations and theory are shown in Figs. 2 and 3 for creep and fatigue loadings. Similar comparable correlations for constant stress rate, constant strain rate, stress relaxation, other temperatures, and a discussion of the parameters used in the model to obtain these correlations are detailed elsewhere [5,7]. One of the most pleasing aspects of the model was how nearly the best-fit parameters used to predict behavior compared with accepted or theoretical values from other related studies.

Extension of the basic concepts presented herein to copolymer or other two-phase polymeric systems is suggested. The theoretical approach is certainly feasible although the experimental use of ESR techniques to verify such an approach is limited to selective polymeric systems. For the nylon 6 and 66 fibers studied, these methods not only provide a reliable technique for predicting macroscopic behavior, but perhaps more importantly they provide insight into methods that may enhance the behavior of alternation of the basic chemical properties or microscopic structural arrangement of the two-phase structure. Such insight would be extremely valuable in other composite systems if these techniques proved successful in their extension.

Filled Rubbers

Specific details of the ESR study in filled rubbers are presented in a more complete paper [11]. In short, it was found that the glass-filled EPDM fractured with no detectable production of free radicals; the sodium-chloride-filled rubber produced easily detectable concentrations of radicals during fracture; and the HiSil-filled rubber produced an order of magnitude more radicals than in the sodium-chloride system. Quantitatively these can be expressed as: (i) undetectable amounts for the glass beads; (ii) $+3 \times 10^{14}$ to 3×10^{15} free radicals/cm^3, corresponding to 10^4 to 10^5 free radicals per particle or $+6 \times 10^{10}$ to 4×10^{11} free radicals per cm^2 of filler surface for sodium-chloride; and (iii) 8×10^{14} to 10^{16}

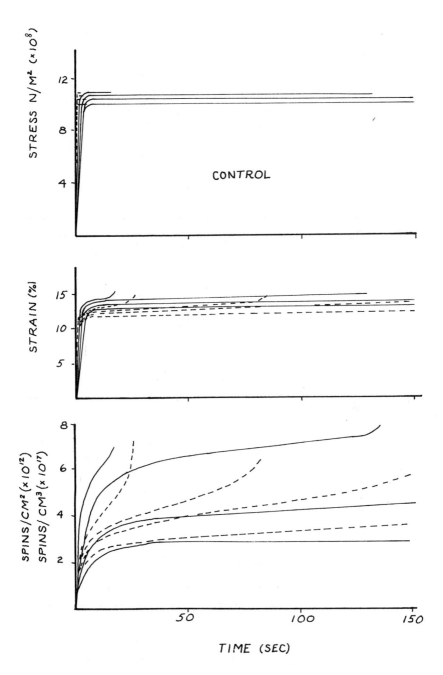

FIG. 2—*Constant-stress (creep) test. Solid line: experimental (spin/cm³); dashed line: theory (spin/cm²).*

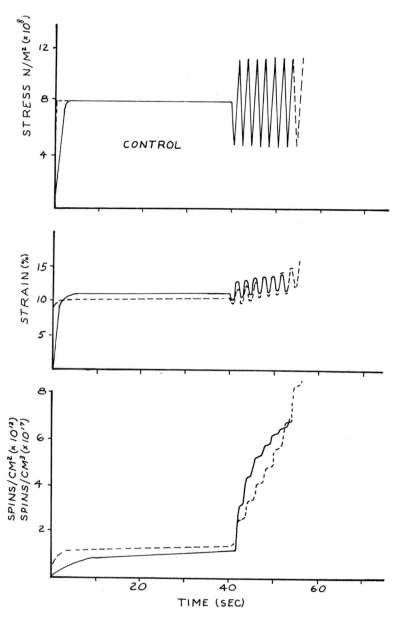

FIG. 3—*Cyclic-stress fatigue test. Solid line: experimental (spin/cm³); dashed line: theory (spin/cm²).*

free radicals/cm^3, corresponding to $+10^5$ to 10^6 free radicals per particle or 3×10^{11} to 3×10^{12} free radicals per cm^2 of filler surface for HiSil at $-102\,°C$ ($-152\,°F$). Here the filler surface area is estimated from the number, size, and shape of the filler particle.

Scanning electron micrographs (SEM) also clearly indicate different fracture mechanisms in the three cases. These are shown in Fig. 4. The glass-filled system begins to dewet at low strain (five to ten percent at room temperature). After this initial dewetting is complete, the vacuoles enlarge as the material is elongated and the filler no longer has a significant strengthening effect. As the loading is continued, a point is reached where the stress between voids is greater than the load failure stress, and the remaining material fails. At this time, insufficient chain scission has occurred for detection by ESR. In the sodium-chloride-filled system, dewetting is also present but occurs at much larger strains. Closer examination of fracture micrographs indicates much rougher voids left by the filler particles. Finally, in the HiSil system there is a much less disruptive nature to the fracture surface with no evidence of dewetting, and SEM micrographs indicate an almost completely cohesive failure. In this case, the filler has its largest strengthening effect. This is better shown by the toughness of the materials as determined from Instron tests at $-86\,°C$ ($-123\,°F$). For sodium-chloride and HiSil the toughness is 1.2×10^6 joules/m^3 and 17×10^6 joules/m^3 respectively.

Free radicals are inherently unstable and, with time, decay by annihiliation reactions with each other or impurities. Our studies indicate that they are much more short lived in rubbers than in other polymers which we have investigated. As expected, the rate of decay is very sensitive to temperature. The radicals were sufficiently stable in this study for our purposes only at temperatures below $-60\,°C$ ($-76\,°F$). As a consequence, ESR studies were conducted at temperatures lower than this. It is realized that most elastomer usage is at higher temperatures, where the material is more rubberlike. It is, therefore, unfortunate that the experimental difficulties related to free radical decay preclude ESR studies except at low temperatures. To help resolve the question of how much of the low-temperature ESR results might be applicable at higher temperatures, micrographs of samples fractured were made at seven intervals between room temperature and $-102\,°C$ ($-152\,°F$). Figures 5 and 6 show these for room temperatures and $-102\,°C$ ($-152\,°F$). For a given material, some slight difference in fracture characteristics can be seen with temperature; however, the basic nature of the fracture surface does not seem to be modified over this temperature range. Certainly there is a much greater difference in the nature of the fracture surface in comparing the two materials than there is in comparing the fracture surfaces at different temperatures for one of the materials.

Testing has just begun in our laboratory on the effects of coupling

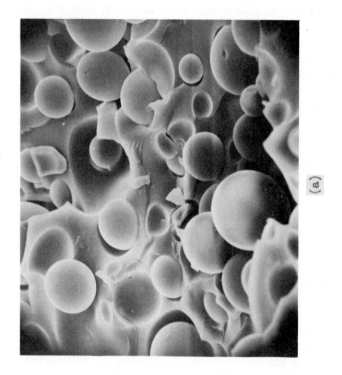

(a)

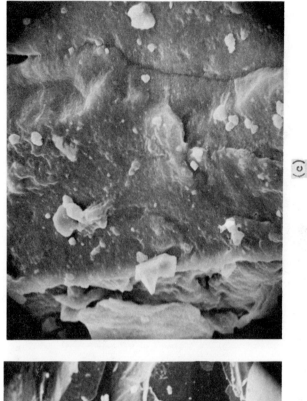

FIG. 4—*Fracture surfaces of filled rubbers at* − 102°C (− 152°F): (a) *glass-filled EPDM, X490 field of view, 0.079 in.;* (b) *sodium-chloride-filled polyisoprene, X102 field of view, 0.038 in.;* (c) *HiSil-filled polyisoprene, X935 field of view, 0.004 in.*

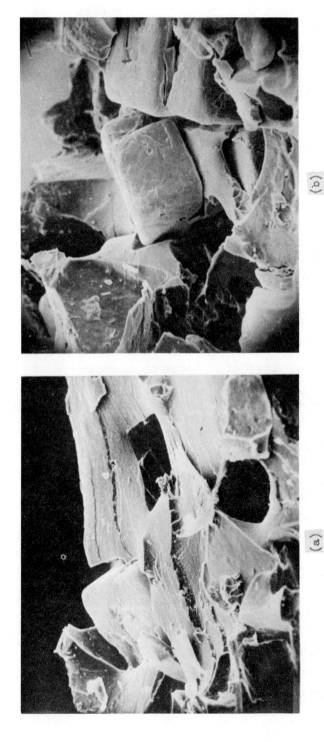

FIG. 5.—Fracture surfaces of sodium-chloride-filled polyisoprene: (a) at room temperature, X128 field of view, 0.03 in.; and (b) at −102°C (−152°F) X102 field of view, 0.038 in.

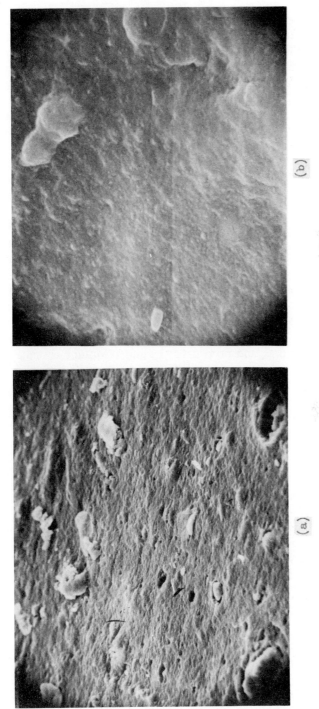

FIG. 6—Fracture surfaces of HiSil-filled polyisoprene: (a) at room temperature, X451 field of view, 0.0085 in.; and (b) at −102°C (−152°F) X468 field of view, 0.0082 in.

agents in enhancing the interaction between filler and matrix. Preliminary results indicate that the treating of glass beads with the silane does indeed increase the ability of the filler to strengthen and reinforce the material. Quantatively this is shown by the fact that the plain glass-filled material yields no EPR signal at failure at $-102\,°C$ ($-152\,°F$) while the treated glass beads show a free radical concentration of 10^{14} to 10^{15} spins/cm^3 at failure. The toughness for the plain glass beads is 9×10^6 joules/m^3 at $-86\,°C$ ($-123\,°F$) while for the treated glass beads it is 14×10^6 joules/m^3.

Filler matrix interaction is an important property of filled materials. The breakdown of the adhesive bonding between filler and matrix which results in the formation of vacuoles or voids in the material is commonly known as "dewetting." Dewetting is reported to occur when the adhesive strength between filler and matrix is less than the cohesive strength of either material [12,13]. On the other hand, when the adhesive strength is large, failure can involve little or no dewetting. One might expect fracture in the former case to occur with comparatively little primary bond rupture in comparison with the latter case. The fillers exhibiting little or no dewetting do exhibit the larger number of free radicals at failure and the larger values of toughness. This is further shown by the increase in number of spins and toughness when a coupling agent is introduced to a poorly interacting filler such as glass. Also, it is worth noting that should a single crack initiate and propagate to failure, forming a single fracture plane, the number of chains ruptured would be insufficient for detection by ESR. Normally gum rubbers fail in this manner. The large number of free radicals present at fracture in the strongly interacting filler systems can be interpreted as evidence for the effectiveness of the filler particles as crack arresters.

It appears that ESR can be used to investigate mechanical breakdown in filled polymer systems at least at low temperatures. The technique should be useful in investigating the effectiveness of fillers and the effect of surface treatment such as coupling agents in enhancing the reinforcing properties of fillers. While the ESR investigation was at low temperatures, micrographs indicate that there is a strong correspondence between fracture behavior at these and higher (rubbery) temperatures. The authors feel some extrapolation of other results can easily be made from the low temperatures to those in the rubbery region.

Conclusions

In conclusion, it appears that the mechanical behavior of both single-component and filled composites depends on the "composite" nature of the structure. An understanding of the interaction of the various components in the structure is useful in predicting behavior as well as giving insight into mechanisms by which the structure might be altered or modified to improve properties. Modern analytical methods such as ESR can be used to experimentally observe phenomena that can be directly related to atomic occurrences. The use of these methods has led to an improved reaction-rate model for failure in fibers and a better insight into matrix-filler interaction in filled rubbers.

Acknowledgments

Portions of this research have been supported by the National Science Foundation and the National Aeronautics and Space Administration. The assistance of M. L. Williams is also appreciated.

References

[1] Zhurkov, S. N., Zakrevskii, V. A., Korsukov, V. E., and Kuksenka, V. S., *Soviet Physics—Solid State,* Vol. 13, No. 7, 1972, p. 1680.

[2] Zhurkov, S. N. and Tomashevskii, E. E., *Proceedings of the Conference on the Physical Basis of Yield and Fracture,* Oxford University Press, Oxford, 1966.

[3] Roylance, D. K., DeVries, K. L., and Williams, M. L., *Fracture,* P. Pratt, Ed., Chapman and Hall, London, 1969, p. 551.

[4] DeVries, K. L., Roylance, D. K., and Williams, M. L., *Journal of Polymer Science,* Part A-1, Vol. 8, 1970, p. 237.

[5] Lloyd, B. A., DeVries, K. L., and Williams, M. L., *Journal of Polymer Science,* Part A-2, Vol. 10, 1972, p. 1415.

[6] Peterlin, A., *Journal of Polymer Science,* Part A-2, Vol. 7, 1969, p. 1151.

[7] DeVries, K. L., Lloyd, B. A., and Williams, M. L., *Journal of Applied Physics,* Vol. 42, 1971, p. 4644.

[8] DeVries, K. L., Roylance, D. K., and Williams, M. L., *International Journal of Fracture Mechanics,* Vol. 7, 1971, p. 1.

[9] Tobolsky, A. and Eyring, H., *Journal of Chemical Physics,* Vol. 11, 1943, p. 125.

[10] Treloar, L. R. G., *Polymer,* Vol. 1, 1960, p. 95.

[11] DeVries, K. L., Wilde, T. B., and Williams, M. L., *Journal of Macromolecular Science, Physics,* Vol. B7, No. 4, 1973, p. 633.

[12] Obert, A. E., *Rubber Chemistry and Technology,* Vol. 40, 1969.

[13] Struik, L. C. E., Bree, H. W., and Schwarzl, F. R., *Proceedings of the International Rubber Conference,* Brighton, England, 1967, MacLaren and Sons, London.

H. J. Konish, Jr.,[1] *and T. A. Cruse*[2]

Determination of Fracture Strength in Orthotropic Graphite-Epoxy Laminates*

REFERENCE: Konish, H. J., Jr., and Cruse, T. A., "**Determination of Fracture Strength in Orthotropic Graphite-Epoxy Laminates,**" *Composite Reliability, ASTM STP 580,* American Society for Testing and Materials, 1975, pp. 490–503.

ABSTRACT: A fracture test program performed on orthotropic graphite-epoxy laminates is reported. The test data are used to evaluate the effects of specimen size and specimen configuration on the measured value of laminate fracture strength. It is shown that apparent fracture strength is independent of specimen configuration and specimen thickness, but varies significantly with respect to crack length. As crack length increases, however, the apparent fracture strength is found to asymptotically approach a limiting value, taken to be the valid laminate fracture toughness.

The test data are also used to evaluate two analytical models for predicting laminate fracture toughness. The first model links basic ply properties and the fracture toughness of angle-ply laminates, while the second model relates the fracture toughness of an arbitrary orthotropic laminate to the fracture properties of its angle-ply components. Both models show good agreement with the test data.

It is concluded that linear elastic fracture mechanics does provide a meaningful characterization of crack growth in orthotropic composite laminates, if some specified conditions are met. Study of cases which do not meet these conditions is recommended for future work.

KEY WORDS: composite materials, fracture properties, crack propagation, laminates, epoxy resins, deformation, models, graphite

The experimental program reported herein is largely a continuation of an earlier test program *[1].*[3] The results of this earlier test series indicate that metals-based linear elastic fracture mechanics (LEFM), when suitably modified for material anisotropy, can be usefully applied to laminated

*This work sponsored by Air Force Contract F33615-73-C-5505, Air Force Materials Laboratory.

[1] National Research Council research associate, Air Force Materials Laboratory, Wright-Patterson Air Force Base, Ohio 45433. Presently Advanced Reactor Division, Westinghouse Electric Corp., Madison, Pa. 15663.

[2] Senior assistant project engineer, Pratt and Whitney Aircraft Division, United Aircraft Corp., East Hartford, Conn. 06108.

[3] The italic numbers in brackets refer to the list of references appended to this paper.

fiber composites. Because of the limited scope of the first test program, however, several critical questions have remained unanswered. Two of these questions are especially significant:

1. Is composite fracture strength independent of specimen size, including laminate thickness?
2. Is composite fracture strength independent of specimen configuration?

Answers to these questions are of fundamental importance to the application of LEFM to fiber composite laminates.

Also of interest is the need to systematically account for the effects of laminate construction parameters, such as ply thickness, ply orientation, and stacking sequence, on laminate fracture strength. Two models for relating fracture strength to certain laminate parameters have been developed, based on the data [1]. The first of these models [2] predicts the fracture strengths of symmetrically loaded angle-ply laminates; the second model [3] predicts the fracture strengths of symmetrically loaded orthotropic laminates having several distinct angle-ply components. Both of these models must be regarded as somewhat tentative, in view of the limited data from which they were developed. Further investigation of these models is thus necessary.

Answers to the foregoing questions regarding the measurement of composite fracture strength must be based on test data. Test data are also required to verify the fracture strength models reported in Refs 2 and 3. Such data have been obtained from the experimental program described herein.

Experimental Program

Test Specimens

The selection of test specimens[4] was dictated by the program objectives noted previously. The effects of specimen configuration were evaluated by comparing the fracture strengths obtained from edge-notched bend specimens (Fig. 1a) and center-notched tension specimens (Fig. 1b) of the same laminate. This comparison also provided some information on the effects of laminate thickness, which differed significantly between the two specimen geometries (0.35 to 0.07 in.). The effects of specimen size were further assessed by comparing the fracture strengths obtained from three geometrically similar center-notched tension specimens of the same laminate. All dimensions of these three specimens, except the laminate thickness, were scaled by factors of one, two, and five, respectively. The

---

[4] The test specimens were furnished under contract by the Convair Aerospace Division of General Dynamics Corp., Fort Worth, Tex.

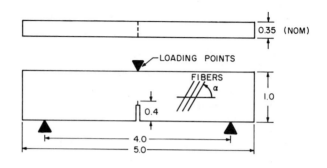

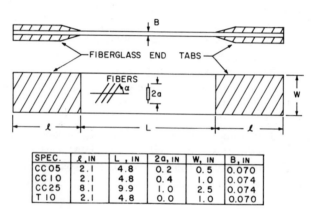

SPEC.	ℓ, IN	L , IN	2a, IN	W, IN	B, IN
CC 05	2.1	4.8	0.2	0.5	0.070
CC 10	2.1	4.8	0.4	1.0	0.074
CC 25	8.1	9.9	1.0	2.5	0.074
T 10	2.1	4.8	0.0	1.0	0.070

FIG. 1—*Test specimen geometry; edge-notched bend specimens* (a) *and tensile specimens* (b), *both unnotched and center-notched, were used. Laminate orientation given by* α. *Specimens were notched by ultrasonically sharpening a machined slot to a width of approximately 0.01 in. at the notch tip.*

fracture strength models were evaluated with data obtained from the bend specimens, which were fabricated from both simple angle-ply laminates and more complex orthotropic laminates having several angle-ply components.

A total of 54 specimens—42 edge-notched bend specimens, 9 center-notched tension specimens, and 3 unnotched tension specimens—was tested. The specimen type, specimen dimensions, and laminate of each test configuration are listed in Table 1. The specimens were notched by ultrasonically sharpening a machined slot to a width of approximately 0.01 in. at the crack tip.

All specimens were fabricated from untwisted tows of Thornel 300 graphite fibers in a Narmco 5208 epoxy resin matrix; the ply properties for this material system are listed in Table 2. All specimen laminates were

TABLE 1—*Specimen descriptions.*

Edge-Notched Bend Specimens

Specimen No.	L^a	S	W	a	B^b	Laminate^c	Number of Specimens
B49	5.0	4.0	1.0	0.4	0.352	(0)	3
B51	5.0	4.0	1.0	0.4	0.352	$(\pm 15)_s$	3
B53	5.0	4.0	1.0	0.4	0.352	$(\pm 30)_s$	3
B55	5.0	4.0	1.0	0.4	0.352	$(\pm 45)_s$	3
B57	5.0	4.0	1.0	0.4	0.352	$(\pm 60)_s$	3
B59	5.0	4.0	1.0	0.4	0.352	$(\pm 75)_s$	3
B61^d	5.0	4.0	1.0	0.4	0.363	$(90/\pm 45)_s$	5
B63	5.0	4.0	1.0	0.4	0.363	$(90/\pm 45)_s$	5
B65	5.0	4.0	1.0	0.4	0.352	$(0_2/\pm 45)_s$	4
B67^e	5.0	4.0	1.0	0.4	0.352	$(90_3/\pm 45)_s$	5
B69	5.0	4.0	1.0	0.4	0.363	$(0/\pm 45)_s$	5

Tension Specimens

Specimen No.	L^a	l	W	a	B^f	Laminate	Number of Specimens
CC05	4.8	2.1	0.5	0.1	0.070	$(0/\pm 45)_s$	3
CC10	4.8	2.1	1.0	0.2	0.074	$(0/\pm 45)_s$	3
CC25	10.0	8.0	2.5	0.5	0.074	$(0/\pm 45)_s$	3
T10	4.8	2.1	1.0	...	0.076	$(0/\pm 45)_s$	3

^{a}All dimensions in inches.
^{b}Nominal ply thickness is 0.0055 in.
^{c}Laminate described by ply orientation angle α (see Fig. 1).
^{d}Manufacturing error; intended to be $(0/\pm 45)_s$.
^{e}Manufacturing error; intended to be $(90_2/\pm 45)_s$.
^{f}Nominal ply thickness is 0.0064 in.

TABLE 2—*Material properties*^{a,b} *Thornel 300^c/Narmco 5208.*

Elastic Constants	Orthotropic Allowables
$E_{11} = 20.5 \times 10^6$ psi	$\sigma_{1u} = 213 \times 10^3$ psi
$E_{22} = 1.37 \times 10^6$ psi	$\sigma_{2u} = 6.1 \times 10^3$ psi
$G_{12} = 0.752 \times 10^6$ psi	$\varepsilon_{1u} = 9.672 \times 10^{-3}$ in./in.
$\nu_{12} = 0.31$	$\varepsilon_{2u} = 4.532 \times 10^{-3}$ in./in.

^{a}Obtained from Convair Aerospace Division, General Dynamics Corporation, Fort Worth, Tex.
^{b}All properties are average values over five tests; specimens made of 0.0061-in.-thick plies.
^{c}Untwisted tows.

midplane symmetric and orthotropic with respect to the loading direction. Each test configuration, that is, a unique combination of specimen type, specimen dimensions, and laminate, was represented by at least three specimens.

Test Procedures

The differences among the test configurations utilized in this program necessitated some variation in test procedures. The edge-notched specimens were placed in the three-point bend test fixture described in Ref *1*, and monotonically loaded to failure in a dispacement-controlled Instron test machine of 10 000-lb capacity. The loading rate was controlled by the fixed rate of motion of the test machine crosshead; a crosshead speed of 0.02 in./min was used throughout the test program to minimize any possible dynamic loading effects.

During each bend test, the applied load and specimen deformation were monitored and recorded continuously. The load was measured directly, using the test machine load cell, and plotted as a function of specimen deformation. The deformation parameter used was the relative displacement of the two notch faces, measured by a double cantilever clip gage of the type prescribed for fracture testing of metals *[4]*. The clip gage was attached to the specimen with knife-edge metal tabs, which were bonded to the specimen using common strain-gage cement.

The tension specimens, both notched and unnotched, were loaded by friction grips or, in the case of the largest center-notched specimens, by pin-and-clevis grips in the bonded fiberglass end tabs. As in the case of bend specimens, the tension specimens were loaded to failure in the Instron test machine at a crosshead speed of 0.02 in./min. The behavior of each specimen was recorded by a plot of applied load as a function of specimen deformation. Except for the largest center-notched configuration, however, the deformation of the tension specimens was characterized by specimen elongation, rather than the notch-face separation used for the bend specimens. This change in the test procedure was clearly justified in the case of the unnotched tension specimens, since the failure site could not be determined *a priori*, and location of the clip gage was, therefore, impossible. In the case of the smaller center-notched specimens, specimen elongation was chosen as the measure of specimen deformation to eliminate any possible constraint of the notch faces by the clip gage tabs. The suitability of specimen elongation as a test parameter was verified by computing fracture strengths for the large center-notched specimens using both of the deformation parameters noted previously. The results of this comparison indicated that notch separation and specimen elongation are reasonably comparable characterizations of deformation for center-notched tension specimens. Gross specimen deformation is not, however, a suitable parameter for bend specimens.

Data Reduction

Despite some variation in the test procedures, the test record obtained for each specimen consists of a plot of applied load as a function of specimen deformation. From these data, it is necessary to extract that value of the load corresponding to the initiation of unstable crack growth. The procedure for obtaining these critical loads is based on the form of the test records.

The idealized curves shown in Fig. 2 represent the three types of test record forms encountered in this program. In all three cases, the initial portion of the test record is nonlinear, with increasing positive slope; this region reflects both specimen behavior and tightening of the load train. The next portion of the test records is linear, corresponding to linear elastic specimen behavior. In some instances, as illustrated in Fig. 2a, this linear behavior was maintained to failure, which coincided with the maximum value of applied load. The initiation of unstable crack growth occurred at peak load in these cases, since any significant crack growth prior to specimen failure would have altered the slope of the test record.

Test records of the type represented by Fig. 2b exhibit a marked discontinuity in slope, which indicates an abrupt change in specimen compliance. In metals, such behavior corresponds to an increment of rapid crack growth; in composites, the slope discontinuity may also result from the failure of fibers aligned with the loading direction or specimen delamination near the crack tip. Although these latter possibilities do not represent classical crack growth, they are abrupt and significant degradations of the material, caused by the existing crack. Thus, in these cases, the load corresponding to the initiation of fracture is defined by the break in the test record.

The initiation of fracture is not well defined by test records of the type shown in Fig. 2c, where the linear portion of the data curve is followed by a nonlinear region of decreasing slope. This last region of the data record corresponds to the accumulation of damage in the region near the crack tip. A significant amount of such damage, in a manner analogous to

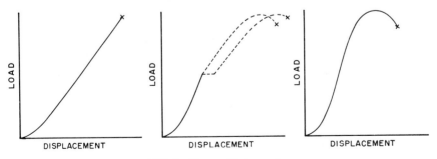

FIG. 2—*Types of test records.*

plasticity in fracture testing of metals, will alter both the geometry of the crack tip and the material properties of the region surrounding it. Thus, only a limited amount of damage can be incurred without invalidating the LEFM characterization of crack growth. In order to maintain the validity of the LEFM model, the data reduction procedure prescribed for fracture testing of metals [4] was employed. From this procedure, a fracture load is obtained corresponding to either a limited amount of damage in the crack-tip region or actual crack growth.

The data reduction methods just described were used, as appropriate, to obtain the fracture load P_Q. The laminate fracture strength was then calculated from the relations [4]

$$K_Q = P_Q S \sqrt{a} f_b(a/W)/BW^2 \tag{1}$$

for the edge-notched bend specimens and, for the center-notched tension specimens

$$K_Q = P_Q \sqrt{a} f_t(a/W)/BW \tag{2}$$

where

S = span of the bend specimen,
a = crack half-length,
B = specimen (laminate) thickness, and
W = specimen width.

The terms $f_b(a/W)$ and $f_t(a/W)$ represent known functions of specimen geometry [5], which describe the interaction between the specimen boundaries and the stresses near the crack tip. The applicability of these isotropic correction factors to composite fracture specimens is discussed in Ref 6. Average values of fracture strength K_Q for each test configuration are listed in Table 3.

Critical strain energy release rates, denoted by G_Q, were also calculated for each of the test specimens, using the expression [7]

$$G_Q = -K_Q^2 \beta_{yy} \text{Im} \{(\mu_1 + \mu_2)/2\mu_1\mu_2\} \tag{3}$$

where β_{yy} is the laminate compliance *transverse to the crack*, and the μ_1 are the roots of the characteristic equation for the laminate. Average values of the critical strain energy release rate G_Q for each test configuration are shown in Table 3.

Results and Discussion

Measurement of Fracture Strength

Fracture testing experience in metals indicates that apparent fracture

TABLE 3—*Average fracture strength and critical strain energy release rate.*

Specimen No.	K_Q (psi$\sqrt{\text{in.}}$)	Variation, %	G_Q (in $\cdot$ lb/^{2})	Variation, %
B49	44 371	+ 1.5/ − 1.7	281.59	+ 2.5/ − 3.3
B51	41 422	+ 3.3/ − 2.2	187.37	+ 6.6/ − 4.4
B53	34 668	+ 5.2/ − 2.6	150.32	+ 10.5/ − 5.3
B55	24 073	+ 3.3/ − 2.9	107.29	+ 6.7/ − 5.8
B57	16 171	+ 3.7/ − 3.9	68.97	+ 7.4/ − 7.8
B59	9 267	+ 2.0/ − 2.8	32.92	+ 4.0/ − 5.6
B61	19 931	+ 1.9/ − 2.0	69.27	+ 3.7/ − 3.9
B63	20 280	+ 2.8/ − 3.1	71.73	+ 5.6/ − 6.2
B65	42 041	+ 1.7/ − 2.0	188.40	+ 3.5/ − 4.0
B67	14 205	+ 2.2/ − 4.9	44.66	+ 4.4/ − 9.6
B69	36 019	+ 6.1/ − 5.5	148.09	+ 12.8/ − 10.9
CC05	24 574	+ 1.9/ − 1.7	68.76	+ 3.8/ − 3.3
CC10	32 999	+ 4.4/ − 3.5	124.10	+ 8.9/ − 6.9
CC25	36 202	+ 2.0/ − 2.1	149.11	+ 4.1/ − 4.1

strength varies significantly with crack length and specimen thickness, unless both dimensions are large compared with the size of the plastic zone around the crack tip [5]. A similar variation of composite fracture strength with crack length is shown by the results obtained from the three center-notched test configurations. The metals methodology, of course, does not apply directly to composite laminates, since they exhibit little plastic behavior; however, the damage zone caused by overloading fibers and matrix near the crack tip in a composite fracture specimen is analogous to the plastic zone in metals. Thus, in composites as in metals, the apparent fracture strength is expected to approach some limiting value with increasing crack length. This expectation is confirmed by the test results for the (0/ ± 45)$_s$ laminate, as shown in Fig. 3. The asymptotic limit of the test results shown in Fig. 4 may be considered the valid fracture toughness K_{IC} of the (0/ ± 45)$_s$ laminate.

A second dimension of interest is specimen thickness; this dimension is quite important in fracture testing of metals, where plane strain conditions are required to limit the size of the plastic zone. However, the excellent agreement among the results obtained from the thick B69 test specimens, the largest (CC25) center-cracked specimens, and some thin-bend test specimens [8], encompassing a thickness range from 0.07 to 0.35 in., indicates that specimen thickness is of minor importance in fracture testing of composites. This conclusion will remain valid as long as the amount of delamination in the crack-tip region is small and unaffected by laminate thickness.

The agreement between the bend specimen data and the center-cracked specimen data also suggests that a unique fracture toughness parameter may be obtained from different test specimen geometries; however, each specimen type must satisfy appropriate dimensional criteria for a valid

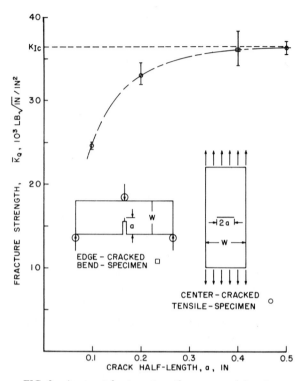

FIG. 3—*Apparent fracture strength versus crack length.*

fracture test. The principal validity criterion appears to be that of sufficient crack length. This criterion cannot be applied, however, without some quantitative measure of sufficiency for crack length. While such a measure cannot be conclusively developed from the data reported here, several possibilities may be considered.

One possible measure of sufficient crack length is the size of the crack relative to the size of the damage zone, which may be estimated [2] from the tensile strength of a laminate and its apparent fracture strength. For the $(0/ \pm 45)_s$ the laminate considered in this program, the damage zone size is approximately 0.035 in. in the B69 edge-notched bend specimens and the largest center-cracked tension specimens. In these cases, the half length of the crack is more than an order of magnitude larger than the damage zone size. In the smallest center-cracked tension specimens, however, the half length of the crack is only about six times the estimated damage zone size of 0.016 in. Thus, a sufficiently large crack might be defined as one at least ten times larger than its corresponding damage zone.

The size of the damage zone might also be compared to the size of the

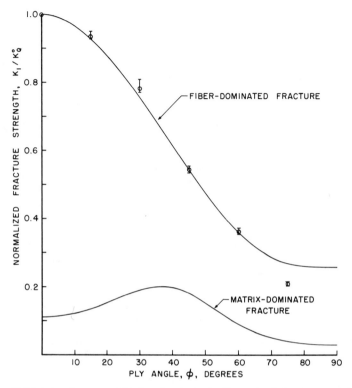

FIG. 4—*Predicted and measured fracture toughness for the angle-ply laminate* $\alpha = (\pm\phi)_s$.

elastic singularity around the crack tip, since it is this latter region which is characterized by LEFM. For the three center-cracked test configurations, in ascending order of size, the respective sizes of the elastic singularity are approximately 0.02, 0.04, and 0.10 in. [2]. Only in the case of the largest center-cracked tension specimens is the elastic singularity significantly larger than the damage zone. It follows that, for the smaller center-cracked test configurations, LEFM does not adequately describe the behavior of the crack-tip region, and thus cannot provide a meaningful characterization of crack growth.

The size of the elastic singularity may also be considered in relation to the width of the notch tip. As just noted, the width was maintained at a fixed value of approximately 0.010 in. in all specimens, because fatigue sharpening of the notch was not possible. In the smaller center-cracked test configurations, the elastic singularity is not much larger than the notch width; the notches in these specimens were thus relatively blunt, compared with the notches in the CC25 test configuration. This bluntness may partially explain the low apparent fracture strengths measured for the CC05 and CC10 test specimens. In any event, whatever size criteria do actually govern the validity of composite fracture tests, it seems clear that those criteria are satisfied by the CC25 and B69 specimen geometries, but not by the CC05 and CC10 configurations.

The various crack length criteria just considered are similar in that they are applicable only to test results, which poses significant problems in designing valid composite fracture test specimens. These problems may be circumvented by stating a sufficiency condition for crack length in terms of some known specimen size parameter. Several size parameters, both microstructural (ply thickness, fiber diameter) and macrostructural (width of the tip of the implanted flaw), have been suggested. However, additional investigations into the effects of these parameters is required before any crack length criterion may be based upon them.

Prediction of Fracture Strength

Two models have been developed [2,3] which can be combined to predict the fracture strength of any midplane symmetric orthotropic laminate having a crack parallel to one principal direction and loaded parallel to the other principal direction. Both models require that the uniform through-thickness strain assumption of lamination theory [9] be satisfied near the crack tip, and thus are restricted to cases in which extensive delamination is not a part of the failure mechanism.

Angle-ply Laminates

The first of these models [2] is applicable only to angle-ply laminates, that is, those described by $\alpha = (\pm\phi)_s$, where α is the angle between the fibers and the applied load (Fig. 1). This model is based on the assumption that crack growth occurs when either σ_1, the ply stress parallel to the fibers, or σ_2, the ply stress transverse to the fibers, reaches its ultimate tensile value, σ_{1u} or σ_{2u}, at some specified distance ahead of the crack. Thus, for each value of ϕ, two predictions of fracture strength, corresponding to fiber-dominated fracture ($\sigma_1 = \sigma_{1u}$) and matrix-dominated fracture ($\sigma_2 = \sigma_{2u}$), are obtained. As discussed in Ref 2, the fiber-dominated fracture strength is expected to govern the behavior of most angle-ply laminates, though a transition to matrix-dominated behavior must occur as ϕ approaches 90 deg (all fibers parallel to the crack). The angle-ply bend specimens of the current test program provided data to validate this model.

Predicted values of K_Q for both fiber-dominated and matrix-dominated fracture were obtained from the angle-ply model using the material properties given in Table 2. These values, normalized with respect to $K_Q{}^\circ$, the fracture strength of a unidirectional 0-deg laminate, are shown as functions of ϕ in Fig. 4. The measured fracture strengths of the angle-ply bend specimens (Table 3), similarly normalized with respect to $K_Q{}^\circ$, are also plotted in Fig. 4. The agreement between the experimental results and the analytical predictions is generally good, though the expected transition from fiber-dominated to matrix-dominated behavior is observed at ϕ = 75 deg. This result strongly indicates that the fracture strength of most angle-ply laminates is governed by fiber strength. Furthermore, it appears that the measured fracture strength of any one angle-ply laminate may be used to predict the fracture strengths of all angle-ply laminates of the same ply material, as long as the fracture of such laminates is fiber dominated.

Orthotropic Laminates

Simple angle-ply laminates are rarely used in real structures, so the angle-ply model considered previously would appear to have limited applicability. However, any orthotropic laminate may be viewed as a combination of angle-ply constituents. Thus, if the fracture strengths of such laminates can be related to the fracture strengths of the angle-ply components, a single fracture test of an angle-ply laminate can be used to predict the fracture strengths of all symmetrically loaded orthotropic laminates of the same ply material.

A method has been developed [3] for predicting the fracture strength of an orthotropic laminate from the fracture strengths of its angle-ply components. The model is based on the argument that d, the transverse stretch at the crack tip, is identical in all components of an orthotropic laminate. From this argument, which is valid in the absence of general delamination near the crack tip, it may be shown that, for an orthotropic laminate having N angle-ply components [3]

$$G_Q = \sum_{i=1}^{N} G_{Qi} t_i / T \tag{4}$$

where

G_Q = predicted value of the critical strain energy release rate for the orthotropic laminate,

G_{Qi} = critical energy release rate of the ith angle-ply component, and

t_i/T = relative thickness of the ith angle-ply component.

Since G_{Qi} can be obtained from the angle-ply model using Eq 3, it is seen that Eq 4 does provide the desired link between the angle-ply model and structural orthotropic laminates. However, it should be recognized that Eq 4 is predicated on the absence of any dissipative mechanism other than self-similar crack growth, and thus cannot be applied to problems involving inter-ply cracking, or independent matrix cracks within individual plies.

The data obtained from the current test program may be used to substantiate the orthotropic laminate fracture strength model. The critical strain energy release rates measured for the angle-ply laminates (Table 3) were used in Eq 4 to obtain predicted values of G_Q for the orthotropic laminates employed in the test program. These predicted values, denoted by G_Q^*, are listed in Table 4; also listed in Table 4 are the average measured values of the critical energy release rate for the orthotropic test laminates, denoted by G_Q, and the ratio G_Q^*/G_Q. The values of G_Q and G_Q^* are seen to agree very well, except in the case of the small CC05 and CC10 center-cracked tension specimens; however, as noted previously, these specimens do not yield valid test results because of insufficient crack length. It should also be noted that the difference between G_Q^* and G_Q is typically no more than the scatterband associated with G_Q. Thus, it may be concluded that Eq 4 is an accurate means for predicting the fracture strength of symmetrically loaded orthotropic laminates.

TABLE 4—*Predicted and measured critical strain energy release rates.*

Specimen No.	G_Q^* (in · lb/in.²)[a]	G_Q (in · lb/in.²)[b]	G_Q^*/G_Q
B61	71.53	69.27	1.033
B63	71.53	71.73	0.997
B65	194.44	188.40	1.032
B67	42.92	44.66	0.961
B69	165.39	148.09	1.117
CC05	165.39	68.76	2.405
CC10	165.39	124.10	1.333
CC25	165.39	149.11	1.109

[a]Predicted value, using angle-ply data (Table 3) and Eq 5; G_Q for 90-deg plies assumed negligible.
[b]Calculated from experimental data (Table 3).

Conclusions

The experimental results reported herein support the application of metals-based LEFM to orthotropic fiber composite laminates. For such materials, a laminate fracture toughness K_{Ic} can be measured using a "valid" composite fracture test; as long as the criteria for test validity are met, the resulting fracture toughness is independent of specimen size and specimen configuration. The test validity criterion for the graphite-epoxy laminates considered in the current experimental program appears to be one of sufficient crack length. The principal measure of such sufficiency seems to be based on the size of the damage zone around the crack tip at failure; however, such size parameters as notch-tip width, ply thickness, and fiber diameter may also be significant. The test results do seem insensitive to specimen configuration and specimen thickness.

The test data also substantiate two analytical models for predicting the fracture toughness of orthotropic laminates. The first of these models relates ply properties to the fracture toughness of angle-ply laminates in which crack growth is fiber dominated. The second model relates the fracture toughness of a general orthotropic laminate to the fracture properties of its angle-ply components. Both models are in good agreement with the experimental data; the models are, however, applicable only to cases in which crack growth is fiber dominated, self similar, and not preceded by extensive delamination. The conditions do not limit the models to an excessive degree, however, as they are satisfied in many significant problems.

Additional investigations are required in several areas. The effects of such laminate variables as fiber diameter, ply thickness, and stacking sequence on laminate fracture toughness must be assessed. Criteria for a valid composite fracture test must be further refined; the possibility of determining the validity of a fracture test configuration prior to actual testing should be considered. Finally, the characterization of fracture modes peculiar to composites, for example, delamination, is a problem area of major importance. These refinements of the current model are certainly justified by the successes achieved to date.

References

[1] Konish, H. J., Jr., Swedlow, J. L., and Cruse, T. A., *Journal of Composite Materials,* Vol. 6, No. 1, Jan. 1972, pp. 114–124.

[2] Konish, H. J., Jr., Cruse, T. A., and Swedlow, J. L., "Method for Estimating Fracture Strength of Specially Orthotropic Composite Laminates," *Analysis of the Test Methods for High Modulus Fibers and Composites, ASTM STP 521,* American Society for Testing and Materials, 1973, pp. 133–142.

[3] Cruse, T. A., *Journal of Composite Materials,* Vol. 7, No. 2, April 1973, pp. 218–229.

[4] Tentative Method of Test E 399 for Plane Strain Fracture Toughness of Metallic Materials, *Annual Book of ASTM Standards,* Part 31, American Society for Testing and Materials, 1970, pp. 911–928.

[5] Srawley, J. E. and Brown, W. F., Jr., *Plane Strain Crack Toughness Testing of High Metallic Materials, ASTM STP 410,* American Society for Testing and Materials, 1969.

[6] Cruse, T. A. and Snyder, M. D., *International Journal of Fracture* (to appear).

[7] Sih, G. C., Paris, P. C., and Irwin, G. R., *International Journal of Fracture Mechanics,* Vol. 1, No. 3, Sept. 1965, pp. 189–302.

[8] Eisenmann, J. R., Convair Aerospace Division, General Dynamics Corporation, Fort Worth, Tex., private communication, 1973.

[9] Ashton, J. E., Halpin, J. C., and Petit, P. H., *Primer on Composite Materials: Analysis,* Technomic Publishing Co., Inc., Stamford, Conn., 1969.

A. S. Yue[1] *and B. T. Kaba*[1]

Fracture Behavior of Unidirectionally Solidified Ti-Ti₅Ge₃ Eutectic Composites

REFERENCE: Yue, A. S. and Kaba, B. T., "**Fracture Behavior of Unidirectionally Solidified Ti-Ti₅Ge₃ Eutectic Composites,**" *Composite Reliability, ASTM STP 580,* American Society for Testing and Materials, 1975, pp. 504–514.

ABSTRACT: A titanium-21 weight percent germanium eutectic alloy was unidirectionally solidified at two different rates to produce a composite material strengthened by intermetallic Ti₅Ge₃ fibers. The higher solidification rate produced a composite with fibers of finer diameters. The fracture behavior of this material was determined from work of fracture and impact experiments. A brittle-to-ductile transition was found, through the work of fracture experiments, to be 1150 °F (621 °C). This transition was raised by some 450 °F (232 °C) under impact loading. The large increase in the work of fracture corresponding to this transition has been attributed to the increased ductility of the titanium matrix. It was also found in this experiment that the composite with larger fiber diameters was tougher than that with smaller fiber diameters. Macroscopic and microscopic observation of the fracture surface revealed that failure occurred in a brittle fashion below 800 °F (427 °C) and by normal rupture between 800 and 1200 °F (427 and 649 °C).

KEY WORDS: composite materials, intermetallics, fibers, eutectics, solidification, fracturing, impact tests, transition temperature

Eutectic solidification as a technique to produce fibrous metal-matrix composites has received much attention within the past decade, especially in regard to the cobalt- and nickel-base superalloys [1–3].[2] High strength at elevated temperatures seems to be the desired product of most research in this field because of the stability that the high-strength reinforcing fibers exhibit at temperatures approaching the melting point of the material. Although providing superior mechanical strength at elevated temperatures, many fibrous eutectic composites are questioned in terms of their resistance to fracture throughout the temperature range of use, because

[1] Professor of engineering and applied science and graduate student, respectively, Materials Department, University of California, Los Angeles, Calif. 90024.
[2] The italic numbers in brackets refer to the list of references appended to this paper.

some of these materials have exhibited low (1 percent) fracture strains [2,3].

It would seem imperative to obtain data to characterize the fracture behavior of a eutectic composite material. The most direct approach would be to use linear elastic fracture mechanics to obtain the parameter K_{Ic}, called the plane-strain fracture toughness. But a fracture mechanics treatment would be useful only if the material to be tested were completely elastic or if sufficiently large specimens were used to obtain plane-strain conditions, which involves keeping the plastic zone size at the crack tip small compared with the thickness of the specimen [4]. Thus an alternative method for characterizing the fracture behavior of a nonelastic, small-specimen (Charpy size) material would have to be employed.

Two methods which give an indication of the fracture behavior of a material are the work-of-fracture method employed by Tattersall [5] and the Charpy impact test [6,7]. These two methods were employed in this study of the fibrous eutectic composite Ti-Ti$_5$Ge$_3$ since the material preparation technique limited the size of the specimen and thus plane-strain conditions are not always met when testing at various temperatures.

Experimental Procedure

Materials

Titanium of 99.9$^+$ percent purity and germanium of 99.99 percent purity were used in this study. The phase diagram [8] for this system predicts a eutectic alloy at 21.0 weight percent germanium. The two phases present are the α-titanium matrix and the titanium 5-germanium 3 (Ti$_5$Ge$_3$) intermetallic fibers.

Material Preparation

It was previously found [9] that titanium-base eutectic alloys reacted with most crucible materials, thus introducing impurities into the molten alloy. To prevent this contamination, an electron beam floating zone melting technique [9] was employed, preceded by the alloying of the titanium and germanium in a watercooled copper crucible arc furnace. The specimens produced by this method—unidirectionally solidified at two different rates, 0.4 in./h and 6.0 in./h—were of cylindrical shape, 2.5 in. long and 0.3 in. in diameter. The Ti$_5$Ge$_3$ intermetallic fibers were unidirectionally aligned parallel to the cylinder axis (Fig. 1).

The cylindrical specimens were then machined to substandard Charpy dimensions 0.197 in. by 0.197 in. by 2.165 in. in accordance with the ASTM Standard Methods for Notched Bar Impact Testing of Metallic Materials (E 23-66). The type of notch used for the impact test specimen

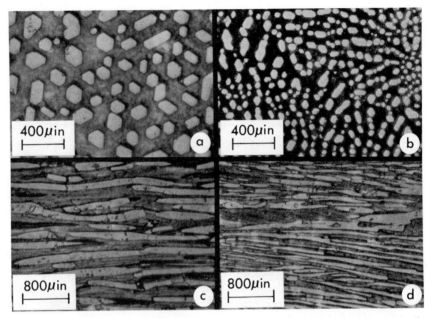

FIG. 1—*Titanium-germanium eutectic microstructure:* (a) *transverse section, 0.4 in./h;* (b) *transverse section, 6.0 in./h;* (c) *longitudinal section, 0.4 in./h;* (d) *longitudinal section, 6.0 in./h.*

differed from that of the work-of-fracture test specimen. A simple slit of root radius 0.010 in. was used for the impact test, while two slits were cut into the work-of-fracture test specimen to reduce the square cross-sectional area to an isosceles triangle cross-sectional area. This method was in accordance with the one employed by Tattersall [5] to obtain the work of fracture.

Work-of-Fracture Testing

The work of fracture, G_F [10], has been shown [5,10] to be a parameter which shows the resistance to fracture a particular material may have. This parameter has been determined by testing the specially notched specimen in three-point loading at a constant rate of beam deflection (0.002 in./min) with the use of an Instron Tensile Testing Machine. A 10 000-lb load cell was used on the 0 to 200-lb load scale. A load-versus-deflection curve is obtained (Fig. 2) from this experiment, and the area under this curve, divided by the area of the triangular fracture surface, will give the work of fracture, G_F. This experiment in its entirety has been described by Tattersall [5]. Both specimens, 0.4 in./h and 6.0 in./h, are tested in this manner at various temperatures from 72 to 1200°F (22 to 649°C). Each test is then followed by macroscopic and microscopic observation with the use of a scanning electron microscope (SEM).

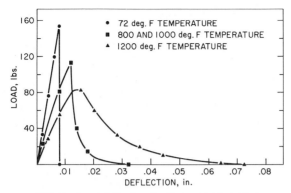

FIG. 2—*Load-deflection for three-point bend test.*

Impact Testing

Three-point loading was also employed in this test by means of a Baldwin Impact Testing Machine at its lowest energy scale (25 ft·lb). In this test it was desired to find the Charpy energy, C_v, as a function of temperature. To achieve a temperature variation among the specimens, each specimen was heated to temperatures between 1300 and 1800 °F (704 and 982 °C) for one hour in a separate furnace. The samples were then transferred from the furnace to the impact testing machine. It was found that the temperature of the specimens dropped by as much as 200 °F (93 °C) during the transfer, so superheating of the specimen was necessary. The amount of superheating was determined by multiple temperature tests using dummy specimens which were connected to a thermocouple and a storage oscilloscope.

At these testing temperatures, it was found that the specimens formed an oxide scale of thickness varying from 0.001 to 0.005 in., so the Charpy energy, C_v, was divided by the metallic area of the fracture face to correct for any area discrepancies. Thus the data reported here are in terms of C_v/A, where A is the metallic area of the fracture face.

Macroscopic and microscopic observation of the fracture surfaces also follow the impact test, and these observations are used to clarify some salient features of these data.

Results and Discussion

Microstructure

As can be seen from Fig. 1, the resulting microstructure of the Ti-Ti_5Ge_3 eutectic consists of discontinuous, needle-like Ti_5Ge_3 intermetallic fibers dispersed parallel to the solidification direction, in an α-titanium matrix *[11]*. The hexagonal-shaped Ti_5Ge_3 fibers have been found to occupy 34 volume percent of the composite, in agreement with theoretical prediction.

The effect of changing the solidification rate from 0.4 in./h to 6.0 in./h is also shown in Fig. 1. The 0.4 in./h solidification rate provided fibers of apparent diameter of 120 to 200 μin. and an interfiber spacing of 280 μin. The 6.0-in./h solidification rate provided a fiber diameter of 60 to 80 μin. and an interfiber spacing of 160 μin. Thus the effect of increasing the solidification rate is to nucleate and grow a larger number of fibers, which results in a smaller fiber diameter and interfiber spacing.

Work of Fracture

The results of the three-point bend test on the specially notched specimen *[5]* are shown in graphical form in Fig. 3. The following are the salient features of these data and each is discussed separately with the aid of macroscopic and microscopic observation: The work of fracture, G_F, for the 6.0 in./h specimens is lower than that for the 0.4 in./h specimens to temperatures of 1000°F (538°C). Between 72 and 1000°F (22 and 538°C), G_F increases slightly as the temperature is raised and between 1100 and 1200°F (593 and 649°C), G_F rises abruptly. The curves in Fig. 3 cross at a temperature just below 1200°F (649°C). The value of G_F at

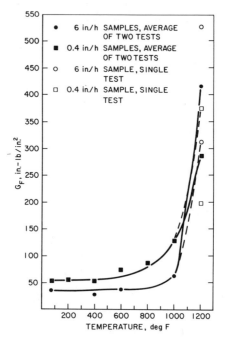

FIG. 3—*Work-of-fracture versus temperature.*

various temperatures is compared with the value of G_F for some selected engineering materials.

The variation in G_F between the 0.4-in./h and 6.0-in./h specimens is primarily due to the number and the diameter size of the Ti_5Ge_3 fibers present. As can be seen from Fig. 1, the 6.0-in./h specimens display a larger number of fibers of much finer diameters (60 to 80 μin.) than the 0.4-in./h specimens (120 to 200 μin.). This seems to follow previous findings [12,13] which state that the toughness or work of fracture [10] increases as the fiber diameter is increased, regardless of whether the fiber is brittle or ductile.

Microscopic and macroscopic observation of the fracture surface indicates only a slight difference between the 0.4-in./h and 6-in./h specimens. This difference occurs on the microscopic level where the fractured fibers are more easily detectable in the 0.4-in./h specimens. Thus the photographs of the 0.4 in./h specimen shown in Fig. 4 are characteristic for both specimens tested at these temperatures.

Tests run at the lower temperatures [less than 800 and 600°F (427 and 316°C) for the 6.0 in./h and 0.4 in./h specimens, respectively] all resulted in the specimens failing catastrophically, with load-deflection curves (Fig. 2) resembling the 72°F (22°C) curve. On a macroscopic level, the fracture appeared to be brittle as the fracture surface was relatively flat

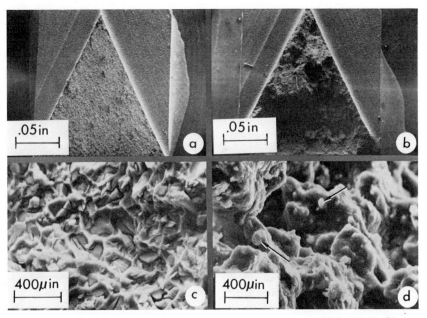

FIG. 4—*Work-of-fracture test fracture surfaces:* (a) *temperature, 72°F (22°C);* (b) *temperature, 1200°F (649°C);* (c) *temperature, 72°F (22°C);* (d) *temperature, 1200°F (649°C).*

(Fig. 4a). Microscopic observation reveals that fracture had indeed occurred in a brittle fashion where cleavage seemed to propagate right through the fiber-matrix interface, indicating a very strong interfacial bond (Fig. 4c).

At temperatures between 800 and 1000 °F (427 and 538 °C), the load-deflection curve (Fig. 2) begins to change. Instead of catastrophic failure where the load on the specimen drops almost immediately to zero, an initial drop in load occurs to ⅓ of the maximum load at a certain deflection, followed by a gradual decrease to zero of the remaining load. Macroscopic observation of the fracture surface also bears out this fact as the top portion of the triangular cross section is flat (as in Fig. 4a), whereas the bottom portion of the cross section exhibits a rough topography (as in Fig. 4b). Microscopic observation indicates that fracture still occurs by cleavage in the macroscopically flat region, but in the rough portion of the fracture surface, rupture of the matrix occurs though the fibers still fail by cleavage. This behavior characterizes a change in the mode of fracture of the matrix from cleavage (unstable or fast fracture) to rupture (stable or slow fracture). The change in the mode of fracture has been attributed not only to the change in temperature [7], but also to the geometry of the specimen's notch. A high stress is concentrated at the tip of the triangular cross section (Fig. 4a) and this stress is sufficient to initiate a cleavage crack which can propagate unstably. But as this crack propagates, it moves into a progressively larger area, so that much of the energy driving the crack is expanded. Additional, external work is needed to keep the crack moving [5], since matrix plastic deformation and a larger area have used up the energy driving the cleavage crack. The external work is provided by the continuing deflection of the specimen, but now the crack cannot propagate unstably due to the matrix plastic deformation. So the crack continues to grow in a stable manner, by ductile fracture (rupture). This explains the initial drop in load, followed by a gradual decrease in load for the specimens tested at 800 to 1000 °F (427 to 538 °C) (Fig. 2).

Observations of the oxidation properties of the specimens at various temperatures have been noted. As the testing temperature was raised above 400 °F (204 °C), oxidation of the specimens began. Between 600 and 800 °F (316 and 427 °C), the specimens developed a metallic, purple tarnish on the surface. Above 1000 °F (538 °C), a definite oxide coating formed and the metallic luster on the specimens disappeared.

Figure 3 also indicates that G_F increases slightly as the temperature is raised from room temperature to 1000 °F (538 °C). This is an unexpected phenomenon since the yield strength decreases with an increase in temperature [14], and Tetelman [7] gives an expression for the toughness, G_{Ic}, which can be correlated with G_F [10], which increases with the decrease in yield strength (where fracture occurs before general yielding).

The most striking feature of the tests performed at 1200 °F (649 °C) is the large jump in the work of fracture for both samples, three and seven times for the 0.4 in./h and 6.0 in./h specimens, respectively. This indicates that the composite material undergoes a brittle to ductile transition at about 1200 °F (649 °C). The load-deflection curve (Fig. 2) shows that the failure of the specimen no longer occurs catastrophically, but rather in a stable manner.

Through macroscopic and microscopic observation, it has been found that the matrix plays the major role in increasing G_F at the brittle-to-ductile transition. From Fig. 4b it is seen that large chunks of material have been pulled out of the fracture surface. Figure 4d indicates that the matrix failed in a ductile manner, while the fibers continued to fail by cleavage.

Another possibility which may increase the work of fracture is the mechanism of fiber decohesion and pullout [7,12,15]. At high temperatures, it is possible that the fiber-matrix interface may be rendered very weak and thus be susceptible to decohesion and pullout, as a moving crack intersects this interface. There is some evidence of this from other photomicrographs, but this evidence (observation of fiber pullout) is rather small for both specimens.

If the average value of G_F is taken at 1200 °F (649 °C), the two curves in Fig. 3 will cross, indicating that the specimens with finer fiber diameters will be more resistant to fracture than the larger fiber diameter specimens. This is not expected from previous findings [12,13], so, in an attempt to correlate the results of this experiment with its expectations, the broken-line curves in Fig. 3 have been added. These curves lead to a single test result at 1200 °F (649 °C). Obviously, much more data must be obtained in the region to eliminate the scatter of results and thus provide a clear picture of the actual physical occurrence.

Typically, the work of fracture for the Ti-Ti$_5$Ge$_3$ eutectic specimens ranges from 50 (lb·in.)/in.^{2} at 72 °F (22 °C) to about 500 (lb·in.)/in.^{2} at 1200 °F (649 °C). In comparison with dural and copper [5] with G_F values of 8×10^2 (lb·in.)/in.^{2} and 2.85×10^2 (lb·in.)/in.^{2}, respectively, the room temperature work of fracture for Ti-Ti$_5$Ge$_3$ is about one order of magnitude smaller while the 1200 °F (649 °C) specimens are similar in toughness to these two materials.

It is also of interest to note that the work of fracture of a brittle eutectic composite, AuPb$_3$–Pb [16], is only 2.5 (lb·in.)/in.^{2}, whereas the work of fracture of a 66 percent boron-epoxy composite [10] is 200 (lb·in.)/in.^{2}.

Impact Testing

Results of the impact testing in the temperature range 1300 to 1800 °F

(704 to 982 °C) are given in Fig. 5. Both the 0.4-in./h and 6.0 in./h specimens exhibited a jump in Charpy energy at a certain temperature. To determine a temperature characterizing this energy jump, the average energy criterion [7] is used. This criterion simply identifies a temperature corresponding to an energy which is one-half the sum of the maximum and minimum energies. Thus, the temperature characterizing the 0.4 in./h specimens is 1594 °F (868 °C), and for the 6.0 in./h specimens is 1612 °F (878 °C). The maximum energy, expressed in terms of Charpy energy divided by the fracture face area (C_v/A), has a value of 700 (in·lb)/in.^{2} for the 6.0 in./h specimens, while the 0.4 in./h specimens have a maximum of 360 (in·lb)/in.^{2}.

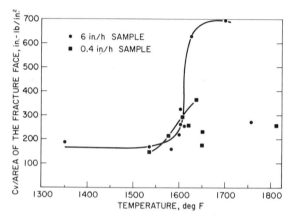

FIG. 5—*Charpy energy versus temperature.*

Although impact data, as in Fig. 5, are relatively easy to obtain, it has been pointed out [7] that data of this nature can only provide a comparison between different materials in terms of relative changes in the impact energy as a function of temperature. It has been suggested [7] that when a brittle-to-ductile transition temperature is determined by the impact test, a criterion based on the fracture appearance must also be made.

In this study, the fracture faces of the test specimens were observed and the fracture face appearance was in qualitative accord with the impact energy results. Those specimens at the minimum Charpy energy had fracture surfaces which resembled those in Fig. 4a and 4c (brittle fracture), while the specimens at the maximum Charpy energy had fracture surfaces as in Fig. 6b and 6d (normal rupture). The usefulness of the impact test is that it substantiates a brittle-to-ductile transition which was initially shown by the work of fracture measurements. By looking only at the work of fracture results, it could possibly be argued that the jump in G_F at 1200 °F (649 °C) was not due to a true brittle-to-ductile transition. It is possible that an increase in G_F could have been due to the fiber-matrix interface breaking down at 1200 °F (649 °C), which would lead to debonding and crack blunting. But the impact

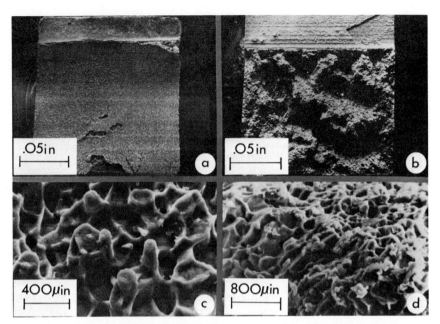

FIG. 6—*Impact test fracture surfaces:* (a) *upper-shelf energy, 0.4 in./h;* (b) *upper-shelf energy, 6.0 in./h;* (c) *upper-shelf energy, 0.4 in./h;* (d) *upper-shelf energy, 6.0 in./h.*

test shows that even at temperatures as high as 1550°F (843°C), cracks can continuously propagate through the matrix and fibers, indicating that the fiber-matrix interfacial bonding has not been broken down.

Figure 5 shows that the maximum Charpy energy for the 6.0-in./h specimens is higher than that for the 0.4-in./h specimens. One explanation for this is the scatter of data, which is an inherent problem with impact testing, especially when heavy oxidation of the specimens occurs. The geometry of the notch can be drastically changed from specimen to specimen due to oxidation, so that the energy values can have a wide variation.

The fracture surfaces were then observed to seek another explanation for this behavior. But instead, a peculiarity has been revealed which has not been explained at this time. In Fig. 6a, failure seems to occur in a brittle manner, and in Fig. 6b a ductile failure mode is detected. However, on a microscopic level, both specimens exhibit extensive plastic deformation (Fig. 6b and 6d). It is possible that the 0.4-in./h specimen failed by shear lip [7], but if this was the case the Charpy energy of the 0.4-in./h specimen should be higher than the 6.0-in./h specimen, which failed by normal rupture.

Acknowledgments

The study of the fracture behavior of Ti-Ti$_5$Ge$_3$ eutectic composites was supported by the U.S. Army Research Office under Grant No. DA-ARO-D-31-124-73-G94. The authors would like to thank M. Doruk and N. Akdas for their technical assistance and B. K. Yue for his help in the preparation of the composite material.

References

[1] Henry, M. F., *Proceedings of the Conference on In Situ Composites,* National Materials Advisory Board, V. 308II, Jan. 1973, pp. 173–185.

[2] Bibring, H., *Proceedings of the Conference on In Situ Composites,* National Materials Advisory Board, V. 308II, Jan. 1973 pp. 1–69.

[3] Sahm, P. R. and Varga, T., *Proceedings of the Conference on In Situ Composites,* National Materials Advisory Board, V. 308II, Jan. 1973, pp. 239–249.

[4] Brown, W. F., Jr. and Srawley, J. E. in *Plane Strain Crack Toughness Testing of High-Strength Metallic Materials, ASTM STP 410,* American Society for Testing and Materials, 1967.

[5] Tattersall, H. G. and Tappin, G., *Journal of Materials Science,* Vol. 1, 1966, pp. 296–301.

[6] ASTM Designation E 23-66, "Standard Methods for Notched Bar Impact Testing of Metallic Materials," Vol. 31, 1971.

[7] Tetelman, A. S. and McEvily, A. J., *Fracture of Structural Materials,* Wiley, New York, 1967.

[8] Hansen, M., *Constitution of Binary Alloys,* 2nd ed., McGraw-Hill, New York, 1958, pp. 777–778.

[9] Crossman, F. W. and Yue, A. S., *Metallurgical Transactions,* Vol. 2, June 1971, pp. 1545–1555.

[10] Beaumont, P. W. R. and Tetelman, A. S., "The Fracture Strength and Toughness of Fibrous Composites," UCLA School of Engineering and Applied Science Report, UCLA-Eng.-7269, University of California, Los Angeles, Aug. 1972.

[11] Yue, A. S. and Crossman, F. W., *Metallurgical Transactions,* Vol. 1, 1970, pp. 322–323.

[12] Cooper, G. A. and Kelly, A., *Journal of the Mechanics and Physics of Solids,* Vol. 15, 1967, pp. 279–297.

[13] Piggott, M. R., *Journal of Materials Science,* Vol. 5, 1970, pp. 669–675.

[14] Akdas, N. M., "Unidirectionally Solidified Ti-Ti$_5$Ge$_3$ Eutectic Composites," Masters Thesis, University of California, Los Angeles, 1972.

[15] Cooper, G. A., *Journal of Materials Science,* Vol. 5, 1970, pp. 645–654.

[16] Zambelli, G. and Kurz, W., *Proceedings of the Conference on In Situ Composites,* National Materials Advisory Board, V. 308II, Jan. 1973, pp. 135–148.

J. F. Mandell[1]

Fatigue Crack Propagation Rates in Woven and Nonwoven Fiber Glass Laminates

REFERENCE: Mandell, J. F., "**Fatigue Crack Propagation Rates in Woven and Nonwoven Fiber Glass Laminates,**" *Composite Reliability, ASTM STP 580,* American Society for Testing and Materials, 1975, pp. 515–527.

ABSTRACT: The characteristics of fatigue crack propagation are described for fiber glass laminates containing woven fabric, woven roving, chopped fiber mat, and unidirectional ply reinforcement. The mode of crack propagation is shown to be a stepwise, ligament by ligament advance of the crack front. The rate of crack propagation is predicted to vary exponentially with the stress intensity factor by an approximate theory based on the fracture toughness, unnotched fatigue life curve, and microstructural characteristics. Good agreement is demonstrated between theory and experiment for each material. The crack growth rate data are normalized to a single relationship for all woven reinforcements, and to a second relationship for nonwoven reinforcements.

KEY WORDS: composite materials, fatigue, fatigue (materials), crack propagation, fiber glass reinforced plastics

The rate of fatigue crack growth in metals has been the topic of numerous studies which have, in most cases, established a linear relationship between the rate of crack growth, dc/dN, and some power of the range of the stress intensity factor, K_I [1].[2] A recent study of fatigue crack propagation in a 0/90 crossplied glass-epoxy laminate [2] indicates an exponential relationship between dc/dN and K_I which can be predicted by an approximate theory. The present paper describes the development of an improved test specimen for measuring fatigue crack growth in certain composites and compares theoretical and experimental crack growth rates for several important classes of fiber glass laminates typical of marine applications.

[1] Research associate, Department of Materials Science and Engineering, Massachusetts Institute of Technology, Cambridge, Mass. 02139.

[2] The italic numbers in brackets refer to the list of references appended to this paper.

Theory

The mode of fatigue crack propagation in crossplied 0/90 glass-epoxy has been described previously [2] as a series of ligament failures. As depicted in Fig. 1, the crack tip in the 0-deg plies (plies having fibers perpendicular to the crack) remains stationary in a given position for a number of cycles of stress until a ligament of material fails, whereupon the crack extends by one ligament width, d, and the process is repeated. Thus, the main crack extends in a stepwise fashion and the crack growth rate is taken as the ligament width divided by the number of cycles necessary to fail the ligament. For purposes of discussion, crack extension is

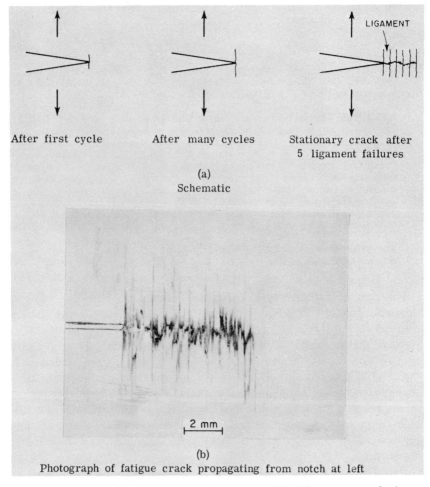

After first cycle   After many cycles   Stationary crack after
                                              5 ligament failures

(a)
Schematic

2 mm

(b)
Photograph of fatigue crack propagating from notch at left

FIG. 1—*Fatigue crack propagating in 0-deg ply of (90/0/90/0/90) glass-epoxy laminate.*

defined as extension of the main crack in its original direction as distinct from extension of the subcrack parallel to the fibers.

The rate of crack growth may be predicted by an approximate theory which assumes that the ligament of material at the crack tip fails according to the fatigue life curve of an unnotched strip of material, but at the local crack tip stress level [2]. If the stress versus log cycles to failure (S-N) curve for the material can be approximated as linear over the stress domain of interest, then the fatigue life of the ligament will be given by

$$\log N = \frac{\sigma_f - \sigma_l}{S} \tag{1}$$

where σ_f is the ultimate tensile strength at the appropriate strain rate, σ_l is the local stress in the ligament, and S is the slope of the S-N curve. The value of σ_l is determined by assuming a linear increase in local stress with K_I up to the critical stress intensity factor, K_Q, at which point σ_l must equal σ_f, so that

$$\sigma_l = \sigma_f \left(\frac{K_I}{K_Q} \right) \tag{2}$$

Substituting Eq 2 into Eq 1, the crack growth rate for a ligament width d will be

$$\frac{dc}{dN} = d \Big/ \exp \left[2.3 \frac{\sigma_f}{S} (1 - K_I/K_Q) \right] \tag{3}$$

Although Eq 3 neglects cumulative damage effects for ligaments ahead of the crack tip, Ref 2 has indicated that for ligament widths of 0.25 mm and greater, such effects are negligible because of the high stress gradients in the crack tip region.

Materials and Test Methods

The four types of E-glass reinforcement used in the study are described in Fig. 2 and Table 1; in each case the fibers were supplied with a polyester compatible finish by the manufacturer (Uniglass Industries). The matrix used in all cases was Laminac 4155 (American Cyanamid Company) with 0.5 percent MEK peroxide. Laminates were fabricated by hand layup followed by compression molding at 0.35 MN/m² and room temperature for one day, then postcure at 100°C (212°F) for two hours.

Test specimens were machined to the sizes indicated in Figs. 4 and 6 using a diamond-edged wheel and TensilKut router; the initial crack was cut with a 0.63-mm-thick diamond-edged wheel. Unnotched tension speci-

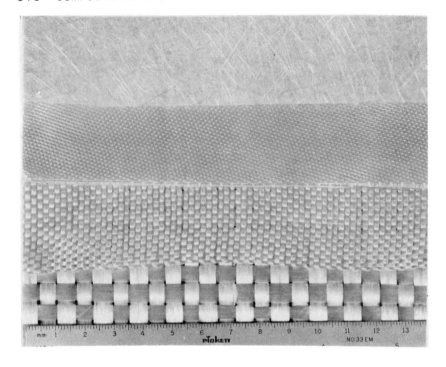

FIG. 2—*Types of E-glass fiber reinforcement* (top to bottom): *random chopped fiber mat; Styles 181 and 1800 woven fabric; and Style 61 woven roving, with centimeter scale.*

mens for woven roving laminates were machined to a larger size, 3.8 cm wide in the gage section, due to the increased material heterogeneity. Ultimate strength and K_Q values were obtained at the displacement rates indicated in Table 1 using an Instron universal or Model 1251 machine; because of the strain rate dependence of strength and toughness [3], tests were conducted at a similar strain rate to that used in the fatigue tests. Fatigue crack growth data were obtained on an Instron Model 1211 dynamic cycler at constant load amplitude with an approximately sinusoidal load-versus-time variation at a frequency of 4 to 7 Hz. All fatigue loading was approximately 0-tension, with a minimum load of 0.5 MN to avoid gripping problems. Tests were conducted in an uncontrolled laboratory environment using wedge-action grips for unnotched specimens and pin loading for crack growth specimens. A replication factor of four was used in all monotonic tests.

The value of stress intensity factor was determined from the relationship [4]

$$K_I = \frac{3.46P(C/H + 0.7)}{BH^{1/2}} \tag{4}$$

TABLE 1—*Physical and mechanical properties.*[a]

Reinforcement (E-glass)	Woven			Nonwoven	
	Fabric Style		Woven Roving Style 61	Chopped Fiber Mat	90/0/90/0/90 Crossplied[c]
	181	1800			
Matrix	polyester	polyester	polyester	polyester	epoxy
Yarn count, yarns/cm					
Warp	22.5	6.3	1.6[b]	...	...
Fill	21.3	5.5	1.6	...	...
Fabric weave	satin	plain	plain	...	...
Fabric weight, kg/m²	0.303	0.329	0.611	0.458	...
No. Plies/thickness, cm					
Specimen unnotched	10/0.254	9/0.254	5/0.229	5/0.303	5/0.127
Crack growth	36/0.915	33/0.915	20/0.915	15/0.915	5/0.127
Fiber volume fraction	0.47	0.47	0.52	0.29	0.50
Ultimate tensile strength, σ_f (MN/m²)[d]	429	339	450	134	418
Slope of S-N curve, S[(MN/m²)/decade]	70.8	58.0	71.9	12.9	42.5
K_Q (MN/m$^{3/2}$)[d]	32.3	26.7	45.4	14.0	26.4
Ligament width, d, cm	0.05	0.05	0.05	0.32	0.025

[a]Fabric description is from manufacturer's data; thickness, fiber volume fraction, and mechanical properties are average values; and ligament width is estimated as described in the text.

[b]Although yarn count is balanced, the amount of fiber is approximately in the ratio of 5:8 in the fill:warp directions.

[c]Scotchply Type 1002 unidirectional ply, 3M Company.

[d]Monotonic tests were conducted at a displacement rate of 0.85 cm/s.

where P is the applied force in MN and B is the thickness (B, C, and H are in meters). This relationship was derived for isotropic constants and is in slight error when applied to anisotropic materials, but has been found to give invariant toughness results for various crack lengths in laminates similar to those used in this study [5]. In all cases the crack was propagated parallel to the warp direction of fabric-reinforced specimens to reduce instances of deviation of the crack from the intended direction of propagation.

Results and Discussion

The ligament-by-ligament nature of crack propagation was observed for all materials tested in this study. The ligament width, d, was clearly evident from polished cross sections for the woven reinforcements as shown in Fig. 3; the ligament width for the random chopped mat laminates was less definite, and an approximate value was determined from crack length versus time curves.

Figure 4 indicates that the S-N curves for unnotched samples were

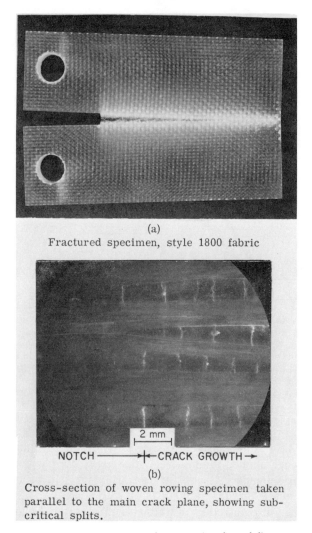

(a)
Fractured specimen, style 1800 fabric

NOTCH ─────────►|◄─CRACK GROWTH ►
(b)
Cross-section of woven roving specimen taken
parallel to the main crack plane, showing subcritical splits.

FIG. 3—*Fractured specimen and cross section through ligaments.*

typically linear down to some low stress level, where a knee in the curve
was evident for woven fabrics. The approximately linear portions of the
S-N curves in Figs. 4 and 5 were fit by a least-squares program to obtain
values for σ_f and S to be used in the dc/dN prediction for each material.
The relatively steep S-N curves for the woven materials apparently result
from the development of cracks at the crossover points of the weave [6];
such cracks are clearly observable (see Fig. 9), and are quickly followed
by failure in the case of the unnotched samples. Table 1 gives the experi-

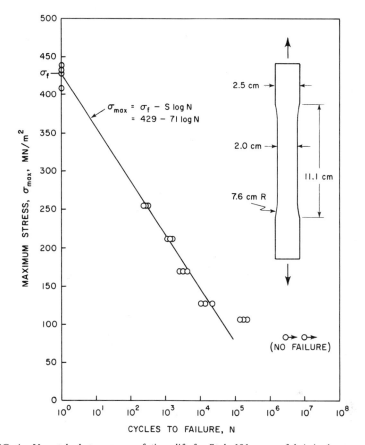

FIG. 4—*Unnotched stress versus fatigue life for Style 181 woven fabric/polyester matrix.*

mentally determined values for d, σ_f, S, and K_Q to be used as material properties in Eq 3.

Figures 6 and 7 indicate approximate agreement between experimental and predicted crack growth data for all four materials. Figure 8 indicates that all data along with previous data for glass-epoxy [2] can be normalized to fall along one of two lines when plotted K_I/K_Q versus log $(dc/dN)/d$. All of the woven reinforcement data fall along a line given by Eq 3 with $\sigma_f/S = 6$, while data from the nonwoven materials fall along a line given by $\sigma_f/S = 10$. The scale for $(K_I)_{max}$ in Figs. 6 and 7 was expanded because of the steepness of the curves; in conventional metals technology dc/dN varies with K_I to some power, typically in the range of 3 to 6 [1], while the results in Figs. 6 and 7 indicate approximate exponents between 9 for the woven roving and 13 for the chopped fiber mat if the data are approximated by a straight line.

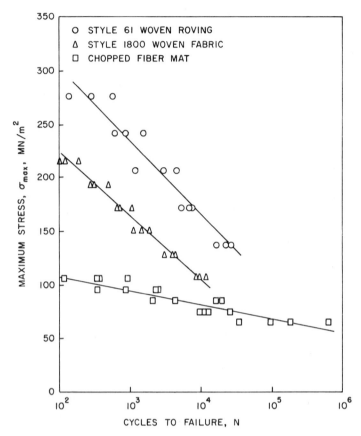

FIG. 5—*Unnotched stress versus fatigue life curves for various reinforcements/polyester matrix.*

Several problems were encountered in the development of the fatigue crack growth test. The cleavage-type sample without side-grooving is useful only for materials in which the crack has a strong tendency to propagate down the length of the specimen. If the woven roving, for example, were oriented with the warp direction perpendicular to the specimen length, the crack would still propagate parallel to the warp, perpendicular to the desired direction. Heating of the crack growth specimens at high frequencies was also a problem. Although preliminary tests did not indicate a significant dependence of dc/dN on frequency below 10 Hz, some specimens, particularly the woven roving, became warm to the touch near the crack tip; however, the heating problem was not studied in detail. Difficulty was also encountered in measuring the crack length because of the stepwise nature of the crack growth and the extensive damage region associated with the crack tip. The lack of any fatigue striations typical

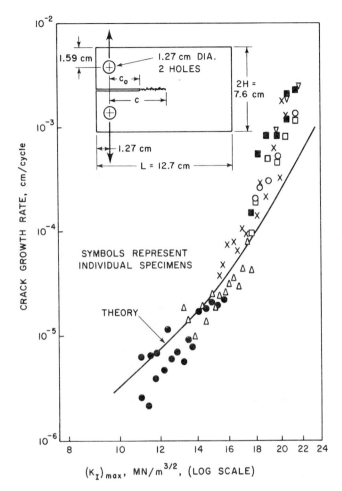

FIG. 6—*Theoretical versus experimental fatigue crack growth rates for Style 181 E-glass woven fabric with polyester matrix.*

of homogeneous materials [1] made it necessary to estimate the position of the crack tip on the specimen surface by optical inspection at low magnification.

The reduction of the test data by classical fracture mechanics techniques may have introduced some inaccuracy. Although fundamental aspects of the applicability of classical fracture mechanics to similar materials have been questioned in the past [3], recent unpublished analytical modeling of subcracking of the type shown in Fig. 1 indicates that the $r^{-1/2}$ stress singularity is maintained for in-plane stresses outside of a very local region at the immediate crack tip. Other studies [3,7] have suggested that a crack length correction factor should be applied to account for subcracking at

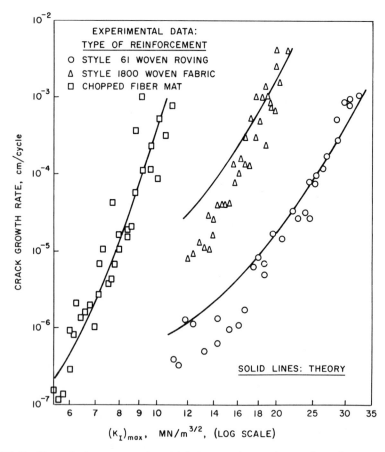

FIG. 7—*Theoretical versus experimental fatigue crack growth rates for polyester matrix with various forms of E-glass reinforcement.*

the crack tip, but results for the cleavage-type sample with its longer crack length suggest that such a correction factor is unnecessary [5]. The use of an isotropic K-calibration introduces some error which will vary with the degree of anisotropy [5] as discussed previously, and the combined effects of microcracking for significant distances away from the crack tip and near the loading points, evident in Fig. 3, and the effects of time on the modulus in regions of high stress may further alter the K-calibration. Another possible complication is the use of specimens of different thickness for the unnotched and crack growth tests; however, previous results have indicated no significant effect of laminate thickness on K_Q over a broad range for similar materials [3].

The results in Figs. 5–8 provide convincing evidence that the fatigue crack growth rate for these specific materials and testing conditions

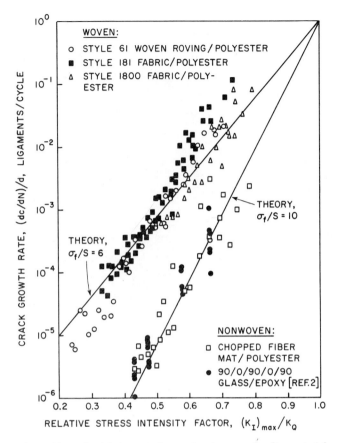

FIG. 8—*Normalized fatigue crack growth rate curves for five materials.*

can be deduced from the fracture toughness and S-N parameters combined with microstructural observations. The underlying mechanisms which lead to the fatigue failure are contained in the S-N curve, and the results suggest that no additional mechanisms are introduced by the sharp crack. Other investigators have associated the fatigue failure of unnotched material with the extension of microcracks [8] and the formation of cracks at the weave crossover points [6]. The absence of macroscopic heating in the unnotched specimens suggests that fatigue failure may result from local stress concentrations in the vicinity of microcracks or the abrasion of the exposed fibers as the microcracks open and close in fatigue. The latter explanation appears to be particularly likely in the case of the woven fabric where the crack formed at the weave crossovers is relatively large, and significant friction is to be expected during cycling.

Analytical procedures are not yet available for the prediction of the

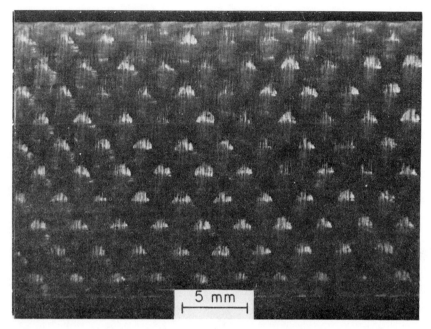

FIG. 9—*Formation of cracks at weave crossover points in unnotched Style 1800 woven fabric/polyester specimen.*

ligament size, but it is observed to be approximately 0.025 to 0.050 cm in all cases except for the random chopped mat. The apparent ligament size for the random chopped-mat specimens appears to be more a function of statistical point-to-point variations in fiber content and orientation rather than any fundamental mechanism which may be operable in the other cases.

Conclusions

It appears that the relationship between the fatigue crack growth rate and the stress intensity factor can be predicted by Eq 3 for a variety of fiber glass laminates, using the *S-N* curve as a material property, for the simple case of pulsating opening-mode loading. The crack growth rate curves can be normalized to a single relationship for all woven reinforcements tested, and to a second relationship for nonwoven reinforcements.

Acknowledgments

The general research program on the fracture behavior of fibrous reinforced composites, from which this report derives, receives support from The Dow Chemical Company, the Air Force Materials Laboratory (USAF Contract F33615-73-C-5169), the NOAA Office of Sea Grant, Grant No.

NG-43-72, and the Massachusetts Institute of Technology Center for Materials Science and Engineering (NSF Contract GH-33653). This support is gratefully acknowledged by the author.

References

[1] Tetelman, A. S. and McEvily, A. J., Jr., *Fracture of Structural Materials,* Wiley, New York, 1967.

[2] Mandell, J. F. and Meier, U. in *Fatigue of Composite Materials, ASTM STP 569,* American Society for Testing and Materials, 1975, pp. 28–44.

[3] Mandell, J. F., McGarry, F. J., Kashihara, R., and Bishop, W. O., "Engineering Aspects of Fracture Toughness: Fiber Reinforced Laminates," Paper No. 17D, *Proceedings,* 29th Reinforced Plastics/Composites Division, SPI, 1974.

[4] Gross, B. and Srawley, J. E., "Stress Intensity Factors by Boundary Collocation for Single-Edge Notch Specimens Subject to Splitting Forces," NASA Technical Note D-3295, National Aeronautics and Space Administration, 1966.

[5] Mandell, J. F., McGarry, F. J., Wang, S. S., and Im, J., "Stress Intensity Factors for Anisotropic Fracture Test Specimens of Several Geometries," *Journal of Composite Materials* (to be published).

[6] McGarry, F. J. and Desai, M. B., "Failure Mechanisms in Fiberglass Reinforced Plastics," *Proceedings,* 14th Conference, Reinforced Plastics Division, Section 16-E, Society of the Plastics Industry, 1959.

[7] Owen, M. J. and Bishop, P. T., *Journal of Composite Materials,* Vol. 7, 1973, p. 141.

[8] Broutman, L. J. and Sahu, S., "A New Theory to Predict Cumulative Fatigue Damage in Fiberglass Reinforced Plastics," Paper 11D, 24th Annual Technical Conference, Reinforced Plastics/Composites Division, Society of the Plastics Industry, 1969.

G. P. Sendeckyj,[1] *M. D. Richardson,*[1] *and J. E. Pappas*[1]

Fracture Behavior of Thornel 300/5208 Graphite-Epoxy Laminates—Part 1: Unnotched Laminates

REFERENCE: Sendeckyj, G. P., Richardson, M. D., and Pappas, J. E., "**Fracture Behavior of Thornel 300/5208 Graphite-Epoxy Laminates—Part 1: Unnotched Laminates,**" *Composite Reliability, ASTM STP 580,* pp. 528–546.

ABSTRACT: Basic stress-strain and strength data generated as part of a systematic investigation of the fracture behavior of 8-ply Thornel 300/5208 graphite-epoxy laminates are compared with theoretically predicted response curves based on single-ply stress-strain curves. Results are given for $(\pm\theta)_{2s}$, $(0/\pm\theta/0)_s$, $(90/\pm\theta/90)_s$, $(0/\pm45/90)_s$, and $(90/\pm45/0)_s$ laminates where $\theta = 0$, 15, 30, 45, 60, 75, and 90 deg.

KEY WORDS: composite materials, phase diagrams, nonlinear systems, stress strain diagrams, strength, laminates, mechanical properties

The increased use of advanced fiber-reinforced composites in aircraft structures, in conjunction with current aircraft damage tolerance criteria, underscores the need for understanding the fracture behavior of composite laminates. Even though considerable effort has been expended in fracture mechanics, few if any systematic studies have been performed. Moreover, the available studies suffer from incomplete reporting of experimental results, with the main omissions normally being the fiber volume and void contents and laminate stacking sequence.

The present paper (the first of a sequence) discusses the basic stress-strain and strength data generated as part of a systematic investigation of the fracture behavior of 8-ply Thornel 300/5208 graphite-epoxy laminates. Specifically, the stress-strain curves as determined from strain-gage data for 21 distinct 8-ply laminate configurations are compared with theoretically predicted response curves based on single-ply stress-strain data. This comparison shows that the method of Sandhu [1,2][2] for predicting the

---

[1] Aerospace engineer, project engineer, and instrumentation engineer, respectively, Structures Division, Air Force Flight Dynamics Laboratory, Wright-Patterson Air Force Base, Dayton, Ohio 45433.
[2] The italic numbers in brackets refer to the list of references appended to this paper.

nonlinear response of balanced laminates gives excellent results up to first-ply failure. Beyond first-ply failure, the agreement is not as good. The lack of agreement is shown to result from the particular failed-ply unloading mechanisms assumed in the analysis. Finally, the strength data are shown to be consistent with the measured fiber volume contents and theoretical strength predictions.

Experimental Results

Sixty-six tension coupons, instrumented with a single centrally located strain-gage rossette, were tested to determine the stress-strain response of 21 distinct 8-ply Thornel 300/5208 graphite-epoxy laminates. All tests were performed at room temperature (68 to 72°F) (20 to 22°C) and 60 percent relative humidity on an Instron universal testing machine at a crosshead travel rate of 0.05 in./min. Upon examining the load versus crosshead-travel records, we observed that the curves had a gentle break in slope at about 500-lb load. Comparisons with strain-gage data showed that this was a peculiarity due to the gripping arrangement used. Since soft aluminum tabs were being used, we concluded that this was due to plastic flow of the tab material in the grips. This is partially substantiated by the nature of the indentations observed on the gripped surfaces of the tabs. Hence, the strain rate was *not* constant during the tests.

The specimens, manufactured by Monsanto Research Corp., had the geometry shown in Fig. 1. See Ref *3* for specimen fabrication details.

Fiber volume and void fractions, determined by Monsanto, are summarized in Table 1. As can be seen, the fiber volume content of the laminates varies by ±2 percent from a nominal value of 66.4 percent. The high fiber volume content of the (±30)$_{2s}$ laminate is suspect.

In the process of determining fiber volume contents, Monsanto researchers ran into a problem apparently encountered by others. The fiber density (1.78 g/cm^3) quoted by the prepreg supplier (Whittaker Corp.) results in consistently negative void contents. Upon measuring the density

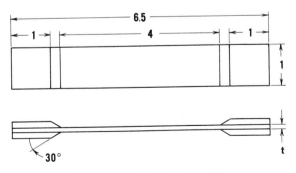

FIG. 1—*Test specimen geometry.*

TABLE 1—*Laminate failure data.*

Laminate Configuration	Fiber, volume, %	Matrix, volume, %	Voids, volume, %	Failure, psi	Stress, MN/m²	Coefficient of Variation, %
(0)₈	68.3	30.4	1.3	234 800	1618.9	6.9
(±15)₂ₛ	66.6	32.8	0.6	106 370	733.4	2.3
(±30)₂ₛ	71.3	25.3	3.4	68 300	470.9	4.1
(±45)₂ₛ	66.6	31.9	1.5	21 980	151.5	2.8
(±60)₂ₛ	66.9	31.7	1.4	9 570	66.0	2.7
(±75)₂ₛ	65.8	33.3	0.9	6 110	42.1	7.4
(90)₈	67.8	31.0	1.2	7 190	49.6	1.3
(0/±15/0)ₛ	65.1	33.7	1.2	155 130	1069.6	6.1
(0/±30/0)ₛ	66.8	32.1	1.1	140 730	970.3	2.4
(0/±45/0)ₛ	66.9	31.5	1.6	127 120	876.5	6.0
(0/±60/0)ₛ	65.2	33.3	1.5	105 360	726.4	5.4
(0/±75/0)ₛ	66.0	33.1	0.9	81 045	558.8	4.3
(0/90/90/0)ₛ	66.3	33.0	0.7	86 520	596.5	5.2
(90/0/0/90)ₛ	66.9	31.7	1.4	119 530	824.1	2.1
(90/±15/90)ₛ	67.1	31.3	1.6	66 570	459.0	2.7
(90/±30/90)ₛ	66.4	32.2	1.4	40 050	276.1	3.5
(90/±45/90)ₛ	64.3	34.5	1.2	24 570	169.4	5.5
(90/±60/90)ₛ	67.1	31.3	1.6	11 130	76.7	4.1
(90/±75/90)ₛ	65.8	33.7	0.5	4 990	34.4	9.6
(0/±45/90)ₛ	67.6	30.8	1.6	71 350	491.9	5.8
(90/±45/0)ₛ	67.5	31.0	1.5	76 120	524.8	1.5

of fibers extracted from the prepreg, Monsanto [3] found the density varied from 1.79 to 1.82 g/cm³. Because of the experimental method used (fibers extracted by N-methylpyrrolodone were tested in a water pycnometer), the 1.82-g/cm³ value was accepted as being most accurate. Hence, it was used in calculating the fiber volume and void contents given in Table 1.

The average failure stresses and coefficients of variation for the 21 laminate configurations are also given in Table 1. With the exception of the (±45)₂ₛ laminate, the failure stresses are the averages of three test results. Six specimens were tested for the (±45)₂ₛ configuration. An additional three (0) specimens from the panel used in the present program were tested independently by Thornton and Kozik [4]. They obtained an average failure stress of 226 970 psi with a 0.82 percent coefficient of variation.

Experimentally measured stress-strain curves are shown in Figs. 2 through 23. Figures 2 through 4 show the basic stress-strain response curves for a unidirectional laminate under tensile and shear loading conditions. The laminate longitudinal (0) stress versus longitudinal (0) and transverse (90) strain curves as determined from strain-gage data are given by the open and solid symbols, respectively, in Fig. 2. Each symbol shape indicates data generated on a different specimen. The solid and dashed curves show the average longitudinal stress-strain and longitudinal stress-transverse strain curves, which are used in subsequent analysis of the laminate stress-strain data. The average curves were generated as follows.

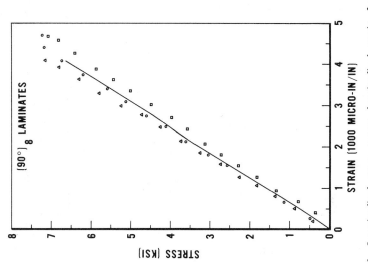

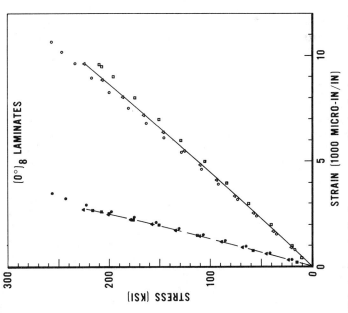

FIG. 3—*Longitudinal stress versus longitudinal strain for* (90)₈ *laminate.*

FIG. 2—*Longitudinal stress versus longitudinal (open symbols and solid curve) and transverse (solid symbols and long dashed curve) strain for* (0)₈ *laminate.*

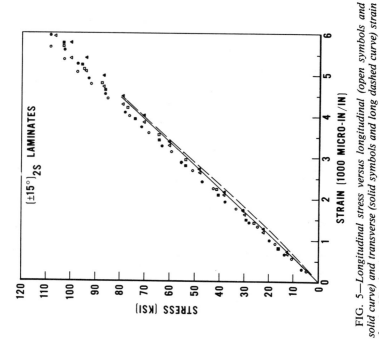

FIG. 5—Longitudinal stress versus longitudinal (open symbols and solid curve) and transverse (solid symbols and long dashed curve) strain for (±15)$_{2s}$ laminate.

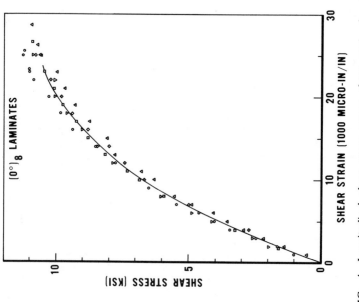

FIG. 4—Longitudinal shear stress versus shear strain for (0)$_8$ laminate.

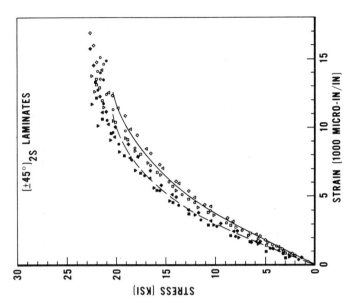

FIG. 7—Longitudinal stress versus longitudinal (open symbols and solid curve) and transverse (solid symbols and long dashed curve) strain for (± 45)$_{2s}$ laminate.

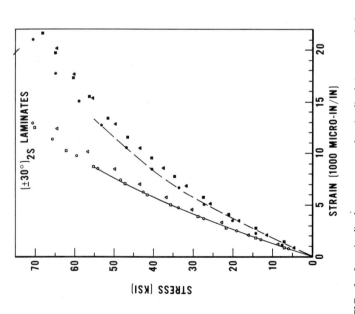

FIG. 6—Longitudinal stress versus longitudinal (open symbols and solid curve) and transverse (solid symbols and long dashed curve) strain for (± 30)$_{2s}$ laminate.

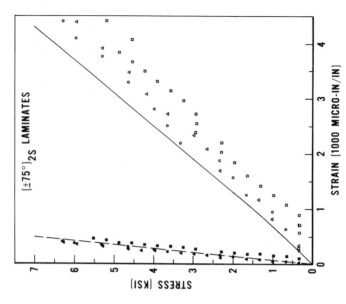

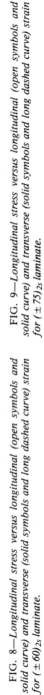

FIG. 9—Longitudinal stress versus longitudinal (open symbols and solid curve) and transverse (solid symbols and long dashed curve) strain for (±75)₂s laminate.

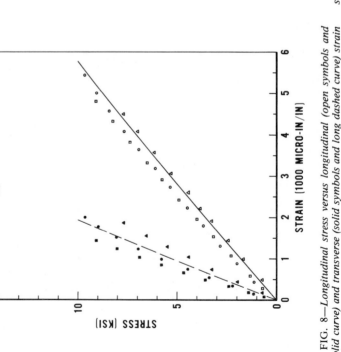

FIG. 8—Longitudinal stress versus longitudinal (open symbols and solid curve) and transverse (solid symbols and long dashed curve) strain for (±60)₂s laminate.

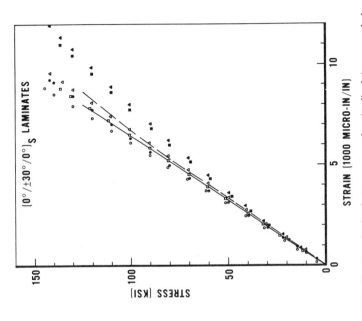

FIG. 11—Longitudinal stress versus longitudinal (open symbols and solid curve) and transverse (solid symbols and long dashed curve) strain for (0/±30/0)$_s$ laminate.

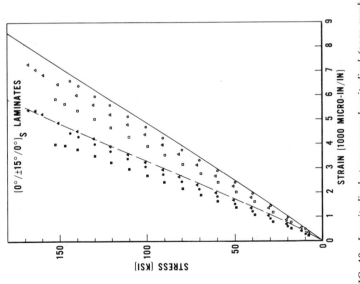

FIG. 10—Longitudinal stress versus longitudinal (open symbols and solid curve) and transverse (solid symbols and long dashed curve) strain for (0/±15/0)$_s$ laminate.

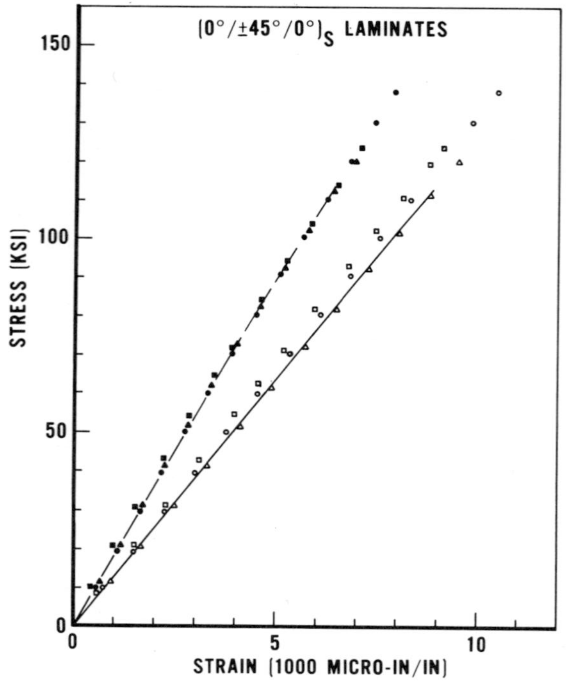

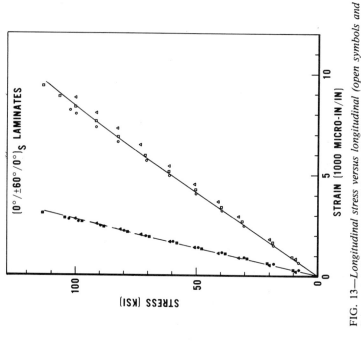

FIG. 13—*Longitudinal stress versus longitudinal (open symbols and solid curve) and transverse (solid symbols and long dashed curve) strain for (0/ ± 60/0)s laminate.*

FIG. 12—*Longitudinal stress versus longitudinal (open symbols and solid curve) and transverse (solid symbols and long dashed curve) strain for (0/ ± 45/0)s laminate.*

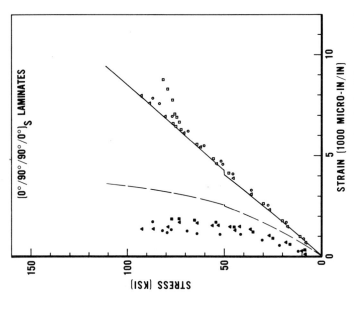

FIG. 15—Longitudinal stress versus longitudinal (open symbols and solid curve) and 10 times the transverse (solid symbols and long dashed curve) strain for (0/90/90/0)ₛ laminate.

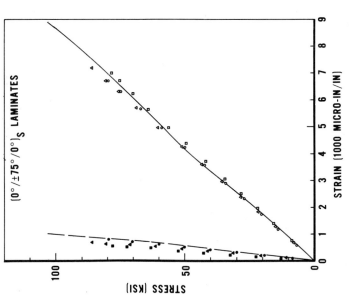

FIG. 14—Longitudinal stress versus longitudinal (open symbols and solid curve) and transverse (solid symbols and long dashed curve) strain for (0/±75/0)ₛ laminate.

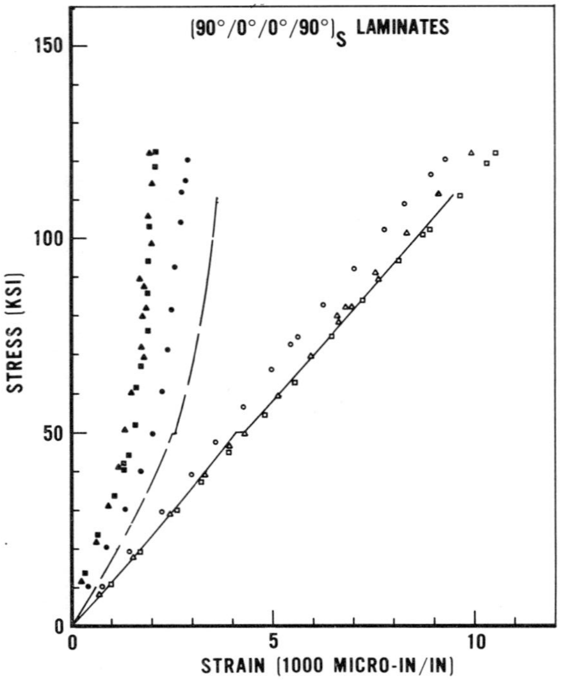

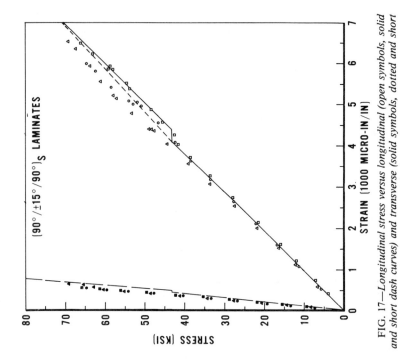

FIG. 17—Longitudinal stress versus longitudinal (open symbols, solid and short dash curves) and transverse (solid symbols, dotted and short dashed curves) strain for (90/±15/90)ₛ laminate.

FIG. 16—Longitudinal stress versus longitudinal (open symbols and solid curve) and transverse (solid symbols and long dashed curve) strain for (90/0/0/90)ₛ laminate.

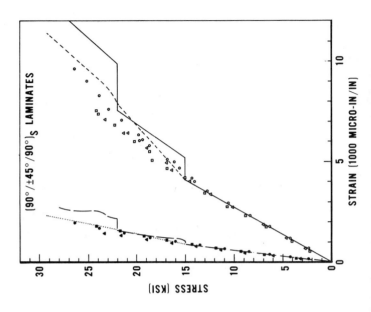

FIG. 19—Longitudinal stress versus longitudinal (open symbols, solid and short dash curves) and transverse (solid symbols, dotted and short dashed curves) strain for (90/±45/90)$_s$ laminate.

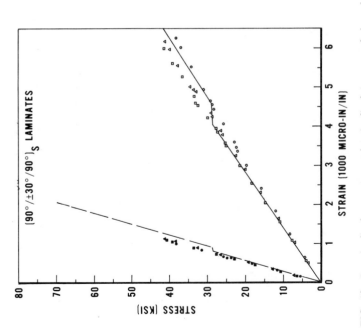

FIG. 18—Longitudinal stress versus longitudinal (open symbols and solid curve) and transverse (solid symbols and long dashed curve) strain for (90/±30/90)$_s$ laminate.

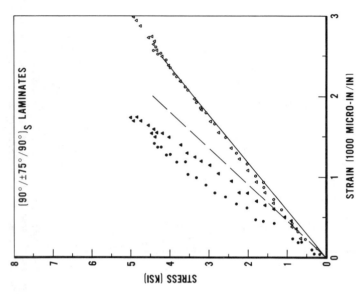

FIG. 21—Longitudinal stress versus longitudinal (open symbols and solid curve) and transverse (solid symbols and long dashed curve) strain for (90/±75/90)ₛ laminate.

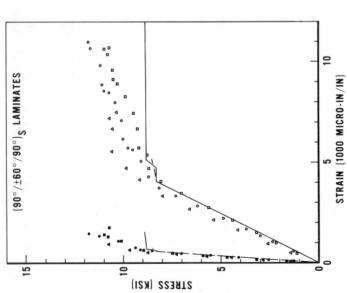

FIG. 20—Longitudinal stress versus longitudinal (open symbols, solid and long dashed curves) and transverse (solid symbols, dotted and short dashed curves) strain for (90/±60/90)ₛ laminate.

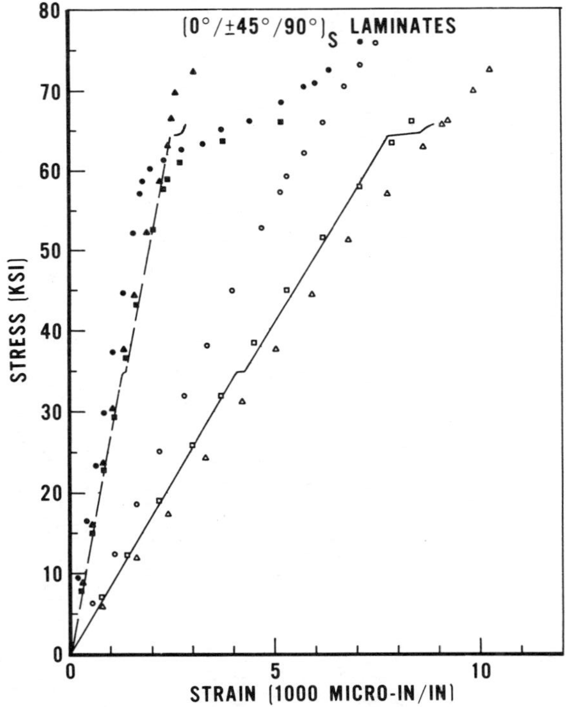

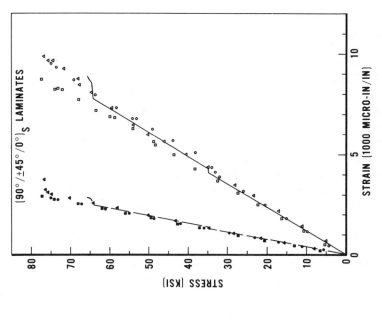

FIG. 23—Longitudinal stress versus longitudinal (open symbols and solid curve) and transverse (solid symbols and long dashed curve) strain for (90/±45/0)_s laminate.

FIG. 22—Longitudinal stress versus longitudinal (open symbols and solid curve) and transverse (solid symbols and long dashed curve) strain for (0/±45/90)_s laminate.

Cubic spline functions were used to fit the data points on the individual experimentally determined stress-strain curves. This gave a smooth curve fit of the experimental data. Using this smooth curve fit, stresses were computed for a set of preselected strain values for all the experimental stress-strain curves. The stresses for each strain value were next averaged to give a single average stress-strain curve. The average curves are shown in Fig. 2. Transverse (90) stress versus transverse (90) strain is shown in Fig. 3. The solid curve is the cubic spline average of the experimental data. Figure 4 shows the shear stress-strain response of the unidirectional laminate. The data points were calculated from $(\pm 45)_{2s}$ laminate response curves by the method proposed by Rosen [5]. Again, the solid curve is the cubic spline fit of the experimental results. Figures 5 through 23 show a comparison of the experimentally determined stress-strain curves with theoretical predictions for all laminate configurations investigated. The following section contains a discussion of the theory-experiment comparison.

Analysis of Experimental Results

Since the fiber volume contents of all the laminates investigated were approximately the same, one would expect the initial moduli of the laminates to be consistent with classical laminated plate theory. From the unidirectional lamina data (Figs. 2 to 4), we have

$$E_l = 23 \times 10^6 \text{ psi}$$

$$E_t = 1.6 \times 10^6 \text{ psi}$$

$$G_{lt} = 0.77 \times 10^6 \text{ psi}$$

$$\nu_{lt} = 0.30 \tag{1}$$

as the best estimates for the initial-ply longitudinal Young's modulus, transverse Young's modulus, shear modulus, and major Poisson's ratio. Moreover, E_l is a monotonically increasing function of strain (or stress), reaching a maximum value of 25×10^6 psi at failure. This is consistent with the nonlinearity of the fiber Young's modulus and fiber volume content of the (0) laminate. The major Poisson's ratio decreases from a value greater than 0.3 at small strain levels (at which strain-gage data are normally inaccurate) to about 0.29 at failure. The transverse Young's modulus is essentially constant to failure. The shear modulus decreases with increasing strain level.

Using the initial lamina elastic constant data (Eq 1) gives initial laminate Young's modulus and major Poisson's ratios that are fully consistent with experimental data. This implies that lamina data, in conjunction with classical laminated plate theory, are sufficient to define laminate moduli to be used in generating fracture specimen calibration curves.

It is also obvious that the initial moduli data are insufficient for predicting the complete laminate stress-strain response. Complete and accurate representations of the lamina stress-strain curves are needed. Unfortunately, these are not available at present. Even though stress-strain curves for tensile and shear loading were obtained experimentally (Figs. 2 to 4), reliable compression response curves are not available and, hence, they must be assumed. We assume here that (a) the lamina has the same stress-strain curves in compression as in tension, (b) the failure stress for longitudinal extension is the same as for compression, and (c) the failure stress in transverse compression is 24 ksi. Moreover, the transverse compression stress-strain curve is linear to failure. Of the foregoing assumptions, the one with respect to transverse compression is the most questionable and, hence, needs justification.

Kaminski [6], using a sandwich-beam test setup, obtained an average transverse compressive strength of 24.2 ksi. At the time of our communications, the modulus data were not reduced, but he suggested assuming a linear response to failure. Hofer [7], using an Illinois Institute of Technology Research Institute compression test fixture, obtained a transverse compression strength of 32 ksi. Moreover, his stress-strain curves were highly nonlinear beyond 24 ksi. Since the available compression data are extremely sketchy, we feel that our assumptions are justified.

The lamina stress-strain data were used to predict the nonlinear response of angle- and multi-ply laminates by the method of Sandhu [1,2]. Its main features are as follows:

1. Cubic spline functions are used to fit accurately all nonlinear lamina stress-strain curves. Hence, the method starts with a better representation of the basic data than those proposed by Petit and Waddoups [8], Hahn [9], and Hashin et al [10]. Specifically, Petit and Waddoups [8] use a piecewise linear representation of the lamina data; Hahn [9] uses an analytical cubic representation of the shear stress-strain response curve; and Hashin et al [10] use a Ramberg-Osgood representation of the shear and transverse stress-strain curves.

2. A predictor-corrector technique, in conjunction with classical laminated plate theory, is used to give the best estimate of the nonlinear multidirectional laminate response. This is computationally more accurate than the predictor technique used in the other methods [8–10]. See Ref 1 for a discussion of the computational aspects of the method.

3. The method allows various options for unloading of failed plies. The two options used in the present work are (a) ply strain redistribution at fixed laminate stress levels (corresponding to opening of cracks in failed plies) and (b) gradual stress and strain redistribution on the ply level after first-ply failure. This is done by reversing the sign of the ply moduli affected by the ply failure until the failed ply unloads. Of the two options,

Option (a) is appropriate for constant stress rate testing of the laminate. Option (b) is more appropriate for constant strain rate test results.

The predicted stress-strain curves for angle- and multi-ply laminates are compared with experimental data in Figs. 5 through 23. In the figures, open symbols represent data points on the experimentally determined longitudinal stress-longitudinal strain curves, while the solid symbols define the experimental longitudinal stress-transverse strain response. The solid curves are the predicted longitudinal stress-longitudinal strain curves, assuming that failed plies unload instantaneously at constant laminate stress by readjustment of lamina stresses and strains (Option a). The long dashed curves are the corresponding predicted longitudinal stress-transverse strain curves (Option a). The short dashed curves in Figs. 17, 19, and 20 show the predicted longitudinal stress-longitudinal strain response, assuming that the failed plies unload gradually (Option b). Finally, the dotted curves show the longitudinal stress-transverse strain response predicted using Option b.

On examining Figs. 5 through 9, we see that the theoretically predicted stress-strain curves for the $(\pm 15)_{2s}$, $(\pm 30)_{2s}$, $(\pm 45)_{2s}$, and $(\pm 60)_{2s}$ laminates fall within the scatter bands of the experimental data. For the $(\pm 75)_{2s}$ laminate, the longitudinal stress-longitudinal strain data are extremely irregular and, hence, the theory-experiment comparison is poor. There is excellent agreement between theory and experiment for the longitudinal stress-transverse strain response curve. Even though the failure stresses are predicted accurately, the failure strains are underestimated for the (± 45) laminates. This is due to the fact that in generating the shear stress-strain curve we assumed that the failure strain is the least failure strain obtained experimentally. This has the effect of making the predicted failure strains lower than those actually measured.

The theoretical curves were terminated by applying on the ply level a strength criterion proposed by Sandhu [1,2]. The criterion is

$$K_1 \int_{e_1} \sigma_1 de_1 + K_2 \int_{e_2} \sigma_2 de_2 + K_6 \int_{e_6} \sigma_6 de_6 = 1 \qquad (2)$$

where

$$K_i = \left[\int_{e_{iult}} \sigma_i de_i \right]^{-1}, \qquad (i = 1,2,6) \qquad (3)$$

Here, σ_i and e_i are stress and strain components on the ply level, e_{iult} are the lamina failure strains, and K_i are the energies under the lamina stress-strain curves. The use of this criterion requires knowledge of all lamina stress-strain curves to failure. As was pointed out in the preceding section, these data are not available at present for the Thornel 300/5208 system. The necessary curves were assumed in the present paper.

Upon examining Figs. 5 through 9, we see that the strength criterion underestimates the strength of the $(\pm 15)_{2s}$ and $(\pm 30)_{2s}$ laminates. This lack of agreement is due to the poor assumption about the transverse stress versus transverse strain response of the lamina in compression since examination of the lamina stress-strain state at incipient failure indicates failure by transverse compression of the lamina. Resolution of this point must await reliable transverse compression data for the lamina.

Figures 10 through 14 show a comparison of experimental results with theoretically predicted stress-strain curves for $(0/\pm \theta/0)_s$ laminates with θ = 15, 30, 45, 60, and 75 deg. As can be seen, the comparison is good. The strength predictions are high for the $(0/\pm 15/0)_s$ and low for $(0/\pm 30/0)_s$ and $(0/\pm 45/0)_s$ laminates. Again this is due to the poor assumption of the transverse compressive response of the lamina.

Theoretical predictions are compared with experimental data for $(0/90/90/0)_s$ and $(90/0/0/90)_s$ laminates in Figs. 15 and 16. The predicted longitudinal stress-longitudinal strain curves are in excellent agreement with experimental results. Agreement is poor for the longitudinal stress-transverse strain curves. Theoretical strength is in excellent agreement with the experimental values for the $(90/0/0/90)_s$ laminate. The $(0/90/90/0)_s$ laminate had a much lower strength. This is due to damage of the surface 0-deg plies during specimen handling and fabrication. Moreover, the horizontal jogs in the theoretical curves indicate failure of the transverse plies in the laminate. They reflect readjustment of the lamina stress-strain state upon failure of the 90-deg plies and the assumed failed ply unloading mode (unloading of the failed ply at constant laminate stress level).

Figures 17 through 21 show the comparison of theoretical and experimental stress-strain curves for $(90/\pm \theta/90)_s$ laminates with θ = 15, 30, 45, 60, and 75 deg. From these figures, it is seen that failed-ply unloading Option *b* gives better predictions than Option *a*. This is as expected since the tests were run at constant crosshead travel rate and not constant stress rate. In general, theory-experiment comparison is good.

Finally, Figs. 22 and 23 show excellent agreement between the theoretical and experimental results for the $(0/\pm 45/90)_s$ and $(90/\pm 45/0)_s$ laminates. The observed difference in experimental stress-strain curves is due to the differences in the deformation and failure modes of the two laminates.

The $(0/\pm 45/90)_s$ laminate began edge-delaminating at about 40 ksi at the specimen midpoint. The edge delamination progressed slowly until the edges were completely delaminated at approximately 60 ksi. As further load was applied, the edge cracks opened more. This opening of the edge cracks is reflected in the change in slope of the measured longitudinal stress-transverse strain curve (since the transverse gage of the rossette was off-center). In contrast, the $(90/\pm 45/0)_s$ specimen did not edge-delaminate and no change in slope was observed.

Conclusion

Based on the theory-experiment comparison, it can be concluded that laminated plate theory is sufficiently accurate for predicting the nonlinear response of multi-ply laminates provided that (1) accurate representations of the nonlinear stress-strain curves of the lamina and (2) realistic modeling of the unloading of failed plies are used. Of these two requirements, modeling of ply failure requires considerably more effort. Specifically, failed-ply unloading at fixed laminate strain levels must be modeled successfully. Such a model would predict load drops of the type observed during constant strain rate tests.

References

[1] Sandhu, R. S., "Ultimate Strength Analysis of Symmetric Laminates," AFFDL-TR-73-137, Air Force Flight Dynamic Laboratory.

[2] Sandhu, R. S., "Nonlinear Response of Unidirectional and Angle Ply Laminates," AIAA Paper No. 74-380, presented at the 15th AIAA/ASME Structures, Structural Dynamics, and Materials Conference, Las Vegas, Nev., 17–19 April 1974.

[3] Sendeckyj, G. P. and Richardson, M. D., "Fracture Behavior of Thornel 300/5208 Graphite-Epoxy Laminates: Specimen Fabrication, Test Procedures, and Strength Data," AFFDL-TM-74-51-FBC, Air Force Flight Dynamic Laboratory, April 1974.

[4] Thornton, H. R. and Kozik, T. J., "Investigation of Fatigue Strength of Multi-layered Advanced Fiber Composites," Progress Report from 18 June 1973 to 1 Feb. 1974 on NASA Grant No. NGR 44-001-149, Texas A&M University Report TEES-2992-74-001, Feb. 1974.

[5] Rosen, B. W., *Journal of Composite Materials,* Vol. 6, 1972, p. 552.

[6] Kaminski, B., private communication.

[7] Hofer, K., private communication.

[8] Petit, P. H. and Waddoups, M. E., *Journal of Composite Materials,* Vol. 3, 1969, p. 2.

[9] Hahn, H. T., *Journal of Composite Materials,* Vol. 7, 1973, p. 257.

[10] Hashin, Z., Bagchi, D., and Rosen, B. W., "Nonlinear Behavior of Fiber Composite Laminates," Report TFR/7309, Materials Science Corp., prepared under Contract NAS1-11284, Sept. 1973.

Characterization and
Materials Development

L. H. Miner,[1] *R. A. Wolffe,*[1] *and C. H. Zweben*[1]

Fatigue, Creep, and Impact Resistance of Aramid Fiber Reinforced Composites

REFERENCE: Miner, L. H., Wolffe, R. A., and Zweben, C. H., "**Fatigue, Creep, and Impact Resistance of Aramid Fiber Reinforced Composites,**" *Composite Reliability, ASTM STP 580,* American Society for Testing and Materials, 1975, pp. 549–559.

ABSTRACT: Kevlar® 49 a high-strength, high-modulus, low-density organic fiber has gained significant acceptance as a weight-reducing replacement for E-glass in aircraft applications and for S-glass in filament-wound missile components. New end-use applications require a better understanding of the static and dynamic fatigue and impact resistance of these composites. The tension-tension fatigue life of both unidirectional fiber and fabric-reinforced laminates was greater than that of comparable glass-reinforced composites. The creep rate under continuous tensile stress was comparable to that of glass composites. The ball-drop impact resistance of Kevlar 49 fabric laminate-faced sandwich panels was dependent on fabric weave construction and number of face sheet plies. This relationship was significantly different for sandwich beams having glass-reinforced facings.

KEY WORDS: composite materials, reinforced plastics, fiber glass, boron, aluminum, fatigue tests, creep strength, impact strength

The utility of Kevlar 49[2] (formerly designated PRD-49) organic yarns, rovings, and woven fabrics as lower weight, higher tensile strength, and higher modulus replacements for glass fiber products has already been well established in applications such as commercial aircraft and helicopters [1–3].[3] Moreover, the combination of high specific tensile strength (strength/density), specific modulus (Fig. 1), and ease of processing has led to promising evaluations of Kevlar 49 as a filament-wound reinforcement for rocket motor cases [4,5] and as an overwrap for metal-lined cryogenic bottles and tanks [6]. Some applications require an understanding of the long-term and dynamic properties of these reinforced com-

---

[1]Technical marketing representative, technical marketing specialist, and senior research engineer, respectively, E. I. du Pont de Nemours & Co., Inc., Industrial Fibers Division, Textile Fibers Department, Wilmington, Del. 19898.
[2]Kevlar is du Pont's trademark for its aramid fiber.
[3]The italic numbers in brackets refer to the list of references appended to this paper.

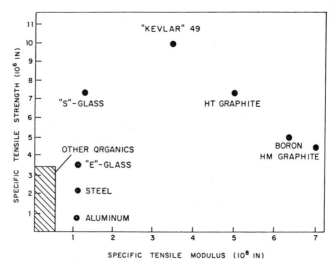

FIG. 1—*Specific tensile strength and specific tensile modulus of reinforcing fibers.*

posites. Earlier work showed that these composites were superior to fiberglass reinforced plastics (GRP) and aluminum in fatigue [6,7], creep [8,9], and impact resistance [10].

The objective of this paper is to report the latest results on the fatigue, creep, and impact testing of these composites.

Fatigue of Unidirectional Composites

Kevlar 49 composites must withstand continuous fluctuating tensile stresses in some end uses, such as the lined pressure vessels just mentioned. Chiao [9] showed that these composites have a superior stress rupture resistance versus glass-reinforced plastics, but the dynamic tension-tension fatigue behavior had been evaluated only on preproduction PRD-49-I fibers [7].

Recent axial tension fatigue tests were conducted on straight-sided aligned fiber-reinforced epoxy composites autoclave-molded from 3M Company SP-306 prepreg tape. Fiber volume fraction was 0.63. Specimen width and thickness were 0.5 in. (12.7 mm) and 0.020 in. (0.51 mm), respectively, with a gage length of 3 in. (76.2 mm). These specimens, which had tapered, fiber glass/epoxy end tabs, were loaded in tension with a ratio of minimum-to-maximum stress of 0.1. Loading rate on a Gilmore hydraulic testing machine was 1800 cpm (30 Hz).

The tension-tension fatigue resistance of these unidirectional composites (Fig. 2) was comparable to that of unidirectional boron-epoxy, which is recognized as best among composite materials. The advantage over GRP and a conventional aluminum (2024-T3) is significant. All materials were

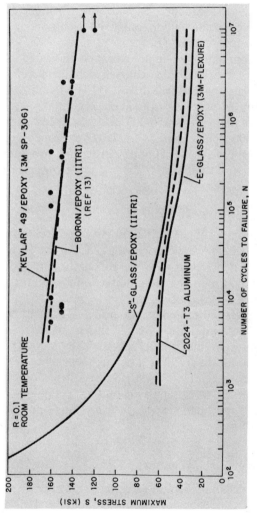

FIG. 2—*Tension-tension fatigue behavior of unidirectional composites and aluminum.*

tested at the same load rate. Each point on the curve, which was plotted by best-fit analysis, represents one test.

One specimen was chosen to determine the effect of fatigue stresses on residual ultimate properties. The sample was tested to run out at 10×10^6 cycles at a maximum stress of 120 000 lb/in.^{2} (827 MN/m^2) and then tested statically. Tensile strength and modulus were 199 000 lb/in.^{2} (1372 MN/m^2) and 12.3×10^6 lb/in.^{2} (84 800 MN/m^2), typical of reported results for unfatigued aramid fiber composites. This single result is consistent with findings of Hoggatt [6].

The results from another single specimen indicated that these composites may share the load-rate sensitivity characteristic of other fiber-reinforced materials. At 160 000 lb/in.^{2} (1103 MN/m^2) maximum stress, representing a full 80 percent of the average ultimate tensile strength, the average cycles to failure was 150 300 at a test speed of 1800 cpm while one sample at 600 cpm endured 1 327 700 cycles before fracture. The 1800-cpm rate, however, was retained during this program for both ease of comparison with published data and economic considerations.

Fatigue of Fabric Reinforced Composites

The fatigue program included Kevlar 49 fabric reinforced epoxy composites. The specimens were autoclave-molded from Hexcel Corporation F-155 preimpregnated Kevlar 49 Style 181 cloth. The specimen geometry was the same as that used for the unidirectional specimens; load rate was again 1800 cpm.

The straight-sides, glass-epoxy tab-ended specimens were marginally acceptable for determining the dynamic fatigue of these fabric reinforced laminates. Failures in the vicinity of the tabs were frequent and undoubtedly penalized the results. Despite these limitations, the fatigue resistance appears to be above Style 181 reinforced GRP (Fig. 3, Ref 11). The Kevlar 49 curve is thus far based on only six points, but the trend is significant. Other specimen shapes, such as "dog-bone" and "bow-tie," are being evaluated.

Creep of Unidirectional Composites

A concern associated with use of an organic fiber in a reinforcing application is its creep behavior under continuous static stress. Organic fibers, such as nylon or Dacron polyester, do not exhibit particularly good creep resistance at elevated stresses. The creep rates of reinforcing fibers such as fiber glass, graphite, and boron are low by comparison, although fiber glass is susceptible to creep-rupture.

Creep specimens were also fabricated from 3M SP-306 unidirectional tape. The samples were instrumented with strain gages so that creep strain

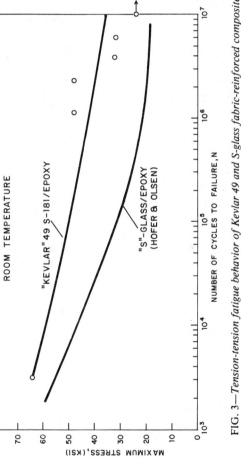

FIG. 3—*Tension-tension fatigue behavior of Kevlar 49 and S-glass fabric-reinforced composites.*

and subsequent recovery behavior could be monitored accurately and continuously.

The creep rate at 100 000 lb/in.^{2} (689 MN/m^2, 50 percent of ultimate tensile strength) of Kevlar 49 composites in the 100 to 1000-min time period is similar to that of GRP; namely, 1.7 $\times$ 10^{-4} μin./in./min versus 1.3 $\times$ 10^{-4} μin./in./min (Fig. 4). The relative positions of the plotted data on the graph reflect the approximately two-times difference in initial modulus of the two materials. Significantly the GRP control stress-ruptured within 100 h at this stress level. The strain recovery after unloading these composites at 48 h occurs at a rate of 2.1 $\times$ 10^{-4} μin./in./min in the 100 to 1000-min time period.

Creep behavior, however, is only one aspect of a material's resistance to long-term static stresses. Since these composites exhibit good creep-rupture resistance at relatively high stress levels [8,9], creep and recovery at stresses greater than 75 percent of ultimate tensile strength are being determined.

Impact of Sandwich Panels

Kevlar 49 composites are generally as impact-resistant as similar glass laminates at lower weight, and significantly better than graphite composites [10,12]. Impact resistance was determined on sandwich panels comprising Kevlar 49 fabric-reinforced epoxy face sheets and Nomex aramid honeycomb core. The honeycomb core was 0.325 in. (8.25 mm) thick with 3/16 in. (4.76 mm) cell size, weighing 5.8 lb/ft^3 (92.9 kg/m^3). The face sheets were fabricated from Dexter Hysol 9704 prepreg fabric.

The ball-drop impact tester was a version of a General Electric-Gardner #8569 film impact tester (Fig. 5). The specimen rested on a solidly supported metal base and was struck by a falling 2-lb (0.91-kg), ¾-in.-diameter (19-mm) spherical-nosed missile guided within a vertical cylinder. Failure was defined as a crack or break in the honeycomb panel face.

Variables were fabric weave design and number of plies used in the construction of the facing laminate. The former parameter was important since du Pont has introduced a number of new Kevlar 49 fabric styles woven from heavy denier yarns using plain-weave, balanced constructions (Table 1). For example, although Styles 181 and 281 have identical basis weight (5.0 oz/yd^2, 169.8 g/m^2), and thickness per ply (10 mils, 0.25 mm), the S-181 is a 50-end by 50-pick (380 denier) 8-harness satin construction, while S-281 is a 17 $\times$ 17 (1140 denier) plain weave.

The ball-drop results (Table 2) show that Kevlar 49 fabric weave design has a pronounced effect on impact resistance. For sandwich panels composed of single-ply face sheets, impact strength is doubled by substituting heavy-denier Styles 281 or 328 for Style 181. For glass fabric-reinforced face sheets, however, impact resistance for Styles 181 (analog of the same

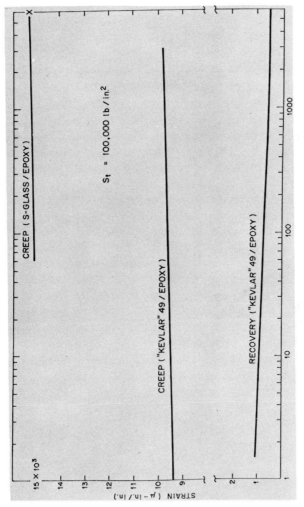

FIG. 4—*Creep and recovery behavior of Kevlar 49 and S-glass unidirectional composites.*

FIG. 5—*Ball-drop impact tester.*

TABLE 1—*Kevlar 49 woven fabric description.*

Style	oz/yd²	Construction Ends/in. (Yarn denier)[a]	Weave	Thickness, mils
120	1.8	34 (195d) × 34 (195d)	plain	4.5
143	5.6	100 (380d) × 20 (195d)	crowfoot	10
181	5.0	50 (380d) × 50 (380d)	8-HS	11
220	2.2	22 (380d) × 22 (380d)]	plain	4.7
243X	6.7	38 (1140d) × 18 (380d)	crowfoot	11
281	5.0	17 (1140d) × 17 (1140d)	plain	10
328	6.8	17 (1420d) × 17 (1420d)	plain	13

Note—The designation "X" refers to the experimental nature of these constructions.
[a] Denier weight in grams of 9000 m.

Kevlar 49 style) and 2542 (the best analog for Kevlar 49 Style 281 is nearly equal. The same weave design dependence exists for both two-ply and three-ply face sheets (Table 2).

One explanation for this behavior involves weave crimp. Since warp (longitudinal) and fill (transverse) yarns in plain weaves are arranged in a one-over, one-under pattern, crimp, or nonstraightness, is much more pronounced than in 8-harness satin weaves which are of 7-over, 1-under design (Fig. 6). Increased crimp may provide a "softer" foundation for impact, allowing the yarns to straighten as part of the energy-absorption mechanism. The effect of weave crimp in the glass fabric facings may be overriden by the crack propagation mechanism inherent to fiberglass. Since the unique compressive yielding behavior may also be a contribution to impact behavior, a complete explanation will require careful analysis and more testing.

The results (Table 2) also indicate that impact strength is a function of the number of face sheet plies, and that the reduction of impact resistance *per ply* is less for glass fabrics than for aramid fibers. For example, Kevlar 49 Style 281 reinforced face sheet ball-drop impact resistance decreases from 45 in·lb/ply (0.52 m·kg/ply) in single-ply layup to 20 in·lb/ply

TABLE 2—*Impact resistance of honeycomb sandwich panels faced with glass and Kevlar 49 fabric epoxy laminates.*

Fabric	Weave	Ply Thickness, mils	Impact Resistance (in·lb) One-Ply	Two-Plies	Three-Plies
Style 181 Kevlar 49	8-HS	10	25	30	40
Style 181 E-Glass	8-HS	10	25	50	60
Style 281 Kevlar 49	plain	10	45	50	60
Style 2542 E-Glass	plain	10	22	...	...
Style 328 Kevlar 49	plain	13	50	55	...

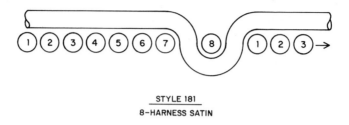

STYLE 181
8-HARNESS SATIN

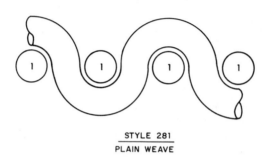

STYLE 281
PLAIN WEAVE

FIG. 6—*Comparison of weave construction of Kevlar 49 fabrics.*

(0.23 m·kg/ply) in three-ply construction. GRP (Style 181) facings decrease from 25 to 20 in·lb/ply (0.29 to 0.23 m·kg/ply) in similar tests.
This decrease in impact resistance per ply for multiple-ply laminates may
be related to the difference between Kevlar 49 and fiber glass in compressive behavior, to resin properties such as modulus and shear strength, or
to the properties at the interface of the individual plies. Further work is
required to define these effects.

In all these experiments, an effort was made to keep other composite
variables constant—for example, void fraction, sheet porosity, resin content—since these can have significant effects on impact resistance. In
particular, for sandwich structures, face sheet porosity had a large deleterious effect on impact strength.

The introduction of the heavy-denier aramid fabrics provides designers
much more latitude in the development of impact-resistant parts. Impact-
critical aramid composite designs should reflect the advantages of using
the heavy-denier fabric styles and as few plies as possible to obtain a
given thickness.

Summary and Conclusions

Tension-tension fatigue tests show that both Kevlar 49 unidirectional
fiber and fabric-reinforced epoxy composites are very resistant to dynamic
fatigue. The behavior of fabric composites was affected by specimen geometry.

The creep behavior of Kevlar 49 unidirectional composites is similar to that of GRP. Previous results indicated that the static fatigue, or creep-rupture, resistance of these composites is significantly better than that of GRP. Evaluations of Kevlar 49/epoxy-faced honeycomb core sandwich panels show that their ball-drop impact strength for a given thickness is increased when the weave crimp is maximized and the number of plies minimized. Glass fabric facings are relatively insensitive to weave crimp.

References

[1] Stone, R. H., "Advanced Organic Fibers for L-1011 Interior Structures," 17th National Society of Aerospace Materials and Process Engineering Symposium, Los Angeles, Calif., April 11-13, 1972, pp. V-A-SIX 1-19.

[2] Hooker, D. M., "PRD-49—A New Composite Material, Its Characteristics and Its Application to the BO-105 Helicopter," Paper No. 915, 31st Annual Conference, Society of Aeronautical Weight Engineering, Inc., Atlanta, Ga., May 22-25, 1972.

[3] Wooley, J. H., Paschal, D. R., and Crilly, E. R., "Flight Service Evaluation of PRD-40/Epoxy Composite Panels in Wide-Bodied Commercial Transport Aircraft," Final Report NASA CR-11-2250, Contract NASI-11621, National Aeronautics and Space Administration.

[4] Wright, O. C., Jr., "Development of a High Performance PRD-49-III Filament-Wound Chamber for Trident I (C4) Third Stage," Paper No. 73-1259, 9th Propulsion Conference, American Institute of Aeronautics and Astronautics, Las Vegas, Nev., Nov. 5-7, 1973.

[5] Woodberry, R. F. H., and Borgmeier, D. E., "Application of Advanced Fibers to Chambers for Solid Rocket Motors (U)," 1973 JANNAF Propulsion Meeting, CPIA Publication 242 (Vol. 2, Oct. 1973), Las Vegas, Nev., Nov. 6-8, 1973, pp. 41-65.

[6] Hoggatt, J. T., "High Performance Filament-Wound Composites for Pressure Vessel Applications," presented at National Society of Aerospace Materials and Process Engineering Technical Conference, Huntsville, Ala., Oct. 5-7, 1972.

[7] Stratton, W. K., "Evaluation of Du Pont's High Modulus Organic Fiber PRD-49 Type I," presented at 16th National SAMPE Symposium and Exhibition, Anaheim, Calif., April 22, 1971.

[8] Moore, J. W., "PRD-49, A New Organic High Modulus Reinforcing Fiber," presented at 27th Annual Society of the Plastics Industry Meeting, Washington, D.C., Feb. 8-11, 1972.

[9] Chiao, T. T., Wells, J. E., Moore, R. L. and Hamstad, M. A. in *Composite Materials: Testing and Design (Third Conference), ASTM STP 546,* American Society for Testing and Materials, 1974, pp. 209-224.

[10] Wolffe, R. A., et al., "New PRD-49 Products for Aerospace and Commercial Applications," presented at 18th National Society of Aerospace Materials and Process Engineering Symposium and Exhibition, April 3-5, 1973, Los Angeles, Calif.

[11] Hofer, K. E., Jr. and Olsen, E. M., "An Investigation of the Fatigue and Creep Properties of Glass Reinforced Plastics for Primary Aircraft Structures," Paper No. AD652415, Naval Air Systems Command, April 1967.

[12] Beaumont, P. W. R. et al in *Foreign Object Impact Damage to Composites, ASTM STP 568,* American Society for Testing and Materials, 1975, pp. 134-158.

[13] IIT Research Institute, "Development of Engineering Data on the Mechanical and Physical Properties of Advanced Composites Materials," AFML-TR-72-205, Air Force Materials Laboratory, Part I, Sept. 1, 1972.

I. L. Kalnin[1]

Thermal Conductivity of High-Modulus Carbon Fibers

REFERENCE: Kalnin, I. L., "**Thermal Conductivity of High-Modulus Carbon Fibers**," *Composite Reliability, ASTM STP 580,* American Society for Testing and Materials, 1975, pp. 560–573.

ABSTRACT: The axial thermal conductivity of high-modulus carbon fibers near room temperature is determined from the measured thermal conductivity of their unidirectional composites and also directly on a dry fiber bundle. A device providing the necessary thermal and electrical connections to the heated fiber bundle is described.

The thermal conductivity of 14 commercial carbon fiber grades ranged from 1.42 W/cm°C for the highest-modulus (GY-70) fiber to 0.03 for the low-modulus (VYB) one. Correlations are given between the thermal and the electrical conductivities and the fiber moduli. Above 0.1 W/cm°C the thermal conductivity increases linearly with the electrical conductivity or the elastic modulus, whereas below that value it becomes nearly independent of modulus, and is accompanied by a sharply decreased electrical conductivity.

KEY WORDS: composite materials, carbon fibers, fibers, fiber composites, graphite composites, reinforced plastics, thermal conductivity, electrical conductivity, electrical resistivity, density, stiffness, test equipment

As the number of applications for the advanced engineering fibers increases, so does the need for information on the properties of the fibers themselves as well as their composites. While in the past, most testing and evaluation focused on the mechanical behavior, new applications requiring data on the graphite fiber thermal and thermomechanical properties are becoming more prominent. It has been shown, for instance, that the ablative plastics reinforced with high-modulus graphite fiber provide a greater load-carrying ability at elevated temperatures, a less catastrophic mode of failure, a higher radiative heat dissipation, and a better thermal shock resistance than the more conventional asbestos-phenolic or glass-phenolic ablative composites [1,2].[2] It is obvious that knowledge of the graphite fiber thermal properties, such as thermal conductivity (TC),

---

[1] Research associate, Celanese Research Co., Summit, N.J. 07901.
[2] The italic numbers in brackets refer to the list of references appended to this paper.

thermal expansion, and heat capacity, is needed not only to improve the effectiveness of ablative materials, but even more so to modify the thermal properties of a composite by knowledgable selection of reinforcements having optimal thermal characteristics.

This paper, by providing the axial TC data on many commonly used graphite fiber grades near room temperature, 23 to 52 °C (73 to 126 °F), represents one of the first steps toward that objective. Two different methods of measurement were used: a conventional one, utilizing a unidirectional fiber-epoxy resin composite; and a direct one, developed at Celanese, utilizing an electrically heated small fiber bundle. The respective apparatus and the measuring procedures used are discussed briefly in the following section.

Experimental Procedures

Fiber TC from Unidirectional Composites

The most prominent feature of the graphite fiber is its high anistropy, caused by preferred orientation of the crystallite basal planes in the direction of the fiber axis. As a result, some mechanical properties, such as strength and modulus, as well as some of the physical properties, including electrical and thermal conductivities, are relatively high along the fiber axis and much lower transversely to it. Consequently, not one but two principal thermal conductivities, one in the fiber direction, k_l, and the other one transversely to it, k_t, should be known. This paper is concerned only with k_l, which is readily determined from the TC of a unidirectionally reinforced bulk composite by means of the well-known rule of mixtures [3,4]

$$k_{cl} = k_{fl}\phi_f + k_r\phi_r$$

where k is the thermal conductivity and ϕ the volume fraction; The first subscripts (c, f, r) indicate a property pertaining to the composite, fiber, or resin, respectively; the second subscripts (l or t) denote the longitudinal (axial) and transverse directionalities. Since k_l of graphite fiber is usually at least 20 times greater than k_r of the epoxy resin, the second term may be disregarded and the simplified formula $k_{fl} \cong (k_c/\phi_f)$ used.

The measuring instrument was a Colora thermoconductometer which is based on the method and apparatus devised by Schroeder [5] in Germany.[3] It is composed of an upper and lower vessel connected thermally by the test specimen. Each vessel contains a low-boiling liquid with a different boiling point, the difference between these being 10 to 20 °C (50 to 68 °F). Experimentally, one measures the time required to transport through the

---

[3] Distributed in the United States by Dynatech Co., Cambridge, Mass.

test specimen a constant amount of heat, indicated by the filling of a standard volume with the distilled-over lower boiling liquid. The sample TC is then calculated from the time, the sample dimensions, and a calibration constant determined previously by means of a set of reference samples of known TC. The instrument can cover a wide TC range, from 10^{-3} to >1 W/cm °C, and is therefore suitable for plastics, semiconductors, and some metals. On the other hand, its temperature capability is only 23 to 170 °C (73 to 340 °F).

The test specimens were round or square coupons 12 to 18 mm wide and 2 to 20 mm thick. The coupons were obtained from composite rods fabricated by impregnating a unidirectional fiber bundle, weighing 15 to 20 g, with a conventional low-viscosity epoxy-hardener mixture and pressure-molding the wet layup at 93 °C (200 °F) into a rod containing 43 to 68 volume percent fiber. The coupons were sliced off the rod with a diamond saw and finished by conventional machining. Ordinarily two to five specimens were used for the TC determination, each specimen being measured three to six times. The repeatability was found to be within ± 6 percent. On the basis of the observed range of values it is felt that the measurement of the TC is accurate to ± 10 percent and that occasional larger deviations from the expected values are due to fluctuations in the composited fiber alignment, fiber distribution, or porosity.

Fiber TC by Direct Measurement

The selection of a suitable method for determining the TC of carbon fibers presented a problem owing to an almost total lack of background information on methods of measurement for oriented fibrous materials at or near room temperature. Techniques for measuring the TC of wire at elevated temperatures by means of optical pyrometry, although well known [6], are not readily adaptable to ambient temperatures. Following the indications of a literature survey and the advice of several authorities on the subject, we decided to concentrate on techniques based on the method of Kohlrausch [7,8].

Briefly, the original method of Kohlrausch consists of firmly attaching the ends of a long straight test bar or rod to two heat sinks maintained at a temperature T_a. The sample is then heated by electrical current until a steady-state condition is established in which the heat generated flows symmetrically from the center of the specimen to the terminal heat sinks at the ends. Knowing the electrical resistivity, ϱ, the potential drop across the specimen, V, and the maximum temperature at the center, T_m, the thermal conductivity, k, can be calculated from the equation

$$ k = \frac{V^2}{8\varrho(T_m - T_a)} \quad \text{(Watt/cm °C)} $$

The Kohlrausch equation is applicable exactly only to very long, thin test specimens showing a temperature-independent electrical resistivity and negligible lateral heat losses. For a carbon fiber test bundle, the first condition is partially fulfilled provided the temperature differential $\Delta T (= T_m - T_a)$ is not too large. Measurements of the electrical resistance of two typical medium- and high-modulus graphite fiber grades, Type II and GY-70, respectively, at 25 °C (77 °F) and 100 °C (212 °F), showed a resistivity drop of about 2.5 percent for the former and 11 percent for the latter grade, indicating that for very accurate TC determinations or large ΔT values a resistivity correction would have to be applied. Since in the present work the ΔT was mostly <50 °C (122 °F), no such correction was made. The second condition—no lateral heat losses—was not fulfilled, however, because the extremely large fiber surface/volume ratio and the high emissivity of graphite are contributing to radiative heat losses at rates that might greatly exceed the conductive heat flux rate along the fiber bundle [9]. In addition, the conductive heat loss along thermocouple wires could be substantial unless the size of the wire is minimized.

Nevertheless the Kohlrausch equation, expressed in a slightly different form, could be utilized to calculate an apparent fiber TC, k_a

$$k_a = \left(\frac{Ild}{D}\right)^2 \cdot \frac{\varrho}{\Delta T} \cdot 10^{11} \quad (\text{W/cm} \,^\circ\text{C})$$

where

I = electrical current, A,
ϱ = yarn resistivity, Ω/cm,
$\Delta T = T_m - T_a$, deg C,
T_m = temperature at center of yarn,
T_a = temperature at clamped ends of yarn,
l = gage length of yarn, cm,
D = yarn denier, g/9000 m, and
d = fiber density, g/cc.

A corrected TC, k, was then derived from the k_a by extrapolation as discussed in the following.

The dry fiber TC measurement was made in a special fixture designed and built at the Celanese Research Company to provide the necessary thermal and electrical contacts.

Its main components are two sets of water-cooled, spring-loaded copper blocks for clamping of the yarn ends, with the current and voltage leads and the two outer thermocouples located in front of the blocks. The distance between the blocks, that is, the fiber gage length, is adjustable stepwise from approximately 8 to 1 cm. The whole assembly is mounted on a 15-in. Cenco vacuum plate to permit measurements in a mechanical pump vacuum. The details of the construction are given in Ref 9.

Due to a varying contact resistance at the yarn bundle/holder interface, the yarn resistivity was determined prior to the actual TC measurement by means of a standard four-point Kelvin bridge. A functional diagram of the apparatus, referred to as the Dry Fiber Thermoconductometer, comprising the holder, an ac (50Hz) voltage and power supply, an ac voltmeter, and a potentiometer to measure the thermocouple emf's, is shown in Fig. 1. The lateral heat losses were decreased as far as possible for this setup by minimizing: (*a*) the fiber surface/volume ratio (increasing the bundle denier); (*b*) the temperature difference between the center of the fiber bundle and the ambient; (*c*) the gage length; and (*d*) by using vacuum to eliminate any heat loss by convection. Experimentally, it was found that the smallest practicable bundle denier was ≈ 4000, while denier values $>10\ 000$ were likely to give contact resistance problems. The conduction loss was minimized by employing the smallest thermocouple wire available (38 B&S gage, approximately 100 μm diameter). To establish a good contact between the center thermocouple bead and the surrounding filaments, the thermocouple junction was securely embedded in the fiber bundle and tied in place with a thermally resistant polymer string.

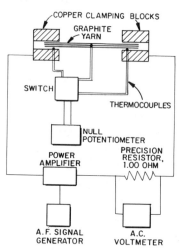

FIG. 1—*Diagram of the Dry Fiber Thermoconductometer assembly.*

The preferred test specimens were 8000 to 10 000-denier bundles, 15 to 20 cm long, weighing approximately 0.2 g per specimen. The TC measurements were made at several ΔT values or gage lengths on two specimens taken from different locations of the sample bobbin.

Other Fiber Properties

The fiber modulus was determined from 10 to 40 single filament measurements, and the fiber resistivity from 2 to 4 dry bundle measurements, in accordance with the techniques described by McMahon [10]. The fiber density was determined by the ASTM Test for Density of Plastics by the Density-Gradient Technique (D 1505) while the composite density was calculated from the weight and dimensions of the molded specimen. The fiber content of the carbon-epoxy composites was determined by chemical digestion, ASTM Test for Fiber Content of Reinforced Resin Composites (ASTM D 3171), and their void content from the volume fractions and densities of the components, ASTM Test for Void Content of Reinforced Plastics (D 2734).

Results and Discussion

Previous Studies

The large amount of past experimental and theoretical work concerning the TC of bulk graphites has been thoroughly reviewed by Kelly [11,12]. Basically, the TC of graphitic materials depends on the size of the crystallites, their perfection and orientation, and the amount of nongraphitic carbon present. Owing to the anisotropy of the graphite lattice, the crystallites themselves are quite anisotropic, having a high TC in the basal plane ("a") directions and a very low TC transversely to it ("c" direction). Consequently, the anistropy of the TC of a graphitic material can vary from highly anisotropic (for example, pyrolytic graphite) to practically isotropic (for example, Poco graphite). In all cases, however, the TC increases rapidly as the temperature rises from absolute zero, reaching a maximum the magnitude and location of which depend on the microstructure, the composition, and the fabrication history of the material. Ordinarily it peaks between 100 and 300 K, and its magnitude may vary approximately from 0.5 to 50 W/cm degree in the high TC direction and from 0.02 to 2 transversely. The observed temperature dependence and other TC features are fairly well understood theoretically [11,12], and good agreement between the experimental and calculated TC values has been observed [13].

The TC studies on graphitic fiber, on the other hand, have been confined to room temperature with only a few data reported so far. The TC of Thornel 40 is given as 0.8 W/cm°C by Blakslee et al [14], while that of Thornel 50 was reported as 1.18 W/cm°C at room temperature [15] and ~0.9 at 1600 K [16]. With respect to the graphitic fibers made from polyacrylonitrile precursor, the only TC data found were those reported by Knibbs et al [17] for the so-called Type I and Type II fibers as 1.02 and 0.22 W/cm°C, respectively, in addition to a previous value of 0.5 on a Type I fiber [18]. The behavior of the temperature dependence of the TC remains yet to be explored, although it may be expected, by analogy with bulk pyrolytic carbon, that the room-temperature values will not be much lower than the TC peak values located probably around 250 K.

Thermal Conductivity of Composited Fiber

The average thermal conductivities taken at a mean temperature of 52 °C (126 °F) of a number of commercial graphite fibers and their unidirectional composites are listed in Table 1 together with other pertinent fiber properties. The composite TC has been corrected for voids using a linear correction [19]: $k = k_0(1 - 2.3v)$, where k_0 is the void-free TC and v the fractional void content. Since most of the void contents are low, the correction is not too significant. Because of the appreciable data scatter range, ± 5 percent and ± 3 percent respectively, the modulus E and electric conductivity σ data are rounded off correspondingly. It is seen that of all the listed fiber properties the TC experiences the largest changes. While the E and σ change by roughly a factor of ten, the TC shows a forty-fold change—from 1.42 W/cm °C for the GY-70 fiber to 0.03 for the low-modulus VYB.

Thermal Conductivity of Dry Fiber

Extensive attempts to measure the dry fiber TC with the existing Colora thermoconductometer, using test plugs cut from a bundle of graphite fibers enclosed in a shrinkable plastic tube, were not successful.

After the Dry Fiber Thermoconductometer was built and put into use, it was established that the large contribution of radiative heat losses from the heated fiber bundle, even near room temperature, interferes with the direct determination of the TC. A theoretical correction for the radiative heat loss as a function of gage length would have to take into account the emissivity of the graphite fiber, which depends on its surface composition and morphology, the emissivity of the surrounding medium, the effective radiating bundle perimeter which changes with the shape and size of the mounted test yarn, and the geometry of the test fixture into which the fiber bundle radiates. Since such a calculation was beyond the scope of the present effort, empirical approaches were used to minimize the effects of the radiative heat loss. Since the radiative heat loss rate is proportional to $(T_m^4 - T_a^4)$, where T_m and T_a are the temperatures of the conductor and the surroundings respectively [20], the first approach was to employ as small a temperature difference ($\Delta T = T_m - T_a$) as possible without excessive loss of reproducibility. Indeed it was found possible to determine a reasonably accurate k by plotting the apparent thermal conductivities, k_a, calculated for a series of successively smaller ΔT, for example, from approximately 50 to 10 °C (122 to 50 °F), at a constant gage length of 7.7 cm, and extrapolating the resulting curve. The extrapolation can be done either linearly from a plot of k_a versus ΔT, extrapolating to $\Delta T = 1$, or

TABLE 1—*Thermal conductivities^a and other physical properties of commercial carbon fibers and their unidirectional composites.*

Fiber Manufacturer	Grade	Unidirectional Composite				Fiber TC, W/cm°C	Electrical Conductivity, ohm⁻¹cm⁻¹	Density, g/cm³	Tensile Modulus	
		Density, g/cm³	Fiber Content, volume %	Void Content, volume %	TC, W/cm°C				million psi	GN/m²
Celanese	Celion GY-70	1.58	56	3.0	0.80	1.42	1610	1.98	77	530
Courtaulds	HMS	1.49	49	2.5	0.46	0.97	1260	1.88	62	430
Union Carbide	Thornel 50	1.39	64	5.5	0.38	0.60	950	1.63	49	340
Morgan	Type II	...	50	...	0.098	0.20	770	1.82	38	260
Courtaulds	HTS	1.42	56.5	4	0.092	0.17	700	1.68	36	250
Union Carbide	Thornel 300	1.60	52	1	0.050	0.094	560	1.75	36	250
Union Carbide	Thornel 400	1.57	60	2.5	0.048	0.080	480	1.78	33	230
Hercules	Grafil A	1.56	59	0	0.036	0.060	500	1.80	36	250
Great Lakes Carbon Co.	Fortafil 3T	1.51	51	1	0.034	0.067	510	1.76	32	220
Hitco	CY-2-1	1.34	57	2	0.022	0.038	270	1.47	...	...
Union Carbide	VYB	1.35	52	4.5	0.016	0.030	130	1.53	6	40
Epoxy Resin (Epi-Rez 510/HHPA)		...	...	...	2.2×10^{-3}*	...	...	...	...	...

^{a}Measured at an average temperature of 52°C (126°F).

alternatively from a plot of k_a versus log ΔT and extrapolating to log $\Delta T = 1$. The first kind of extrapolation seems preferable when reliable k_a data are present at low-temperature differences, say 20 °C (68 °F) or less. The log-log approach, on the other hand, gives more consistent curves for the low TC fibers or at large ΔT values, the 30 to 60 °C (86 to 140 °F) range. Table 2 gives a comparison between the fiber TC data calculated

TABLE 2—*Comparison of fiber thermal conductivities determined by indirect and direct methods.*

Manufacturer	Grade	TC from Unidirectional Composite, W/cm °C	TC of Dry Fiber by Extrapolation of ΔT, W/cm °C
Celanese	GY-70	1.42	1.38
Courtaulds	HMS	0.97	0.90
Union Carbide	Thornel 50	0.60	0.61
Morgan	Type II	0.20	0.17
Courtaulds	HTS	0.17	0.21
Hitco	CY-2-1	0.038	0.18
Union Carbide	VYB	0.030	0.18

by the composite route and those obtained directly from the dry yarn measurement by extrapolation. It is seen that the agreement is reasonably good for fiber TC values above 0.18 W/cm °C. It could not be used, however, on the low TC fibers, because the extrapolation plots tend to converge to a $k_a \approx 0.16$. Other techniques, based on the extrapolation of k_a to shorter gage lengths or the use of other than the Kolrausch equation, were then developed to determine the TC of carbon fiber bundles in the lower TC range, 0.02 to 0.2 W/cm °C. The details of these developments are given elsewhere [21]. A comparison between the low TC fiber data obtained by the composite route and directly from the dry fiber measurement is given in Table 3, in addition to data on some fibers not available in sufficient quantity for compositing. In all cases the mean temperature of the measurement, $\frac{1}{2}(T_m - T_a)$, ranged from 20 to 25 °C (68 to 73 °F).

Relationship Between Thermal Conductivity and Other Physical Properties

The most widely known relationship between the thermal and electrical conductivities, k and σ, is the Wiedemann-Franz rule: $k/\sigma T = $ constant $= 2.45 \times 10^{-8}$ (V/K)^2, which is not valid for graphite except near absolute zero [22]. It has been noted, however, that for numerous bulk graphites at high temperatures the ratio k/σ becomes nearly constant and independent of temperature [23], a value of 0.36×10^{-3} V^2/°C having been quoted for >1500 K [24]. Even at room temperature (300 K) the k/σ has been found to be fairly constant for many graphites [25] with a numerical

TABLE 3—Thermal conductivities and other physical properties of some lower TC carbon fibers.

Manufacturer	Grade[a]	Fiber TC		Electrical Conductivity, ohm⁻¹cm⁻¹	Density, g/cm³	Tensile Modulus	
		From Unidirectional Composite, W/cm°C	By Extrapolation of Gage Length, W/cm°C			million psi	GN/m²
Union Carbide	Thornel 300	0.094	0.092	560	1.75	36	250
Stackpole	Panex A	...[a]	0.10	550	1.76	33	225
Hercules	Grafil A	0.060	0.075	500	1.80	36	250
Great Lakes Carbon Co.	Fortafil 3T	0.067	0.063	510	1.76	32	220
	Fortafil 4R	...[a]	0.16	750	1.75	41	285
Celanese	Experimental						
	2-374-02	0.022	0.021	25	1.78	16	110
	2-374-03	0.030	0.025	62	1.83	20	140
	2-374-04	0.038	0.034	250	1.82	24	165

[a] A sufficient amount for compositing was not available.

value around 1 to 1.3 × 10⁻³ V²/°C *[17,23]*. As far as graphitic fibers are concerned, Knibbs *[17]* indicated that the British Type I and II fibers have widely differing k/σ ratios at room temperature. The present results fully confirm this: the k/σ decreases progressively from 0.88 × 10⁻³ V²/°C for the high-modulus GY-70 to 0.12 × 10⁻³ for the Grafil A tow. The relationship between the k and σ of the commercial high-modulus fibers, however, is linear above 0.2 W/cm °C but much less so at lower k values, as shown in Fig. 2. For fibers having moduli of 40 million psi (275 GN/m²) or more, these can be correlated satisfactorily by either of the following expressions: $k = 3.55 \log\sigma - 10.0$, having a correlation coefficient, $r = 0.995$; or $k = 1.4 \times 10^{-3} \sigma - 0.85$ (W/cm °C), where $r = 0.994$. Another type of correlation, used for bulk graphites *[26]*, appears to be valid only for graphite fibers having elastic moduli of 50 milllion psi or more

$$\frac{1}{k} = 2.3 \times 10^3 \left(\frac{1}{\sigma}\right) - 0.70 \quad (W/cm\,°C)$$

In the range of 10 to 300 ohm⁻¹cm⁻¹, the relationship $k = 0.016 \log\sigma$ may be used for estimating the fiber TC. Between 300 and 600 ohm⁻¹cm⁻¹, however, there is a considerable scatter of both the thermal and electrical conductivity data, indicating that the microstructure of these fibers is rather varied.

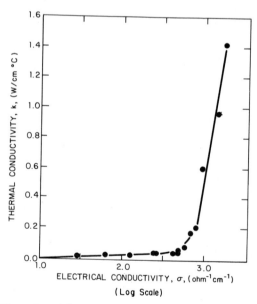

FIG. 2—*Thermal conductivity and electrical conductivity of carbon fibers.*

The change in k with fiber modulus E is depicted in Fig. 3. Again, at 40 million psi or above, the k increases linearly with the fiber modulus according to

$$k = 0.032 E - 1.0, (E \text{ in million psi}) \text{ with } r = 0.996$$

At lower moduli the k values show little dependence on the modulus.

The relationship between the E and σ above 38 million psi modulus ($\sigma > 600 \text{ ohm}^{-1}\text{cm}^{-1}$) is given by either

$$E = 0.044\sigma + 5.7; \text{ correlation coefficient, } r = 0.996$$

or

$$E = 110.9 \log\sigma - 280; r = 0.994$$

with E in million psi. Similar relationships have been reported previously for graphitic fibers originating from both rayon or PAN precursors [10,27,28]. The approximate linearity between the axial fiber modulus and the electrical or thermal conductivities indicates that, once the graphite basal planes have become highly oriented, further changes in the aforementioned properties are largely determined by the intercrystalline microstructure, that is, by the microposity and the density, composition, and nature of the intercrystalline boundary. Below 30 million psi modulus level, however, additional, not clearly identifiable effects appear, causing a rapid decrease in the fiber electrical conductivity.

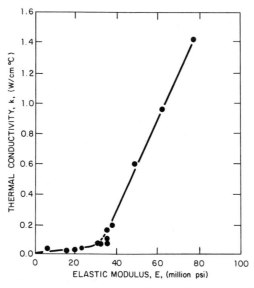

FIG. 3—*Thermal conductivity and elastic modulus of carbon fibers.*

Summary

The axial thermal conductivity of a number of high-modulus graphitic fibers, manufactured mostly by pyrolysis of a PAN precursor, was determined near room temperature either from the measured TC of their unidirectional composites or by a direct method, or both. A device for the direct determination of the as-received carbon fiber TC utilizing electrical heating of the fiber bundle was constructed and evaluated. Because of the large radiative heat losses, the correct TC values could not be measured directly, but had to be obtained by extrapolation to lower temperature differentials or shorter gage lengths. The TC of fourteen commercial carbon fiber grades was measured and found to vary from 1.42 W/cm °C for the very high-modulus GY-70 to 0.03 for the VYB grade yarn. Above 0.1 W/cm °C (>600 ohm⁻¹cm⁻¹), the TC increases linearly with increasing electrical conductivity or elastic modulus. Below 0.06 W/cm °C, however, a decreasing TC is accompanied by a sharply lower electric conductivity and little dependence on the modulus. In general, the TC of the carbon fibers is considerably lower than expected from the available TC data on pyrolytic bulk graphites [29], probably because of the reportedly small basal plane crystallite sizes [30]. The very low thermal and electrical conductivities encountered in some low-modulus carbon fibers, however, must be ascribed to additional intracrystalline lattice distortions causing large deviations from lattice periodicity.

Acknowledgment

This work was sponsored by the Air Force Materials Laboratory, Nonmetallic Materials Division, under the guidance of the late H. M. Ezekiel as project engineer. The permission by AFML and by Celanese Co. to publish this paper is gratefully acknowledged. I also wish to thank both G. J. Breckenridge and G. Brenn, who showed great skill and dexterity in developing reliable operating procedures for the respective dry fiber and composite fiber thermoconductometers.

References

[1] Schmidt, D. L., in *Environmental Effects on Polymeric Materials,* D. V. Rosato and R. T. Schwartz, Eds., Interscience, New York, 1968, Chapters 5, 6.

[2] Marks, B. S., Technical Report NASA CR-1723, National Aeronautics and Space Administration, Washington, D.C., May 1971.

[3] Springer, G. S. and Tsai, W. S., *Journal of Composite Materials,* Vol. 1, No. 2, 1967, p. 166.

[4] Behrens, E., *Journal of Composite Materials,* Vol. 2, No. 1, 1968, p. 1.

[5] Schroeder, J., *Review of Scientific Instruments,* Vol. 34, 1963, p. 615.

[6] Flynn, D. R., in *Thermal Conductivity,* R. P. Tye, Ed., Academic Press, New York, 1969, Vol. 1, Ch. 5.

[7] Kohlrausch, F., *Annalen Physik,* Vol. 1, 1900, p. 132.

[8] Jaeger, W. and Diesselhorst, H., *Abhandlungen Physikalisch-Technischer Reichsanstalt,* Vol. 3, 1900, p. 269.

[9] Kalnin, I. L. et al, Technical Report AFML-TR-72-151 Part I., Air Force Materials Laboratory, Dayton, Ohio, Nov. 1972.

[10] McMahon, P. E., in *Analysis of Test Methods for High Modulus Fibers and Composites, ASTM STP 521,* American Society for Testing and Materials, 1973, pp. 372–377.

[11] Kelly, B. T. in *Chemistry and Physics of Carbon,* P. L. Walker, Jr., Ed., Marcel Dekker, New York, Vol. 5, 1969, pp. 119–215.

[12] Kelly, B. T. and Taylor, R. in *Chemistry and Physics of Carbon,* P. L. Walker, Jr., Ed., Marcel Dekker, New York, Vol. 10, 1973, pp. 1–140.

[13] Taylor, R. et al, *Carbon,* Vol. 6, 1968, pp. 537–544.

[14] Blakslee, O. L. et al, *Proceedings,* National SAMPE Symposium, Society of Aerospace Materials and Process Engineering, Anaheim, Calif., Vol. 12, 1967, AC-6.

[15] Union Carbide Co., Technical Information Bulletin 465-217 jj, no date.

[16] Taylor, R. E., Technical Report AFML-TR-72-9, Air Force Materials Laboratory, Dayton, Ohio, Feb. 1972.

[17] Knibbs, R. H. et al, *Proceedings,* Annual Technical Conference on Reinforced Plastics/ Composites Division, Society of the Plastics Industry, Vol. 26, 1971, 8-F.

[18] Johnson, W. and Watt, W., *Nature,* Vol. 215, July 22, 1967, p. 384.

[19] Hutcheon, J. M. and Price, M. S. T., *Proceedings 4th Carbon Conference,* Pergamon Press, New York, London, 1960, p. 645.

[20] Holland, F. A. et al, *Heat Transfer,* Elsevier, New York, 1970, p. 529.

[21] Kalnin, I. L. et al, Technical Report AFML-TR-73-191, Air Force Materials Laboratory, Dayton, Ohio, Aug. 1973.

[22] Reynolds, W. N., *Physical Properties of Graphite,* Elsevier, New York, 1968, pp. 73–80.

[23] Bowman, J. C. et al, *1st Conference on Carbon and Graphite,* Society of Chemical Industry, London, 1958, p. 52.

[24] Lutcov, A. I. et al, *Carbon,* Vol. 8, 1970, p. 753.

[25] Lutcov, A. I. et al, *Inzhenerno-fizicheskii Zhurnal,* Vol. 22, No. 5, 1972, p. 932.

[26] Mason, I. B. and Knibbs, R. H., Technical Report UK AEA R-3973, Harwell, England, 1962.

[27] Bacon, R. and Schalamon, W. A., *Applied Polymer Symposia,* Vol. 9, 1969, p. 285–292.

[28] Ezekiel, H. M., *Journal of Applied Physics,* Vol. 41, No. 13, 1970, p. 5351.

[29] Moore, A. W. in *Chemistry and Physics of Carbon,* P. L. Walker, Jr. and P. A. Thrower, Eds., Marcel Dekker, New York, 1973, Vol. 11, p. 106.

[30] Johnson, D. J. and Tyson, C. N., *British Journal of Applied Physics (Journal of Physics D.),* Series 2, Vol. 2, 1970, p. 787; Vol. 3, 1970, p. 526.

A. S. D. Wang,[1] R. B. Pipes,[2] and A. Ahmadi[3]

Thermoelastic Expansion of Graphite-Epoxy Unidirectional and Angle-Ply Composites

REFERENCE: Wang, A. S. D., Pipes, R. B., and Ahmadi, A., "**Thermoelastic Expansion of Graphite-Epoxy Unidirectional and Angle-Ply Composites,**" *Composite Reliability, ASTM STP 580,* American Society for Testing and Materials, 1975, pp. 574–585.

ABSTRACT: An experimental investigation of the thermal expansion of a unidirectional fiber-reinforced composite material is described herein. The basic material used in the tests was a prepreg graphite-epoxy tape, designated as Modmor-II, supplied by NARMCO. Unidirectional and angel-ply laminates were made from the prepreg tape and were tested for their linear thermal expansion in the temperature range between 25 and 150 °C (77 and 302 °F). The experimental results compared reasonably well with the predicted values of the thermal expansion coefficients calculated based on several existing linear elastic micromechanics theories and lamination theories.

KEY WORDS: composite materials, thermal expansion, mechanical properties, elastic theory, laminates, fibers

Thermal elastic analyses of structural composite materials require the knowledge of their thermomechanical properties. Generally speaking, the thermal and mechanical properties of materials are closely coupled, even for elastic, homogeneous, and isotropic solids. In practice, however, the evaluation of the thermal properties for some structural composites often excludes consideration of their simultaneous mechanical responses such as internal stress relaxation. Furthermore, for a relatively small temperature change—typically in the range of 25 to 150 °C (77 to 302 °F)—the affected thermal strains in composites are often assumed to be a linear function of the change of temperature. These assumptions are adopted of course only

---

[1] Visiting professor, National Taiwan University and Chung-Shan Research Institute of Science and Technology, Taiwan, China.

[2] Associate professor of mechanical and aerospace engineering, University of Delaware, Newark, Del. 19711.

[3] Visiting assistant professor of civil engineering, Drexel University, Philadelphia, Pa. 19104.

for simplicity, since it is well known that composites of polymeric phases are essentially viscoelastic in nature, and to some extent the polymeric phase materials have been found to behave nonlinearly under thermal or mechanical loads.

The problem of predicting the effective thermal expansion coefficients (TEC) for multiphase composites has been studied by many authors. Here, we mention the works by Schapery [1],[4] who developed an energy method calculating the bounds for the effective TEC of composite materials made of isotropic phases. Explicit formulas were given for volumetric and linear TEC of both elastic and viscoelastic composites. Recently, Schneider [2] computed the effective TEC for unidirectional fiber-reinforced composites by solving an elasticity problem assuming elastic isotropic phases. A hexagonal cylindrical assemblage was used in the solution following a similar procedure by Rosen and Hashin [3]. Basically, these theories attempt to relate the effective TEC of the composite in terms of their constituent properties. When the directionally dependent TEC of an individual lamina are known, the effective TEC for multilayered laminates can also be reasonably evaluated by means of lamination theory [4,5].

The purpose of the present paper is to investigate experimentally the thermal (equilibrium) responses of a typical graphite-epoxy system subject to temperature changes from approximately 25 to 150°C (77 to 302°F). The composite system is made of epoxy resin and Modmor-II graphite fibers, both of which were supplied by the Whitaker Division, NARMCO. An examination of the mechanical properties of the epoxy resin was first carried out, followed by the measurements of the effective TEC for: the epoxy, the unidirectional laminates, and the angle-ply laminates. The experimental results for the TEC are shown to compare reasonably well with the analytical predictions, using the formulas given both by Schapery [1] (when specialized to elastic unidirectional composite) and by Schneider [2] for the unidirectional laminates, and the formulas given by Halpin and Pagano [6] for the angle-ply laminates.

Experiment

Description of Specimens and Tests

Three basic types of specimens were used in the tests:

(a) Dog-bone-shaped epoxy coupons which were machined from a cast billet. The effective portion of the coupon (excluding end tabs) had a uniform thickness of 0.25 cm, a width of 0.75 cm, and a length of 7.5 cm.

(b) Unidirectional laminates made by stacking eight layers of the prepreg tape. The laminates were autoclave cured in accordance with the recommended procedures.

---

[4]The italic numbers in brackets refer to the list of references appended to this paper.

(c) Balanced ±45-deg angle-ply laminates eight layers thick. The overall thickness of the laminates was about 0.125 cm, and the fiber volume fraction determined from photomicrographs was 57.7 percent.

The following two basic tests were undertaken to determine the thermal (equilibrium) elastic responses:

(a) Uniaxial static and creep tension tests for the epoxy resin at four equal temperature levels ranging from 25 to 150 °C (77 to 302 °F). The static tension tests were performed using an Instron test machine at a constant strain rate of 0.1 min⁻¹. The creep tests were conducted using a deadweight apparatus at various stress levels.

(b) Thermal strain measurement at six temperatures from 25 to 150 °C (77 to 302 °F). Thermal expansion coefficients were determined for the epoxy resin, for the unidirectional laminates along their two principal directions as well as along a set of directions 15 deg and −65 deg from the fibers, and for the ±45-deg laminates also along a set of principle axes 45 deg from the fibers.

In addition to these two basic tests, a series of static and creep tests was also performed for 0-deg laminates. Since in this case the loading axis is parallel to the fibers, the test results were used to provide information about the behavior of the fibers.

In all the tests, a pair of 90-deg strain-gage rosettes was installed on both sides of each specimen in the same orientation. The readings in the strains of the corresponding gages were averaged to represent the strain in a given orientation of the specimen.

Thermal Strain Measurement

In the thermal strain measurement, we followed the common procedure of employing a wheatstone-bridge along with an electric oven capable of controlling a temperature to within ±0.5 °C in the range −40 to 300 °C (−40 to 572 °F). Thermal strain readings (apparent strain) were taken for at least six temperature increments from room temperature [approximately 25 °C (77 °F)] to 150 °C (302 °F). For each temperature increment, a thermal equilibrium period of as long as half an hour was allowed before a reading was taken.

The change in resistance of a typical resistance strain gage subjected to a change in temperature is produced by three effects [6]: (a) The gage grid elongation ($\Delta L/L = \alpha \Delta T$); (b) the base material upon which the gage is mounted elongation ($\Delta L/L = \beta \Delta T$); and (c) the change in resistivity of the gage material ($\Delta R/R = \gamma \Delta T$). Thus, if ε is the apparent strain, the true thermal strain of the base material is given by [6]

$$\beta \Delta T = \varepsilon + \alpha \Delta T - \gamma \Delta T / S_g \qquad (1)$$

where α and β are the TEC of the gage and the base materials, respectively,

γ is the coefficient of resistivity of the gage, and S_g is the gage factor of the strain gage.

In the present tests, the gage rosettes used were made of 2024-T4 aluminum whose TEC is approximately constant ($23.4 \times 10^{-6}/°C$) in the temperature range of interest. In order to determine the quantity γ/S_g, a pair of the gage rosettes was mounted on both sides of a 5 by 5 by 0.75 cm 2024-T4 aluminum plate which was then subjected to the same temperature environment as those other specimens. Since the base and the gage were of the same material, $\alpha = \beta$, it follows from Eq 1 that after a sufficient period of thermal equilibrium

$$\gamma\Delta T = \varepsilon S_g = (\Delta R/R)|_{\Delta T}, \qquad \alpha = \beta \qquad (2)$$

where ΔT is the change in temperature from the reference temperature.

Figure 1 shows the average apparent thermal strain ε of the aluminum plate as a function of temperature. Note that the slope of the ε-ΔT curve gives the value for γ/S_g. In the case, the curve is quite nonlinear and is represented by piecewise linear segments as shown in the figure. Hence, one calculates the TEC of the base material from Eq 1.

Temperature Elastic Moduli of Epoxy and Composite Laminates

The uniaxial and creep test results indicate considerable viscoelasticity of the epoxy resin. In fact, the material responses were also found to be nonlinear when the stress and the temperature levels are high. Figure 2

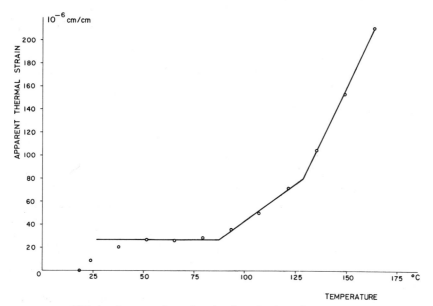

FIG. 1—*Apparent thermal strain of an aluminum-base material.*

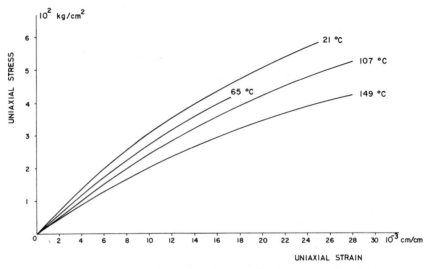

FIG. 2—*Static stress-strain relation of epoxy at various temperature levels.*

shows the static stress-strain curves at different temperatures. It is seen that the transition from linear to nonlinear is not apparent. It is rather difficult, for example, to determine the Young's modulus for each curve. The creep data indicate also a nonlinearity for the epoxy (detailed creep data analyses are contained in separate reports *[7,8]*). It was observed however, that the response of the epoxy is primarily linearly viscoelastic for temperatures below 100 °C (212 °F) and at stress levels less than 30 percent of ultimate. Figure 3 shows the relaxation moduli, $E_m(t)$, for the epoxy specimens subjected to about 20 percent of ultimate stress at various temperatures. At this low stress level, the curves are seen to possess the usual trend of parallel straight lines as they are plotted in a semi-log scale. If these lines could be extended to very small time, one would obtain the 'instantaneous' Young's modulus E_m. But practical difficulty exists because of the insufficient data collected for short-time responses. Here, in the face of being less vigorous, we simply determine E_m by extending the straight lines to 1 s of time from Fig. 3. These values are compared with those best estimated using Fig. 2. The comparison is illustrated in Fig. 4. In Fig. 5, a similar comparison is displayed for the Poisson ratio v_m. Here, it should be remarked that at low stress levels (up to 30 percent of ultimate) the Poisson ratio is essentially constant in time and is affected slightly by an increase of temperature up to 100 °C (212 °F). The average value of v_m is 0.42. When the stress or temperature levels increase, however, the Poisson ratio varies considerably with time and temperature *[8]*.

In the static and creep tests for the 0-deg laminates, it was found that

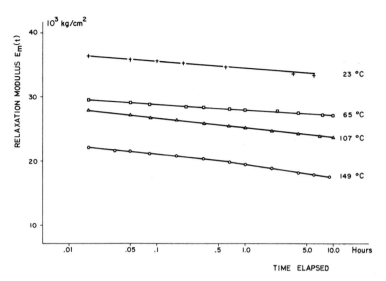

FIG. 3—*Relaxation modulus of epoxy at various temperature levels.*

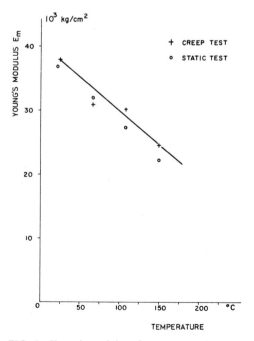

FIG. 4—*Young's modulus of epoxy versus temperature.*

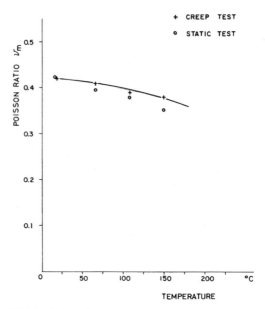

FIG. 5—*Poisson's ratio of epoxy versus temperature.*

the laminate (and hence the fibers) is essentially linear elastic when the applied load in the direction of the fibers is under 80 percent of ultimate, and the temperature is below 150 °C (302 °F).

If the usual rule-of-mixtures

$$E_L = V_m E_m + V_f E_f, \qquad v_{LT} = V_m v_m + V_f v_f \tag{3}$$

holds, we can determine E_f and v_f by measuring directly the values of E_L and v_{LT} and with prior knowledge of the fiber volume fraction $V_f = (1 - V_m)$, and the constants E_m, v_m. These are found to be

$$E_f \cong 2.355 \text{ kg/cm}^2 \ (33.5 \times 10^6 \text{ psi}), \qquad v_f \cong 0.1 \tag{4}$$

which are in agreement with data for the Morganite II fiber (35×10^6 psi and 0.1, respectively).

It should be pointed out that graphite fiber is generally anisotropic; therefore the value for v_f found by Eq 3 is probably relevant only to the unidirectional laminates used in the present setting. It is not clear what value v_f should have when there is stress applied transverse to the fibers. It is believed generally that the value is not far from ± 0.1, and hence the influence in the composite is insignificant.

From the preceding analysis it is concluded that, although the epoxy resin definitely behaves viscoelastically, its linear elastic moduli could be used, at least as a first approximation, to predict the TEC of epoxy reinforced with graphite fibers. It was also found that the anisotropy of the fibers could also be neglected.

Discussion of Results for TEC

TEC of Unidirectional Laminates

The TEC for epoxy, β_m, obtained experimentally is shown in Fig. 6. At room temperature it has a value of $51 \times 10^{-6}/°C$. It increases slightly with temperature and its glass transition point seems to lie around $150°C$ ($302°F$) although it is not readily apparent from the limited data. As for the TEC of the graphite fiber, it is believed to be very small, and we set $\beta_f \cong 0$.

According to the formulas given by Schapery (when specialized to unidirectional fibrous composite) and by Schneider, the TEC in the fiber direction of the unidirectional laminates is

$$\beta_L = \frac{\beta_f E_f V_f + \beta_m E_m V_m}{E_f V_f + E_m V_m} \tag{5}$$

The TEC transverse to the fibers of the unidirectional laminates given by Schapery has the form

$$\beta_T = \beta_f V_f (1 + \nu_f) + \beta_m V_m (1 + \nu_m) - \beta_L (\nu_f V_f + \nu_m V_m) \tag{6}$$

while Schneider gives a more complicated form

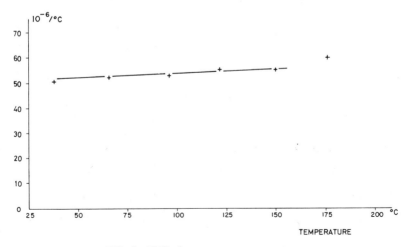

FIG. 6—*TEC of epoxy versus temperature.*

$$\beta_T = \beta_f K + \beta_m (1 - K) \qquad (7)$$

where

$$K = \frac{a_1{}^2 v_m - 2a_1(1 - v_m) - 4}{2(a_2 + a_1 a_3 - a_4) E_m D} - \frac{v_m R}{D + R}$$

and

$$a_1 = \frac{2v_f D + 2v_m R}{D + R} \qquad a_2 = -\left(\frac{v_m}{E_m} + \frac{1}{E_m D[1 - 1.1V_f]E_m}\right)$$

$$a_3 = \frac{v_f}{E_f} + \frac{v_m}{E_m} \qquad a_4 = \frac{1 - v_f}{E_f}$$

$$R = E_f/E_m \qquad D = \frac{1 - 1.1V_f}{1.1V_f}$$

For small β_f and v_f and large E_f/E_m, Eq 6 and 7 may be approximated by the same equation

$$\beta_T = \beta_f V_f + \beta_m V_m (1 - v_m) \qquad (8)$$

which is the rule of mixtures.

Figure 7 shows the comparison between the experimental β_L and β_T and the corresponding predictions using Eqs 5, 6, 7, and 8. Except for the TEC calculated using Eq 7, close agreement is indicated.[5] Both β_L and β_T differ slightly from a constant value, due to the nonlinear effect of the epoxy resin.

When β_L and β_T of the unidirectional composite are used in a linear coordinate transformation, one obtains β_x and β_y in terms of β_L and β_T

$$\beta_x = \beta_L \cos^2\theta + \beta_T \sin^2\theta$$
$$\beta_y = \beta_L \sin^2\theta + \beta_T \cos^2\theta \qquad (9)$$

where θ is the angle of a rotation between the x-y and L-T axes. Figure 8 shows the comparison between β_x, β_y calculated from Eq 9 and those measured experimentally for 15-deg off-angle specimens.

[5] In a recent paper [9], Kalnin modified the Schneider equation and computed β_T for high-modulus graphite-epoxy unidirectional composites wherein the constants E_f, v_f, and β_f are measured transverse to the fibers. It is not clear what procedures were employed in determining these quantities.

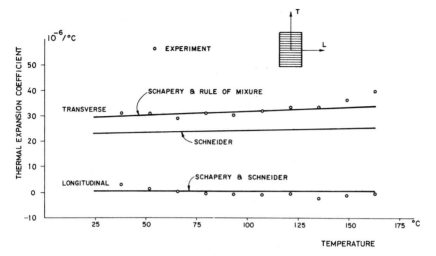

FIG. 7—*Comparison of the TEC between experiment and theory.*

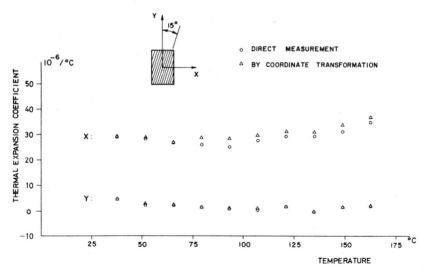

FIG. 8—*Comparison of the TEC between direct measurement and coordinate transformation.*

TEC of ±45-deg Angle-Ply Laminates

For laminates of zero bending-extension coupling, Halpin and Pagano *[10]* formulated an exact expression for the TEC. The TEC computed using the Halpin-Pagano formulation are illustrated in Fig. 9 along with the experimental results. The comparison shows reasonable agreement.

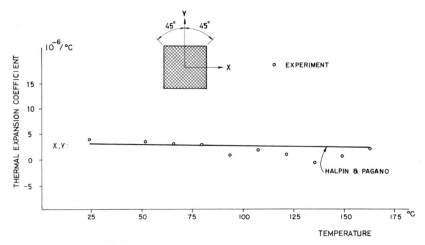

FIG. 9—*Comparison of the TEC for a ±45-deg laminate between experiment and theory.*

Concluding Remark

In conclusion, the linear theories predicting the TEC for unidirectional and angle-ply laminates are shown to be satisfactory for the graphite-epoxy system used, even though the effects of viscoelasticity of the epoxy and the possible anisotropy of the graphite fibers were neglected. Because of the rather long time period necessary for observation of the TEC for the laminates, stress relaxation in the epoxy is inevitable at higher temperatures. Use of the elastic moduli of epoxy in the various theories predicting the TEC is probably inadequate at high temperature levels, as can be seen in the results. The agreement between the theory and experiment could be improved somewhat if Schapery's viscoelastic formulation [1] was adopted in the formulation.

References

[1] Schapery, R. A., *Journal of Composite Materials,* Vol. 2, No. 3, July 1968, pp. 380–404.
[2] Schneider, W., *Kunststoffe,* Vol. 61, No. 4, April 1971, pp. 273–277.
[3] Rosen, B. W. and Hashin, Z., *International Journal of Engineering Science,* Vol. 8, 1970, pp. 157–173.
[4] Ashton, J. E., Halpin, J. C., and Petit, P. H., *Primer on Composite Materials: Analysis,* Technomic, Stamford, Conn., 1969, pp. 88–91.
[5] Chou, P. C., Carleone, J., and Hsu, C., *Journal of Composite Materials,* Vol. 6, No. 1, 1972, pp. 80–93.
[6] Dally, J. W. and Riley, W. F., *Experimental Stress Analysis,* McGraw-Hill, New York, 1965, pp. 377–379.
[7] Wang, A. S. D., McQuillen, E. J., and Ahmadi, A., *Proceedings,* The 1974 Symposium on Mechanical Behavior of Materials, Kyoto, Japan, pp. II-9(2).

[8] Ahmadi, A., "Theoretical and Experimental Studies on the Creep Behavior of a Graphite-Epoxy Composite Material," Ph.D. thesis, Drexel University, Philadelphia, Pa., 1974.

[9] Kalnin, I. L., *Proceedings,* The Society of the Plastic Industry, Vol. 29, 1974, Section 21-C, pp. 1–8.

[10] Halpin, J. C. and Pagano, N. J., "Consequences of Environmentally Induced Dilation in Solids," Technical Report AFML-TR-68-395, Air Force Materials Laboratory, Dayton, Ohio, 1969.

M. B. Kasen[1]

Properties of Filamentary-Reinforced Composites at Cryogenic Temperatures

REFERENCE: Kasen, M. B., **"Properties of Filamentary-Reinforced Composites at Cryogenic Temperatures,"** *Composite Reliability, ASTM STP 580,* American Society for Testing and Materials, 1975, pp. 586–611.

ABSTRACT: This paper presents a review of a series of significant publications on the mechanical and thermal properties of filamentary-reinforced structural composites in the cryogenic temperature range. The objective, scope of work, and significant conclusions of the selected works are discussed. The temperature dependence of the ultimate tensile strength, tensile modulus, thermal conductivity, and thermal contraction (expansion) is presented for selected composites developed in each program. Problem areas are defined and suggestions are made for future work.

KEY WORDS: composite materials, reviews, structural composites, cryogenics, glass, boron, graphite, reinforced plastics, aluminum, tensile strength, modulus of elasticity, thermal conductivity, thermal expansion

Nomenclature

NOL   Naval Ordinance Laboratory
UFW   Uniaxial filament-wound
BFW   Biaxial filament-wound
GFRP   Glass fiber reinforced plastic
CFRP   Carbon fiber reinforced plastic
BFRP   Boron fiber reinforced plastic
NMA   Nadic methyl anhydride
BDMA   Benzyldimethylamine
L-100   Polyurethane resin (Adiprene)
MOCA   4, 4'-methylenedianiline
DSA   Dodecenyl succinic anhydride

The primary impetus for structural composite development has arisen

[1] Staff scientist, Cryogenic, NBS-Institute for Basic Standards, Boulder, Colo. 80302.

from the desire to obtain improved mechanical properties at room and elevated temperatures, to save weight, and to reduce the cost for current and future aerospace hardware applications. Comparatively little effort has been expended on development of composites for use at cryogenic temperatures. A notable exception has been a fairly extensive body of work sponsored by the National Aeronautics and Space Administration (NASA) and the U.S. Air Force (USAF) wherein a series of glass-reinforced composites was evaluated down to 20 K. Such materials were subsequently successfully used as baffles and structural support components in various aerospace applications. The other major field of cryogenic composite development has been filament-winding for fabrication of cryogenic pressure vessels. In recent years, advanced fibers have also been investigated for the latter application. To a large extent, the remaining published data reflect work in which cryogenic properties were peripheral to the main work objective.

The relative lack of emphasis on cryogenic structural composites is understandable, as the majority of the applications are presently satisfied by well-characterized metals and alloys. Why then should one consider composites for such applications? The answer lies in the increasingly stringent demands being made on materials in advancing cryogenic technology, of which the development of superconducting machinery may serve as an example. While the first generation of such machines will be almost entirely dependent on metals technology, it is highly probable that succeeding generations will capitalize on composite technology for reasons of increased reliability, reduced weight, and increased overall efficiency, as composites offer higher specific strengths and moduli combined with a wider range of thermal and electrical properties than are available with any metal or alloy.

A major barrier to the wider use of structural composites for cryogenic applications is the lack of broad characterization and handbook-type data describing the properties and performance of such materials under cryogenic conditions. The Cryogenic Division of the National Bureau of Standards (NBS) has therefore undertaken a comprehensive survey of the literature on the mechanical and thermal properties of structural composites from about 1960 to the present time. In the course of the survey, it became apparent that there existed several bodies of work that were particularly outstanding and which deserved more detailed analysis than was possible in the more comprehensive review. It is the intent of the present paper to consider the results of these selected studies, reviewing their objectives, the scope of the work undertaken, and the general conclusions reached by the authors. Subsequently, selected composite types developed in each program are discussed in some detail. In the interest of brevity, discussions of the properties are restricted to ultimate tensile strength, tensile modulus, tensile fatigue, thermal contraction, and thermal conductivities, as these properties are of most interest to the potential users.

The discussion of properties given herein does not take into consideration the effect of variations in fiber/resin ratio of specific types of composites and test specimens, as this characteristic was not reported for all referenced works. Composite properties are strongly influenced by this ratio. The property data discussed in this paper reflect actual values and trends reported for specific composites. Controlled variations in many of the properties are obtainable in practice by specific variation of the fiber content of the composite.

As composites are frequently used where weight is critical, or where specific strengths are required, typical composite densities have been summarized in Table 1.

TABLE 1—*Typical composite densities.*

Composite System	Fiber/Resin Ratio	Density, $lb \cdot ft^{-3}$ ($kg \cdot m^{-3}$)
S-glass-epoxy	60–67	0.068–0.074 (1.09–1.19)
Kevlar 49/epoxy	60–65	0.047–0.050 (0.753–0.801)
Boron-epoxy	55	0.070–0.074 (1.12–1.19)
Graphite-epoxy	55–60	0.050–0.055 (0.801–0.881)
Boron-aluminum (4 mil)	50	0.10

It must be emphasized that this survey is not exhaustive, that the results reported have not been experimentally confirmed by NBS, and that the conclusions and evaluations presented in this paper reflect those of the cited authors and do not imply approval, endorsement, or recommendation of any commercial product by NBS.

The presentation is in two parts—the first considering the work on glass-reinforced materials and the second considering a variety of advanced-fiber reinforced materials.

Glass-Reinforced Composites

Overview

Brink, Chamberlain, and their associates made the initial significant contribution to understanding the cryogenic behavior of glass-fiber reinforced plastic (GFRP) materials in report ASD-TDR-62-794 to the USAF, Part I of which was published in 1962 [1][2] and Part II in 1964 [2]. Part I of this work evaluated the mechanical properties of commercial composite products which conformed to existing military specifications.

[2] The italic numbers in brackets refer to the list of references appended to this paper.

Tensile, flexure, compressive, and fatigue properties were evaluated from 295 K to 20 K in epoxy, phenolic, polyester, and silicone matrices reinforced with 181 glass cloth. The results indicated a general increase in strength as the temperature was lowered, while the same relative fatigue resistance was observed at cryogenic temperatures as at room temperature, the cryogenic fatigue properties being equal to or above the room temperature values. Similar resin systems were found to produce similar trends on cooling, and toughness of the GFRP composites was maintained at cryogenic temperatures while the rate of cooling was not found to be important. Part II of this work investigated a series of additional resins, including Teflon,[3] polyurethane, phenyl silane and polybenzimidazole (PBI or Imidite), which were recommended by the manufacturers for use at low temperatures. Bearing yield strength, tensile fatigue, and impact properties were evaluated in addition to the properties investigated in Part I. In general, the properties of composites made with the modified resins were found to be inferior to those of the commercial materials studied in Part I. The authors concluded that epoxies were the most desirable matrix materials, with polyesters running a close second. Flexibilized matrix systems were judged useful only if flexibility was of paramount importance. The authors concluded that there existed a need for standardization of test procedures, a conclusion which is unfortunately still valid today.

Chronologically, the next major contribution was made by Toth et al in 1966 [3]. This report covered a three-year effort which had the following objectives: (a) to critically evaluate test methods for use at cryogenic temperatures, (b) to establish the relationship between test results and design performance, and (c) to apply the developed techniques to the evaluation of a variety of glass-polymeric composites. Unidirectional as well as woven cloth reinforcement of conventional and modified epoxy resins was studied. A limited test series was also run on silicon carbide whiskers combined with S-glass as reinforcement for an epoxy resin. Test temperatures ranged from 295 K to 20 K. The authors concluded that valid test procedures had been developed and proven by subsequent model testing. The test program included tensile, flexural, compressive, interlaminar, and bearing strength as well as thermal conductivity and thermal expansion. The S-glass in an epoxy of the Polaris formulation[4] was judged by Toth [3] to have the most optimum overall properties for cryogenic use. (Commercial designations for the Polaris resin are E-787 and 58-68R.)

---

[3] The use in this paper of trade names of specific products is essential to the proper understanding of the work presented. Their use in no way implies approval, endorsement, or recommendation by NBS.

[4] The Polaris resin consists of Epon 828/Epon 1031/NMA/BDMA in proportions 50/50/90/0.55 pbw. It is referred to as the Polaris resin because of its successful use in that missile.

Two major reports appeared in 1967. In January the publication of the work of Soffer and Molho *[4]* reported the results of an intensive effort to develop improved epoxy resins for use in filament-wound cryogenic pressure vessels. Forty-one candidate resins were evaluated for mechanical properties and for suitability in filament-winding operations. Composite specimens using S-901 glass were evaluated in tension, interlaminar shear, and thermal expansion. As a result of this work, Soffer and Molho selected a modified epoxy system designated Resin 2 as superior for cryogenic use.[5] As a final evaluation, Resin 2 was compared with 58-68R (E 787) in a series of burst tests on metal-lined, S-901 glass filament-wound pressure vessels, the results showing Resin 2 to be clearly superior in the longitudinal filament stress level developed in the vessels at 77 and 20 K.

The second significant publication in 1967 was that of Lewis and Bush *[5]*. Again oriented toward filament-wound cryogenic tankage, the objective was to determine the extent to which various fiber finishes and coupling agents could be used to improve the cryogenic properties of composites reinforced with Aerojet General Hi-Stren glass. Naval Ordinance Laboratory (NOL) rings and flat specimens were used to obtain tensile, interlaminar shear, and thermal expansion data. The study also evaluated various modified epoxy matrices in an attempt to improve impact strength, toughness, and extensibility at cryogenic temperatures. It was concluded that glass finishing treatments could be used to improve bonding of filaments to the resin, thereby improving the mechanical properties, but that coupling agents were effective only in improvement of wet strength. At 77 K and 20 K, the highest pressure vessel longitudinal and hoop-filament tensile strengths were again developed with Resin 2.

The foregoing studies encompassed 45 separate types of glass-reinforced composites which varied not only in the glass/polymer combination, but in methods of fabrication and testing. The present paper makes no effort to discuss all of the results in detail; rather, we shall confine our attention to the tensile strength, tensile modulus, thermal contraction, and thermal conductivity properties reported for the best of the composites evaluated in these works. We shall consider only uniaxial filament-wound (UFW), biaxially filament wound (BFW) of 0/90 orientation, and woven-cloth layups. Data for UFW composites are restricted to the longitudinal properties, while data for the BFW and cloth composites refer to properties parallel to one major fiber direction unless otherwise noted.

Mechanical Properties

Figure 1 shows the expected superiority of the UFW glass-epoxy

[5] Epon 828/DSA/EMPOL 1040/BDMA in proportions 100/115.9/20/1 pbw. As this formulation was developed under NASA sponsorship, it will henceforth be referred to as NASA Resin 2.

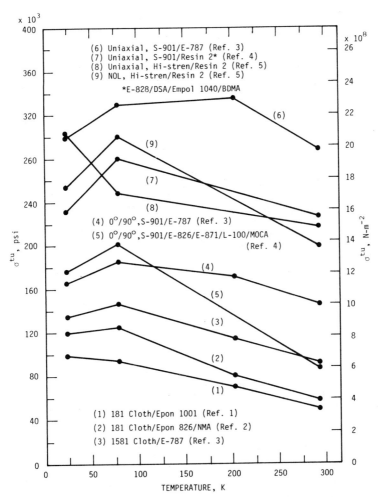

FIG. 1—*Ultimate tensile strength, σ^{tu}, of glass-epoxy composites at cryogenic temperatures.*

composites in ultimate tensile strength, with the BFW and cloth composites having sequentially lower strengths. The strength increased for all composite types upon cooling to 77 K; however, below 77 K the data appear erratic. The latter phenomenon is observed to some extent in all of the mechanical properties of filamentary-reinforced polymeric-matrix composites.

These data suggest that one can expect a maximum tensile strength on the order of 100 to 140 ksi at 77 K for cloth-reinforced epoxies, while BFW composites are capable of developing considerably higher strengths, on the order of 180 to 200 ksi at this temperature. More scatter is observed in the UFW data, which is somewhat surprising, as the tensile strength in this orientation should be essentially fiber controlled.

It may be that, within the cryogenic temperature range, the temperature-sensitive properties of the matrix are affecting the overall strength even in the UFW composites, possibly by altering the neighbor fiber interactions at fracture sites. It may also be that the difficulty in obtaining valid test data from UFW composites at cryogenic temperatures accounts for some of this scatter. Nevertheless, it appears that about 280 ksi is not an unreasonable expectation for the tensile strength of UFW composites in the fiber direction at 77 K. It is this exceptional strength coupled with comparatively low cost that has maintained the popularity of glass-fiber reinforced composites.

Curve 5 has been included on Fig. 1 to illustrate the results obtained with an epoxy polyblend designed for greater flexibility at low temperatures. The strength of this polyblend[6] is low at 295 K, but increases rapidly on cooling. On the basis of the mechanical properties at cryogenic temperatures, this particular polyblend, designated Resin 4A by Soffer and Molho, was considered by them to be the best of the resins they studied, as it was the only resin tested that did not crack during thermal shock and impact testing at cryogenic temperatures, and its notch toughness was superior to all other resins tested in the program. The authors concluded, however, that the processing characteristics of this polyblend were unfavorable, and the NASA Resin 2 formulation was selected as their overall choice of matrix material for filament-wound composites.

The UFW composite data of Fig. 1 illustrate the results reported for the epoxy formulations E-787 (58-68R) and NASA Resin 2. On the basis of these data, E-787 (58-68R) produces the higher tensile values, at least to 77 K. However, these data may not be directly comparable because of possible differences in fiber/resin ratios. Composite tensile strengths of a specific specimen are dependent on this ratio (as well as on fiber orientation), higher fiber contents yielding higher composite strengths and moduli in the direction of the reinforcement. Also, the work of Soffer and Molho has shown that the specific application may affect the choice of matrix resin. At this point it must be concluded that both of these resins should receive equal consideration for cryogenic applications.

The initial tensile moduli for the same composites appear in Fig. 2. The moduli generally tend to increase upon cooling to 77 K; however, there does not appear to be consistent behavior, even among composites of the same type and layup, possibly due to resin content variations. As with the tensile strength, the tensile modulus appears to become erratic upon further cooling to 20 K.

The cloth-reinforced composites have the lowest modulus, ranging from 4-5 × 10^6 psi at 77 K, the highest of these being reported for 1581/E-787. The S-901/E-787 BFW composite has a substantially higher modulus at

---

[6] Epon 826/Epon 871/L-100/MOCA (35/15/50/27.6 pbw).

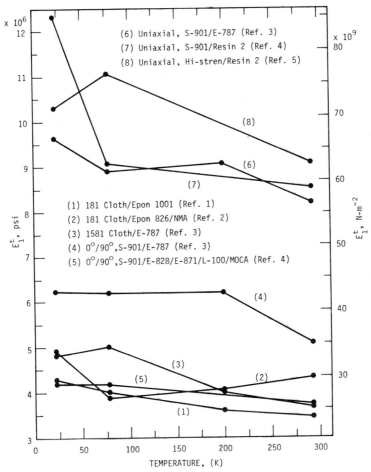

FIG. 2—*Initial tensile moduli, E_1^t, of glass-epoxy composites at cryogenic temperatures.*

slightly over 6×10^6 psi at this temperature. Note, however, that the polyblend BFW composite has a tensile modulus no better than that of the cloth-reinforced materials and shows very little temperature sensitivity. The UFW composites have the highest moduli, as is expected. The Hi-Stren/NASA Resin 2 composite appears to have the highest modulus; however, it should also be noted that Hi-Stren glass has a modulus 8 percent higher than S-901 glass. The latter data resulted from a series of tests investigating the effects of glass finishes on the mechanical properties, and the reported higher values of composite moduli may reflect superior bonding at the glass-matrix interface as well as higher fiber modulus. It would appear from these data that an initial tensile modulus of from 9 to 10×10^6 psi might reasonably be expected from UFW glass-epoxy composites at 77 K. It is these low moduli of glass-reinforced composites that have stimulated the development of advanced-fiber composites.

It is apparent from Figs. 1 and 2 that if one wishes to speak with any degree of specificity about the temperature dependence of the tensile properties of a glass-fiber reinforced composite in the cryogenic region, one is pretty well constrained to talk about a specific composite and fiber/resin ratio, particularly for temperatures below 77 K. This is further illustrated in Fig. 3, which is a frequency histogram compiled from all available literature data on the temperature dependence of the tensile properties of glass-epoxy composites of the three considered layup types. Figure 3a of this diagram shows that cooling from 295 K to 77 K produces an increase in tensile strength in all cases, the extent of the increase ranging from 10 ksi to as much as 130 ksi, with the highest probability of obtaining an increase on the order of 30 to 60 ksi. However, on cooling further to 20 K these data suggest a high probability of little or no change in tensile strength, but with the distinct possibility of a strength loss of as much as 70 ksi or a strength gain of as much as

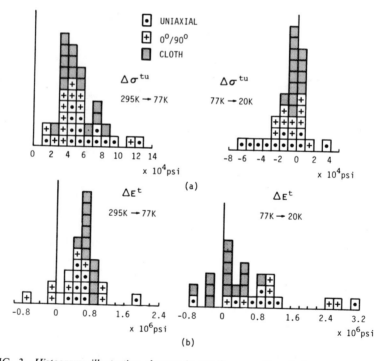

FIG. 3—*Histograms illustrating changes in tensile properties of glass-epoxy composites upon cooling into the cryogenic range. The ordinate represents the number of literature references reporting property changes of a given magnitude.*

40 ksi. The data also indicate that the probability of a strength change of a given magnitude is independent of the layup type, which, by inference, suggests that the erratic behavior below 77 K is a matrix-controlled phenomenon.

Comparable statistical data for the tensile modulus of glass-epoxy composites presented in Fig. 3b indicate the probability of a modest modulus increase on the order of from 0.6 to 0.8 × 10⁶ psi on cooling to 77 K, but with a finite chance that the modulus may decrease by as much as 0.8 × 10⁶ psi or that it may increase by as much as 2 × 10⁶ psi. The results of further cooling to 20 K are more difficult to interpret. In general, the data seem to cluster around a small increase of modulus up to about 0.6 × 10⁶ psi for cloth reinforcement and suggest that a somewhat larger increase on the order of from 0.6 to 1.3 × 10⁶ psi could be obtained with crossply or uniaxial composites. Nevertheless, the range of scatter from −0.8 to 3.2 × 10⁶ psi is again indicative of very erratic behavior upon cooling below 77 K. Microbuckling of fibers due to resin shrinkage and minimal stress relaxation at cryogenic temperatures may lead to variations in initial tensile modulus and account for some of data scatter.

This erratic behavior in strength and modulus when testing at 20 K cannot be attributed to a sudden embrittling of the epoxy matrix, as 77 K is already far below the glass-transition temperature of the matrix. Nor can it be reasonably attributed to a sudden increase in the difficulty of obtaining reliable test data, as there is no *a priori* reason for a test method giving reliable data at 77 K to become entirely unsuitable at 20 K. The author does not know the answer to this problem. However, in searching for an explanation, consideration should be given to the results of some recent studies which have shown that, at least in the linear polymers of the polycarbonate and polyethylene terepthalate types, the medium in which a low-temperature test is conducted can strongly affect the resultant mechanical properties [6,7]. These studies indicate that yield and fracture of such polymers in the cryogenic temperature range are controlled by a crazing phenomenon which is strongly influenced by the activity of the gas or liquid in contact with the polymer surface. As all reported data on the mechanical properties of composites at cryogenic temperatures have been obtained at liquid nitrogen or liquid hydrogen temperatures, it must be considered at least a possibility that the observed anomolous behavior is a synergistic effect of a given type of polymer in contact with a given ambient medium.

Thermal Properties

Figure 4 presents the data reported by Toth et al [3] for the temperature dependence of the thermal contraction of several of the E 787 matrix

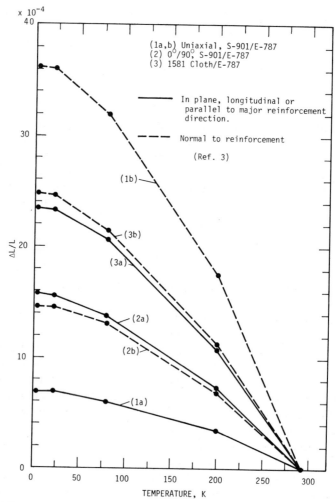

FIG. 4—*Thermal contraction, ΔL/L, of glass-epoxy composites at cryogenic temperatures.*

composites that appear in Figs. 1 and 2. As the thermal contraction of the epoxy is significantly larger than that of the glass, there will generally be a difference between the thermal contraction in the plane of reinforcement and that normal to the plane (thickness direction). Contraction in the reinforcement direction in the case of a UFW composite is held to a minimum by restraint of the glass, as shown by curve 1a, while contraction in the reinforcement-normal direction in this type of composite is very large, curve 1b, the glass providing negligible restraint in the latter case. In the BFW case, the contraction parallel to a major fiber direction is about twice that of the UFW composite, about proportional to the decrease in fiber density. However, contraction in the reinforcement-normal direction in this type of layup is also quite low, curve 2b, reflecting the effective restraint provided by the crossplied glass fibers, which are in close proximity. The in-plane contraction of the cloth composite is the highest of the group as shown by curve 3a, reflecting the lower glass content of such composites and the lesser restraint provided by the convoluted fibers, which, in general, do not lie parallel to the reinforcement plane. The reinforcement-normal contraction is also high for composites of this type, due both to the lesser total glass content and to the lesser restraint provided by the layered cloth.

It should be noted that, in general, the literature reports a reinforcement-normal contraction about twice that of the in-plane contraction for balanced-weave cloth-reinforced glass-polymeric composites in contrast to the similar values reported by Toth for 1581/E-787.

Thermal conductivity is also an important parameter in cryogenic design. Unfortunately, improper experimental technique invalidates some of the data in the literature—primarily, failure to properly compensate for radiation losses, which can introduce errors on the order of 100 to 200 percent in the higher temperature ranges. Figure 5 presents what the author believes to be the best available data for glass-epoxy composites, based on the work of Campbell et al [8] and of Hertz [10].

Thermal conductivity differs from the other thermal properties of composites in that it is significantly affected by the ambient atmosphere in which the test is conducted. The literature data suggest that, compared with the values obtained in helium, data taken in nitrogen will average about 7 percent lower, while data taken in vacuum will average about 20 percent lower. Campbell [8] suggests that the low value in vacuum primarily reflects the difficulty of obtaining good contact between the composite specimen and the mating parts of the thermal conductivity apparatus. An ambient atmosphere of nitrogen or helium increases the measured conductivity by reducing this contact resistance; however, diffusion of the gas (particularly of helium) into pores within the composite was also found to contribute to an increase in conductivity, as the gas provides an overall improvement in the thermal path within the composite. This explanation appears plausible, as it is consistent with the effect of the ambient atmosphere being observed over the entire 20 K to 295 K temperature range. The present author believes, however, that consideration should also be given to the effect on thermal conductivity of a matrix which has cracked due to thermal contraction at very low temperatures. The effect of the latter would be to increase the spread between conductivities measured in the various ambient media.

As the data taken in vacuum appear to be subject to the largest error, the data appearing on Fig. 5 are averages reported for tests in nitrogen and helium.

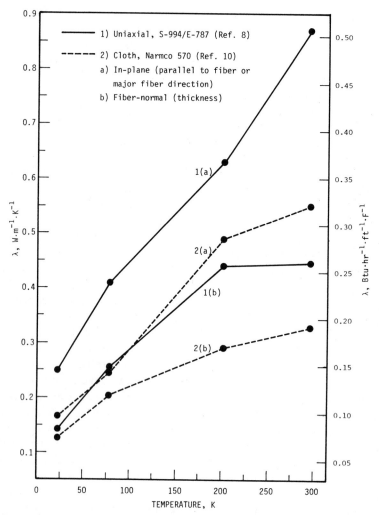

FIG. 5—*Thermal conductivities, λ, of glass-epoxy composites at cryogenic temperatures.*

Thermal conductivity at 20 K is 30 to 40 percent of that at 295 K. The difference between both the fiber-normal and the in-plane conductivities and the absolute spread of values is widest at room temperature, converging as the temperature is lowered. Conductivity is the highest for the UFW composite in the fiber direction, reflecting both the high density of fibers and the higher conductivity of glass as compared with the epoxy matrix. Fiber normal conductivity in the UFW composite is much lower than the in-plane value. Lower conductivity in both directions is observed for the cloth-reinforced composite, reflecting the lower fiber density of such composites. No reliable data were available for a 0/90 crossply; however, such a composite layup would be expected to develop intermediate conductivities in both directions, the in-plane conductivity being lower than the UFW due to lower fiber density in the direction of heat flow, while the plane-normal value should be higher than that for cloth due to the overall higher fiber density.

Other Matrices

For the sake of brevity, the author has had to confine the discussion thus far to epoxy matrix composites, although the referenced works contain data on many other matrix materials. Concentration on the epoxies is somewhat justified in that such materials are today the almost universal choice for demanding cryogenic service, based on their generally superior performance qualities. For example, if the tensile strength of cloth-epoxy specimens is taken at 100 ksi at 77 K, the next strongest composites consisting of the polyurethanes, polyesters, phenolics, Teflons, and polybenzimidazoles would form a group at about 70 to 80 ksi. The silicones, phenyl silanes, and polyimides form a third and lower strength group at about 40 to 50 ksi. The epoxies also excel in flexural and compressive strength. Only in modulus are the epoxies equaled (and often exceeded) by the phenolics, polybenzimidazoles, and phenyl silanes.

Fatigue

The author wishes to conclude this section on glass-reinforced composites with a brief discussion of the tensile fatigue studies of Brink [1] and of Chamberlain et al [2], as these data constitute almost the entire body of research on the dynamic properties of glass-reinforced composites at cryogenic temperatures. The only other work known to the author is the study by Fontana [11] using a reciprocating-beam method and by Lavengood and Anderson [12] in torsion.

The work of Brink and Chamberlain was, with one exception, conducted with 181-cloth reinforced composites and included the variety of matrix material listed in Fig. 6, which is a plot of the failure stress of each material after 10^6 cycles at the various temperatures. Figure 6 also records the percent of the original single-cycle ultimate tensile strength retained by each composite type after 10^6 cycles. Glass-reinforced polymers have reduced fatigue performance when compared with many alloys or with the advanced composites. However, these data show that the absolute magnitude of the stress required to induce failure after 10^6 cycles generally increases with decreasing temperature. At 200 K and 20 K, the polybenzimidazoles showed superior performance, while equaling the best at 77 K. Furthermore, the percentage of original strength retained by the polybenzimidazoles was consistently among the highest of the group. The better fatigue performance of this material may be accounted for by the

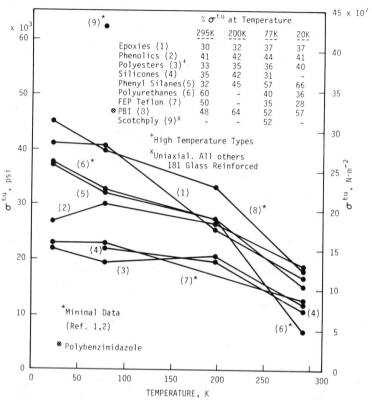

FIG. 6—*Failure stress of glass-reinforced composites, n^{tu}, as a function of temperature after 10^6 fatigue cycles.*

very low in-plane thermal contraction of polybenzimidazole composites—about one-third that of the epoxies—which decreases the residual stress at the glass-matrix interface at cryogenic temperatures. As the polybenzimidazole composites also compare well with the epoxies in static strength properties, another look at the polybenzimidazole types may be warranted for cryogenic applications requiring good dynamic performance.

The epoxies also look comparatively good, but primarily because of their high initial strength—their percentage of retained strength was among the lowest of the group. In general, the polyurethanes, phenyl silanes, and phenolics grouped into intermediate performance, while the polyesters, silicones, and Teflons had distinctly lower fatigue properties. Figure 6 contains only one data point for a UFW glass-epoxy composite at 77 K. This material had a much higher absolute strength after 10^6 cycles than any of the cloth-reinforced materials; however, it retained only about 52 percent of its original strength.

The available data are insufficient to either prove or disprove the existence of a fatigue limit at cryogenic temperatures, although the S-N curve reported by Brink [1] for 181/Epon 1001 did appear to be reaching a limit at about 30 percent of the original strength at temperatures below 77 K.

Advanced Composites

Overview

The application of carbon fiber reinforced epoxy composites to filament-wound cryogenic tankage was investigated by Simon, Larsen, and Alfring, their results appearing in a series of reports in 1970, 1971, and 1972 [13–15]. Their initial task was to evaluate the tensile, flexural, interlaminar shear, bending fatigue, and thermal expansion properties of several fibers and resins in the form of strands, bars, and NOL rings from 295 K to 20 K. The tensile modulus of these CFRP composites was observed to increase up to 20 percent on cooling to 77 K, concomitant with a decrease in ultimate tensile strength by as much as 30 percent. Bending fatigue at 50 percent of the tensile ultimate was found to cause less deterioration after 1000 cycles at cryogenic temperatures than at room temperature. The thermal contraction tests revealed a slight negative coefficient, indicating that the resin matrix might see up to 1.5 percent strain when cooled. The second task was the design and testing of filament-wound tanks using Morganite (Modmor) II and Thornel 50 fibers in a NASA Resin 2 matrix. Results indicated that these CFRP overwrapped tanks would be competitive with boron-reinforced tanks and possibly competitive with glass reinforcement in terms of strength/weight ratio.[7]

A third task undertook to study the effect of elastomeric additions on the strength and fracture toughness of epoxy resins and of CFRP composites. Results were generally unimpressive except for a CBTN-modified ERLB 4617 resin composite which demonstrated significantly improved tensile and short-beam shear strength at cryogenic temperatures at the expense of a decrease in room temperature shear strength. The remaining tasks in this program were directed at a continued study of the effect of elastomer additions to the epoxy matrix. Simon and Larsen concluded that, based on their data, Courtaulds HT-S fiber in a NASA Resin 2 matrix was a satisfactory combination for general cryogenic use for both UFW and BFW composites.

In 1972, Hertz, Christian, Varlas, et al published the results of a com-

---

[7] More recent work with improved graphite fibers indicates 295 K pressure vessel strength/weight ratios higher than for glass and slightly lower than for PRD 49-III (Kevlar 49).

prehensive study on the materials development portion of a larger program investigating advanced composites for specific uses in spacecraft and missiles [16]. The associated studies on the structural development part of this program may be found in Ref 17, while the development of hardware is reported in Ref 18. The objective of the study was to select advanced composites systems capable of operating for relatively short times over a 77 to 450 K temperature range. Work was directed toward the selection of two types of CRFP composites, one of high modulus and one of high strength. Boron-fiber reinforced aluminum (6061) was also studied to relate variations in mechanical properties to variables in production method or in fiber diameter. Boron-fiber reinforced plastic (BFRP) composites in the form of the commercial SP-272 material were also investigated. The mechanical and thermal properties of these materials were characterized from 77 to 450 K, including thermal expansion, thermal conductivity, specific heat, electrical resistivity, and thermo-optical properties. Three materials—5.7-mil Borsic/6061 aluminum, HT-S/X-904 epoxy, and a hybrid CFRP system utilizing both GY-70 and HM-S fibers in an X-904 epoxy matrix—were selected for determination of design allowable data. Some data on the effects of various environments on the mechanical and thermal properties of the selected composites were also reported.

Hoggatt in 1971 [19] and Hanson [20] in 1972 published the initial data on the cryogenic properties of PRD-49/epoxy composites. Hoggatt first investigated the suitability of PRD-49[8] for filament-winding applications and subsequently determined the basic property data (tensile, interlaminar shear, and thermal expansion) down to 20 K. These data were then used in the design, fabrication, and testing of a series of cryogenic pressure vessels. Results indicated that the specific strength of vessels made with PRD-49-I fiber was about the same as that for S-glass; however, the specific modulus of the PRD-49 tanks was almost three times higher. These data were obtained with epoxy matrices of both the NASA Resin 2 and ERLA 4617/CL type. Hoggatt concluded that the results justified further investigation of PRD-49 for cryogenic applications. Some recent work by Chiao et al [20] supports this conclusion, showing that pressure vessels reinforced with PRD 49-III fiber may develop specific strengths 30 to 50 percent higher than that of comparable glass-reinforced vessels at both room and cryogenic temperatures.

The studies of Hanson [21] considered both the strength and creep behavior of PRD-49-I and PRD-49-III composites from 20 to 477 K, using an ERLA 4617 epoxy matrix. At 20 K, the ultimate tensile strength of the PRD-49-III composite was found to be about 90 percent of that at room temperature, while an increase in tensile modulus by about 40 percent was noted. The creep tests, all conducted at or above room temperature,

[8] Product of the E. I. DuPont Company now called Kevlar 49.

showed the presence of an initial accelerated stage, followed by a much lower secondary creep rate.

Mechanical and Thermal Properties

Figures 7-12 illustrate the temperature dependence of the ultimate tensile strength, tensile modulus, thermal contraction (expansion), and thermal conductivities of a series of advanced composites selected by the authors of the aforementioned studies as being most useful in cryogenic applications. These data show the commercial BFRP and Borsic-aluminum composites to be almost in a class by themselves, having the highest

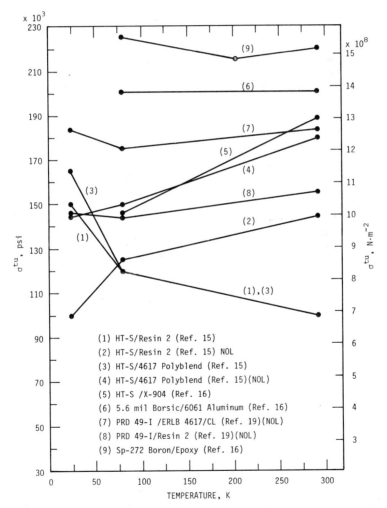

FIG. 7—*Uniaxial longitudinal ultimate tensile strengths,* σ^{tu}, *of advanced composites at cryogenic temperatures.*

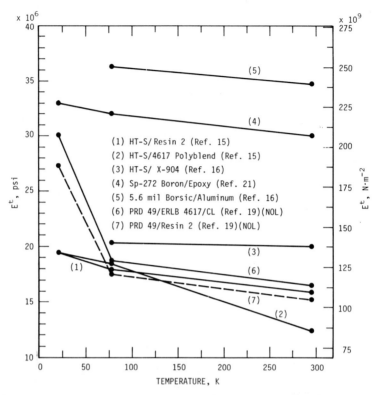

FIG. 8—*Uniaxial longitudinal tensile moduli,* E^t, *of advanced composites at cryogenic temperatures.*

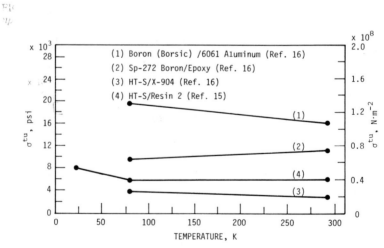

FIG. 9—*Uniaxial transverse ultimate tensile strengths,* σ^{tu}, *of advanced composites at cryogenic temperatures.*

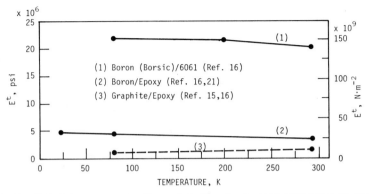

FIG. 10—*Uniaxial transverse tensile moduli,* E^t, *of advanced composites at cryogenic temperatures.*

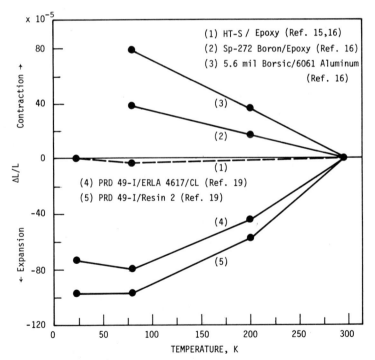

FIG. 11—*Uniaxial longitudinal thermal expansion and contraction,* $\Delta L/L$, *of advanced composites at cryogenic temperatures.*

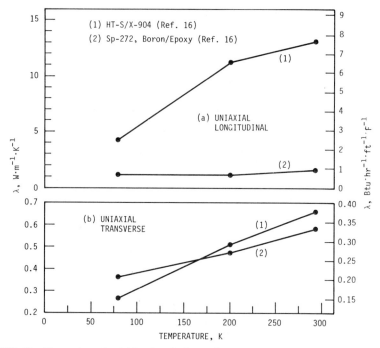

FIG. 12—*Thermal conductivities, λ, of advanced composites at cryogenic temperatures.*

strengths, highest moduli, and undergoing thermal contraction during cooling. Conversely, the CFRP and PRD-49 materials have somewhat lower strengths, considerably lower moduli, and undergo varying degrees of expansion upon cooling.

The strongest of these materials is the boron-epoxy, which develops about 225 ksi at 77 K and for which the tensile strength shows a relatively small temperature dependence. The modulus of this material is also very high, about 32×10^6 psi at 77 K, with the modulus appearing to slightly increase on cooling. Boron-epoxy contracts a relatively modest amount in the fiber direction, with the transverse contraction being about half of that in the fiber direction. The data shown on Fig. 7 are for the commercial SP-272 product reinforced with 4.2-mil boron fiber. Nadler et al [22] have also evaluated this product as well as an equivalent material, Narmco 5505, reporting strength data very close to that of Hertz. The tensile modulus data plotted in Fig. 8 reflect the work of Nadler, as Hertz did not evaluate this parameter. The 4.2-mil fiber is currently being replaced by 5.6-mil fiber in many applications, as the latter produces a less costly composite with slightly higher tensile properties. The cryogenic properties of the 5.6-mil composites have not been reported.

The uniaxial transverse tensile strength of the BFRP material is lower than that of boron-aluminum but is higher than that of the CFRP material. The uniaxial transverse modulus is about 5×10^6 psi, distinctly lower than the boron-aluminum, but again higher than that of the CFRP material. The thermal conductivity is very low, particularly in the fiber-normal direction, which is an attribute in many cryogenic applications.

The plotted data illustrate the results reported by Hertz for the 5.6-mil boron fiber in its Borsic variant as a reinforcement for 6061 aluminum. Conventional 5.6-mil and 4.2-mil boron-reinforced 6061 alloys were also investigated; however, the ultimate tensile strengths of the latter were reported to be about 20 ksi lower than that for the Borsic reinforcement. Borsic (or boron) reinforced aluminum alloy appears to be an excellent choice for cryogenic applications wherever the high thermal contraction and high thermal conductivity can be tolerated. Hertz reports an ultimate tensile strength of 200 ksi at 77 K for uniaxial longitudinal Borsic/6061 combined with a very high tensile modulus of about 35×10^6 psi. The 20-ksi transverse tensile strength and a transverse tensile modulus in excess of 20×10^6 psi at 77 K are also impressive compared with the values for the other types of composites. These properties appear to have very little temperature sensitivity. No data were available on the thermal conductivity of boron-aluminum composites at cryogenic temperatures; however, it is certain to be matrix-dominated and very high.

Hoggatt's data for PRD 49 gives some evidence of why this new fiber is considered important. The present data suggest that the PRD 49/ERLB 4617/CL composite ranks next to the boron-aluminum in strength with a respectable 180 ksi, although the same fiber in a Resin 2 matrix comes in considerably lower at just over 140 ksi. Being NOL ring data, these values may be conservative, as the latter test is not strictly uniaxial. The moduli values of 18 to 19×10^6 psi at 77 K do not appear at first to be outstanding; however, they are in the same range as the HT-S CFRP composites, and, furthermore, this value would be compared with the 10×10^6 psi maximum modulus available for glass-reinforced composites for which PRD 49 is seen as a substitute. PRD 49 looks even better in modulus at 20 K, if the extremely large increase observed by Hoggatt in his NOL ring tests proves to be a real effect.

The data show PRD 49 composites to have a very high negative coefficient of thermal contraction—much higher than that of the CFRP composites. Normally, this would produce a sufficiently high interfacial strain at cryogenic temperatures to cause significant degrading of the mechanical properties. This does not appear to be the case with PRD 49 fiber.

Finally, a look at the CFRP data for the HT-S fiber in a series of epoxy matrices illustrates some of the problems encountered in attempting to characterize CFRP material for cryogenic use. While Simon and Larsen have shown that HT-S fiber can be put to good practical use in filament-wound cryogenic vessels, the tensile strength data appearing in Fig. 7 would hardly justify optimism in this respect. As may be seen by comparing Curve 1 with Curve 2 and Curve 3 with Curve 4, the same composites show widely varying strengths and widely varying temperature sensitivities of strength depending on whether the test was conducted on flat uniaxial tension coupons or with NOL rings. This is, at the very least, good evidence of the need for more reliable test methods for use at cryogenic temperatures.

The moduli of the HT-S CFRP composites (all flat uniaxial coupons) show much less scatter and a tendency to converge to about 19 to 20×10^6 psi at the lower temperatures. As regards the uniaxial transverse properties, the strength of the CFRP composites appears to be no more than half that of the BFRP composite at best, while the transverse moduli are extremely low, on the order of 10^6 psi. Curve 3 of Fig. 10 is dashed to indicate an approximate value, the actual data showing a spread from 0.5 to 1.2×10^6 psi at 77 K.

The HT-S fiber composites have a very small negative coefficient of thermal contraction to 77 K. Curve 1 of Fig. 11 is also dashed to indicate approximate values. The slight reversal in contraction indicated below 77 K for this material (seen also in the PRD 49 composite in Curve 4) is apparently a real effect. Finally, from Fig. 12 we observe that the thermal conductivity of the CFRP composites is much higher in the fiber direction than is the case for the BFRP material, reflecting the relatively high thermal conductivity of the graphite itself. This difference largely disappears in the transverse direction.

Summary

Glass-reinforced polymers will continue to be used in cryogenic applications requiring high tensile strength combined with high toughness but where stiffness is not required and where cyclic fatigue is not a major problem. The data reviewed in this paper suggest that, at this time, glass filament-wound with either Resin 2 or the Polaris formulation is satisfactory for cryogenic applications. When considering the use of NASA Resin 2, the reader should be aware that this resin formulation has been optimized for cryogenic service and therefore has relatively poor elevated temperature properties. Care must be taken to properly support components made with this resin whenever elevated temperature vacuum degassing of an assembly is required.

The commercial boron-epoxy and boron-aluminum materials appear to perform very well at cryogenic temperatures and should be among the first materials considered for applications requiring very good strength combined with exceptional stiffness.

The carbon fiber reinforced epoxies seem less advantageous, as their mechanical properties appear to become substantially degraded upon cooling; however, some of this adverse behavior may reflect problems in obtaining valid test data on CFRP materials at cryogenic temperatures, as examples do exist of successful practical applications of CFRP structural materials in the cryogenic range.

The data on the cryogenic properties of composites made with PRD 49 fiber, although not very extensive, suggest that this relatively new material may be superior to carbon fibers for cryogenic use, although the large negative coefficient of thermal contraction may pose problems in some applications. In general, it appears that the epoxy resins most successful with glass-reinforcement are also very suitable for use with the advanced fibers.

This review suggests that the following work would be of value in implementing expanded use of structural composites for demanding cryogenic structural applications such as would be encountered in superconducting machinery:

1. The reason for the erratic mechanical property behavior in polymeric-matrix composites below 77 K must be ascertained. In particular, it is imperative to determine whether or not the type of cryogen in which tests are conducted has a significant effect on the mechanical properties.

2. Material research and evaluation must be directed toward obtaining the type of basic composite cryogenic property data which will be of most value to the design engineer. Contemporary composite theory requires full characterization of a uniaxial lamella of the composite of interest, that is, an experimental determination of the strength and moduli values is required for the prediction of limiting property values in complex crossply layups. Accurate tensile and compression data are required in the longitudinal and transverse modes plus accurate values for intralaminar (in-plane) shear. Even at room temperature, tension and compression testing in the reinforcement direction has proven difficult to perform with acceptable accuracy. Testing problems will be further complicated at cryogenic temperatures; however, these problems must be solved.

3. Having come to terms with the problems posed in (1) and (2), the static mechanical property data for the best of the glass-reinforced composites and of the state-of-the-art commercial boron-epoxy and boron (Borsic)-aluminum materials should be extended down to 4 K. Subsequently, PRD 49/epoxy composites should be evaluated over the entire cryogenic range and another look should be given to the CFRP materials, as the presently available data have an unacceptably large scatter which may well reflect difficulties in the testing procedures rather than inherent scatter in the material itself. All materials must be thoroughly characterized for resin/fiber density, void content, and fiber alignment.

4. Data on the performance of composites under dynamic loading conditions at cryogenic temperatures are minimal to nonexistent. Yet, these

types of data are mandatory if composites are to be used in cryogenic machinery. The available data are encouraging in that they suggest that fatigue performance at cryogenic temperatures is generally superior to that at room temperature. However, this will have to be more fully documented. As high-cycle fatigue testing at 4 K is very expensive, the materials included in such a testing program must be carefully selected. For this purpose, it would be very desirable to have an efficient screening type of test capable of correlating incipient damage with expected fatigue life. Data on thermal fatigue are also required, that is, the effect of repeated cooldowns on both the static and dynamic properties of composites must be determined.

Acknowledgments

The author wishes to thank Dr. R. P. Reed for his consultation and for review of the completed manuscript. This research was supported by the Advanced Research Projects Agency.

References

[1] Brink, N. O., "Determination of the Performance of Plastic Laminates Under Cryogenic Temperatures," ASD-TDR-62-794, (AD 288 944), Air Force Systems Command, Wright-Patterson Air Force Base, Ohio, Aug. 1962.

[2] Chamberlain, D. W., Lloyd, B. R., and Tennant, R. L., "Determination of the Performance of Plastic Laminates at Cryogenic Temperatures," ASD-TDR-62-794, Part II, (N64-24212), Air Force Systems Command, Wright-Patterson Air Force Base, Ohio, March 1964.

[3] Toth, L. W., Boller, T. J., Butcher, I. R., Kariotis, A. H., and Yoder, F. D., "Program for the Evaluation of Structural Reinforced Plastic Materials at Cryogenic Temperatures," NASA CR-80061 (Final), (N67-12051), National Aeronautics and Space Administration, Marshall Space Flight Center, Ala., Aug. 1966.

[4] Soffer, L. M. and Molho, R., "Cryogenic Resins for Glass Filament-Wound Composites," NASA CR-72114 (Final), (N67-25076), National Aeronautics and Space Administration, Lewis Research Center, Cleveland, Ohio, Jan. 1967.

[5] Lewis, A. and Bush, G. E., "Improved Cryogenic Resin-Glass Filament Wound Composites," NASA CR-72163 (Final), (N67-31856), National Aeronautics and Space Administration, Lewis Research Center, Cleveland, Ohio, March 1967.

[6] Kastelic, J. R., Hiltner, A., and Baer, E., Journal of Macromolecular Science-Physics, Vol. B7, No. 4, 1973, pp. 679–703.

[7] Relationships Between Structure and Mechanical Behavior in Polymeric Solids, ASM Materials Science Seminar, Chicago, Ill., 1973 (to be published by American Society for Metals).

[8] Campbell, M. D., O'Barr, G. L., Haskins, J. F., and Hertz, J., "Thermophysical Properties of Plastic Materials and Composites to Liquid Hydrogen Temperature ($-423°F$)," ML-TDR-64-33, Part III, (AD 468 155), Air Force Materials Laboratory, Wright-Patterson Air Force Base, Ohio, Aug. 1965.

[9] Haskins, J. F., Campbell, M. C., Hertz, J., Percy, J. L., "Thermophysical Properties of Plastic Materials and Composites to Liquid Hydrogen Temperature ($-423°F$)," ML-TDR-64-33, Part I, (AD 601 337), Air Force Materials Laboratory, Wright-Patterson Air Force Base, Ohio, June 1964.

[10] Hertz, J., "Investigation of Potential Low Temperature Insulations," General Dynamics/Astronautics Report GS/A-ERR-AN-688, Dec. 1964.

[11] Fontana, M. B., Bishop, S. M. and Spretnak, J. W., "Investigation of Mechanical Properties and Physical Metallurgy of Aircraft Alloys at Very Low Temperatures, Part 5—Mechanical Properties of Metals and a Plastic Laminate at Low Temperatures," AF Technical Report 5662, Part 5, (AD 27726), Air Force Materials Laboratory, Wright-Patterson Air Force Base, Ohio, Dec. 1953.

[12] Lavengood, R. E. and Anderson, R. M., *Technical Papers,* 24th Annual Technical Conference, Society of the Plastics Industry, Section 11-E, 1969, pp. 107.

[13] Simon, R. A. and Alfring, R., "Properties of Graphite Fiber Composites at Cryogenic Temperatures," NASA CR-72642, (AD 746 885), National Aeronautics and Space Administration, Lewis Research Center, Cleveland, Ohio, May 1970.

[14] Larsen, J. V., "Properties of Graphite Fiber Composites at Cryogenic Temperatures—Effect of Elastomeric Additions to Resin Systems," NASA CR-72804, (AD 882 972), National Aeronautics and Space Administration, Lewis Research Center, Cleveland, Ohio, March 1971.

[15] Larsen, J. V. and Simon, R. A., "Carbon Fiber Composites for Cryogenic Filament-Wound Vessels," NASA CR-120889, (N73-11553), National Aeronautics and Space Administration, Lewis Research Center, Cleveland, Ohio, May 1972.

[16] Hertz, J., Christian, J. L., and Varlas, M., "Advanced Composites Applications for for Spacecraft and Missiles, Phase I Final Report, Volume II: Material Development," AFML-TR 71-186, Vol. 2, (AD 893 715L), Air Force Materials Laboratory, Wright Patterson Air Force Base, Ohio, March 1972.

[17] Forest, J. D., Fujimoto, A. F., and Foelsch, G. F., "Advanced Composite Applications for Spacecraft and Missiles, Phase I Final Report, Volume I: Structural Development," AFML-TR 71-186, Vol. 1, Air Force Materials Laboratory, Wright-Patterson Air Force Base, Ohio, March 1972.

[18] Forest, J. D. and Varlas, M., "Advanced Composites Applications for Spacecraft and Missiles, Final Report," AFML-TR 72-278, Air Force Materials Laboratory, Wright-Patterson Air Force Base, Ohio, March 1972.

[19] Hoggatt, J. T., "Development of Cryogenic PRD 49-I Filament-Wound Tanks," NASA CR-120835, (N72-24941), National Aeronautics and Space Administration, Lewis Research Center, Cleveland, Ohio, Dec. 1971 (also in *SAMPE,* Vol. 3, 1971, pp. 157-167).

[20] Chiao, T. T., Hamstead, M. A., Marcon, M. A., and Hanasee, J. E., "Filament-Wound Kevlar 49/Epoxy Pressure Vessels," NASA CR-134506, National Aeronautics and Space Administration, Lewis Research Center, Cleveland, Ohio, 1973.

[21] Hanson, M. P., "Effects of Temperature and Creep Characteristics of PRD-49 Fiber/Epoxy Composites," NASA TN D-7120, (N73-12607), National Aeronautics and Space Administration, Lewis Research Center, Cleveland, Ohio, Nov. 1972.

[22] Nadler, M. A., Yoshino, S. Y., and Darms, F. J., "Boron/Epoxy Support Strut for Non-Integral Cryogenic Tankage," North American Rockwell Space Division Report SD-68-99501, Feb. 25, 1969 (see also 15th National Symposium, SAMPE, April 1969).

T. T. Chiao,[1] M. A. Hamstad,[1] and E. S. Jessop[1]

Tensile Properties of an Ultrahigh-Strength Graphite Fiber in an Epoxy Matrix

REFERENCE: Chiao, T. T., Hamstad, M. A., and Jessop, E. S., "Tensile Properties of an Ultrahigh-Strength Graphite Fiber in an Epoxy Matrix," *Composite Reliability, ASTM STP 580,* American Society for Testing and Materials, 1975, pp. 612–620.

ABSTRACT: The fiber performance and potential as a reinforcement for fiber composites of a special PAN-based graphite fiber were evaluated by testing the fiber's tensile properties in an epoxy matrix. Representative strand samples were taken from 30 spools (∼4 kg) of single-end, 1500-filament fiber to make over 5000 fiber-epoxy strand specimens using the filament-winding process. Characteristics studied were fiber uniformity, strength and modulus distributions at room and liquid nitrogen temperatures, stress-strain behavior, the effect of strain rate on fiber strength, and acoustic emission during tensile loading to failure. The fiber was found to have a 3570-MPa (517 ksi) failure stress, a 1.7 percent failure strain, a 206-GPa (30 × 10^6 psi) modulus, and a density of 1.77 Mg/m^3 at 23 °C (73 °F). Liquid nitrogen temperature and various strain rates had no significant effect on fiber tensile properties.

KEY WORDS: composite materials, carbon fibers, epoxy resins, fibers, performance, acoustics, emission

We have been searching for extra high-strength, low-density graphite fibers to be used in filament-wound pressure vessels for possible space shuttle applications. A PAN-based fiber recently became available by special order. The properties claimed by the manufacturer[2] seemed very attractive for tensile-critical applications. We therefore decided to thoroughly characterize this fiber in fiber-epoxy composites from an

---

[1] Chemist, mechanical engineer, and technical associate, respectively, University of California, Lawrence Livermore Laboratory, Livermore, Calif. 94550.
[2] Union Carbide Corp., Thornel "Special" fiber. Reference to a company or product name does not imply approval or recommendation of the product by the University of California or the U.S. Atomic Energy Commission to the exclusion of others that may be suitable.

engineering point of view: fiber uniformity, distribution of various tensile properties, stress-rupture behavior, fiber processibility in the filament-winding process, and performance in pressure vessels. This paper summarizes the fiber properties and the behavior of the basic building blocks of various composite fiber-epoxy strands.

Experimental Results and Discussion

The fiber is made from a single-end, 1500-filament PAN precursor. The elemental analysis is carbon 88.59 percent, hydrogen 0.30 percent, nitrogen 7.609 percent, chlorine 3.00 percent, ash 0.04 percent, and oxygen 0.47 percent (by difference). The fiber strand contains small amounts of twist, approximately 0.15 turns/cm. Its average density from three tests, where it was immersed in kerosene and compared against a calibrated quartz standard, is 1.77 mg/m³ at 23 °C (73 °F). In many ways this fiber is similar to the commercially available Thornel-400 graphite fiber (Union Carbide Corp.), which we have studied recently [1].³

Thirty spools of fiber were selected from several batches. We took three 2.54-m-long specimens from each spool and checked the weight variation of the fiber strands. Figure 1 is a summary of these data in denier (g/9000 m). The equivalent cross-sectional area of the fiber strands was calculated using the fiber density and the average fiber mass of the three specimens from each spool. The results are shown in Fig. 2. The coefficient of variation (CV) of 3.5 percent is considered small. We think that the average area of 4.022×10^{-4} cm² can be used in converting tensile load to fiber stress in most engineering calculations.

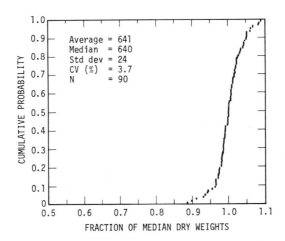

FIG. 1—*Denier variation of the special graphite-epoxy fiber.*

³ The italic numbers in brackets refer to the list of references appended to this paper.

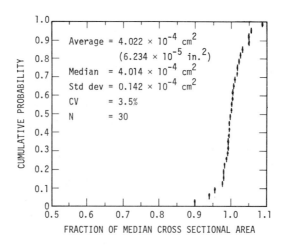

FIG. 2—*Cross-sectional area of the special graphite-epoxy fiber.*

Matrix System

We used a room-temperature-curable epoxy system, DER 332[4] Jeffamine T-403[5] (100/36), throughout the study. The pure resin system, when jelled at ambient temperature overnight and cured at 74°C (165°F) for 3 h, has a typical tensile rupture strength of 75.2 MPa (10.9 ksi), a rupture elongation of 5 percent, and a modulus of 3.4 GPa (494 ksi). We have recently studied this resin system in detail [2].

Fiber-Epoxy Strands

The epoxy-impregnated fiber strand is the simplest composite and is the basic building block of many composite structures. We used this type of specimen to determine the tensile properties of the fiber. Over 5000 fiber strands (approximately 180 from each spool) were fabricated using the vacuum filament-winding process shown in Fig. 3. As many as 180 specimens can be wound onto each of the fixtures. From a random spool of fiber we made almost 2000 specimens to study the effect of strain rate and liquid nitrogen temperature on fiber tensile strength. These same specimens are also being used to check the stress-rupture behavior of the fiber composite. The strands were impregnated with the previously mentioned epoxy system and cured according to the same schedule. Ten fiber-epoxy strands were randomly selected from each group of 180 specimens to determine fiber volume content. The fiber content of these strands averaged 64.2 percent by volume with a CV of 8.7 percent from 300 specimens. The fiber filament shapes are shown in Fig. 4.

[4] Dow Chemical Company.
[5] Jefferson Chemical Company.

FIG. 3—*Vacuum winding of fiber-epoxy strands.*

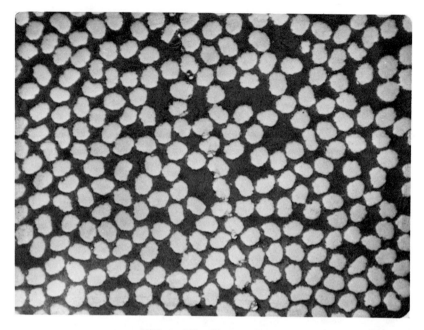

FIG. 4—*Fiber filament shapes.*

Using a 25.4-cm gage length, we tested the strands in tension at a constant crosshead speed of 1 cm/min with a simple clamping arrangement *[3]*. Our machine compliance was measured by varying the gage length of the specimens *[4]*. We used over 500 strand specimens to study the stress-strain behavior of the fiber. Figure 5 shows a typical stress-strain curve. The ordinate indicates only the fiber stress,[6] not the composite stress. The distribution of the fiber failure properties, and the fiber modulus, are summarized in Fig. 6. The average fiber properties—a failure stress of 3570 MPa (517 ksi), a failure strain of 1.7 percent, and a modulus of 206 GPa (30 × 10⁶ psi)—are truly outstanding among graphite fibers. The data scatter, however, as indicated by a coefficient of variation of over 9 percent, is undesirably high.

The effect of low temperature on fiber strength was determined by immersing the specimens directly into liquid nitrogen. We used 12.7-cm gage length in this case. Details of our setup and test procedure were reported previously *[1]*. On the basis of tests performed at room and liquid nitrogen temperatures (see Table 1), it is apparent that temperature does not affect the fiber tensile properties.

The strain rate effect on the fiber tensile properties is of interest to many researchers. Table 2 shows such data based on strand specimens from the spool of fiber mentioned previously. The rate effect, if any, is minimal.

---

[6] Fiber stress was calculated by ignoring the matrix contribution in the strands.

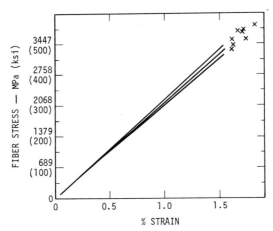

FIG. 5—*Typical stress-strain curve of the special graphite fiber calculated from epoxy-impregnated strands.*

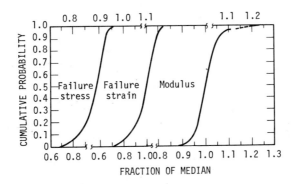

FIG. 6—*Tensile properties of special graphite-fiber-epoxy strands.*

TABLE 1—*Effect of liquid nitrogen temperature on the tensile properties of the special graphite fiber-epoxy strands.*

	21°C (70°F)	−196°C (−321°F)
Number of specimens [a]	50	25
Average tensile rupture stress of fiber [b]	3830 MPa (555 ksi)	3860 MPa (560 ksi)
Coefficient of variation	4.0%	7.5%
Fiber modulus at 0.5% strain	205 GPa (29.8 × 10⁶ psi)	201 GPa (29.0 × 10⁶ psi)
Coefficient of variation	3.1%	5.4%
Rupture strain	1.8%	1.9%
Coefficient of variation	5.2%	9.6%

[a] All test specimens were from a single spool of fiber.
[b] Fiber stress was calculated by ignoring the matrix contribution in the strands.

TABLE 2—*Strain rate effect on the tensile properties of the fiber-epoxy strands.*

Strain Rate,[a] min⁻¹	Fiber Properties	Average Value	Coefficient of Variation, %	Number of Specimens
1.97	rupture stress	3860 MPa (560 ksi)	5.6	10
1.97×10^{-1}	rupture stress	3880 MPa (563 ksi)	4.0	10
1.97×10^{-2}	rupture stress	3780 MPa (548 ksi)	7.4	10
	secant modulus at 0.5% strain	209 GPa (30×10^6 psi)	1.1	
	rupture strain	1.7%	8.2	
1.97×10^{-3}	rupture stress	3650 MPa (530 ksi)	4.1	10
	secant modulus at 0.5% strain	208 GPa (30×10^6 psi)	2.2	
	rupture strain	1.7%	5.1	
1.97×10^{-4}	rupture stress	3690 MPa (535 ksi)	2.5	10
	secant modulus at 0.5% strain	208 GPa (30×10^6 psi)	2.8	
	rupture strain	1.7%	3.5	

[a]Crosshead speed divided by specimen gage length.

We would like to point out that the minimal strain rate and liquid nitrogen temperature effect on the fiber tensile properties are consistent with our previous data on many advanced fibers [1,5,6].

In searching for a nondestructive test to study the failure of fiber composites, we have found that the acoustic emission technique (AE) is a promising tool. We tested 30 fiber-epoxy strands under tensile loading using AE monitoring. A typical summation of acoustic emission versus fiber stress is shown in Fig. 7. As previously reported [7], the signal counts are mainly associated with fiber failures. As indicated in Fig. 7, there was no detectable fiber damage until the applied load exceeded 1380 MPa (200 ksi), which is approximately one third of the ultimate fiber failure stress.

Presently we are studying the long-term performance (stress-rupture) of the special graphite fiber-epoxy strands. We took 100 specimens made from the spool mentioned previously and loaded them to 90 percent of the average fiber failure stress. Only 25 specimens have failed thus far, with a failure life ranging from 0.01 h to over 661 h. These limited data show that, in the properties tested, this special graphite fiber is superior to

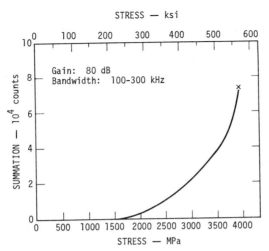

FIG. 7—*Typical curve of fiber stress versus acoustic signal counts under tensile loading of the special graphite fiber-epoxy strands.*

such other composite systems as the organic fiber-epoxy *[8]* or S-glass-epoxy system *[9]*.

Conclusions

1. The fiber tensile properties of this special graphite fiber in an epoxy matrix are: a modulus of 206 GPa (30 × 10⁶ psi), a rupture tensile stress of 3570 MPa (517 ksi), a rupture strain of 1.7 percent. At liquid nitrogen temperature or various quasi-static strain rates, the fiber tensile properties remain approximately the same. The data scatter, however, is on the undesirably high side.

2. For long-term, tensile-critical applications where composite density is also a key consideration, we consider this fiber to be one of the best candidates among the known fibers for composites. Extensive study on the performance of filament-wound vessels is in progress.

3. For applications where the environment is hostile and where shear and compressive stresses are also present, we consider that this is one of the most attractive fibers that could be made commercially available, but its quality consistency (large CV), must be improved in order for it to become an acceptable engineering material.

Acknowledgments

We wish to thank our colleagues M. A. Marcon, R. L. Moore, and Robert Patterson for their assistance.

This work was performed under the joint auspices of the National Aeronautics and Space Administration-Lewis Research Center (contract No. C-13980-C) and the U.S. Atomic Energy Commission.

References

[1] Chiao, T. T., Moore, R. L., and Walkup, C. M., *SAMPE Quarterly,* Society of Aerospace Materials and Process Engineering, Vol. 4, No. 4, 1973, p. 7.

[2] Chiao, T. T. and Moore, R. L., "A Room-Temperature-Curable Epoxy For Advanced Fiber Composites," *Proceedings,* Society of the Plastics Industry Reinforced Plastics/Composites Institute, 29th Annual Technical and Management Conference, Washington D.C., 5–8 Feb. 1974.

[3] Chiao, T. T. and Moore, R. L., *Journal of Composite Materials,* Vol. 4, 1970, p. 118.

[4] Gloor, W. H., "Estimation of True Fiber Modulus from Instron Data," AFML Report TM-MAN-68-15, Air Force Materials Laboratory, Dayton, Ohio, 1968.

[5] Chiao, T. T. and Moore, R. L., *Journal of Composite Materials,* Vol. 6, 1972, p. 547.

[6] Chiao, T. T. and Moore, R. L., *Journal of Composite Materials,* Vol. 5, 1971, p. 124.

[7] Hamstad, M. A. and Chiao, T. T., *Journal of Composite Materials,* Vol. 7, 1973, p. 321.

[8] Chiao, T. T., Wells, J. E., Moore, R. L., and Hamstad, M. A., "Stress-Rupture Behavior of Strands of An Organic Fiber/Epoxy Matrix," *Proceedings,* ASTM 3rd Symposium on Composite Materials, Testing and Design, Williamsburg, Va., 21–22 March 1973.

[9] Chiao, T. T., Lepper, J. K., Hetherington, N. W., and Moore, R. L., *Journal of Composite Materials,* Vol. 6, 1972, p. 358.

J. T. Staley[1]

Heat-Treatable Cladding for New Aluminum Alloy 7050-T76 Sheet

REFERENCE: Staley, J. T., "**Heat-Treatable Cladding for New Aluminum Alloy 7050-T76 Sheet,**" *Composite Reliability, ASTM STP 580,* American Society for Testing and Materials, 1975, pp. 621-632.

ABSTRACT: Four alloys were evaluated as candidates for a cladding on aluminum alloy 7050-T76 sheet. An alloy containing nominally 5 percent zinc, 1.2 percent magnesium, 0.1 percent zirconium, 0.1 percent maximum silicon, and 0.1 percent maximum iron, balance aluminum, provided good electrochemical protection to alloy 7050, and the composite of 7050-T76 clad with this alloy developed a useful combination of static and cyclic mechanical properties. Composites of 7050-T76 sheet clad with alloys containing higher amounts of zinc and magnesium developed comparable static mechanical properties and greater fatigue strengths, but were susceptible to stress-corrosion cracking of the cladding, and, consequently, are unacceptable.

KEY WORDS: composite materials, reliability, aluminum alloys, crack propagation, mechanical properties, fatigue strength, cladding

Conventional alclad 7XXX sheet is a laminar composite of a heat-treatable Al-Zn-Mg-Cu alloy clad with a low-strength Al-1Zn alloy which is anodic to the core. This composite is used on commercial aircraft where the cladding provides electrochemical protection from corrosion. Designers of high-performance aircraft, however, often specify bare 7XXX sheet because the weight penalty associated with the lower mechanical properties of alclad sheet is unacceptable. In recent years, heat-treatable claddings which provide electrochemical protection have been developed for 7075, and 7008 alclad 7075 and 7011 alclad 7075 provide significantly improved mechanical properties. Alloys 7008 and 7011 are not suitable claddings for the recently introduced alloy 7050, however, because the composite could not be recycled to make alloy 7050. Consequently, a new alloy was needed to provide alclad 7050 sheet with a highly desirable combination of high-strength, good fatigue characteristics, and high-resistance to corrosion.

[1] Section head, Alcoa Laboratories, Alcoa Technical Center, Alcoa Center, Pa. 15069.

Alloy Selection

Target compositions of alloys selected as candidates for claddings on the basis of recyclability, corrosion characteristics, and ability to age harden are presented in Table 1. Alloy 1 has the same zinc and magnesium contents as 7008, a heat-treatable cladding for 7075, but contains zirconium in place of chromium. Avoidance of chromium permits adjustment of the recycled composite to meet the 7050 specification, while zirconium is added for grain size control of the cladding alloy. Limitations on impurity elements, particularly iron, are stringent to maintain a high electronegative potential of the alclad sheet surface. Alloy 2 is similar to Alloy 1 except for silicon. The 0.8 percent silicon addition was included as a variant designed to develop additional strength by precipitation heat treatment at 325°F (436 K) through Mg_2Si precipitation. Alloys 3 and 4 are higher solute versions of Alloys 1 and 2, respectively, and were included in an attempt to develop higher mechanical properties.

TABLE 1—Target compositions of 7050 and cladding alloys.

Alloy	Zn	Mg	Cu	Zr	Si	Fe	Ti	Cr	Mn
7050	6.2	2.25	2.3	0.10	0.12[a]	0.15[a]	0.05[a]	0.04[a]	0.10[a]
1	5.0	1.2	0.03[a]	0.10	0.10[a]	0.10[a]	0.05[a]	0.03[a]	0.03[a]
2	5.0	1.2	0.03[a]	0.10	0.8	0.10[a]	0.05[a]	0.03[a]	0.03[a]
3	6.5	1.8	0.03[a]	0.10	0.10[a]	0.10[a]	0.05[a]	0.03[a]	0.03[a]
4	6.5	1.8	0.03[a]	0.10	0.8	0.10[a]	0.05[a]	0.03[a]	0.03[a]

[a] = maximum.

Material and Procedures

Chemical analyses of the conventional, direct chill cast ingots (Table 2) indicated that the compositions were close to the targets. Alclad sheets 4.8 mm thick with nominal 2½ percent cladding per side and 1.6 mm thick with nominal 4 percent cladding per side were fabricated from these ingots by conventional roll bonding procedures (Fig. 1), and bare 7050 sheet was prepared for comparison.

Metallographic examination of the alclad sheet revealed that two of the 1.6-mm sheets were inadvertently clad one side with Alloy 1 and one side with Alloy 2. This composite sheet was retained in the experiment because it provided the opportunity to compare two cladding alloys on the identical core.

Heat treatment of the sheet was conventional. Panels were solution heat-treated at 895°F (752 K), quenched in cold water, stretched 1 to 1½ percent to flatten, and aged 24 h at 250°F (394 K) plus 9 h at 325°F (436 K) to the T76 temper.

TABLE 2—Chemical analyses.

Alloy	Use	Zn	Mg	Cu	Zr	Si	Fe	Ti	Cr	Mn
7050	0.187 in. core bare and 0.062-in.	6.00	2.25	2.40	0.10	0.06	0.06	0.03	0.00	0.00
7050	core	6.12	2.30	2.37	0.10	0.04	0.04	0.02	0.00	0.00
1	cladding	4.92	1.13	0.00	0.10	0.04	0.08	0.03	0.00	0.00
2	cladding	5.03	1.16	0.00	0.10	0.74	0.09	0.03	0.00	0.00
3	cladding	6.55	1.78	0.00	0.09	0.04	0.08	0.03	0.00	0.00
4	cladding	6.50	1.80	0.00	0.10	0.76	0.09	0.03	0.00	0.00
	interliner[a]	2.21	0.00	0.00	0.00	0.04	0.04	0.03	0.00	0.00

[a] A magnesium-free interliner was used to facilitate the bonding of two magnesium-bearing alloys.

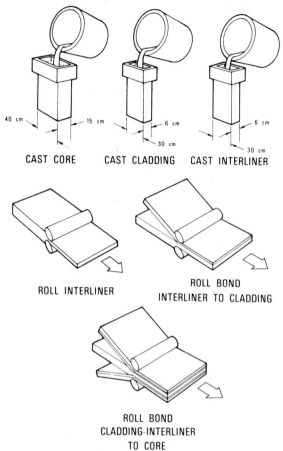

40 cm   15 cm   6 cm   6 cm
30 cm   30 cm

CAST CORE   CAST CLADDING   CAST INTERLINER

ROLL INTERLINER

ROLL BOND
INTERLINER TO CLADDING

ROLL BOND
CLADDING-INTERLINER
TO CORE

FIG. 1—*Fabrication procedure of alclad 7050 sheet.*

Metallographic examination and microprobe analysis of the heat-treated sheet indicated that diffusion had eliminated any evidence of the interliner.

Results and Discussion

Mechanical Properties

Static mechanical properties were evaluated using tension, tear [1],[2] and 3-in.-wide (75 mm) edge-notched tension [2] specimens.

Tensile Properties—To evaluate effectiveness of the claddings in minimizing loss in strength, tensile strengths of standard 2-in. gage length full-thickness specimens of the 4.8-mm-thick composite sheet were

[2] The italic numbers in brackets refer to the list of references appended to this paper.

compared with tensile strengths of specimens machined from the core. The differences in 0.2 percent offset yield strengths were comparable to the differences between yield strengths of bare 7075-T6 sheet and 7011 alclad 7075-T6 sheet, while the differences in ultimate tensile strengths were significantly smaller. These results indicated that all of the candidate alloys were acceptable on the basis of static strength.

Notch Toughness—Ratios of notch-tensile strength to yield strength and tear strength to yield strength of the 4.8-mm sheet were used as indicators of ability to deform plastically in the presence of a stress raiser. The values determined for the composite sheet are not considered to be significantly different from the notch-yield and tear-yield ratios of the bare sheet (Table 3); no effect of cladding alloy was apparent. These results indicated that all of the candidate alloys were acceptable on the basis of notch toughness.

Fatigue—Fatigue characteristics were evaluated initially by comparing axial-stress *S-N* curves of smooth and mildly notched (K_t = 3) specimens of the 1.6-mm-thick bare and alclad 7050-T76 sheet. The *S-N* curves (Fig. 2) were analytically determined using the method of Reemsnyder [3].

Effectiveness of the heat-treatable alloy claddings was evaluated by comparing the difference between the fatigue strengths of bare and alclad 7050-T76 sheet at ten million cycles with previously observed differences

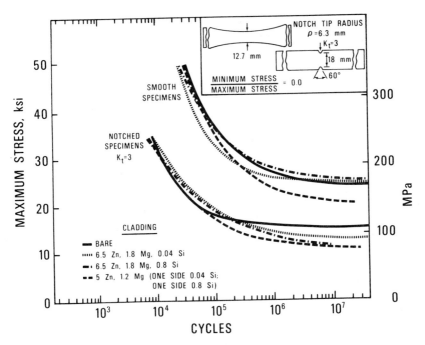

FIG. 2—*Axial fatigue curves for 7050-T76 and alclad 7050-T76 sheet.*

TABLE 3—Notch toughness of bare and alclad 7050-T76 sheet.

Cladding Alloy No.	Variant	Longitudinal			Transverse		
		Yield Strength ksi (MPa)	Notch Tensile Strength / Yield Strength	Tear Strength / Yield Strength	Yield Strength ksi (MPa)	Notch Tensile Strength / Yield Strength	Tear Strength / Yield Strength
	bare 7050	76.8 (530)	0.74	1.14	75.0 (517)	0.69	1.07
1	5.0 Zn, 1.2 Mg, 0.04 Si	76.2 (525)	0.86	1.21	74.5 (514)	0.69	1.10
2	5.0 Zn, 1.2 Mg, 0.8 Si	77.4 (534)	0.89	1.18	75.1 (518)	0.69	1.07
3	6.5 Zn, 1.8 Mg, 0.04 Si	78.4 (540)	0.81	1.16	76.2 (525)	0.69	1.16
4	6.5 Zn, 1.8 Mg, 0.8 Si	78.5 (541)	0.79	1.13	75.7 (522)	0.71	1.06

between the fatigue strengths of commercially available bare and conventional alclad 7XXX sheet determined at Alcoa Laboratories under similar test conditions. Relative performance of the composites in the axial fatigue tests depended on the stress intensity factor. The performances of smooth specimens ($K_t = 1$) of the alclad 7050-T76 sheet clad with the alloys containing 6.5 percent zinc and 1.8 percent magnesium were superior. In contrast to the 6-ksi (41 MPa) difference usually found between the fatigue strengths of bare and 7072 alclad 7075-T6 sheet, the fatigue strengths of these composites equaled the fatigue strengths of bare 7050-T76 sheet. When tested as mildly notched specimens ($K_t = 3$), the fatigue strengths of all of the composites were below that of the bare sheet. However, the 3 to 5-ksi (20 to 34-MPa) difference between the notch fatigue strengths of bare and alclad 7050-T76 sheet was substantially less than the 9-ksi (61-MPa) difference observed between the notch fatigue strengths of similar specimens of bare and alclad 7475-T61 sheet.

These results indicated that the alloys containing 6.5 percent zinc and 1.8 percent magnesium were superior to the alloys containing lower zinc and magnesium as claddings for 7050-T76 on the basis of fatigue strengths of the composites. However, the fatigue performance of a composite of the lower solute cladding alloys on 7075-T76 sheet was also acceptable.

Solution Potential

The difference in solution potential between cladding and core in an alclad product is a criterion of the protection which will be afforded by the cladding. Solution potentials versus 0.1N calomel electrode measured in a standard aqueous solution of 53 g NaCl and 9 ml of 30 percent H_2O_2 revealed that the solution potentials of the claddings were 970 to 1050 negative mV, while the solution potentials of the core were 798 to 806 negative mV. The 170 to 230 mV is substantially higher than the usual 100-mV difference in potential found between the cladding and core of standard alclad products.

Corrosion

The ability of the cladding to protect the core was confirmed using alclad 7050-T76 panels grooved to expose the core. These panels, along with similar bare 7050-T76 and alclad 7075-T6 panels, were exposed for two weeks in an acidified salt spray test *[4]* which is commonly used to evaluate resistance to exfoliation corrosion, and for one year in the 3.5 percent sodium-chloride alternate immersion test using granulated salt and tap water (10 min exposed, 50 min drying).

Performances in the acidified salt spray test and in the alternate immersion test were comparable. As indicated by the extent of corrosion in the machined grooves (Fig. 3), all of the experimental cladding alloys protected 7050-T76 at least as well as 7072 protected 7075-T6.

Examination of metallographic cross sections of specimens exposed in the salt spray test confirmed the beneficial effect of the cladding in protecting the core (Fig. 4). The freedom from corrosion in the machined groove of the specimens of alclad 7050-T76 contrasts with the corrosion in the groove of the bare specimens of 7050-T76.

The ability of the claddings to prevent a loss in mechanical properties

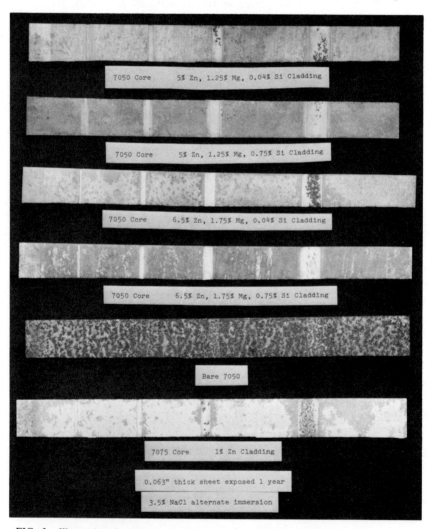

FIG. 3—*Illustrating that all experimental claddings protect 7050-T76 at least as well as alloy 7072 (Al-1Zn) protects 7075-T6.*

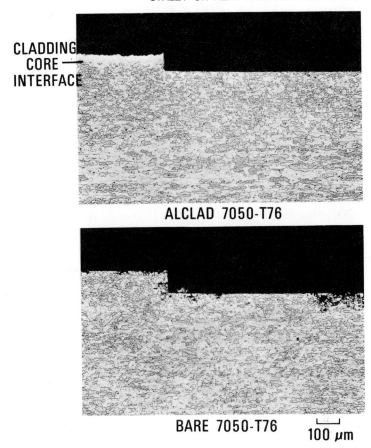

CLADDING
CORE
INTERFACE

ALCLAD 7050-T76

BARE 7050-T76   ⊢———⊣
                    100 μm

FIG. 4—*Illustrating protection afforded to core by 5.0 zinc, 1.2 magnesium, 0.04 silicon cladding in two-week test in acidified 5 percent sodium-chloride intermittent spray.*

of the composite sheet under corrosive conditions was determined using 1.6-mm-thick, standard 2-in. gage length, long-transverse specimens. Unstressed specimens were exposed for either 144 days in the 3.5 percent sodium-chloride alternate immersion test or one year in the seacoast environment at Point Judith, R. I. The ultimate tensile strengths of the alclad specimens tested after exposure equaled those of unexposed specimens, while strengths of bare specimens exposed in the accelerated and natural environments were 20 and 7 percent lower, respectively. These results indicated that all of the experimental alloys were acceptable on the basis of electrochemical protection for the 7050 core.

Stress-Corrosion

Resistances to stress-corrosion cracking of the sheet in the long-transverse direction were determined using 1.6-mm-thick plastically deformed (preform) specimens *[5]* and 1.6 and 4.8-mm-thick standard tension specimens stressed to 75 percent of their yield strengths. Triplicate specimens were exposed for eight months in the 3.5 percent sodium chloride alternate immersion test according to Federal Test Method 823, and for one year in the inland industrial atmosphere at New Kensington, Pa., and the seacoast environment at Point Judith, R. I.

Plastically deformed specimens of the sheet clad with Alloys 3 or 4 (6.5 percent zinc, 1.8 percent magnesium) fractured during exposure in the alternate immersion test, and metallographic examinations of specimens which either fractured during the accelerated test or were removed intact from the seacoast environment after one year indicated that intergranular stress-corrosion cracks initiated in the cladding. Because these cracks propagated into the core in a transgranular manner and because no bare specimens have failed, the core is considered to be resistant to stress-corrosion cracking. On the basis of these tests, alloys containing 6.5 percent zinc and 1.8 percent magnesium were not acceptable for use as claddings.

Because their stress-corrosion susceptibility eliminated the higher solute alloys from consideration, and because the high silicon content offered no apparent advantage, the alloy containing 5 percent zinc, 1.2 percent magnesium, 0.1 percent zirconium, and 0.04 percent silicon was selected for further investigation. The fatigue crack growth characteristics of 4.8-mm-thick bare 7075-T76 sheet and 7050-T76 sheet clad with this alloy were determined and compared with the fatigue crack growth characteristics of bare and alclad 7075-T6 sheet.

The rate of fatigue crack propagation was determined using constant-load-amplitude fatigue tests conducted at a stress ratio, R (minimum stress/maximum stress), of one third at a frequency of 13.3 Hz. The relative humidity was controlled during the test to provide either dry (relative humidity $\leqslant$10 percent) or humid (relative humidity >90 percent) air.

The results, Figs. 5 and 6, indicate that fatigue crack propagation rates of alclad 7050-T76 sheet and bare 7050-T76 sheet were equal in either environment.

Conclusions

An aluminum alloy containing nominally 5 percent zinc, 1.2 percent magnesium, 0.1 percent zirconium, 0.1 percent maximum silicon, and 0.1 percent maximum iron developed the most desirable combination of properties for use as a cladding on aluminum alloy 7050-T76 sheet. When applied as a cladding, it electrochemically protected alloy 7050 at least as well as alloy 7072 protected 7075-T6, and fatigue crack propagation characteristics, static strength, notch toughness, and notch fatigue

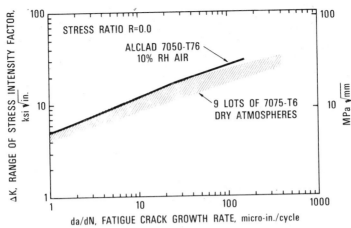

FIG. 5—*Illustrating low-fatigue crack growth rate of alclad 7050-T76 sheet in dry air.*

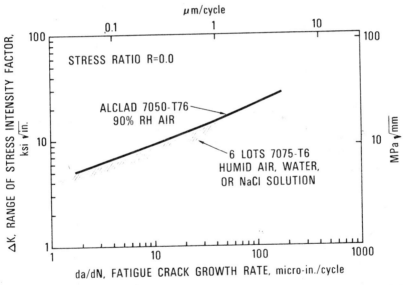

FIG. 6—*Illustrating low-fatigue crack growth rate of alclad 7050-T76 sheet in humid air.*

strengths of a composite of 7050-T76 sheet clad with this alloy equaled or approached the properties of bare 7050-T76 sheet. Composites of 7050-T76 sheet clad with alloys containing higher amounts of zinc and magnesium developed comparable static mechanical properties and greater fatigue strength, but were susceptible to stress-corrosion cracking of the cladding and, consequently, are unacceptable.

Acknowledgment

This work was sponsored by the U.S. Naval Air Systems Command under Contract No. N00019-72-C-0146.

References

[1] Kaufman, J. G. and Knoll, A. H., *Materials Research and Standards,* Vol. 4, No. 4, April 1964, p. 151.

[2] Kaufman, J. G. in *Proceedings,* American Society for Testing and Materials, Vol. 65, 1965, p. 626.

[3] Reemsnyder, H. S., *Journal of the Structural Division, Proceedings,* American Society of Civil Engineers, Vol. 95, No. ST7, July 1969.

[4] Lifka, B. W. and Sprowls, D. O., *Corrosion,* Vol. 22, No. 1, 1966.

[5] Proceedings, American Society for Testing and Materials, Vol. 65, 1965, p. 182.